6808353 GALLOWAY, ANNALS OF COAL MINING
AND THE COAL
£6. 622.33 R.L. TRADE.

HERTFORDSHIRE LIBRARY SERVICE

This book is due for return on or before the date shown. You
may extend its loan by bringing the book to the library or,
once only, by post or telephone, quoting the date of return,
the letter and number on the date card, if applicable, and the
information at the top of this label.

The loan of books ~~in demand cannot be extended~~

**RENEWAL
INFORM-
ATION**

L.32A   9/12

D1610639

Please renew/return this item by the last date shown.

So that your telephone call is charged at local rate,
please call the numbers as set out below:

	From Area codes 01923 or 0208:	From the rest of Herts:
Renewals:	01923 471373	01438 737373
Enquiries:	01923 471333	01438 737333
Minicom:	01923 471599	01438 737599

L32b   Checked 17/9/11

26 OCT 1995

21 NOV 1995

24 JUN 2000

18 DEC 2003

Norfolk
17/1/05.

-3 JAN 2006
9/12

L 33

ISBN 0 7153 4980 5
Annals of Coal Mining and the Coal Trade, First Series,
was originally published in 1898 by
The Colliery Guardian Company Limited, London
Reprinted by the present publishers in 1971
© 1971 Introduction by Baron F. Duckham

HERTFORDSHIRE
COUNTY LIBRARY

622.33

6808353

Printed in Great Britain by
Stephen Austin & Sons Limited Hertford
for David & Charles (Publishers) Limited
South Devon House Newton Abbot Devon

INTRODUCTION TO THE 1970 EDITION

The author of the *Annals of Coal Mining and the Coal Trade,* Robert Lindsay Galloway, was born in 1844, the third son of the Paisley coal- and ironmaster William Galloway, JP. He qualified as a certificated colliery manager and mining engineer and spent the greater portion of his career on Tyneside and in his native Scotland. He had, in addition, some direct experience of south Wales, where his distinguished brother, Sir William Galloway, was a sometime Professor of Mining at University College, Cardiff. Robert contributed to the discussion of papers at the North of England and Scottish Institutes of Mining Engineers on several occasions, but it was as an historian rather than as an engineer or manager that he became best known in his lifetime and subsequently. He married Elizabeth Baird, who predeceased him, and died at Mine House, Bridge of Allan, on 24 February 1908 of a long-standing heart disease.

Besides the *Annals,* his chief publications were: *The Steam Engine and its Inventors* (1880); 'An Account of some of the Earliest Records connected with the working of coal on the Banks of the River Tyne', *Archaeologia Aeliana,* ns, VIII (1880); *A History of Coal Mining in Great Britain* (1882, reprinted with an introduction summarising technical developments to the Great War, 1969); and *Papers relating to the History of the Coal Trade and the Invention of the Steam Engine* (1906). Galloway also helped to organise the Glasgow Mining Exhibition of 1886 and wrote a 'Review of the Progressive Improvement of Mining in Scotland' as an introduction to its catalogue.

The tremendous saga of the British coal industry has never, in recent times, lacked its historians; nor, for that matter, has it wanted even its poets or artists. Quite apart from the industry's understandable attraction for scholars, economists and social or political reformers, it has provided by turns a dramatic milieu, a subject of awe, a background of conflict or a symbol of man's elemental struggle with nature's more forbidding side, for creative writers of every kind.

No other way of human breadwinning, except the call of the sea and perhaps agriculture, has exerted a similar hold on the artistic imagination. From the delicately handled colliery scenes of the watercolourist Thomas Hair, to the sinewy coal hewers of Henry Moore's early drawings; from ballads like the *Collier's Wedding* or the *Trapper's Petition* and the vigorous traditional verse of the northeast, to simple, heartfelt poems such as Wilfred Owen's *Miners,* or to a large and uneven scatter of novels — the way of life, hardships and sacrifices of the mining communities have engaged the attention of a wide variety of men. Though comparatively few people remember much from their school days about nineteenth century social conditions, most can probably recall, if only vaguely, something of lessons about child and female labour in the mines. Somehow the arduous and dangerous business of getting coal has found for itself a place in the national consciousness like that of no other industry.

This is perhaps an eccentric way in which to introduce one of the great classics of industrial history, but the wider public interest in mining development needs to be borne in mind if the 'feel' of this work is to be fully understood in a society and age for which coal is no longer king.

Galloway lived at a time when coal miners accounted for the largest single group of male industrial workers in the economy — there were roughly a million of them in the year of his death — when mining appeared destined for continued expansion until resources ran down, when coal occupied a fair volume of British shipping space and when economic growth without abundant supplies of this fuel seemed unthinkable. In 1915 the expert commentator H.S. Jevons was still able to forecast a prodigious increase of output over the following few decades. This is not to say that the chronological context of the writing of the *Annals* makes it an unbalanced history or one which lacks perspective. Quite the reverse is true; but it is assuredly a work which in its own scholarly way celebrates the greatness of a mighty industry.

It is at one and the same time the finest technical history we possess of any major British industrial activity and an account in almost heroic terms of the ceaseless battles, victories and defeats of a long list of mining engineers, both famous and obscure. The Speddings, father and son; the Buddles; William Brown of Throckley or Thomas Barnes of Walker Colliery: these are the protagonists of volume one. Though not written to illustrate any thesis nor conceived even mainly on biographical lines, it yet deserves to stand against Samuel Smiles's more obviously hagiographical work on the celebrated mechanical and civil engineers. The story of the great coal viewers has never, oddly enough, been written. This book is still the nearest we have to it.

Galloway's earlier and shorter book, *A History of Coal Mining in Great Britain* (1882, reprint 1969 by David & Charles), was his sighting shot for this later and very much fuller work, parts of which originally appeared as articles in the pages of the *Colliery Guardian*. Through its majestic scale and its very wealth of detail, the *Annals* quickly and deservedly acquired its pre-eminent position as the foremost work of reference on the technical development of British coal mining — with the word 'technical', let it be understood, being generously interpreted. The importance of transport improvement to coal exploitation is stressed — Galloway even grasped the significance of the Sankey Brook Navigation in the emergence of the canal age — and the role of developing steam power for pumping, winding and locomotion is seen in its wider context.

True, Galloway tells us comparatively little directly about the miners themselves or their social organisations, though there are many indirect references, especially in volume one. One will find only the briefest mention of Scottish collier serfdom, for instance, and virtually nothing on the early efforts by miners to form and nurture trade unions. The bigger strikes in the north-east are briefly described, as is the binding system, but there is no attempt by the author to analyse the growing tensions between masters and men. Labour history, the place of coal mining in politics and all but the most general economics of the industry were all subjects which the author felt to be outside his frame of reference. Nonetheless, the *Annals* is never a narrow book and one has only to glance through the footnotes of almost any article or monograph on the history of mining to realise how much scholars have continued to draw on the work.

An astonishing fact about the *Annals* is that it was compiled almost exclusively from sources in print. At the date when Galloway wrote, the vast riches of county record offices with their collections of family papers, often so relevant to mining history, scarcely existed. Coalowners and colliery proprietors were then both equally unlikely to allow access to their archives, while for an amateur historian (which is after all what Galloway was) working far outside London, the difficulties in the way of making full use of either the British Museum or Public Record Office were well nigh insuperable. But as far as the printed word went, and despite a busy life as a mining engineer, Galloway allowed nothing to escape him. While much reliance was inevitably placed on the earlier works by Bourne, Brand, Dodds and Bell on the Newcastle area or by Dunn and Bald on coal viewing, there was hardly a mining treatise, a local history or a local record series that was not efficiently ransacked for information. For the second volume in particular, the number of Parliamentary Papers and the many contributions to the *Transactions* of the mining

institutes provided invaluable material. Only an unrealistic or pedantic
view of scholarship would condemn the *Annals* — as this writer once
heard it described — as a magnificent compilation of existing knowledge rather than a work of research. But however designated, its
continuing worth is not in question.

Galloway, it must be realised, wrote originally for a professional or
semi-professional readership. As a professional himself it was naturally
the story of technical change, broadly defined, which chiefly interested him. But, a good historian, he always sought to link his narrative
to more general national events and processes. The success of this
integration of course varies. If this aspect of his work is occasionally
unsatisfactory, we must bear in mind that he put pen to paper at a
period when the disciplines of economic and social history (especially
the latter) had by no means clearly emerged; at least not in a form
yet capable of influencing strongly the amateur worker. If we
remember this we shall be astonished at the breadth of Galloway's
vision and at the good sense of most of his conclusions. Though
teachers of history would undoubtedly agree that we need a good
outline of the economic development of the coal industry from
where Nef left off up to modern times, they would in all probability
accept that the distinctive contribution of Galloway in his chosen
area will never be wholly replaced. Unlike some present day reprints,
these volumes need no word of apology. They still provide their own
justification.

One regret which may be felt by some readers is that Galloway's
narrative breaks off in the middle of the nineteenth century. This is
the more lamentable because the real beginnings of machine mining
did not come until the years after 1870. Although the impact of
mechanisation up to 1914 was in Great Britain comparatively slight —
only 9.1 per cent of our coal production was mechanically cut and
much less mechanically handled by face conveyors in that year — the
regional differences were already considerable. Scotland, for example,
produced some 23 per cent of its coal by cutters in 1914, the
economics of thinner and often dirtier seams demanding a more
rapid investment in such equipment. One manufacturer of coal
cutters, Sam Mavor, was strictly correct when, with Scotland largely
in mind, he declared in 1906: 'it is not too much to say that the
existence of a number of collieries now absolutely depends on
machines'. The general impact of technological change has of course
been explored for the period 1850 to 1914 — notably by Professor
A.J. Taylor — but we still lack the careful chronicle of early machine
mining which Galloway was uniquely in a position to write.

There is also some discrepancy of balance and treatment between
volumes one and two (or the first and second *series,* as the author
preferred to call them). This is most obvious in the time-span covered:

whereas the first volume takes us from ancient times into the nine-teenth century, its sequel scarcely covers a generation of mining history. The treatment, too, tends at times to report or summarise rather than to weigh and consider. To a large extent the difference can be accounted for in the change in the type of source used. It is only with the select committees on the coal trade of 1830 and that on accidents of 1835 that the magnificent series of 'Blue Books' on the coal industry really begins. Given Galloway's natural interest in the woeful record of mining fatalities — to name only one theme — it is easy to understand how he became somewhat embarrassed by the very abundance of material. And this was even before he reached the inspectors' reports which commence in the 1850s. In fact he never did advance far enough to be able to use and analyse this invaluable source.

When one considers the enormous storehouse of information in the Parliamentary Papers for the period beyond 1850, it must be admitted as highly unlikely that Galloway could ever have brought his book up to date and at the same time retained the scale upon which he had embarked in volume two. One is forcibly reminded of Laurence Sterne's humorous threat in *Tristam Shandy:* 'It must follow, an' please your worships, that the more I write, the more I shall have to write — and consequently the more your worships read, the more your worships will have to read.' Although Galloway's detail and occasional digressions, unlike those of Sterne's hero and his immortal Uncle Toby, are very much to the point, they would never have allowed him to reach 1898, let alone 1904! We have simply to be grateful for what was covered and not lament what was left undone.

Fortunately, though there has been no second Galloway (Nef wrote a different kind of book), there have been many excellent articles and monographs on aspects of the industry since 1850 and, of course, on its earlier history as well. I have attempted to assemble references to the most significant additions to the literature in the select bibliography which follows this introductory note.

Every age inevitably mirrors some of its own problems and pre-occupations in its approach to history. Any modern continuation of Galloway would presumably link the history of technical change to at least some comment on economic growth and on social mutation. Galloway himself was able to do this in only a very unsophisticated way even where his subject matter allowed of it. Our present concern with such issues as capital formation, class and labour solidarity, business and management history, together with ever more refined methods of quantification, have already been productive of studies which will one day fill many of the gaps which a broad general history must necessarily leave. We also tend to value most what is no longer with us or is fast disappearing — witness the rash of railway or small sailing vessel preservation societies. The rundown of the modern coal industry is witnessing a physical transformation of the landscape which some of us not so very long ago could hardly have imagined. Pits close, their shafts are filled, their headgear is dismantled; engine houses are razed and even some of the great spoil heaps are slowly moved. Under such circumstances industrial archaeology has sprung into vigorous life, its contribution to mining history coming, with one or two very notable exceptions, somewhat late on the scene. Few scholars are yet entirely agreed upon exactly what constitutes industrial archaeology or about how valuable its findings are for industrial history in its widest context. To some it is merely a new antiquarianism, replacing the cataloguing of medieval churches and their monuments which once kept generations of local historians out of mischief; to others it represents a valid approach which complements and enriches the study of the written document. In mining, where the physical record was large, industrial archaeology will, I believe, amply justify itself. It should certainly bring to life many pages of the *Annals*, which must in any case be considered as required reading for the field worker in this specialised area.

Historical scholarship, it is safe to say, has provided the student of coal mining with more data and interpretation than it has for any other great industry, not even excepting that of cotton. Some writers, like Ashton and Sykes, Nef, (or more recently) Professors Court and Taylor, have opened significantly new fields or approaches. Considerable amounts of work are still being produced at the level of university theses and in the periodical literature. But no one, as yet, has appeared willing to master the secondary sources of the day — as Galloway did for his — to give us the balanced general history which I have already suggested is needed. One of the sadder aspects of modern research in history is that the very detail uncovered by monographs, theses and articles makes the task of producing more general works covering long periods of time increasingly difficult and onerous. It is not simply, nor perhaps even chiefly, because of the labour involved; it stems from a recognition that the complexity of a subject cannot always be adequately treated within the space permitted by publishing economics; and, if we are honest, from a fear that the result will be dismissed by one's colleagues as a mere piece of hack writing. Yet seemingly there are some bad consciences as the grandiloquent titles of articles (the all-embracing being limited to the particular 'case study of ...') sometimes demonstrate. The grand theme or 'sweep' belonged to a more innocent age. Happily the author of this reprint, as a good amateur, was without the worst type of academic inhibition.

Before coming to the select bibliography, some guidance needs giving on the literature dealing with the principal themes of Galloway's book. These remarks should help the reader unfamiliar with the subject to form some idea of the basic reading available on these broadly technological topics. To avoid unnecessary repetition, only the author's name is generally given, together with the date of publication and number of the regional section of the list in which the item appears. Thus 'Atkinson (1966, 2)' refers to F. Atkinson, *The Great Northern Coalfield 1700-1900* (Barnard Castle 1966) in the second section of the bibliography.

Technological history

The serious student of technical change will uncover much vital information in the *Transactions* of the various Mining Institutes. Those of the North East of England Institute of Mining and Mechanical Engineers (the earliest such body) date from 1852-3. For many years now the papers and proceedings of the major institutes have been bound up annually in one volume as *Transactions of the Institute of Mining Engineers*. Other serials of use to the historian are the *Colliery Guardian* (dating from 1858, without a break since 1861), the *Proceedings of the National Association of Colliery Managers* (from 1904), the *Transactions of the Newcomen Society*, *Colliery Engineering* and *Industrial Archaeology*. While on the subject of periodicals it might be remarked that the diamond jubilee issue of the *Colliery Guardian* (1927, 1) contains an excellent selection of articles reviewing technical developments over the preceding sixty years. Of broadly similar scope is the Mining Association's *Historical Review of Coal Mining* (undated: [1925?], 1). The articles, by a number of writers, are generally clear expositions of such subjects as safety in mines, mining legislation, leases, lighting, ventilation, working coal and so on. Though they add little that is new to the period before 1850 (often they inevitably rely on Galloway) they do summarise the changes after that date. I have also attempted a brief summary of such changes between 1880 and 1914 in my introduction to Galloway's *A History of Coal Mining in Great Britain* (1882, reprinted 1969).

The best account of long-term technical progress at any one group of mines is that by Anderson (1967, 3) for Blundell's colleries in Lancashire, a considerable article comprehending developments from the eighteenth to the twentieth centuries. For shorter periods of time the number of contributions to the literature is growing quickly. Swan (1943-5 and 1945-7, 2) has commented on colliery equipment and a sinking operation in the great northern coalfield during the eighteenth century, while Mullineux (1963, 3) and, more particularly, Banks and Schofield (1968, 3) have described the engineering feats of James Brindley at the 3rd Duke of Bridgewater's mines. The second mentioned work is in fact a fascinating marriage of engineering knowledge and careful fieldwork. For Scotland, Carvel (1944, 1946, 1949, 4) has produced company histories of colliery undertakings and manufacturers of mining machinery which include some technical data. Duckham (1968 and 1970, 4) has described the course of technical change in the coalfields north of the Tweed between 1700 and 1815, while the older National Coal Board booklet (1958, 4) provides an admirable outline of technological progress from earliest times. The only district which can so far boast a visual approach to a long period of mining history is the great northern coalfield of Durham and Newcastle. Atkinson (1966, 2) skilfully uses pictures ranging from Hair's 'sketches' to photographs, old and new, of material objects to build up a successful commentary on technical improvement during the two centuries between 1700 and 1900.

Of late the approach of industrial archaeology has borne fruit after a curiously lengthy period of gestation. Perhaps there were always antiquaries who did not mind 'muddying their boots', but at a time when the heavy industries were daily throwing up new physical land-marks, they knew nothing of the urgency of today's worker, even if they were interested in industrial history. T.J. Taylor's 'The Archaeol-ogy of the Coal Trade' (1852, cited by Galloway in the *Annals*, 1, 48, 87-8, etc) was groping in the right direction as was the deservedly famous piece for West Cumberland by Fletcher (1876-7, 3). Some of the works already mentioned here fit happily within the somewhat indeterminate boundaries of industrial archaeology. Recent additions to the literature include contributions by Vinter on the Bristol coal-field (1964-5, 7), Harris on the Ingleton district of Yorkshire's West Riding (1968, 6) and Goodwin on Fife (1959, 4). The regional industrial archaeologies published by David & Charles also contain information on coal mining and the gazetteers of these volumes form an essential guide to sites of importance. Of the areas so far covered, the books dealing with Lancashire by O. Ashmore, the East Midlands by D.L. Smith, the Bristol region by A. Buchanan and N. Cossons and Scotland by J. Butt are most relevant.

Despite the research completed on technical development in mining there has been no major modification of Galloway's account. It is now clear that whim gins (for winding) were in use in Scotland rather earlier than the author of the *Annals* supposed and that the cog and rung gin survived longer on Tyneside than he appears to have assumed. Sir John Clerk of Penicuik, Midlothian, found cog and rung gins still commonplace around Newcastle in 1724 and compared them un-favourably with the 'Scotch gins' (whim variety) of his homeland. Gunpowder, too, was more widely used for blasting rock than one would conclude from the *Annals*. The chronology of early steam locomotion is, of course, now known in much greater detail, while L.T.C. Rolt, in his book *George and Robert Stephenson* (1960) has

given us a fuller account of 'Geordie' Stephenson's role as the independent inventor of a safety lamp. The character of Sir Humphry Davy
appears somewhat less attractive then in the pages of Galloway. But
these are minor points indeed. Most work has tended to confirm the
vigorous outline drawn by Galloway and to paint in the colours rather
than alter the basic sketch.

Colliery transport arrangements and the application of steam power
to mine drainage and winding are two aspects of technological development where our knowledge has been widened without the findings of
the present book being questioned. Both subjects are far too wide to
be fully comprehended by the appended bibliography and reference
is made there only to works of the most direct relevance. Thus
waggonways have been included, but the general development of
canals and railways has not.

Baxter (1966, 1) provides a useful background survey of, and
bibliography for, waggonways and tramroads. More particular, though
briefer, accounts are those by Lee (1937, 6) for the celebrated
Middleton Colliery Railway and by the same writer (1944, 1945-7,
1947-9, 2) for the great northern coalfield, by Harris (1956, 3) for
the St Helen's district of Lancashire, by Dott (1947, 4) for Scotland
and by Mott (1964-5, 1) for eighteenth-century England. Bland
(1932, 7) has reviewed the work of John Curr, the famous colliery
viewer and engineer credited with the introduction of underground
iron tram rails.

Further light on the spread of steam power before the expiry of the
patent of James Watt may be found in a number of sources, among
the chief of which are Mott (1962-3, 1) and Harris (1967, 1) for
Britain generally, Raistrick (1936-7, 2) and Hughes (1949, 2) for
Durham and Tyneside, and Duckham (1969 and 1970, 4) for Scotland. Watkins (1955, 2) has commented on the famous nineteenth-
century vertical winding engines of the great northern coalfield, while
many other writers on mining have made some mention of steam
power. The long-standing debate on the site of the first Newcomen
engine is summarised by Rolt in his *Thomas Newcomen: the Pre-
history of the Steam Engine* (1963). It is now abundantly clear that
the second half of the eighteenth century saw an application of the
Newcomen engine by British collieries on a scale even larger than
that imagined either by Galloway or by later writers such as J. Lord
(*Capital and Steam Power 1750-1800* (1923)). At a very conservative
estimate there must have been well over 300 Newcomen-type engines
which had been purchased by the mining industry before 1800.
Around 70 can be traced for Scotland alone by that date.

The periodic publication of contemporary documents continues
to deepen our understanding of earlier mining practice. One fascinating source is the diary or journal which, when kept by a coal-

master or discriminating traveller, undoubtedly enriches our knowledge of the methods of a bygone age. Several of the writings of the
Scottish mining laird Sir John Clerk II of Penicuik have now been
edited in print. The most relevant concern his visit to Newcastle in
1724 (Atkinson, 1965, 2) and to Whitehaven in 1739 (Prevost, 1965,
3). Another journal well worth consulting is the Hatchett diary
edited by Raistrick (1967, 1).

A fair amount of research has been completed on the remaining
semi-technical topics covered by Galloway: mining accidents (and
safety!) and the growth of legislation concerning the coal industry.
Much of what has been written is in the professional literature, and
falls outside what can properly be designated historical writing, but
a few general references can be given. Both themes are treated briefly
in the Mining Association's publication (1925? 1) already mentioned.
The more infamous accidents are often described in books on trade
union history: R. Page Arnot (1955, 4) on the Blantyre and Knoch-
shinnoch disasters and on that at Senghenydd (1967, 5); F. Machin
on the second Oaks disaster (1958, 6), and so on. Besides drawing on
the official documents of inquiry by the mines inspectors or special
commissioners, such accounts typically make use of newspaper
reports. Quantification of fatal accidents is relatively straightforward
for periods after 1854, when the inspectors' reports became annual;
for the half century or so earlier, Hair (1968, 1) has recently
summarised the known facts.

The social and political background of mining legislation has not
yet attracted quite the degree of attention accorded to state intervention in textile factories — there was no 'mining movement' at all
comparable with the factory movement — but modern scholarship
has at last begun to bring within its orbit the study of the politico-
administrative setting and actual working of the early mines regulations. MacDonagh (1967, 1) has characteristically examined the
first decade of state interference (1842-52), whilst Webb (1955, 1)
has commented on the work of that notable Whig inspector, Seymour
Tremenheere. Older, more general, outlines of, and commentary on,
coal mines legislation may be found in Boyd (1879 and 1892, 1) and,
for Scotland, in Barrowman (1888-9, 4).

During the last two decades the history of technology has been
increasingly integrated with the analysis of social and economic
change. Though economic history has never lacked an awareness of
the importance of invention and innovation, the careful relation of
the study of the practical sciences to that of society is now blossom-
ing. A.E. Musson's and Eric Robinson's *Science and Technology in
the Industrial Revolution* (Manchester 1969), is the fruit of the
considerable labours of both authors over many years to further the
appreciation of the role of technology in the crucial stages of

economic growth. The book contains some valuable references to mining developments. For the later nineteenth and early twentieth centuries two of the essays of Professor A.J. Taylor (1961, 1968, 1) are highly relevant to an understanding of the economic context of the beginnings of machine mining in Britain.

Trade

Galloway saw his book as a history of the coal trade as well as a history of the coal industry. Nonetheless the term 'trade' was understood in a fairly popular sense. Although both volumes say something about the growth of the vend in the north-east, they present no systematic analysis of the coal trade nor any really detailed description of its organisation. Later writers have done much to redress this balance, though much discussion of 'landsale' has often been incidental to transport history. Ashton and Sykes (1929, 1) in their classic account of eighteenth-century mining include chapters on inland and overseas trade and the supply of coal to London. Nef, too, (1932, 1) discusses trade between 1550 and 1700 in his own monumental work. Another American scholar, Sweezy (1938, 1) treated the whole history of monopoly organisation and competition between 1550 and 1850. More recently writers such as Smith (1961, 1) and Fraser-Stephens (1950, 1) have looked at various organisational aspects of the London market. An older book on the metropolitan coal trade is that written by Dale (1912, 1). A useful reference of the same vintage for the export record of coal from 1850 is Thomas (1903, 1). Most modern economic histories comment on the rundown of coal exports from the record year of 1913.

For the supply end of the chain, important contributions have come from the pens of Jevons (1915, 1) though much of his book is social and industrial in approach; Taylor (1955, 2) and Large (1958-9, 2) for the north-east; and Williams (1956, 3) for Whitehaven. Many books not specifically or wholly devoted to the coal industry include important references to the coal trade. The list would be far too long for the present bibliography, but one might instance works by the late Professor Hughes (1952, 2; 1965, 3) and those general studies of trade, T.C. Smout, *Scottish Trade on the Eve of the Union 1660-1707* (Edinburgh 1963) and L.M. Cullen, *Anglo-Irish Trade 1660-1800* (Manchester 1968). The medieval coal trade of the north-east has recently engaged the attention of two scholars, Fraser (1962, 2) and Blake (1967, 2). Geographical analyses of the coal trade are also by no means lacking. Here there is merely room to note the contribution of Elliott (1968, 2), again for Tyneside, and Brookfield (1953, 2) for the inter-war coastwise movement of coal.

B.F.D. October 1969

SELECT BIBLIOGRAPHY

With one or two exceptions, this bibliography contains only those books and articles on the history of coal mining which appeared after the publication of the *Annals*, first series, (1898). Moreover, it is a list dealing almost exclusively with the periods covered in Galloway's work, though including those items which bring the story up to the first world war. The arrangement adopted is regional, but the topics included are wider than those treated in the *Annals*.

GENERAL (1)

Arnot, R.P. *The Miners: A History of the Miners' Federation of Great Britain 1889-1914* (1949) and *Years of Struggle* (1953)

Ashton, T.S. 'The Coal Miners of the 18th Century', *Economic Jnl: Econ Hist Supp*, iii (1928)

Ashton, T.S. and Sykes, J. *The Coal Industry of the Eighteenth Century* (Manchester 1929)

Baxter, B. *Stone Blocks and Iron Rails* (Newton Abbot 1966)

Boyd, R.N. *Coal Mines Inspection: its history and results* (1879)

Boyd, R.N. *Coal Pits and Pitmen. A short history of the coal trade and the legislation affecting it* (1892)

Challinor, R. and Ripley, B. *The Miners' Association: a Trade Union in the Age of the Chartists* (1968)

Colliery Guardian: Diamond Jubilee Issue 1867-1927, ed Sheddon, C.T. (1927)

Court, W.H.B. 'Problems of the British Coal Industry between the Wars', *Econ Hist Rev*, XV (1945)

Dale, H. *Coal and the London Coal Trade* (1912)

Daniel, D. 'Some aspects of mining reform', *Quarterly Rev*, CCLXXVI (1914)

Duckham, Baron F. 'A Colliery History', *Local Historian*, VIII, 7 (1969)

Fraser-Stephen, E. *Two Centuries in the London Coal Trade: the story of Charringtons* (1950)

George, M. Dorothy. 'The London Coal-Heavers ...' *Economic Jnl: Econ Hist Supp*, ii (1927)

Harris, J.R. 'The Employment of Steam Power in the Eighteenth Century', *History*, LII (1967)

Hair, P.E.H. 'Mortality from Violence in British Coal-Mines, 1800-50', *Econ Hist Rev*, 2nd ser, XXI (1968)

Hunt, R. *British Mining* (1884)

Jevons, H.S. *The British Coal Trade* (1915)

Lubin, I. and Everett, H. *The British Coal Dilemma* (New York 1927)

McCormick, B. and Williams, J.E. 'The Miners and the Eight-Hour Day, 1863-1913', *Econ Hist Rev*, 2nd ser, XII, 2 (1959)

MacDonagh, O.O.G.M. 'Coal Mines Regulations: the First Decade, 1842-1852', in *Ideas and Institutions of Victorian Britain: Essays in honour of George Kitson Clark* ed Robson, R. (1967)

Meade, R. *The Coal and Iron Industries of the United Kingdom* (1882)

Mining Association of Great Britain [various authors]: *Historical Review of Coal Mining* (undated: 1925?)

Miners' Federation of Great Britain: *Statistical Report of the Hours worked at Collieries in every Mining District in Great Britain except Durham and Cleveland* (1890)

Moller, Asta. 'Coal Mining in the Seventeenth Century', *Trans Royal Hist Soc*, 4th ser, 8 (1925)

Mott, R.A. 'The Newcomen Engine in the Eighteenth Century', *Trans Newcomen Soc*, XXXV (1962-3)

Mott, R.A. 'English Waggonways of the Eighteenth Century', *Trans Newcomen Soc*, XXXVI (1964-5)

Munro, J.E.C. *Sliding Scales in the Coal and Iron Industries from 1885 to 1889* (Manchester Stat Soc, 1890)

Munro, J.E.C. 'The Probable Effects of an Eight Hours Day on the Production of Coal and the Wages of Miners', *Economic Jnl* (1891)

Nef, J.U. 'Dominance of the Trader in the English Coal Industry in the Seventeenth Century', *Jnl Econ & Business Hist* 1 (1929)

Nef, J.U. *The Rise of the British Coal Industry* (2 vols 1932)

Raistrick, A. (ed) *The Hatchett Diary: A Tour Through the Counties of England and Scotland in 1796 Visiting Mines and Manufactories* (Truro 1967)

Redmayne, R.A.S. *The British Coal Industry During the War* (Oxford 1923)

Simpson, J.B. *Capital and Labour in Coal Mining* (Newcastle 1900)

Simpson, J.B. 'Coal Mining by the Monks', *Trans Inst Mining Engineers*, XXXIX (1910)

Smith, R.A. *Sea-Coal for London: History of the Coal Factors in the London Market* (1961)

Sorley, W.R. 'Mining Royalties and their Effect on the Iron and Coal Trades', *J Royal Stat Soc* LII (1889)

Spring, D. 'The English Landed Estate in the Age of Coal and Iron: 1830-1880', *J Econ Hist*, XI (1951)

Stone, G. *The British Coal Industry* (1919)

Sweezy, P.M. *Monopoly and Competition in the English Coal Trade, 1550-1850* (Cambridge, Mass, 1938)

Taylor, A.J. 'Combination in the Mid-Nineteenth Century Coal Industry', *Trans Royal Hist Soc*, 5th ser, III (1953)

Taylor, A.J. 'The Miners' Association of Great Britain and Ireland, 1842-48: A Study in the Problem of Integration', *Economica*, ns, XXII (1955)

Taylor, A.J. 'The Sub-Contract System in the British Coal Industry' in *Studies in the Industrial Revolution presented to T.S. Ashton*, ed Presnell, L.S. (1960)

Taylor, A.J. 'Labour Productivity and Technological Innovation in the British Coal Industry, 1850-1914', *Econ Hist Rev*, 2nd ser, XIV (1961)

Taylor, A.J. 'The Coal Industry' in *The Development of British Industry and Foreign Competition 1875-1914*, ed Aldcroft, D.H. (1968)

Thomas, D.A. 'The Growth and Direction of our Foreign Trade in Coal during the last half century', *J Royal Stat Soc*, LXVI (1903)

Turner, E.R. 'English Coal Industry in the seventeenth and eighteenth centuries', *American Hist Rev*, XXVII (1922)

Webb, R.K. 'A Whig Inspector' [Seymour Tremenheere], *J Mod Hist*, XXVII (1955)

Williams, R. Price 'The Coal Question', *J Royal Stat Soc*, LII (1889)

THE NORTH-EAST (2)

Archer, M. *A Sketch of the History of the Coal Trade of Northumberland and Durham ... to the year A.D. 1700* (1897)

Atkinson, F. 'Some Northumberland Collieries in 1724', *Trans Arch & Ant Soc of Durham & Northumberland*, XI (1965)

Atkinson, F. *The Great Northern Coalfield 1700-1900* (Barnard Castle 1966)

Best, G. *Bishop Westcott and the Miners*, Westcott Memorial Lecture (Cambridge 1967)

Blake, J.B. 'The Medieval Coal Trade of North East England: some Fourteenth-Century Evidence', *Northern History*, II (1967)

Brookfield, H.C. 'A Study in the Economic Geography of the pre-War Coastwise Coal Trade', *Trans Inst Brit Geographers*, XIX (1953)

Dendy, F.W. (ed) *Records of the Company of Hostmen* (Surtees Soc, CV, 1901)

Elliott, N.R. 'A Geographical Analysis of The Tyne Coal Trade', *Tijdschrift voor Econ en Soc Geografie*, LIX (1968)

Fawcett, J.W. 'Some Durham Bonds', *Proc Soc Antiq of Newcastle,* 4th ser, X (1943)

Fewster, J.M. 'The Keelmen of Tyneside in the Eighteenth Century', *Durham University Jnl,* L (1957-8)

Fraser, C.M. 'The North-East Coal Trade until 1421', *Trans Arch & Ant Soc of Durham & Northumberland,* 4th ser, XI (1962)

Fynes, R. *Miners of Northumberland and Durham* (repr Sunderland 1923)

Galloway, R.L. 'An Account of some of the Earliest Records connected with the working of coal on the Banks of the River Tyne', *Archaeologia Aeliana,* ns, VIII (1880)

Greenwell, G.C. *Glossary of Terms used in the Coal Trade of Northumberland and Durham* (1888)

Hair, P.E.H. 'The binding of the pitmen of the north-east, 1800-9', *Durham University Jnl,* LVIII, 1 (1965)

Hughes, E. 'The First Steam Engine in Durham Coalfield', *Archaeolgia Aeliana,* 4th ser, XXVII (1949)

Hughes, E. *North Country Life in the Eighteenth Century:* vol I, *the north east 1700-1750* (1952)

Large, D. 'The Third Marquess of Londonderry and the End of the Regulation 1844-45' [of the NE Coal Trade], *Durham University Jnl,* LI (1958-59)

Lee, Charles E. 'An ancient underground railway' [at E Kenton Colliery, Northumberland], *Railway Mag,* XC, 533 (1944)

Lee, Charles E. 'The World's Oldest Railway. 300 years of coal conveyance to the Tyne Staiths', *Trans Newcomen Soc,* XXV (1945-7)

Lee, Charles E. 'Tyneside Tram roads of Northumberland', *Trans Newcomen Soc,* XXVI (1947-9)

McCutcheon, J.E. *The Hartley Colliery disaster, 1862* (pub privately, Seaham 1963)

Mott, R.A. 'The London and Newcastle Chaldrons for measuring coal', *Archaeologia Aeliana,* 4th ser, XL (1962)

Raistrick, A. 'The Steam Engine on Tyneside 1715-1778', *Trans Newcomen Soc,* XVII (1936-7)

Scott, H. 'The Miners' Bond in Northumberland and Durham', *Proc Soc of Antiq of Newcastle,* 4th ser, XI (1947)

Spring, D. 'The Earls of Durham and the Great Northern Coalfield', *Canadian Hist Rev,* XXXIII (1952)

Swan, E.W. 'A Durham collieries' stocktaking in 1784', *Trans Newcomen Soc,* XXIV (1943-5)

Swan, E.W. 'Sinking a Northumberland colliery in 1761-2', *Trans Newcomen Soc,* XXV (1945-7)

Taylor, A.J. 'The Third Marquis of Londonderry and the North-Eastern Coal Trade', *Durham Univ Jnl,* XLVIII (1955)

Taylor, T.J. 'The Archaeology of .the Coal Trade', *Proc Archaeological Inst of Newcastle,* I (1852)

Turner, E.R. 'The Keelmen of Newcastle', *American Hist Rev,* XXI (1916)

Watkins, G.M. 'Vertical Winding Engines of Durham', *Trans Newcomen Soc,* XXIX (1955)

Webb, S. *The Story of the Durham Miners 1662-1921* (1921)

Welbourne, E. *The Miners' Unions of Northumberland and Durham* (Cambridge 1923)

THE NORTH-WEST (3)

Anderson, D. 'Blundell's Collieries: the progress of the business'; and 'Wages, disputes and conditions of work', *Trans Hist Soc Lancs & Ches,* CXVI (1964) and CXVII (1965); 'Technical Developments 1776-1966', CXIX (1967)

Bailey, F.A. 'Early Coalmining in Prescot, Lancashire', *Trans Hist Soc Lancs & Ches,* XCIX (1947)

Bankes, Joyce H.M. 'Records of mining in Winstanley and Orrell near Wigan from the 16th century to the 19th century', *Trans Lancs & Ches Ant Soc,* LIV (1939)

Bankes, Joyce H.M. 'A Nineteenth Century Colliery Railway', *Trans Hist Soc Lancs & Ches,* CXIV (1962)

Banks, A.G. and Schofield, R.B. *Brindley at Wet Earth Colliery: An Engineering Study* (Newton Abbot 1968)

Barker, T.C. 'Lancashire Coal, Cheshire Salt and the Rise of Liverpool', *Trans Hist Soc of Lancs & Ches,* CIII (1951)

Barker, T.C. and Harris, J.R. *A Merseyside Town in the Industrial Revolution: St Helens 1750-1900* (Liverpool 1954)

Clegg, H.E. 'Historical Notes on Wigan Coalfields', *Trans Geological & Mining Soc* (1957)

Crofton, H.T. 'Lancashire and Cheshire Coal Mining Records', *Trans Lancs & Ches Ant Soc,* VII (1889)

Fletcher, I. 'The Archaeology of the West Cumberland Coal Trade', *Trans Cumberland & Westmorland Ant & Arch Soc,* os, III (1876-7)

Ford, P. 'Tobacco and Coal: a note on the Economic History of Whitehaven', *Economica,* IX (1929)

Harris, J.R. 'Railways of the St Helen's Coalfield down to 1830: a Note', Jnl *Transport Hist,* II, 3 (1956)

Hughes, E. *North Country Life in the Eighteenth Century,* vol II: *Cumberland and Westmorland 1700-1830* (1965)

Kendall, J.D. 'Notes on the History of Mining in Cumberland and North Lancashire', *Trans N of England Mining Inst,* XXXIV (1884-5)

Mullineux, F. 'The Duke of Bridgewater's Underground Canals at Worsley', *Trans Lancs & Ches Ant Soc,* LXXI (1963)

Prevost, W.A.J. (ed) 'A trip to Whitehaven to visit the coalworks there in 1739 by Sir John Clerk', *Trans Cumberland & Westmorland Arch Soc*, ns, LXV (1965)

Taylor, A.J. 'The Wigan Coalfield, 1851', *Trans Hist Soc of Lancs & Ches*, CVI (1954)

Williams, J.E. 'Whitehaven in the Eighteenth Century', *Econ Hist Rev*, 2nd ser, VIII, 3 (1956)

Wood, O. 'A Cumberland Colliery in the Napoleonic War', *Economica*, ns, XXI (1954)

SCOTLAND (4)

'A.M.' [MacGeorge], *The Bairds of Gartsherrie* (Glasgow 1875)

Anon, 'Slavery in Modern Scotland', *Edin Rev*, CLXXXIX (1899)

Arnot, R.P. *A History of the Scottish Miners from the Earliest Times* (1955)

Barrowman, J. *Glossary of Scotch Mining Terms* (Hamilton 1886)

Barrowman, J. 'Scotch Mining Legislation', *Trans Mining Inst of Scotland*, X (1888-9)

Barrowman, J. 'Slavery in the Coal-Mines of Scotland', *Trans Mining Inst of Scotland*, XIX (1897-8)

Cadell, H.M. *The Rocks of West Lothian: an Account of the Geological and Mining History of the West Lothian District* (1925)

Campbell, R.H. *Carron Company* (Edinburgh 1961) [contains important references to coal mining in late eighteenth century]

Carvel, J.L. *A Hundred Years in Coal: the History of the Alloa Coal Company* (Edinburgh 1944)

Carvel, J.L. *The New Cumnock Coalfield* (Edinburgh 1946)

Carvel, J.L. *Fifty Years of Machine Mining* [Anderson & Boyes] (Glasgow 1949)

Clow, A. and N.L. 'Lord Dundonald', *Econ Hist Rev*, XII (1942) [includes the coal-tar patent of 1781]

Cochran-Patrick, R.W. *Early Records relating to Mining in Scotland* (Edinburgh 1878)

Cunningham, A.S. *Mining in the 'Kingdom' of Fife* (Dunfermline 1913)

Cunningham, A.S. *Fife Coal Company 1872-1922* (Leven 1922)

Cunningham, A.S. *Mining in Mid and East Lothian* (Edinburgh 1925)

Dott, G. *Early Scottish Colliery Waggonways* (repr from *Colliery Engineering*, 1947)

Duckham, Baron F. 'Some Eighteenth-Century Scottish Coal Mining Methods', *Industrial Archaeology*, V, 3 (1968)

Duckham, Baron F. 'Life and Labour in a Scottish Colliery 1698-1755', *Scot Hist Rev*, XLVII, 1 (1968)

Duckham, Baron F. 'The Emergence of the Professional Manager in the Scottish Coal Industry 1760-1815', *Business History Review* XLIII (1969)

Duckham, Baron F. 'Early Application of Steam Power at Scottish Collieries: a Note and Query', *Industrial Archaeology*, VI (1969)

Duckham, Baron F. 'Serfdom in Eighteenth Century Scotland', *History*, LIV (1969)

Duckham, Baron F. *A History of the Scottish Coal Industry: vol I, 1700-1815* (Newton Abbot 1970)

Durland, K. *Among the Fife Miners* (1904)

Goodwin, R. 'Some Physical and Social Factors in the Evolution of a Mining Landscape' [Fife], *Scot Geog Mag*, LXXV, 1 (1959)

Hamilton, H. 'Combination in the West of Scotland Coal Trade, 1790-1817', *Econ History*, II, 5 (1930)

Lebon, J.H.G. 'The Development of the Ayrshire Coalfield', *Scot Geog Mag*, XLIX (1933)

Megaw, R.R.S. 'Women Coal-bearers in Midlothian', *Scottish Studies*, X, 1 (1965)

Muir, A. *The Fife Coal Company Limited; A Short History* (Cambridge 1951)

NCB (Scottish Division), *A Short History of the Scottish Coal Mining Industry* (Edinburgh & Glasgow 1958)

Payne, P.L. 'The Govan Collieries, 1804-5', *Business History*, III, 2 (1961)

Scott, N.M. 'Documents relating to Coal Mining in the Saltcoats District in the First Quarter of the Eighteenth Century', *Scot Hist Rev*, XIX (1922)

Slaven, A. 'Earnings and Productivity in the Scottish Coal-mining Industry during the Nineteenth Century: the Dixon Enterprises' in *Studies in Scottish Business History*, ed Payne, P.L. (1967)

Sleight, G.E. 'Ayrshire Coal Mining and Ancillary Industries', *Ayrshire Collections*, 2nd ser, VIII (1966)

Smout, T.C. 'The Erskines of Mar and the Development of Alloa, 1689-1825', *Scottish Studies*, VII, 1 (1963)

Strawhorn, J. (ed), 'Selections from the Auchenharvie Papers' [Saltcoats and Stevenston], *Ayrshire Collections*, 2nd ser, VI (1958-60)

White, K.M. 'Notes on an old coal-working and a wooden shovel from Ormiston, East Lothian', *Proc Soc Antiqu Scotland*, 7th ser, III (1941)

Youngson Brown, A.J. 'Trade Union Policy in the Scots Coalfields, 1855-1885', *Econ Hist Rev*, 2nd ser, VI, 1 (1953)

WALES (5)

Arnot, R.P. *South Wales Miners. Glowyr de Cymru. A History of the South Wales Miners' Federation* (1898-1914) (1967)

Bramwell, H. *The Economics of the South Wales Coalfield* (Cardiff 1920)

Dalziel, A. *The Colliers' Strike of 1871* (Cardiff 1872)

Dalziel, W.G. *The Records of the South Wales Coalowners' Association* (Cardiff 1895)

Davies, H. *The South Wales Coalfield, its Geology and Mines* (Pontypridd 1901)

Dodd, A.H. 'The North Wales Coal Industry during the Industrial Revolution, *Archaeologia Cambrensis*, (1929)

Dodd, A.H. *The Industrial Revolution in North Wales* (2nd ed Cardiff 1951), espec ch VI

Edwards, N. *History of the South Wales Miners* (London 1926)

Edwards, N. *History of the South Wales Miners' Federation*, I, (London 1938)

Evans, D. *Labour Strife in the South Wales Coalfield 1910-11* (Cardiff 1911)

Evans, E.W. *The Miners of South Wales* (Cardiff 1961)

Hare, A.E.C. *Anthracite coal industry of the Swansea district* [mainly econ & social survey] (Cardiff 1940)

John, A.H. 'Iron and Coal on a Glamorgan Estate 1700-1740', *Econ Hist Rev*, XIII, 1 & 2 (1943)

John, A.H. *The Industrial Development of South Wales, 1750-1850* (Cardiff 1950)

Lerry, G.G. *The Collieries of Denbighshire – past and present* (Wrexham & Oswestry 1946)

Lewis, E.D. *The Rhondda valleys: a study in industrial development, 1800 to the present day* (1959)

Morris, J.H. and Williams, L.J. 'The Discharge Note in the South Wales Coal Industry, 1841-1898' *Econ Hist Rev*, 2nd ser, X, 2 (1957)

Morris, J.H. and Williams, L.J. *The South Wales Coal Industry 1841-75* (Cardiff 1958)

Morris, J.H. and Williams, L.J. 'The South Wales sliding scale, 1876-1879: An experiment in Industrial Relations', *Manchester School of Econ & Soc Research* XXVIII (1960)

North, F.J. *Coal and the Coalfields of Wales* (Cardiff 1926)

Phillips, E. *A History of the Pioneers of the South Wales Coalfield* (Cardiff 1925)

Rawson, R.R. 'The coal-mining industry of the Hawarden district on the eve of the Industrial Revolution', *Archaeologia Cambrensis*, XCVI, 2 (1941)

Rees, W. *Industry Before the Industrial Revolution* (Cardiff 1968) vol I [Chapters 1 and 2 deal chiefly with Wales]

Richards, H. and Lewis, P. 'House-building in the South Wales Coalfields 1851-1913', *Manchester School of Econ & Soc Studies*, XXIV (1956)

Rogers, E. (ed Rogers, R.O.) 'The History of Trade Unionism in the Coal Mining Industry of North Wales to 1914: Twelve Years of Sectional Movements (1848-1860)', *Trans Denbighshire Hist Soc,* XVI (1967)

Thomas, B. 'Migration of Labour into the South Wales Coalfield 1861-91', *Economica,* X (1930)

Trueman, A.E. 'Population Changes in the Eastern Half of the South Wales Coalfield', *Geog Jnl,* LIV (1919)

Wilkins, C.W. *The South Wales Coal Trade ... from the Earliest Days to the present time* (Cardiff 1888)

Williams, D.T. *The economic development of Swansea and of the Swansea district to 1921* (Cardiff 1940)

YORKSHIRE AND THE MIDLANDS (6)

Anon, *The Staveley Story* [Staveley Coal & Iron Co, Derbyshire] (undated)

Bolsover Colliery Coy, *The Bolsover Colliery Company Ltd 1889 – 1939* (private printing 1940)

Clayton, A.K. 'Coal mining at Hoyland' [Yorks], *Trans Hunter Arch Soc,* IX (1966)

Court, W.H.B. 'A Warwickshire Colliery in the Eighteenth Century', *Econ Hist Rev,* VII, 2 (1937)

Court, W.H.B. *The Rise of the Midland Industries* (1938)

Daniels, G.W. and Ashton, T.S. 'The Records of a Derbyshire Colliery, 1763-1779', *Econ Hist Rev,* II, I (1929-30)

Green, H. 'The Nottinghamshire and Derbyshire Coal Fields before 1850', *J Derbyshire Arch & Nat Hist Soc,* LVI (1936)

Griffin, A.R. *The Miners of Nottingham: a history of the Nottinghamshire miners' unions* (1962)

Griffin, A.R. 'Methodism and Trade Unionism in the Nottinghamshire–Derbyshire Coalfield, 1844-90', *Proc Wesley Historical Soc,* XXXVIII, I (1969)

Griffin, A.R. 'Bell-Pits and Soughs: Some East Midlands Examples', *Industrial Archaeology,* VI (1969)

Hardy, S.M. 'The Development of Coal Mining in a North Derbyshire Village, 1635-1860', *University of Birmingham Hist Jnl,* V, 2 (1956)

Harris, A. 'The Ingleton Coalfield', *Industrial Archaeology,* V, 4 (1968)

Hopkinson, G.G. 'The development of the S. Yorks & N. Derbyshire coalfield 1500-1775', *Trans Hunter Arch Soc,* VII, 6 (1957)

Jenkins, W.J. 'Early history of coal mining in the Black Country', *Trans Newcomen Soc,* VIII (1927-8)

Johnson, R. 'An Ancient Swanwick Coal Mine', *J Derbyshire Arch Soc,* LXXIII (1953)

Lee, Charles, E. 'The First Steam Railway, Brandling's colliery line between Leeds and Middleton', *Railway Mag*, (Dec 1937)

Lister, J. 'Coal Mining in Halifax' in *Old Yorkshire*, 2nd ser, ed Wheater, W. (1885)

Lones, T.E. *History of Mining in the Black Country* (1898)

Lones, T.E. 'The South Staffordshire and North Worcestershire Mining District and the Relics of Mining Appliances', *Trans Newcomen Soc*, XI (1930-31)

Machin, F. *The Yorkshire Miners – a History*, vol I (Barnsley 1958)

Raybould, T.J. 'The Development and Organization of Lord Dudley's Mineral Estates, 1774-1845', *Econ Hist Rev*, 2nd ser, XXI, 3 (1968)

Rimmer, W.G. 'Middleton Colliery near Leeds, 1770-1830', *Yorks Bulletin of Econ & Soc Research*, VII, 1 (1955)

Scott, H. 'Colliers' Wages in Shropshire, 1830-1850', *Trans Salop Arch Soc* LIII, 1 (1949)

Sorby, E. 'Coal Mining Near Sheffield from 1773 to 1820', *Trans Inst Mining Engineers*, LXV (1923)

Stone, L. 'An Elizabethan Coalmine' [Sheffield Park, Yorks], *Econ Hist Rev* 2nd ser III, 1 (1950-51)

Ward, J.T. 'The Earls Fitzwilliam and the Wentworth Estate in the Nineteenth Century', *Yorks Bulletin Econ & Soc Research*, XII (1960)

Ward, J.T. 'West Riding Landowners and Mining in the Nineteenth Century', *Yorks Bulletin Econ & Soc Research*, XV (1963)

Williams, J.W. *The Derbyshire Miners: A Study in Industrial and Social History* (1962)

Wray, D.A. *The Mining Industry in the Huddersfield District* (Huddersfield 1929)

MISCELLANEOUS (7)

Anstie, J. *Coalfields of Gloucestershire and Somerset and their resources*, (1873)

Bland, F. 'John Curr, Originator of Iron Tram Roads', *Trans Newcomen Soc*, XI (1932)

Bulley, J.A. 'To Mendip for Coal: a Study of the Somersetshire Coalfield before 1830', *Proc Somersetshire Arch & Nat Hist Soc*, XCVII (1952) & XCVIII (1953)

Hart, C.E. *The Free Miners of the Forest of Dean and Hundred of St Briavels* (Gloucester 1953)

Redmayne, R.A.S. *Men, Mines and Memories* (1942)

Vinter, D. 'The Archaeology of the Bristol Coalfield', *J Industrial Archaeology*, I (1964-5)

ANNALS OF COAL MINING
AND THE COAL TRADE

ANNALS OF COAL MINING

AND THE COAL TRADE

THE INVENTION OF THE STEAM ENGINE
AND THE ORIGIN OF THE RAILWAY

BY

ROBERT L. GALLOWAY

MINING ENGINEER AND CERTIFICATED COLLIERY MANAGER; MEMBER OF THE INSTITUTION
OF MINING ENGINEERS; MEMBER OF THE EXAMINATION BOARD FOR THE WESTERN
DISTRICT OF SCOTLAND; AUTHOR OF "THE STEAM ENGINE AND ITS
INVENTORS," "A HISTORY OF COAL MINING IN GREAT
BRITAIN," ETC.

WITH NUMEROUS ILLUSTRATIONS

LONDON
THE COLLIERY GUARDIAN COMPANY, LIMITED
ESSEX STREET, STRAND
1898

All rights reserved

PREFACE.

THE history of the growth of the coal industry, from small and unpromising beginnings to its present magnitude and importance, forms an

> "ample page
> Rich with the spoils of time,"

which has in large measure remained "unrolled."

The bulk of the subject-matter contained in the following pages appeared in a series of articles contributed to the *Colliery Guardian* during the years 1896 and 1897. The whole has been carefully revised, and numerous additions have been made.

R. L. G.

Inscribed to

JOHN BELL SIMPSON, Esq.

OF BRADLEY HALL, RYTON-ON-TYNE,

IN REMEMBRANCE OF A PERIOD OF MUCH INTEREST

SPENT AMONG THE COLLIERIES OF THE

NORTH OF ENGLAND

CONTENTS.

CONTENTS.

LIST OF ILLUSTRATIONS.

PLATES.

The blocks of plates I., II., VII., were prepared for the original series of articles, and have been kindly lent by the proprietors of the *Colliery Guardian.*

ANNALS OF COAL MINING

AND THE COAL TRADE.

CHAPTER I.

PREVIOUS TO 1066 A.D.

Ancient use of mineral fuel by smiths in the south of Europe.   Improbability of coal having been used for fuel by the aboriginal inhabitants of Britain. Used to a small extent by the Romans in Britain.   No foundation for its supposed use by the Early English or Anglo-Saxons.

WHETHER a knowledge of the use of coal, like that of gunpowder and the mariner's compass, was first arrived at in remote Cathay, as some suppose, will perhaps remain a mystery.   So far as western civilization is concerned, in which we are more immediately interested, the mineral begins to be heard of about the time of Alexander the Great.

In this era, the sons of Vulcan in the south of Europe had already discovered the peculiar suitability of coal for the require-ments of their craft, and had adopted it in some places for fuel in their smithies.   This is made known to us by the Greek naturalist and philosopher, Theophrastus, the favourite pupil of Aristotle, and his successor as head of the Peripatetic School at Athens.   In his book about stones this author specifies earthy ones, found in Liguria in the north of Italy—the modern province of Genoa—and in Elis, in Greece, which kindled and burned in the very same manner as charcoal, and were used by smiths.   They had no distinguishing name, but were called just *anthraces*, or charcoals (εὐθὺς ἄνθρακας in Sir John Hill's text, 2nd ed., p. 62), borrowed from the older fuel for which they had been substituted, and to which they bore such a striking affinity in appearance, properties, and uses.

Apart from this notice of the employment of coal by smiths in

Elis and Liguria, while Rome was still young—shared, perhaps, in the latter case with the ironworkers in the neighbouring state of Etruria : the home of the iron-digging Tuscan chief who figures in Macaulay's *Lays* as

> " Seius, whose eight hundred slaves
> Sicken in Ilva's mines "

—no other record exists relating to the use of mineral fuel in ancient times in the countries bordering on the Mediterranean.

The abundance of wood in Britain at this distant period may well have afforded a ready supply of fuel which amply sufficed for the simple wants and ways of the inhabitants. It is improbable that coal was in use among them, previous, at all events, to the Roman invasion. Under the conditions which then prevailed it is difficult to comprehend how coal could have been of any value for fuel.

The family of Smiths—the earliest patrons of coal—though now the largest in the kingdom, must in those days have been a very small one. Iron was so scarce that it ranked as a precious metal. It was coined into money, Cæsar tells us (*De Bell. Gall.*, lib. v., c. 12), in the form of rings of a standard weight; and it was worn round the body and neck, Herodian states (*Octo Libri Hist.*, lib. iii., c. 14), for personal adornment and as a display of wealth.

The limeburner, again, that other manipulator of minerals, who was among the first to adopt mineral fuel in his trade, and for whose requirements likewise it was peculiarly well suited, cannot have begun to ply his vocation at all. It is scarcely to be imagined that lime was used in ancient British agriculture, and buildings of stone and lime were unknown. For architectural and military purposes, in this era, earth formed the leading article.

Thus no want that we know of for coal had arisen. There was no motive, as yet, for digging it for fuel, even supposing suitable implements to have existed with which to dig it.

Several writers have nevertheless endeavoured to carry back the history of the use of coal to this early date, though with no great measure of success. Among these, Whitaker, the historian of Manchester, ranks prominent. But the various matters which he cites in support of the view that coal was commonly used in Britain in ancient times, so far from being at all convincing, are for the most part altogether wide of the mark.

One of his arguments, for example (2nd ed., vol. ii., p. 37), is based upon the word *coal* itself, which he alleges to be a British word, and to subsist among the Irish in their *gual*, and among the

Cornish in their *kolan* to this day. But any evidence of the ancient use of coal supposed to be derived from the antiquity of this word (to whatever language it belongs), is quite subverted by the fact that the name of coal was originally attached to fuel of wood or charcoal, and had no connection whatever with the mineral now known by that name. This supposed proof of early coal burning in Britain may consequently be said to end in smoke.

From another source we have a story of a flint axe, the instrument of the aborigines, having been found stuck in a vein of coal, where it came out to the surface and was exposed to view, in a steep rock, called Craig-y-Park, in Monmouthshire. So frequently has this been quoted as evidence of coal having been dug in Britain in the Stone Age, that, according to a late writer, the axe has been well-nigh worn out in the service.

This oft-told tale is first met with in the pages of Thomas Pennant, the well-known last-century tourist (*Tours in Wales*, vol. i., p. 25, ed. 1810), who refers to the *Philosophical Transactions* (No. 335, p. 500) as his authority. Here the narrator informs his readers that, " In a steep rock, called Craig-y-Park, and others in the parish of Ystrad Dyvodog, we observed divers veins of coal, exposed to light as naked as the rock, and found a flint axe, somewhat like those used by the Americans." So far as this account goes, the statement that the axe was sticking in a vein of coal at all appears to be a purely fanciful assumption on the part of Pennant himself. So that as regards its affording any evidence of the archaic digging of protruding veins of coal, we may, metaphorically speaking, bury this ancient hatchet.

A similar instance of supposed connection between stone implements and coal digging is furnished by Mammatt, in his *Geological Facts* (p. 9), who tells us that, " In Measham (Leicestershire), where the bed was not more than 40 or 50 feet from the surface, indications of ancient workings were found, in stone hammer heads, and large wedges of flint with hazel withes round them, also wheels of solid wood about 18 inches in diameter." Had these stone implements been found in coal workings, they would certainly have lent to them an air of antiquity; but that any connection existed between them and the bed of coal lying beneath appears to be altogether conjectural. It is very doubtful whether such implements· would have at all sufficed either for reaching the coal at the depth stated, or for digging it afterwards.

We hear again of coal being found in what Sir Richard Colt Hoare (*Ancient History of South Wiltshire*, p. 85 ; Wright's *The*

Celt, the Roman, and the Saxon, 5th ed., p. 114) supposed to be
British villages, near Heytesbury, in Wiltshire. Assuming this to
be correct (though probably belonging to the late Roman period),
it may possibly have been used to an insignificant extent for
smithwork, or other special requirement. But it is scarcely
credible that coal should have been employed for ordinary purposes of fuel in the unventilated semi-subterranean abodes in vogue
among the native population, which are conceived to represent the
earliest form of artificial human habitation in Britain; a step in
advance of the cave dwellings; and like them, and also like the
singular underground retreats, known as "weems" in Scotland
(Wilson's *Prehistoric Annals,* vol. i., p. 107), possessing probably
only a single aperture, which was at once doorway, window, and
chimney.

Whether or not coal was used for fuel in Britain in pre-Roman
times, one of its varieties—known as cannel coal in England, from
its blazing and giving light like a candle, and as parrot coal in
Scotland, from the crackling noise which it makes in burning—
being attractive to the eye by reason of its glossy smoothness, and
susceptible of a high degree of polish, appears to have been
occasionally carved into ornaments in far-back vistas of the past.
Sir Charles Lyell, in his *Antiquity of Man* (p. 61, ed. 1873), cites
an instance of a rude ornament of this material having been found
beneath the gravel of an ancient raised sea-beach in the parish
of Dundonald in the west of Scotland, where it had evidently been
deposited by natural causes long ages before; the remoteness of the
period being shown by the fact (Hull's *Coalfields,* 3rd ed., p. 14) that
the relative level of sea and land was 50 feet different from what
it is at the present day. Ornaments of coal have also been found at
Angerton, in Northumberland, associated with flint knives, and supposed to belong to the period about 600 B.C. (Latimer's *Loc. Rec.,*
p. 156).

Reasoning from analogy, it seems probable that the British word
glo, now the Welsh term for coal, simply passed through the same
change as similar words in the case of various other languages; and
from having in the first instance been applied to fuel of wood or
charcoal, became subsequently transferred to coal. If, on the other
hand, this word originally signified a black stone, in that case it is
possible that it may have been applied to cannel, as used for ornamental purposes, or to jet which is also found to have been converted
at an early date into beads, and bracelets, and such like charms, dear
to the feminine heart in all ages and countries.

That the Romans made some use of coal for fuel during their occupation of our island, has been brought to light by the explorations of archæologists. Coal or its ashes, sometimes both, have been obtained among the ruins of many of their stations situated on or near the coalfields. Thus, Dr. Bruce tells us in his *Roman Wall* (3rd ed., p. 93), that the ashes of mineral fuel have been met with in nearly all, and a store of unconsumed coal in some of the stations on the line of the Great Wall from the Tyne to the Solway Firth—that ancient scientific frontier of the Emperor Hadrian, known to those initiated in Romano-British antiquities, as the barrier of the lower isthmus. The anonymous author of the *Picture of Newcastle*, said to have been the Rev. J. Hodgson, the historian of Northumberland, speaks (p. 217, ed. 1812) of coal as intimately mixed with the calcareous flooring of the Roman baths at Lanchester, in Durham; and as forming part of the remains of a Roman smithy discovered at Ebchester, in the same county. Whitaker, in his *History of Manchester* (vol. ii., pp. 37-38), refers to similar remains found there. And Wright, in his *Uriconium* (p. 115, ed. 1872), alludes to coal having been used by the inhabitants of that ancient Roman town, situated at what is now known as Wroxeter, in Shropshire. Other writers, too numerous to mention, advert to the same subject; and the remains have been generally accepted as indubitably belonging to the Roman period.

That coal should have been utilized by the Romans in Britain is not surprising. We know that they manufactured iron in various districts, and coal was the best fuel wherewith to manipulate it. They also used stone and lime for building purposes. But beyond the discoveries above mentioned our information does not go ; and though it would appear that this fuel was even at times employed in the heating chambers or hypocausts of baths and houses, it is evident from various considerations that the use made of the mineral in this era must have been very circumscribed.

No Roman remains have been found in old coal workings, or among heaps of coal ashes. Whitaker, in the passage above referred to, alludes to many beds of cinders heaped up in the fields in the neighbourhood of North Brierley, in the West Riding of Yorkshire, in one of which a number of Roman coins were met with, as a noted instance of the use of coal by the Romans—a case which, on his authority, has been since adduced by many other writers. The "cinders" in question, however, were not the ashes of coal, but the scoriæ, or slag, left by a Roman ironwork, the finding of coins, etc., among which is a matter of very common occurrence. Strange to say they are referred to as such by Whitaker himself on a previous page (p. 28); and that this is the correct view is clear from the letter of Dr. Richardson, in which the original account of them is given (see appendix to Leland's *Itinerary*, vol. i., p. 144, ed. 1768). The term "cinders" or "synders" was, in fact, at one time the usual designation for the refuse of old ironworks, and survives in the names of many places where they exist, such as Cinderhill, Cinderford, etc.

No Roman writer, again, adverts to the use of coal for fuel, either in Britain or anywhere else, with perhaps one exception. This is the indirect and seemingly unconscious allusion made to it by Solinus, a writer of uncertain date, but who preceded St. Jerome, and probably wrote in the third or fourth century. This occurs in his *Collection of Things Memorable* (c. 22), in speaking of the material burnt in the temple of Minerva: the goddess who presided over the warm springs of Britain (used for medicinal purposes) presumably at Bath, a place named by the Romans, on account of its natural thermal fountains, *Aquæ Solis*, or waters of the Sun. The perpetual fires in her shrine, he relates, instead of resulting in the usual white ashes, left a residuum of stony balls (*globos saxeos*); the explanation of what apppeared something miraculous to him doubtless being that coal—which could easily be got not far from Bath—being more durable than wood, and consequently more suitable for the maintenance of the constant fires, was the fuel employed by the priests. That Solinus was not at all conversant with the use of coal for fuel may be accepted as conclusively established by the circumstance of his preserving, as a memorable item of information, this simple fact connected with its ashes.

That coal was little dug by the Romans is further shown by exposed veins, or seams, of it being left undisturbed in some places in close proximity to their encampments (see Mr. T. J. Taylor's memoir on "The Archæology of the Coal Trade," published in the *Proceedings of the Archæological Institute*, at Newcastle, in 1852, vol. i., p. 151). And, in addition to this, their language possessed no term denoting mineral fuel; the Latin *carbo*, like the Greek *anthrax*, properly signifying charcoal.

Gagates—a word which, in rolling down the stream of time, became ground into *geat*, and *jet*—was a famous product of Britain in the Roman period, and was carried for ornamental purposes to Rome, where its praises were recited both in prose and verse. It has been supposed (Fuller's *Worthies*, art. "Yorkshire"; Gough's "Camden," vol. iii., p. 103, ed. 1789) that coal was included under this name. This seems very probable, the allusions to its burning properties being suggestive of coal more than of true jet. Among the various wonderful attributes ascribed to this material, we are told that

> " Water makes it fiercely flame,
> Oyle doth quickly quench the same "

—a somewhat free translation, on the part of Fuller, of a paradoxical saying which may have had its origin in the practice pursued by smiths of sprinkling water on their fires in order to increase the intensity of the heat.

Gagates is also spoken of as remarkably abundant in Britain, which likewise favours the supposition that coal was regarded as such by the Romans. Solinus, in the passage above referred to, characterizes it as the most plentiful and the best stone (*lapis*) in Britain. If this view of the British gagates, of Roman times, be correct, it would follow that while coal was unknown to any Roman writer as a useful fuel, it was in a manner known to many of them as a mineral that burned, and possessed various mysterious properties, and was valuable for the manufacture of articles of *vertu*. Little could they have imagined, however, that it was its destructive use as a fuel that was destined to cause it to become in reality, what Solinus had in another sense already termed it—the best stone in Britain.

Whatever use was made of coal for fuel during the Roman occupation, seems to have come to an end along with it, and many centuries intervene before we come upon the fringes of the coal trade of modern times. The English doubtless knew nothing of coal when they arrived in Britain, on the departure of the Romans in the fifth century ; and with their different manners and customs, had little need for it.

The early English period was *par excellence* the era of wood—of house-bote, hey-bote, fire-bote : wood for building, fencing, burning. Stone and lime were little used for building purposes. When Benedict Biscop (Abbot of Jarrow, died 690) wished to build a monastery of stone, after the Roman fashion (*in more Romanorum*) at Wearmouth, he had to cross to the Continent for masons for the purpose. In the *English or Anglo-Saxon Chronicle*, the expression "to timber" is used as synonymous with to build ; a stone church being said to be *timbered* with stone. Even the ploughs of this period are supposed to have been wholly constructed of wood—one of the laws enacting that no person should guide a plough who could not make one—a circumstance which indicates that iron was extremely scarce.

The fuel employed in this era—the Dark Ages—appears to have consisted of wood, probably supplemented by peat, which was already utilized to a small extent in Germany in the time of Pliny (*H.N.*, xvi. 1). So far as any records of its use are concerned, coal remained wholly neglected.

Bæda, or Bede (the venerable Bede), who spent his life at Jarrow, on the south bank of the Tyne—now the seat of the great shipbuilding works of Sir C. M. Palmer & Co., but then a quiet riparian retreat where the as yet pellucid waters of the river, teeming with the lordly salmon, began to commingle with the green tides of the North Sea—tells us nothing of any use of coal in his day. Writing in the early part of the eighth century he speaks (*Hist. Eccl., lib.* i., c. 1) of the abundance of metalliferous ores in Britain, and almost quotes the words of Solinus regarding gagates; adding the remark, probably taken from Pliny (*H.N.*, xxxvi. 34), that when kindled it drove away serpents. This seems to sufficiently indicate that any practical use of coal, for ordinary purposes of fuel, was altogether unknown to him.

It is usual to quote a solitary passage, from a charter belonging to the ninth century, as evidence that coal was at this time employed for fuel in England, but the words can scarcely be accepted as bearing out the interpretation put upon them.

This charter is inserted in the copy of the *English Chronicle* known as the Laudian MS., which is supposed to have belonged to the Abbey of Peterborough (see the *Anglo-Saxon Chronicle*, by B. Thorpe, London, 1861. A.S., vol. i., p. 122 note, trans. vol. ii., p. 56), but is also found and in a more complete form elsewhere, and has been published by Kemble (*Cod. Diplom.*, ii. 46) and Thorpe (*Diplom. Ang.*, p. 104) in their collections of records of this era. It relates to a lease of some land at Sempringham in Lincolnshire, made by the abbot and monks of Peterborough about the year 852. Among the conditions it was stipulated that the lessee, Wulfred, of Sempringham, besides giving some land at Sleaford in exchange, should pay an annual rent, partly in money, and partly in kind or service. In the latter connection, it was arranged that he should every year supply sixty cartloads (*fothur*) of wood to the dwelling or village (*ham—i.e.* Scottish *hame*, English *home*) in the Wood of Horn, and twelve cartloads of " græfa " (*twælf fothur græfan*), and six cartloads of fagots. The term " græfa " is usually construed as fossil or pit coal—a translation for which Bishop Gibson appears to be primarily responsible ; and such is the meaning attached to it by Bosworth in his *Anglo-Saxon Dictionary*, where he gives a reference to this passage

—the only instance of the use of the word apparently known to him.

With all deference to such eminent authorities, there are what seem to be insuperable difficulties in the way of accepting this rendering of the word. No coal could be got in Lincolnshire, nor within a considerable distance from it, so that it is altogether unlikely it should have been required as payment in kind. We know also that even in the coalfields themselves, where it abounded, it was not till four or five centuries later that householders began to adopt coal for domestic use, the purpose for which the fuel here bargained for appears to have been intended. If coal, again, had ever been known by this name, it seems impossible to account for the appellation having subsequently been completely lost.

On the other hand, the word *græfa* is susceptible of various different interpretations. Thus it occurs, under date 900 A.D. (Thorpe's *Diplom. Ang.*, p. 146), in the compound *thorn-græfan*, translated a "thorn-grove," which points to the possibility of it signifying brushwood.

At the same time this term—which, with the general disuse of the inflection, doubtless subsequently assumed the form of *græfe*, and so passed into the modern word *grave*—appears to have been most largely used in connection with the idea of digging. Earle (quoted in new edition of Bosworth's *A.S. Dictionary*) suggests that it may here mean *gravel*. This is certainly a dug-up substance, and to that extent meets the case; still the rendering is inadmissible, inasmuch as, however useful elsewhere, a dozen cartloads of gravel annually would be a little out of place among fuel.

Peat, however, seems exactly to answer all the conditions, and is most likely what is here referred to. This fuel is dug, or *graven*, as well as coal (*Proc. Arch. Inst.*, Newcastle, 1852, vol. i., p. 154, note), and it could certainly be obtained in Lincolnshire with great facility. We are also not without direct evidence of the word *græfe*, or grave, being used in connection with peat. Thus we find a peatery, or place where peats were dug, termed a "grave" (*Thirty-fifth Report of the Deputy-Keeper of the Public Records*, pp. 10, 29); also peat itself called "turfgrave" (Dugdale's *Monasticon*, vol. v., p. 22); while down till modern times (*Household Books of Naworth Castle*, p. 91, Surtees Society, vol. lxviii.) digging peats continued to be spoken of as "graving peats."

This word also occurs in the name of Gravesend, and perhaps in that of Crieff, in Scotland. Whether it there signifies a peatery, or a grove of wood, may be doubtful, but in neither case could it possibly refer to coal, the one place being situated far to the south and the other far to the north of the coal-producing districts.

It is true that the word *græfe*, variously spelt, was also applied to diggings of other kinds—as, for example, to the fosse outside the walls of a town, or fortification, at one time known as a graffe—and, in particular, to mines, which latter fact may serve to explain how the above passage came to be supposed to refer to coal. But, perhaps, no better evidence could be found that the term had been previously applied to diggings made for peat than is afforded by this passage itself. Regarding this word as used in connection with mines, there will be occasion to speak hereafter.

CHAPTER II.

THE NORMAN PERIOD. 1066-1217 A.D.

Coal first dug in Germany about the tenth century. Not mentioned in Domesday Book. No clear records of its use in England even in the twelfth century. Began to be used in Belgium and Scotland. The Great and Forest Charter.

THE coalfield of Zwickau, in Saxony, Mr. Smyth informs us in his *Treatise on Coal and Coalmining* (p. 3), is considered to have been the earliest worked in Germany; and the digging of coal there is said to be able to be carried back to about the tenth century.

In the north-west of Europe the mineral appears to have received little or no systematic attention till a later date.

Had coal been dug in England at the time of the compilation of Domesday Book, the great survey carried out about 1085 by order of William the Conqueror, some reference would probably have been made to the subject. But while this wonderfully minute and exact record—so much so that it has been said that not a single pig escaped it—makes mention of leadmining works (*plumbariæ*), which were almost all situated in the King's demesnes in Derbyshire, and notes the production of iron in various counties which it traverses, specially referring to an iron mine (*minaria ferri*) discovered in Cheshire, and likewise furnishes particulars regarding the salt industry, both inland and on the coast, it seems to be a blank so far as coal is concerned.

Even in the twelfth century, while the records relating to the working of metalliferous ores—particularly of lead from which the as yet scanty silver coinage of the kingdom was, in part at least, obtained—are both numerous and varied, not a single indubitable and substantial record regarding the digging or use of coal in England has yet been brought to light; any that would seem to point in this direction being of a more or less shadowy and ambiguous character.

References to the use of wood and peats for fuel, on the other hand, are abundant. Thus, in the famous Burgh Laws of David I.—the legislator and founder of many monasteries : the "sair sanct for the croun," king of Scotland—which were intimately connected with, if not in large measure adopted from, the Laws and Customs of the town of Newcastle-on-Tyne, which was in his possession (*Proc. Arch. Inst.*, Newcastle, 1852, vol. i., pp. 25, 154), persons bringing fuel into the burghs were granted a certain degree of immunity from distraint for debt in respect of the wood and peats which they brought (*Ancient Laws and Customs of the Burghs of Scotland*, vol. i., pp. 17, 18—Scottish Burgh Rec. Soc.). Again, in the charter granted by Pudsey (or de Puteaco, or de Puiset), Bishop of Durham, to Gateshead-on-Tyne, in 1164 (*Boldon Buke*, appendix, p. xl.), provision was made for the burgesses obtaining supplies of wood and peats for their own use, but not to sell.

Instances of grants of wood and peats made in the twelfth century to towns and religious houses as fuel for their domestic requirements—and that too in localities where coal could have been obtained with the greatest facility, and where some of the earliest records relating to its use occur at a later date—might be multiplied. But we should probably search in vain in this direction for any references to coal at this early period, inasmuch as the use of mineral fuel appears to have been at first almost, if not solely, confined to smiths and limeburners, and numerous records exist of its employment by these classes and other artisans, for about a century before it began to be adopted in house fires—when indeed the primitive arrangement of the fire-hearth in the centre of the floor, necessitated by the walls being formed of wood, and there being at the same time no provision for getting rid of smoke save simply a hole in the roof above, rendered coal a fuel much less suitable than wood and peat for use in the interior of dwelling houses.

Not yet do we escape from difficulties arising from the ambiguity of words, in which the early history of the use of coal is involved. As already adverted to, the English word "coal," or as it was usually spelt in former times "cole," like the Greek *anthrax* and the Latin *carbo*, properly signified charred wood, or what is now termed charcoal. This circumstance altogether invalidates some of the passages which have been cited as bearing on the use of mineral coal, while it renders others of uncertain import.

The new order of things introduced at the Conquest was undoubtedly, from an industrial point of view, calculated to foster

PLATE I.

MAP SHOWING
SUCCESSION OF GEOLOGICAL FORMATIONS
IN NORTHUMBERLAND AND DURHAM.

Based on map prepared by Professor G. A. Lebour,
Durham College of Science, Newcastle-on-Tyne.

YORKSHIRE

the employment of coal. Then began the erection of numerous feudal castles, churches, and other large buildings of stone and lime (many of the free-masons engaged in the work being said to have come from the Continent), giving rise to a need for fuel, to meet which coal was of all kinds the most suitable. And though we are without clear and direct records relating to the actual employment of the mineral, it is possible that a commencement may have been made to utilize it, to a small extent, even in the Norman period.

Among records of a more or less obscure and ambiguous character which have been supposed, or might be thought, to point to the incipient use of coal, the following may be noticed.

Lanchester, in Durham, where seams of coal and ironstone come out to the surface, has at various epochs been a centre of mining and metallurgical activity. The Romans, as we have seen, are supposed to have made use of coal there, and the great Consett Ironworks of the present day are situated in this district.

An undated and indefinite, but at the same time interesting record relating to a hill in the Lanchester neighbourhood, now called Cold-pike Hill, may be connected with the employment of coal in the Norman period. By an early chapter, a grant of some land at "Kolpihill" was made to St. Cuthbert and his monks of Durham, for the smithy, or workshop of their church (*ad fabricam ecclesiæ*)—the stately Durham minster

> Half church of God, half castle 'gainst the Scot

—the building of which was commenced about the year 1094.

Mr. Surtees, in his admirable *History of Durham* (vol. ii., p. 319), seems to have supposed the name of this hill to have been originally Coal-pit Hill, it being so called in a record of the fourteenth century. There are a few considerations which render this etymology not altogether convincing. Though coal and cold are frequently confused in early documents, it is perhaps doubtful whether the word pit formed the latter part of the name. There is another pike, or peak, in the same neighbourhood, viz., Pontop Pike ; and this term was not uncommonly applied to hills, as in Morton Pike, the Peak of Derby, etc. Coal could also have been got in the hill without any necessity for pits, inasmuch as seams of the mineral (though not of much thickness) pass almost horizontally through this isolated knoll, and come to the surface, or "crop out," all round its sides ; while old ironstone pits at Lanchester were not termed pits, but "delfs,"—a name which Mr. Surtees himself remarks in the same volume (p. 305, note) they still retain.

But irrespective of the etymology of the name, this was undoubtedly a likely spot for coal to have been early discovered. The purpose for which the land was granted was also one for which coal was peculiarly well suited. So that, though containing no actual mention of coal, and consequently not wholly conclusive, this record would almost seem to indicate that a supply of the mineral was probably specially procured from this place, as fuel for the artificers employed in the building of the minster. As to the period of the operations to which the charter belongs, these extending over a great length of time, we are unfortunately without information.

Other evidence exists of coal having been specially dug in the vicinity for the erection of large buildings in early times; and it seems not improbable that the mineral may have been used in this intermittent and isolated manner previous to the existence of any regular coal trade.

Some passages contained in a detailed survey of the See of Durham, made by order of Bishop Pudsey in 1183, and known as the *Boldon Buke* (which has been published with a translation, by the Surtees Society, vol. xxv.), are among those most frequently quoted as evidencing the use of coal in England in the twelfth century, though their tenor is very uncertain. This book furnishes an account of the various services rendered to the bishop by the smaller vassals of the see, in return for land held by them, not yet commuted into payment of rent in money; and in one or two instances the supplying of coal is mentioned in connection with smith-work.

Out of about fourteen smiths enumerated in the survey, in the case of two of them it is stated that they themselves found, or provided, the coal which they required. Thus, at Wearmouth and Tunstall (p. 5) the smith held twelve acres "for the plough-shares (now evidently formed of iron) and the coal (*carbonem*) which he finds." The smith at Sedgefield again (p. 11) held a bovate, or oxgang, of land "for the plough-shares, which he makes, and he finds the coal." And it is further stated (p. 25) that at Escomb, near Bishop Auckland, a certain collier (*carbonarius*) held a toft and a croft and four acres, and found the coals for the plough-shares of the manor of Coundon.

Whether the coal above mentioned consisted of charcoal or mineral coal, and whether the nameless collier (the only one mentioned in the survey) was one of the original colliers or charcoal-burners, or may have been a veritable Troglodite—a digger of "Tartarean coals,"—like the colliers of a later date, we have no means of determining with certainty. An almost parallel, though slightly later, record in the Register of Worcester Priory (p. 56A, Camden Society) obviously relates to the older fuel. Here, under date 1240, we read that " John, the collier, holds a cot-land, for which he pays, etc. ; besides he shall make each *cauk* (*i.e.* cake, coke, or cook) of coal for one penny."

Thus, whatever degree of probability there may be in the supposition that mineral coal is referred to in the *Bolden Buke*, on account of its connection with smith-work, there are no sufficient grounds for confidently assuming it to have been such. The word "finds" (*invenit*) is repeatedly made use of in the book in the simple sense of supplying or providing—men, dogs, horses, etc., for hunting purposes—and without the least intention of conveying the idea of any search being necessary. The carting of "wodlades," or loads of wood for fuel, was also a service commonly required from the vassals, but there is no allusion whatever in the survey to any carting of coal. This book may be regarded as indicating, at all events, that if coal had commenced to be used at all in Durham at this date, its use was extremely rare.

In the adjoining county of Northumberland, coal remains at this period enveloped in profound obscurity. In the Chartulary of New-minster Abbey, near Morpeth (p. 197, Surtees Society, vol. lxvi.), a stream forming part of the boundary of the estate of Stretton, adjoining Shilbottle, near Alnwick, which belonged to this church, is mentioned in the time of Henry II. by the name of Colepethe-burne, and at a later period (p. 202) as Colepeteburne. The first part of this name, it can scarcely be doubted, refers either to charcoal or mineral coal ; but whether the second syllable signifies path, or peat, or pit, we have no means of ascertaining. We know that a forge for the manufacture of iron existed here at an early date, which might account for a traffic in charcoal. If there was likewise a coal-pit in the neighbourhood in the twelfth century, we have no record of the fact.

In this connection it may be mentioned that in the charter granted by Richard I., Cœur de Lion, to Bishop Pudsey, creating him Earl of Northumberland, in order to procure from him a sum of money for crusading purposes—converting, as the king facetiously remarked, an old bishop into a young earl—mines of silver and iron are specified, but there is no allusion to coal.

It can scarcely be doubted that Griff, in Warwickshire, as Dr. Stukeley observes in his *Itinerarium Curiosum* (2nd ed., century II., p. 19), has obtained its name from *digging* having been carried on

there.   Griff—noted as the birthplace of "George Eliot," the
novelist—is situated on the eastern edge of the Warwickshire coalfield.   Its name, as will be noticed, is identical with the word
græfe, already considered in connection with the digging of peat.
Its position certainly favours the hypothesis that this name may
have been given to it from the digging of coal, as Dr. Stukeley
supposed, and it eventually became famous for its coal mines,
though we have no mention of coal in connection with it till long
subsequently.   Griff, as Sir William Dugdale informs us in his
Antiquities of Warwickshire (p. 758, ed. 1765), is not named in Domesday Book.   The earliest mention of it known to him was as the
place of residence of Raphe de Sutlei (or Sudley), who lived 1198-
1241.

It may be remarked with reference to the word *græfe*, as used
in connection with mining, that having no special signification
beyond that of a digging, or excavation, without any regard to
the substance dug, it was applied to mines of coal, lead, and iron,
indifferently ; becoming, in fact, simply the vernacular term for a
mine—just as in the present century the shallow gold mines in
Australia were known as "the diggings."   In addition to Griff, in
Warwickshire, there were at least two other places of the same
name : one in the lead-mining district of Derbyshire, and another in
the north-east of Yorkshire, the latter being probably the seat of
an iron mine.

This word occurs in a large variety of forms, according to different dialects and different ages.   Thus we have the harder and
perhaps older forms of graff, greff, griff (as above), groof, gruff ; and
the softer ones of grave, greave, grove, groove.   Creach (or Criche)
and Cruche, names of mining places in Derbyshire and Somersetshire, if not the same, appear to be cognate words : the former
place, according to Camden, deriving its name from lead mines
there in Saxon times.   And the anonymous author of the *Picture
of Newcastle*, in his account of the coal trade, suggests that Pitten-
crieff, near Dunfermline, in Fife, obtained its name from the digging
of coal there ; though it is of course possible that it may have been
so called from the still older digging of peat, in the vicinity of
this ancient town, which is said to have been a favourite place of
residence of the kings of Scotland.

Though long obscured under the Latin and Norman-French
almost exclusively made use of in written documents for a number
of centuries after the Conquest, through which it only occasionally
rises into view, this word continued in use among the common

people; especially the forms "grove" and "groove," which were still applied to numerous lead mines in Derbyshire, and were also to be met with in the coal district of the north of England, in the eighteenth century; and survive in the name of a coal seam in the neighbourhood of Newcastle-on-Tyne—the Grove, or Groove seam of Walbottle Colliery—to the present day.

So far as coal mines were concerned, this term seems to have been chiefly applied to, and retained by, mines of a more or less horizontal character—the usual form in the earliest period of coal-digging. The common vernacular term for a vertical pit appears to have been "delf"—from the verb to delve—a word which must have been widely applied to coal pits at one time, as it is met with in many of the coalfields, and still exists in the names of coal seams in districts as far apart as the Forest of Dean and Lancashire; its application to the mineral itself probably taking precedence in point of time to that of its application to the place from which it was obtained. But the term "pit" also would seem to have been applied to coal excavations in the north of Northumberland, even in the infancy of coal mining, if the existence of the name of pite-man or pitman there (to be hereafter referred to) may be accepted as affording conclusive evidence of the fact.

Regarding the coal in that ancient mining district, the Forest of Dean, nothing is heard at this period; but it may be here mentioned that a considerable time afterwards we find two individuals basing their claim to the right of taking coal and other things in the forest, on the plea that their ancestors had enjoyed these privileges ever since the Conquest.

The only record which has been supposed to refer to coal in Wales in this era, is contained in the casual remark of Gerald de Barri (*Itin. Camb.*, lib. ii., c. 10) that Coleshulle—adjacent to the town of Flint, which is called Colesul in Domesday Book—signifies the hill of coals (*carbonum collis*). Though this has been cited (Wright's *Domestic Manners*, etc., p. 100) as evidence of coal being now in use, it is so indefinite as to be of little value. The hill referred to was situated in a wooded district, and may have obtained its name (as may also the various other Coleshills have done) from the manufacture of charcoal there: this fuel being extensively employed in mediæval times, notably in making iron, to say nothing of the smelting of other minerals, etc.

Apart, however, from the foregoing somewhat uncertain and unsatisfactory records, there is no doubt that coal did begin to receive some little attention in Belgium and Britain almost simul-

taneously towards the close of the twelfth century. Its discovery
in Belgium, according to the legend, as quoted by Schook in his
"Tractatus de Turffis" (*Groningæ*, 1658, p. 223), was made in 1189 [1]
by a pilgrim, who pointed it out to a smith; while the records of
Holyrood and Newbattle abbeys furnish evidence that it began to
be dug on the south shore of the Firth of Forth, in Scotland, both
at Carriden in Linlithgow and at Preston in East Lothian, before
the end of the reign of William the Lion, or about the year 1200.

Though the changes introduced at the Conquest were in one
sense favourable to the employment of coal for fuel in England,
they were wholly adverse to commerce in general, and particularly
so to the obtaining of a supply of coal for purposes of trade; and
whether or not a commencement had been made to bring it into
use, some further time elapses before we meet with distinct and
direct notices relating to the birth of the coal industry. Meanwhile, certain important political events transpired, which probably
exerted a powerful influence in removing obstacles in the way of
the digging of the mineral. These were the wresting of the Great
Charter from King John by the barons in 1215, and the granting
of the Forest Charter by Henry III. in 1217. By these concessions
on the part of the Crown, the severity of the early Norman rule
was relaxed, and much greater security given to subjects in the
possession of their lands and rights. And though the right to dig
coal in their lands was never formally conceded by the Crown, we
find it subsequently claimed as belonging to them by common law,
the claim being apparently based on the twelfth chapter of the
Forest Charter. This makes no mention of coal, but grants liberty
to every freeman to "erect a mill in his own wood, or upon his
own land, which he hath in the Forest; or make a warren, or pond,
or marle-pit, or ditch, or turn it into arable land, etc."; in short,
concedes the right to dig and break ground, which had previously
been so sternly held in check. At this time mills and warrens,
etc., were matters of more moment than coal. Being granted to
the freemen holding land in the king's forests, these privileges
would, *a fortiori*, be now regarded as legally belonging to all the
freeholders in the kingdom.

Commenting on the above clause of the Forest Charter, Thomson
remarks, in his *Essay on Magna Charta* (p. 351), that the digging of
pits for marle in the neighbourhood of forests, even in ground not

---

[1] Some interesting records have recently been adduced relating to the
working of coal in the Worm coalfield, on the confines of Belgium and
Germany, in 1113 (*Colliery Guardian*, lxxvi. 300).

belonging to the king, was at one time frequently prosecuted in the Forest Courts, and punished with heavy fines, on account of the danger and inconvenience it occasioned in hunting. This was a sport of which the Normans are said to have been passionately fond, and they would no doubt have liked to have preserved England as a happy hunting-ground, only the times would no longer admit of it. The Forest Charter, according to Thomson (p. 337), became a statute of no less importance than the Magna Charta.

The term forest in early times seems to have been almost synonymous with uncultivated land. "The common law," says Mr. Green (*Short History*, p. 63), "ran only where the plough ran; marsh, and moor, and woodland knew no master but the king, no law but his absolute will; and it was this will which was embodied long after Cnut's time in the form of Forest Law."

When the digging of coal commenced, neither king nor subject could have the least conception that it would be followed downwards, and take the form of vast subterranean mines, far exceeding in importance the much-prized mines of the precious metals, so carefully guarded as pertaining to the royal prerogative. Even in the middle of the nineteenth century, the ambassadors from Siam could with difficulty be made to understand that in England men worked underground, and in the dark, in order to obtain coal, because in Siam it was got quite at the surface. So was it in England in the early part of the thirteenth century. Of coal *mines* we have no mention till towards its close. And coal appears to have passed into the hands of subjects, along with peat and other things, as a mere surface material, not worth mentioning, included in the simple right to dig.

CHAPTER III.

THE THIRTEENTH CENTURY. 1217-1307 A.D.

First records relating to coal and coal-digging in England—Northumberland and Durham, the king's forests, Nottinghamshire and Derbyshire, Shropshire, the Forest of Dean, Staffordshire, Lancashire, North Wales, South Wales. Early records of the coal trade—London, Berwick-on-Tweed, Colchester, Dover, etc. Working coal and ironstone by bell pits.

WE reach *terra firma*, both with regard to taking and trading in coal in England, soon after the commencement of the reign of Henry III. The newly-awakened and widespread interest with which the mineral came to be viewed in the thirteenth century, is exhibited by the fact that while it lay to all appearance almost, if not altogether untouched when this king ascended the throne in 1216, between this time and the close of the reign of his son Edward I., in 1307, we have clear records of a beginning having been made to utilize it for fuel in most of the coalfields in the kingdom, and likewise notices of a trade in coals being carried on at many points.

In that classic region of coal, the great northern or Newcastle-on-Tyne coalfield, the mineral must have begun to receive systematic attention in the early part of the reign of Henry III. It is not on the Tyne—the "coaly Tine" of Milton—however, that the first records relating to it are met with. The dawn of the coal trade would seem to have begun further north, where fragments of the mineral, quarried from their native bed by the heavy surge of the North Sea, lay strewn among the shingle on the open Northumberland coast. The strange black stones, which could be burned like charcoal, and were seemingly brought there by the waves themselves—like the associated sea shells and sea weed, a product of the dominions of Neptune—appear to have been here also christened with the peculiar name of "sea coal."

The earliest mention of the mineral in the North under this name refers to sea coal gathered on the shore along with sea weed. This occurs in a grant made to the monks of Newminster Abbey, by Adam de Camhous (now Camboise), of some land on the coast in the vicinity of Blyth ; with a road to the shore for the conveyance of sea weed (*alga maris*) for tillage, and for taking sea coal (*carbo maris*) wherever it could be found, over as much of the shore as belonged to the land (*Chartulary*, p. 55, Surtees Society). The charter is undated, but precedes a covenant between the same monks and Adam, Alan, and Richard de Camhus, dated 1236. The purpose for which the coal was granted is not specified.

Other evidence, to be referred to hereafter, indicates that a small trade in coal already existed on the River Blyth ; and points to the mineral being obtained at Plessey, and shipped to London, at this early period.

In this connection it is curious to find Mr. T. Y. Hall speaking of Blagdon—the seat of Sir Matthew White Ridley, Bart.—which adjoins Plessey, as a point where coal received attention at a remote date. In his list of pits in Durham and Northumberland, in 1854, he particularizes the "Roman Road Old Pit (at the outcrop) near Blagdon, worked 1,000 years ago." Unfortunately we have no means of verifying the statement, but it seems quite probable that coal was got very early at this place.

Nearly simultaneously with the above-mentioned grant of coal at Blyth, the monks of Newminster obtained another similar concession elsewhere. By a charter specially relating to coal (*Chartulary*, p. 201), undated but granted previous to 1240, Nicholas de Aketon gave them the privilege of taking sea coals wherever they could be found in his wood of Middlewood for the forge of their grange of Stretton ; an estate of theirs to which reference has been already made, and which appears to have been situated in the neighbourhood of Shilbottle, near Alnwick. In this case the coal was obviously intended to be used for smith work.

It is noticeable, as indicative of the infantile state of the coal industry in Northumberland at this period, that in the grants of coal to Newminster no reference is made to any process of mining, or even of digging, in order to procure the mineral ; they were to *take* it.

A singular evidence that coal had probably begun to be dug in the middle of this century, in the extreme north of Northumberland, at Holburn, opposite to Lindisfarne, or Holy Island—the abode of St. Cuthbert, and the original seat of the See of Durham—is afforded by the fact that the name piteman, or pitman, is already heard there. About 1240-50 (Raine's *North Durham*, p. 76) James, the son of David de Houburne, confirmed a grant of some land made to the monks of Holy Island by "Roger piteman." In other contemporary records (*ib.*, Appendix, pp. 116, 117) mention also occurs of Alice, daughter of Roger piteman, and of Robert, son of Thomas piteman. If these Pitemans, or Pitmans, obtained their name from a coal pit, as Mr. Raine supposes, it is an exceptionally early instance of the word pit being used in connection with the digging of coal.

Regarding the nascent coal trade of the Tyne there is a dearth of records. It is doubtful, indeed, whether it existed, to any extent at least, before the middle of the thirteenth century. From an account of the trade of Newcastle previous to the reign of Henry III., by Mr. Hodgson Hinde (*Proceedings Archæological Institution*, Newcastle, 1852, vol. i.), coal would appear not to figure among the articles of merchandise exported from Newcastle, or chargeable with tolls and customs, or upon which subsidies were levied in the reign of King John. Even in the reign of Henry III. little is hear of it.

For much of our information as to the early progress of coal mining and the coal trade in the Newcastle-on-Tyne neighbourhood, we are indebted to the records of the struggle on the part of successive bishops of Durham, and priors of Tynemouth, to maintain the ancient rights of their churches to trade freely on the Tyne, against what they considered as the unjustifiable aggression of the townsmen of Newcastle.

In virtue of the incorporation of their town as a royal burgh by King John, in 1213, the burgesses laid claim to an exclusive monopoly of the traffic on the river. This is not surprising, considering the privileged character of such towns in mediæval times, the basis of which was an annual fee-farm rent paid by the burgesses to the Crown, they recouping themselves out of tolls and customs levied upon merchandise of all kinds, and from trading monopolies which they enjoyed. The mediæval burgh was, in fact, the only mercantile town of the district—the residence of its merchants, the seat of its fairs, the market for all its trade—in short, a centre of monopoly. In commerce it could brook no rival near it. To bring their town into this position the burgesses of Newcastle ceaselessly strove, the result being many lively proceedings on their part, and many appeals to the law and the king for protection, on the part o the bishops of Durham, and priors of Tynemouth; the fight continuing throughout several centuries, one king favouring the prelates, another the burgesses, according as the influence of the Church waxed or waned.

The monks of Tynemouth, the picturesque ruins of whose priory, interesting and beautiful even in decay, still adorn the northern heights at the entrance to the river, were probably among the first to dig coal in the valley of the Tyne. They were owners of extensive estates stretching along the north bank of the river, including the manors of Tynemonth, Elswick, Benwell, and Wylam, all which contained easily available coal in abundance. Unfortunately, with the exception of a few excerpts made by Brand, the historian of Newcastle-on-Tyne, the records of this house have not been published. Should they come to be so, they will probably throw some additional light on the early coal trade of the Tyne.

At what date these monks began to turn the coal in their lands to account, we have no precise information; but we have evidence that they were obtaining it in their manor of Tynemouth and shipping it away, in 1269, from the circumstance of its being recorded (*Calendar of Documents Relating to Scotland*, vol. i., p. 511) that in this year certain men of Newcastle were brought before the justices, to answer to the Prior for an alarming and slightly destructive attack which they had made on his infant town of North Shields: one of the counts of the indictment against them being, that they had seized and carried off a ship of his lying there laden with sea coal.

From a statement of the various sources of revenue of their house (Brand, vol. ii., pp. 591, 592) drawn up in 1292, as the basis for the taxation made by Pope Nicholas to procure money for Edward I. engaging in a Crusade, we learn that the Tynemouth monks then derived from their collieries (*carbonariis*) at Tynemouth an average annual income of 61s. 3d.; and had besides another colliery at Wylam, a small village on the western edge of the coalfield famous as the birth-place of George Stephenson, which, in conjunction with a brewhouse there, yielded them annually 20s.

With reference to the above sums it may be remarked that they were not quite so insignificant as they would appear to be. Silver, which formed the chief, indeed, probably the only metallic currency, at this time, was comparatively scarce in Europe previous to the discovery of America, followed by the great influx of this metal, particularly from the rich mines of Potosi. Hence, in the thirteenth century money was from ten to twenty times relatively more valuable than it now is. In Scotland at the present day the word silver, or "siller," continues to be used as synonymous with money; handed down from the time when it really constituted the only money in use, like the word *argent* in France.

While the term "colliery" (*carbonaria* or *carbonarium*) was now used to signify a place where mineral coal was got, it continued long afterwards to be still- likewise applied to an establishment for the manufacture of charcoal. Thus in 1331-32 (Pat. 5 Edw. III., part 1, m. 8) the Prior and Canons of Carlisle claimed to have a colliery in the king's forest of Inglewood, for making coals out of dead wood (*habere carbonarium ad carbones ardendum de mortuo bosco*).

Though we have no direct records relating to other collieries on the Tyne, the growth of a considerable trade in coals on the river, towards the latter part of the thirteenth century, is evidenced by the increase which took place in the revenue of Newcastle-on-Tyne. At an inquest held there by order of Edward I. in 1281 (*Inq. post mort.*, etc., Chancery, 9 Edw. I., No. 85), it was ascertained that when the town was given into the hands of the burgesses by King John, in 1213, at an annual rent of £100, it was then not worth so much ; but it was now so enhanced by coals (*per carbones*) that it was sometimes worth £200 ; though when coals failed it fell much below this value.

On the south side of the Tyne, in the lands of the Bishopric of Durham, the digging of coal would seem to have made little if any progress in the thirteenth century. As late as 1302 the question of the ownership of this hitherto valueless mineral had not been settled between the bishop and his vassals. While no claim was made by the Crown to coal in the lands of subjects, Durham was peculiarly situated in this respect. This formed what is usually described as an *imperium in imperio*, the bishop, in his capacity of a count palatine, enjoying certain quasi-royal prerogatives.

The first notice relating to coal in the bishopric, is in connection with a dispute between the bishop and the freeholders as to the right of the latter to take and trade in the coal found in their lands. This occurs in a petition presented to Edward I. in 1302, by the "Men of the Franchise of Durham between the Tyne and the Tees, against Anthony (Beck) Bishop of Durham," which is given at length in the *Registrum Palatinum Dunelmense* (vol. iii., pp. 41 and 42 ; trans. p. 550). Herein, among other things, it is alleged that "Whereas, where it is lawful for every freeman to make a mill on his own land, and to take coal mine (*prendre myne de carbon*) found in his own land, there come the bailiffs of the bishop, and disturb as well the lords of the vills, as other freeholders, so that they cannot by the things aforesaid make their profit, against the common law of the land."

In the following year (*ib.*, p. 61, trans. p. 557 ; Surtees, vol. i., p. xxxiii.) Bishop Beck effected a reconciliation with the commonalty by the concession, or confirmation, of several important privileges, among which was the right of the freemen to take "mine of coal and of iron" found in their lands.

In the above record, which seems to connect the legal right to take coal mine with the franchises granted by the twelfth chapter of the Forest Charter as already referred to, it will be observed that the word "mine" is used in the sense of ore, or mineral. Such was the original signification of the word, its application to the place where the mineral was got being a later use of the term. Ignorance of this fact has occasionally led translators of mediæval records to construe as "a mine" what should simply be rendered as mine, or mineral—an error which is made in the published translation of this very record.

The same cause has also led to several erroneous attempts to explain the etymology of the word "mine," which, it may be re-marked, is perhaps derived from an Eastern root signifying weight ; stones containing ores being usually heavier than others. Of these the most preposterous is that advanced by Sir John Pettus, who tells us (*Fleta Minor : Essays on Words Metallick*) that he conceives the word "mine" to be no other than a translation of the Latin word *meus* (*i.e.* my own) ; and the word "miners" he thinks may be from *minores* (the lesser), because they are a people of lesser quality than those above ground ! The word "mine" still pre-serves its original meaning in the names of seams or veins of mineral, as in the "Arley Mine" of Lancashire, the "Heathen Mine" of Staffordshire, etc.

It appears to have been in Norman-French, and in the latter part of the fourteenth century, that the word "mine" came to possess its dual meaning, it being then difficult at times to know in which of the two senses the word is used in this language. In Latin the distinction was always preserved, two words being used— viz., *mina* and *minaria* (later *minera*), corresponding to the English words "mine" and "minery"—the former signifying the mineral itself, the latter the place where it was got, and likewise the smelting establishment, which in early times was usually situated in the proximity of the mine. The word "minery" has become obsolete, though at one time in use ; as, for example, in Manlove's metrical version of the Laws and Customs of the lead miners of Derbyshire, where, in allusion to the extraordinary privileges enjoyed by the miners of opening out veins of ore in any man's land—a peculiar, not to say despotic, right quite at variance with common law, doubtless originally acquired by the miners of metal-liferous ores, here and elsewhere, in virtue of the royal prerogative in minerals—it is explained that

> " Churches, houses, gardens, all are free
> From this strange custom of the minery."

Within a few years after the reconciliation had been effected between the bishop and the commonalty we hear of the digging of coal going on in Durham.

In the king's forests the digging of coal, after an irregular fashion and without the sanction of the king, must have begun between 1217 and 1245. The Forest Charter, granted in the former year, contains regulations as to the taking of toll, or cheminage (*i.e.* payment for wayleave, or right of way), from parties obtaining timber, bark, and coal (meaning charcoal), but makes no mention of mineral coal, from which it is clear that the latter had not yet become an object of consideration when the charter was framed. That it was being dug soon afterwards is shown by its being made one of the subject-matters to be examined into by a Royal Commission, appointed in 1245 to investigate regarding encroachments made upon the king's forest since the commencement of the reign of Henry III.: "Let inquiry also be made," says one of the instructions (M. Paris, *Historia Major*, p. 661, ed. 1640), "touching sea coal found within (or below) the forest, and what persons have taken the payment (or bribe) for diggings made on account of that coal, and for cheminage" (*et qui mercedem ceperint pro fossatis faciendis de carbone illo, et pro cheminagio*).

The use of the Latin word *fossatum* (a fosse, or trench) bespeaks the open character of the excavations here referred to. When vertical pits begin to be mentioned in Latin records, at a later period, the word *puteus* (a well hole) is applied to them.

The circumstance of coal smoke being already prevalent in Not-tingham in the middle of the thirteenth century, sufficiently indicates that some progress had been made in the digging of the mineral in the southern portion, at least, of the great coalfield of Yorkshire, Derbyshire, and Nottinghamshire—the "woollen coalfield," as it has been termed. It is recorded in the *Annales de Dunstaplia* under date 1257 A.D. (see also Nichol's *Leicester*, vol. i., p. 143) that Queen Eleanor had been sent to stay at this town during the absence of Henry III. on an expedition into Wales, but had to remove to

Tutbury Castle, Staffordshire, instead, being quite unable to remain
in Nottingham by reason of the smoke of the sea coals.

Records connected with the early working of coal in this coalfield
are few; the demand for coal in inland districts being extremely
small in the thirteenth century, when its use was almost entirely
confined to smiths and limeburners.   There is a notice, however
(*Abbrev. Placit.*, p. 260, rot. 48), of a law suit taking place in 1306-7,
regarding the right to dig coals at Denby, in Derbyshire; and we
know from later evidence that a commencement must have been
made to work coal at Alfreton, in this county, about the same date.

In the small but interesting coalfield of Shropshire, mention
occurs of coal in a right-of-way granted about 1250 (Dugdale's
Monasticon, vol. v., p. 360; Eyton's *Shropshire*. vol. iii., p. 276), by
Philip, Lord of Benthale, to the Abbey of Buildewas, for leading
stones, coals, and timber.   Though mineral coal is probably alluded
to, as the materials seem to have been intended for building purposes,
this record is not quite conclusive.   But a few years later another
occurs (Eyton, vol. iii., p. 27) of a sufficiently definite character.
Between 1260 and 1263 Walter de Clifford, Lord of Corfham,
granted Sir John de Halston license to dig coals in the forest of
La Clie (the Clee Hills) to sell or give away.   Among the receipts
obtained by the Abbot of Wigmore from Kayham and Switton, in
this county, in 1291 (*ib.*, vol. iv., p. 362), there is an item of
"profits from a coalmine 5s."

In the ancient iron-mining district of the Forest of Dean, which,
like the tin-mining district of Cornwall and a portion of the lead-
mining district of Derbyshire, formed part of the demesne lands of
the Crown, coal may have been dug at an early period; but
information regarding it is only obtained in 1282, in connection
with an inquiry into the rights and privileges claimed by the
keepers of the bailiwicks in the forest.   Rudder informs us in his
History of Gloucestershire (p. 34, ed. 1779) that on this occasion six of
the ten bailiffs claimed iron ore and sea coal, dead and dry wood
and windfalls, and had their claims allowed; particularly the bailiff
of Blakeney and Sir Rauf de Abbenhalle, as he and his ancestors
had enjoyed the same ever since the Conquest.   If this latter
statement be literally correct as regards coal, it would point to
the digging of it to a small extent in the Forest of Dean at an
earlier date than any contemporary record seems to indicate.   At
the same time we cannot attach much weight to a mixed claim of
this kind, made so long afterwards, as affording satisfactory evidence that coal was actually dug in the Forest so very far back.

Regarding four of the six bailiffs above mentioned, it is stated that they knew not by what warrant they had these privileges; and the same is said of Nicholas de Lacu, who took coal in his wood of Lideneye. The coal in the other bailiwicks belonged to the king, but the record furnishes no information as to the conditions under which it was worked. In the *Laws and Customs of the Miners in the Forrest of Dean* (published at London in 1687), however, which, according to Mr. Nicholls (*Forest of Dean*, p. 13), incontrovertibly belong to the reign of Edward I., and describe the regulations under which the working of the iron ore was carried on in the Forest, it is set forth (p. 17) that "the sea coal mine is as free in all points as the oare mine." From this it would appear that the coal was worked by the free miners under arrangements with the Crown similar to those relating to the iron ore.

Not yet was Staffordshire the busy hive of industry its rich mineral stores were destined to cause it to become. It was no Black Country in the thirteenth century. Here in the time of Edward I. (W. B. Scott, *Trans. So. Stafford. Inst.*, 1886), Margery La Rous, lady of the moiety of the town of Walsale, granted to Roger Morteyn and his heirs a moiety of the profit of each manner of mine, as well of sea coal as of iron.[1] At Brierley Hill, and up to Dudley, it is said (Midland Mining Commission, *First Report*, p. 63) that mines have existed since 1300 along the line where the measures are brought up to the day by Netherton Hill, etc.

From an inquisition dated 1282-83 (*Inq. post. mort.*, 11 Edw. I., No. 34), it appears that William de Audleye held the manor of Tunstall, in North Staffordshire, of Edmund, son of King Henry, with various pertinents, among which were two mills with pool, etc., an iron mine worth yearly 40s., and a mine of sea coal worth yearly 14s. 8d.

In the coalfield of Lancashire—the "cotton coalfield" as it has been called—coal was being got in the neighbourhood of Colne before the close of the thirteenth century. It was probably here that the monks of Bolton Abbey procured the sea coals we find them buying for their forge in 1294 (Whitaker's *Craven*, 2nd ed., p. 384), as they continued to send to Colne for coal for this special purpose long subsequently. A more direct record, however, occurs (Whitaker's *Whalley*, etc., 4th ed., vol. i., p. 361) immediately

[1] The writer has Mr. P. R. Björling to thank for drawing his attention to this and a number of other records relating to early coal mining in Staffordshire and Yorkshire.

afterwards. In 1295-96 the sea coals at Trahden, in the lands of Henry de Lacy, yielded a revenue of 10s.

According to Pennant (*Tours in Wales*, vol. i., p. 23, ed. 1810), collieries existed at Mostyn, in North Wales, in the time of Edward I., as appears, he says, by an extent of that place in the twenty-third year of his reign (1294-95).

In the great coalfield of South Wales the earliest mention of coal as yet brought to light is contained in the charter granted to Swansea, in 1305, by William de Brews. In this he concedes to the townsmen dead and dry wood, oak for building and for ships, turves and peats, and license to have earth coal (*carbonem terreum*) in Ballywasta, to supply all their necessaries, but not to sell to strangers. (*Charters granted to Swansea*, by G. G. Francis, London, 1867 (not published); Will. de Breuosa: Gower, Swansea, Pat. 33 Edw. I., part 2, *a tergo*.)

Coal was, however, probably dug and exported from Swansea previous to this date. We find sea coal used at the king's silver mines at Byrland, in Devon, in 1301-2, in the accounts of Thomas de Sweneseye (*Archæological Journal*, No. 108, p. 318, 1870), who held the position of Master of the King's Mines in Devon and Cornwall at this period. Coal is also stated (*Mining Journal*, xviii. 23) to have been worked in Monmouthshire in the reign of Edward I.

Contemporaneously with the first mention of sea coal in Northumberland, a ray of light is reflected from a London record regarding the incipient use of the mineral at this "devouring focus." In the year 1228 a person is referred to in a State document (Pipe Roll, 12 Henry III.; Riley's *Memorials of London*, p. xvi.) as hailing from "Sacoles[1] Lane"—the advent of the new fuel in the metropolis having been signalized by a lane in the suburbs, where it was carried and used, being named after it. This lane (Stow's *Survey of London*, p. 705, ed. 1618) was also called Limeburners' Lane, which sufficiently accounts for coal having been so soon attracted to this distant spot, the local demand for it in the north at this early period being no doubt almost *nil*. This habitat of metropolitan limeburners is the first mart we hear of in England for coal as an article of merchandise.

We are also not without some indication of one at least of the

[1] The meaning of the name would appear not to have been quite understood yet in London. Sea Coal Lane still exists in the vicinity of Ludgate Circus, half-buried under modern London. In the thirteenth century it is spoken of as *extra Neugat' in suburbio London'*.

localities from which coal was probably thus early brought to
London.   In a subsequent record of the year 1253, relating to some
houses in "Secole Lane" (*Cartæ Antiquæ*, Chancery, L., No. 20, in
dorso), they are stated to have formerly been the property of William
of Plessey (*Willielmi de Plessetis*).   From this it would appear that
coal was shipped from Plessey to London almost at the beginning of
the reign of Henry III.

Notices relating to the early coal trade between London and the
north are scanty.   There is mention (Patent Roll, 41 Hen. III. ;
Riley's *Memorials,* Introduction, p. xvi., note) of the arrival of ship-
loads of sea coal in London in 1257 ; and payments were made out
of the Exchequer in 1258 and 1259 (Devon's *Issues,* Hen. III.—Hen.
VI. 48, 74) for small quantities of sea coal for forging iron at Westminster Palace.   From the *Liber Albus,* or White Book of London
(Riley's translation, p. 208), we also learn that among the Customs
of Billyngesgate,[1] in the time of Henry III., one of the duties
leviable there was, "For two quarters of sea coal, measured by the
King's quarter, one farthing."   But the quantity brought was
doubtless for a long period very insignificant.

When the volume of trade began to expand it encountered a
remarkable check.   It appears that towards the end of the reign of
Edward I., brewers, dyers, and others who required much fuel, had
then lately commenced to substitute coal for the wood and charcoal
they had previously used in their furnaces.   But unaccustomed as
the London of that time was,

> " to smoke, to the eclipse
> That metropolitan volcanoes make,
> Whose Stygian throats breathe darkness all day long,"

a general revolt took place in 1306 against this innovation as an
intolerable nuisance, corrupting the air of the city, with the result
that these would-be coal consumers were compelled by the King
(Pat. 25 Edw. I., m. 5 d') to eschew the obnoxious mineral and
return to the fuel they had been wont to use of old.   According to
Stow, smiths only were excepted, but shortly afterwards limeburners
also are found continuing to use coal unmolested, as they had long
been doing.

---

[1] Billingsgate long continued to be the headquarters of the London coal
trade.   As late as the middle of the eighteenth century the coal factors
and buyers used to associate together among the fish people in order to
effect purchases of coal.—*Report on the Coal Trade,* 1830, p. 160.

The quarter-chaldron measure—known as the "vat," and holding 9 bushels
of coal—continued in use down till the present century.—*Ibid.,* p. 86.

It has been frequently stated that coal was used for fuel in West minster Palace at the coronation of Edward II. This is altogether improbable, and there is no sufficient foundation for the statement. There is a record (Brand, vol. ii., p. 254) of 10s. worth of sea coal being taken to the palace at this time; the purpose for which it was intended not being specified. But in the case of various purchases of the mineral made by the clerk of the palace previous to and subsequent to this date (Devon's *Issues of the Exchequer*, Henry III. to Henry VI., pp. 48, 74, 130), the fuel is stated to have been bought for the use of smiths. We only hear of the above 10s. worth in connection with a claim for its payment, made about fourteen years after it was got. For three centuries later coal continued to be regarded by the upper classes in London as a most inferior and objectionable fuel.

The importation of coal into Berwick-on-Tweed—first heard of in 1265, in the account of the sheriff of that town, published in the *Rolls of the Chamberlain of Scotland* (vol. i.), where there is recorded a purchase of five chalders of sea coals (*carbones marini*) for the castle there—must have become a regular branch of the trade of the town in the last decade of the thirteenth century, inasmuch as the sale of coal, among other things, out of ships arriving in the port, was regulated by one of the Statutes of the Guild enacted in 1294 (*Ancient Laws and Customs of the Burghs of Scotland*, vol. i., p. 87—Scottish Burgh Records Society). But whether any portion of the coal imported had begun to be used for domestic purposes we have no means of discovering.

Regarding the extent to which coal was being utilized in the town of Colchester, very exact information is available in two taxing bills relating to this place. In the first of these, belonging to the year 1295-96 (*Rot. Parl.*, vol. i., p. 228 *b*), sea coals, valued at 6d. per quarter, are found in the possession of some four householders only. In one case at least the owner of it was evidently a smith, having a store of iron as well as sea coal; and if we make allowance for the possibility of the others being either smiths, limeburners, brewers or dyers, scarcely any margin is left for supposing that coal was being used for domestic purposes in this place; and this seems corroborated by the fact that in the case of the second bill (1300-1) sea coals are only found in the possession of one householder. Curiously, an inhabitant of this town is mentioned by the name of "Sacole sutor," or sea-coal shoemaker, perhaps given to this son of the last from his eccentricity in the matter of fuel.

Various small purchases of sea coal are quoted by Mr. Rogers in

SECTION FROM HEDDON O

HEDDON ON THE WALL

Sea Level

Walbottle

THE NINETY FATHOM DYKE

Benwell

Elswick

NEWCASTLE

HIGH MAIN
BENSHAM
LOW MAIN
BEAUMONT
BROCKWELL

GROOVE SEAM
ENGINE SEAM
SPLINT SEAM

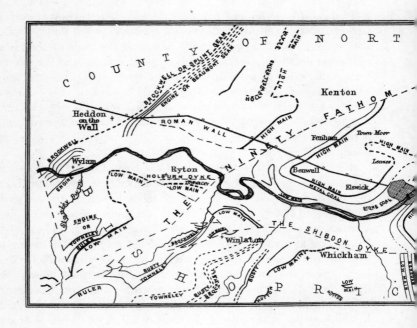

GEOLOGICAL PLAN SHOWING THE OUTCR

I.

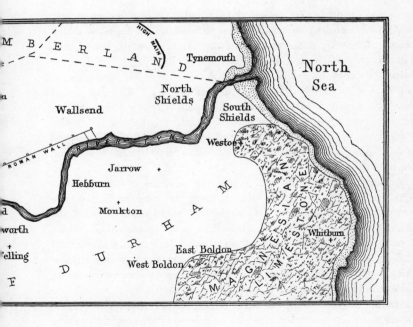

WALL   TO   TYNEMOUTH

Wallsend   Percy Main   TYNEMOUTH   North Sea

HIGH MAIN
BENSHAM
LOW MAIN
BEAUMONT
BROCKWELL

M B E R L A N D   HIGH MAIN   Tynemouth   North Sea

North Shields   South Shields

Wallsend

ROMAN WALL   Westoe

Jarrow   M

Hebburn   A

Monkton   G

worth   N   Whitburn
        E
elling   S

F   D U R H A M   I   East Boldon
                A   West Boldon
                N   L I M E S T O N E

THE COAL SEAMS NEAR THE RIVER TYNE.

his *History of Agriculture and Prices in England* (voi i., p. 422, and
vol. ii., p. 333), as at Dover in 1279, and at Waleton and Weston,
two places in Suffolk and Herts, in 1291 and 1292.   At the same
time exception may be taken to the assertion of this writer that the
coal bought for Dover Castle " must of course have been burnt in a
fireplace with a chimney."   The whole tenor of contemporary records
points to the conclusion that at such an early date it was more probably burnt in the smithy.   Purchases of sea coals for the use of the
smiths and limeburners figure very commonly in the accounts of
castles which were being erected in the early part of the following
century—*e.g.* Dunstanborough, Carnarvon, Beaumaris, etc.

Though we are without a single clear reference to the use of coal
for domestic purposes during the thirteenth century, we know that
about 1300 a commencement was undoubtedly made to admit this
fuel into house fires.   In this connection the grant of coal to
Swansea in 1305—the earliest instance of a grant of coal to a
town—may probably be regarded as an indication of the movement
which had begun to be made in this direction, references to which
became sufficiently numerous and clear soon afterwards, both in the
coalfields themselves and on the east coast.

Greater progress would appear to have been made in the use of
coal in China than in England at this period.   The celebrated
Venetian traveller, Marco Polo, who spent twenty years in that
part of the world in the latter part of the thirteenth century, refers
to black stones dug in the mountains of Cathay, which were used
for fuel, and preferred to wood both because they burned better and
cost less.

In the infancy of the coal trade, the supplies of the new fuel
would doubtless at first be obtained on the very surface of the
ground, as on the sea shore, and at the weathered edges of coal beds,
where it only required to be lifted.   The next process would consist
of removing the surface earth from above a section of the bed, and
forming an open-cast, or quarry work, a method of procuring coal
which continued to be practised at suitable spots for many centuries,
and even at the present day is not altogether extinct.

Another method of obtaining coal and ironstone practised in the
distant past, the character of which sufficiently indicates it to belong
to the very alphabet of mining, was that of sinking what are known
as *bell* or *bee-hive pits*.   Like the open-cast works, this partook more of
digging than of mining, and may be regarded as occupying a tran-
sitional place between the two.   No records of this primitive
system have come down to us, and we only know of it from the

works which have been brought to light by more recent operations. It was practised where the stratum of mineral lay only a few yards beneath the surface, and was probably employed, in the first instance, in procuring ironstone. It consisted in sinking a small pit through the surface cover, which was widened out or "belled" at the bottom, to lay bare as much of the mineral as was consistent with safety ; and when this had been removed the working was abandoned, and a new pit sunk alongside.

These bell pits—veritable baby pits—have been found in many parts of the kingdom, indicating that the system was at one period widely practised.

They have been met with in different parts of Yorkshire, and notably in the neighbourhood of Leeds (*Leeds Mercury Supplement*, May 16, 1885), where they were employed in procuring ironstone. At the Calls works, where a bed 5 or 6 feet in thickness, containing nodules of ironstone, lay under a depth of from 7 to 9 feet of cover, the pits were 3 feet in diameter, and placed 12 feet apart from centre to centre, only admitting of each pit being belled out little more than 1 yard all round, an unwrought shell being left between the excavations. Similar workings have likewise been found at Egton Moor (*Yorkshire Archæolog. Journal*, 1883, part xxix., p. 39), and Burmantofts.

In South Staffordshire also bell pits were made use of for procuring ironstone at a time when coal was of no value whatever, being sunk through coal, the only use made of which was to throw it back with the rubbish to help to fill up the pit after the ore had been got. At the Coppice, Sedgley (*Trans. Fed. Inst.*, vi. 554-5), the pits were 5 feet in diameter at the top, and 12 feet at the bottom, and from 15 to 20 feet deep. The workings were confined to a distance of not more than 8 or 9 feet from the shaft: average about 6 feet. Many bell pits are also stated to have been found when the Eccleshall reservoir was made.

At Ponkey, near Ruabon, in North Wales, ironstone had been worked in a precisely similar manner by means of bell pits, which, here also, had been sunk through coal.

Of the employment of bell pits in the working of coal several notices occur.

In the small coalfield at Stublick, near Hexham, in Northumberland, Mr. Greenwell informs us (*Trans. Manchester Geolog. Soc.*, x. 51) that coal had been worked by means of such pits, placed 8 or 10 yards apart.

Perhaps to this system also may be ascribed the peculiar workings mentioned by Professor Hull (*Coalfields*, 3rd ed., p. 16) as having been found near the outcrop of the Arley mine, not far from Wigan, in Lancashire. Here, in driving a tunnel to divert the course of the river Douglas, the seam was discovered to have been excavated into a series of polygonal chambers, with vertical walls, opening into each other by short passages, presenting on a ground plan something of the appearance of a honeycomb, altogether different from anything within the experience of the miners of the district.

This system is likewise stated to have been pursued in the early period of the working of the thick coal of South Staffordshire (*Proceed. Inst. Mechan. Eng.*, 1860, p. 95), and we have evidence (*Min. Jour.*, xviii. 23) of it having at one time been pursued in the working of coal in Monmouthshire. That it was the best method of procedure under the circumstances is indicated by the fact that it continued to be practised in Yorkshire by the Low Moor, Bowling, and North Brierley companies, for getting ironstone, as recently as the middle of the present century (*Ibid.*, p. 44), at depths of from 20 to 45 feet from the surface. In Derbyshire also the working of ironstone by bell pits was practised equally recently down to depths of 20 or 30 yards (Prof. Phillips' *Report*, p. 38). What is perhaps the nearest approach to a record relating to the bell pit system of working is to be found in one of the ancient laws of the Forest of Dean miners, which fixed the bounds of a mine at the distance to which a miner could throw the rubbish from his pit—a distance at a considerably later period commuted to 12 yards all round. These laws belong to about 1300 A.D., and seem to indicate that at the date of their compilation the Forest miners had scarcely emerged from the bell pit system of procuring minerals.

CHAPTER IV.

THE FOURTEENTH CENTURY. 1307—1400 A.D.

*The Chimney. Leases of coal. Staiths and Keels. Collieries in Elswick.
Royal grants of coal to Newcastle.*

CHIMNEYS, in the modern sense of the word, which has reference to
the outlet for the smoke rather than to the fireplace itself, appear to
have been unknown in dwelling-houses in ancient times.   The hall,
or entrance chamber, which with the Romans was also the cooking
place, or kitchen (*culina*), was designated the black apartment
(*atrium*) ; a name doubtless conferred upon it on account of its
smoke-begrimed aspect, and clearly indicating that the smoke
wended its way through the room before arriving at any " entrance
out."

The central situation of the fireplace in a Roman cottage is illustrated in the concluding stanzas of Macaulay's " Lay of Horatius,"
where, referring to the recital of the story in after years on winter
nights, beside a roaring fire of the good logs of Algidus, he describes
this as being done

" When young and old in circle
Around the firebrands close "

—the fire having in early times been in reality the centre, or *focus*,
of " the family circle."

In his *History of Domestic Manners and Sentiments in England during
the Middle Ages* (p. 98), Mr. Wright informs us that chimneys were
a new characteristic introduced into the more private apartments of
the Norman houses, and especially the castles, the massive walls of
which admitted of flues, or vents, being carried up in their thickness ; though, at the same time, in the hall the piled-up fire in the
middle of the floor was usually still retained.

What is perhaps one of the earliest historical notices relating to a
chimney occurs in Brayley and Britton's *History of the Ancient Palace*

at Westminster (p. 59), where it is recorded that in 1251, Richard of Westminster was commanded that the low chamber in the king's garden should be painted, and that in the same chamber a chimney should be made.

The fuel used in this chimney consisted, however, of wood billets, doubtless of the choicest; though, rather curiously, when it was taken down (or blown down) and rebuilt a few years afterwards (1258-59), some sea coal was present as the favoured fuel of the smiths engaged in strengthening the shaft on the outside. But for several centuries later such chimneys were almost entirely confined to great houses.

Early in the fourteenth century we begin to hear of a domestic invention called an iron chimney (*caminus ferreus*). This was a semi-portable apparatus, not attached to the wall in any way, but capable of being moved from one room to another. The fact of its being considered so important a piece of furniture as to be frequently entailed by will upon son after son in succession (Raine's *North Durham*, p. 101n), illustrates how scarce and valuable iron continued to be.

Whether the iron chimney was specially invented with a view to the employment of coal fuel is perhaps not absolutely certain; but this seems somewhat probable, inasmuch as it makes its appearance just at the period when coal began to be used for domestic purposes, and the two frequently figure together in the same accounts. Thus in a fragmentary inventory of the goods and chattels belonging to Jarrow Monastery in 1310 (Surtees Society, vol. xxix., p. 3), we find the monks there having two iron chimneys in the hall of their house; and in their accounts for the year 1313 (*ib.*, p. 8), which are the earliest extant, sea coals (*carbones maritimi*) are likewise purchased by them.

But even this form of chimney is stated to have been employed by richer people only, such as the religious houses, while the poorer classes must have originally used coal in the ordinary way, though at first, doubtless, merely as an adjunct to other fuel. Indeed, the mixing of coal with other kinds of fuel seems to have been commonly practised during a long period, the new fuel becoming dovetailed on to the old, which it gradually supplanted.

The incipient use of coal for domestic purposes, references to which are met with almost simultaneously in many districts in the first quarter of the fourteenth century, imparted a new importance to the mineral in localities where it had hitherto been of little or no value. Insignificant at the outset, the demand steadily increased in

volume, especially from about the middle of the century, and doubtless contributed in no small degree to bring about the opening out
of additional colleries.

A new feature in connection with the working of coal dates from
the early part of this century. Though supplies could still, and,
indeed, for a long time, be got in some places without the necessity
of mining, this was gradually becoming the exception. In most
cases subterranean works had to be resorted to, in the opening out
of which some preliminary trouble and expense were incurred.
With this altered condition of matters, and the expansion of the
industry at the same time, the custom of letting coal on lease began.
In return for the privilege of working the coal for a stipulated period,
the lessees paid a rent to the landowners ; and likewise undertook,
at their own cost, the preparatory operations necessary for gaining
access to, or as is usually termed "winning," the coal.

In the great northern coalfield of Northumberland and Durham,
the records relating to the working of coal in the fourteenth century
are remarkably full and interesting, and furnish us not only with a
good panorama of the localities where the mineral was being got,
but even with some details of the mining operations carried on
in this coalfield at this early period. Many of the usages and terms
peculiar to coal mining and the coal trade in this district, are found
to have existed since the early years of the industry.

Already on the Tyne the coal was loaded into boats by means of
stagings, known then as now by the antique name of *staiths*. This
early English term, signifying a staying, or stopping place, appears
at one time to have been applied to the bank of a river itself—as in
the *Brut* of Layamon, which belongs to the close of the twelfth
century and reads almost like a foreign language, where this priest
is described as living at Ernley, in North Worcestershire, at a
noble church on Severn's bank, and being well pleased with his
surroundings :

> "he wonede at Ernleye
> at ædhelen are chirechen
> uppen Seuarne stathe
> sel thar him thuhte"

—but it came to be specially employed to designate the stations
on the banks of a river, with their wooden framework partly projecting into it, which were used for loading purposes. These points
were also utilized as depôts for storing coals and other merchandise
so as to be ready for shipment : explaining how the great flood in
the rivers of Northumberland, caused by the melting of snow about

Christmas 1377, is described by Walsingham (*Hist. Angl.*, vol. i., p. 323) as having swept away the pit coals, mill stones, etc., which had been gathered there.

At Hithe, in Kent (*Fossil Fuel*, p. 349), the landing place is called the Stade. And in this form the term still exists in a number of compounds, such as home-stead, farm-stead, etc., and probably also in such names as Stead and Stedman.

Keels too—that ancient craft brought with them by the English when they came to Britain (the germs of our vast modern fleets), which for so many centuries played an important part in the Tyne coal trade, and whose name is so familiar at the present day in connection with the popular air of the "The Keel Row"—thus early plied to and fro between the staiths situated on the shallow upper reaches of the river and the vessels lying below Newcastle bridge.

Among situations favourable to the prosecution of coal mining, the high grounds on both banks of the Tyne, near Newcastle and Gateshead, presented a combination of natural advantages of the rarest description, both from a geological and geographical point of view. Seams of coal, of good thickness and excellent quality, were to be found cropping out, or basseting, on the hillsides. The opening-up of collieries was thus an easy and inexpensive process, while below lay the broad-bosomed river, ready to waft away their produce to numerous markets on the east coast, as well as to others on the opposite shores of the Continent: there being a reference (Brand, vol. ii., p. 255) to a foreign export of coal as early as 1325, when a ship of Pontoise, in France, brought a cargo of corn to Newcastle-on-Tyne, and returned freighted with *charboun de meer*, or sea coal.

In the part of this favoured tract on the north side of the Tyne, and immediately to the west of the town lands of Newcastle, was situated the manor of Elswick, already referred to as forming a portion of the possessions of Tynemouth Priory. Here, at little depth, lay a fine bed of coal, called, from its superior importance, the "Main coal," which, at a later period, made the collieries of the Tyne, and Wallsend Colliery in particular, so far famed.

Though the Tynemouth monks had collieries at Tynemouth and Wylam in 1292, they had not then begun to work coal in Elswick. But we find them obtaining possession of some land and buildings on the staiths (*les stathes*) at Newcastle in 1326 (Gibson's *Mon. of Tynemouth*, vol. i., p. 138), giving them facilities for the shipment of coal from Elswick ; and soon afterwards we hear of coal being worked in this manor and new collieries being opened out, as appears from the following entries in their Chartulary (Brand, vol. ii., p. 255

note), which are the earliest records we have of collieries being let on lease in the great northern coalfield :

"Note that the colliery of Elswick called 'le Heygrove' has been demised to Adam de Colewell, from the feast of St. Martin, 1330 A.D., till the same feast a year after, for 100s.

"Note that the other new colliery, which Hugh de Hecham formerly held, in the west field of Elswick, has been demised to the same Adam de Colewell, for a payment of six marks (80s) ; the year to begin when he has dug it."

It is obvious that these two coal mines, particularly the first mentioned, had been in existence previous to this date. In the latter part of the name of "Heygrove" (*i.e.* the high mine), the vernacular term for a mine (*grove*) is observable. The fact of the uppermost seam of coal at the modern colliery of Walbottle, in this neighbourhood, being known to the present day as the Grove, or Groove seam, as previously referred to, indicates that coal was probably worked here also at an early date, notwithstanding the absence of contemporary records relating to it.

A person of the name of Hugh de Hecham, not unlikely the very individual mentioned above as having been lessee of a colliery in Elswick—the name being a Newcastle one—figures as a metropolitan limeburner, or "lymbrennere," at this period (Riley's *Memorials*, p. 174). He was evidently a person of some weight among the limeburning fraternity in London, and succeeded in inducing his fellow tradesmen to combine together to raise the price of lime, to the great grievance of "the good folks of the ward of Tower." Hugh, however, was brought before the Lord Mayor in 1329, charged with extortion and intimidation, and in the end got sent to prison for his pains.

Regarding the Elswick mines at this early time, we also learn that in 1331 the colliery in the west field, near the road, was leased to one Ralph Bullock, for part of a year, at a rent of 2s. a week. Then, a year or two afterwards, notice occurs of the opening out of an altogether new colliery in Elswick Moor :

"Note that John le Carter, Richard de Colewell, and Geoffrey Lene, of Elswick, have taken one colliery to be newly dug in the moor of Elswick, near Gallowflat, to be held from the feast of All Saints, 1334, till the same feast a year after, for 20s."

The Gallow-flat, or Gala-flat, was the place where the Newcastle gallows were erected, and was reached by a street called the Gallow-gate. Old coal-workings in the Gallow-flat neighbourhood are heard of at a later period in the annals of coal mining.

The above pristine Elswick records illustrate the extreme simplicity of coal-digging on the Tyne at this date, and the facility with which collieries could be inaugurated. The name "Colewell" also savours of an early stage in the history of pit sinking. The unsophisticated character of the leases is shown by the fact of no definite limit being apparently placed on the quantity of coal allowed to be worked in return for the rent paid, nor any stipulations made regarding the manner in which the operations were to be carried on.

In the adjoining town lands of Newcastle-on Tyne, consisting of an extensive tract lying outside the walls of the town, the digging of coal had not yet commenced. Though the town had been given into the hands of the burgesses by King John, to be held direct from the Crown at an annual fee farm rent, no grant had been made of the town lands. The only parts of these lands to which the burgesses had acquired any rights were known as the Castle-field and the Frith; and even in these the privileges conceded extended to certain surface rights alone, the minerals not having been granted by the Crown.

The Castle-field probably owed its name and origin to the fact of its having been detached from the Castle Moor by King John, to be given to certain burgesses as compensation for land of which they had been deprived in connection with the formation of a moat round the castle, from which the town took its name. The Frith was a much later acquisition. It seems to have been at first rented by the burgesses from the Crown, as there is mention (Charleton's *Newcastle Town*, p. 347) of the payment of one mark per annum for rent of "a certain field called Le Frythe." According to Grey (*Chorographia, or a Survey of Newcastle-upon-Tine*, 1649) Edward III. made a gift of it to the town "for the good services of the townsmen": supposed to have been a brave and successful *sortie* which was made in the year 1342, from a postern gate in the Edwardian walls, surprising the Scotch army encamped in the Frith, and taking the Earl of Moray prisoner.

Though the revenue of Newcastle had been so much increased, as we have seen, by the rise of the coal trade subsequent to the fixing of the annual rent, the town was brought very low in the middle of the fourteenth century by the great pestilence known as the Black Death, which swept over town and country in the summer of 1349, and twice successively during the next few years, paralyzing commerce of every description, and indeed carrying off about one half of the population.

PLATE III.

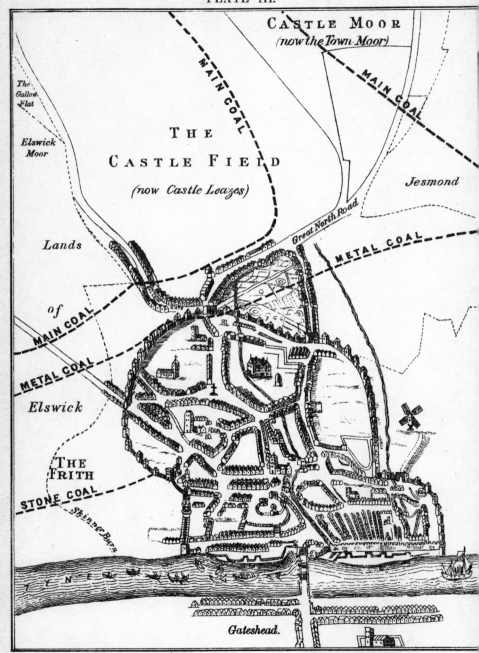

THE GALLOW FLAT

Elswick Moor

THE CASTLE FIELD
(now Castle Leazes)

CASTLE MOOR
(now the Town Moor)

MAIN COAL

MAIN COAL

Jesmond

Great North Road

Lands

of

MAIN COAL

METAL COAL

METAL COAL

Elswick

THE FRITH

STONE COAL

Skinner Burn

TYNE

Gateshead.

PLAN OF NEWCASTLE-ON-TYNE, AND PARTS ADJOINING:

THE TOWN BEING TAKEN FROM SPEED'S MAP, 1610 A.D.

Scale 5 inches to a Mile.

In their difficulties the burgesses of Newcastle petitioned Edward III. for permission to dig, and to take coals and stone, in the common lands of the town outside the walls, in the places called the Castle-field and the Frith, and to make profit therefrom in aid of the payment of their annual rent. And on the 1st of December, in the twenty-fourth year of his reign (1351), by Letters Patent (24 Edw. III., part 3, m. 6), addressed "to his beloved Mayor, and Bailiffs, and good men of our town of Newcastle-on-Tyne," the king granted them this license, to continue during his good pleasure, for 20s. paid into the hamper.

The above is obviously the license said by Gardiner (*England's Grievance*, ch. 3) to have been granted to Newcastle by Henry III., and to which he makes no allusion at this period. That it belongs to the reign of Edward III. is sufficiently attested by its existence on the patent roll of this king, which is further corroborated by the receipt of the 20s. paid for the privilege by the mayor, bailiffs, and good men of Newcastle, being acknowledged on the corresponding Exchequer roll (*Abbrev. Rot. Orig.*, vol. ii., p. 215). In addition to this, the license is referred to in other contemporary records, to be mentioned immediately, as having been recently granted; while it contains internal evidence that it cannot belong to the date hitherto assigned to it. The walls alluded to were undoubtedly those built in the reigns of the Edwards; and the very first words of the license itself, "The king, to his beloved mayor and bailiffs," which are omitted by Gardiner, refute the idea of it belonging to the year 1239, as usually stated, Newcastle at that time not yet having any mayor.

It has been necessary to enter with some detail into this question, as there has hitherto been an error of more than a hundred years as to the date when the digging of coal began in the town lands of Newcastle outside the walls, and as this erroneous view has formed a stereotyped part of all historical notices relating to coal ever since Gardiner wrote in 1665, though some writers had observed a difficulty about it. Brand (vol. ii., p. 253 note) acknowledges that he could not find the grant; which is not surprising, not only on account of its having been misplaced, but because the patent roll of the year to which Gardiner refers it happens to be one of the very few which have been lost.

Whether the townsmen of Newcastle may have previously dug coal under the town, cannot probably now be ascertained. Brand speaks of the existence of subterranean passages; but as to the period when they were constructed, or whether they had any connection with the digging of coal, we have no information.

The Castle-field still retained its early name in 1542, at which date there is mention (Charleton's *Newcastle*, p. 365) of "a place called Spittel Tongs adjoining the Castle Fields." It is now known as the Castle Leazes, or simply as the Leazes (*i.e.* the leas or fields). The Frith was subsequently called the Forth. They were both contiguous to the lands of the manor of Elswick.

A curious light is thrown upon the then recent date of the license to dig coal in these tracts of the town lands, by the fact that a few years later we find the Prior of Tynemouth appealing to the king for protection, alleging that under colour of this royal license, the men of Newcastle were digging in his moor of Elswick, and endeavouring to demolish the drain (*seweram*) from his mine in Elswick Moor, which was the chief source of sustenance of himself and his house. Commissioners were in consequence appointed by the king (Pat. 31 Edw. III., part i., m. 25 d'), on the 26th of January, 1357-58, to ascertain the true boundaries between the town lands of Newcastle and those of Elswick, and to certify the same into Chancery.

A few months afterwards (10th May, 1358) the community of Newcastle obtained an important charter from Edward III. (Charter Roll, 31 Edward III., No. 6), reciting and confirming the various charters and liberties previously conferred upon the town by himself and his ancestors ; and in addition to this, on the representation of the burgesses that the town was so impoverished and destitute of men, by reason of the last pestilence, wars, and other losses, that its ordinary revenue was insufficient to pay the annual rent, the king handed over to them the Castle-field and Castle-moor, within the boundaries recently ascertained ; and gave them the right to dig, and to have mines of coals and stones there, and to make profit of the same in aid of their fee-farm rent, the burgesses paying a fine of 40s. into the hamper.

By the above grant, according to Gardiner (*England's Grievance*, chap. v.), the burgesses obtained "850 acres of ground, besides pasture for all their kine, and coals for all their fuel."

CHAPTER V.

THE FOURTEENTH CENTURY.—Continued.

Collieries, and the coal trade on the south side of the Tyne. Leases of mines in Whickham and Gateshead. Edward III. regulates the coal trade. Working of coal at Winlaton, Fugerhous, Birtley. Coal trade with London. Measurement of keels.

MEANWHILE on the opposite bank of the Tyne, which likewise abounded in mineral riches, the opening out of collieries had been actively going on at various points.

As already remarked, records relating to the working of coal in Durham begin immediately after the agreement had been consummated between Bishop Beck and the vassals of the see in 1303. In a roll of the revenues of the bishopric for the year 1307-8 (Surtees Society, vol. xxv., Appendix ii.), mention occurs of a coal mine in Chester Ward, belonging to the bishop, as yielding 12s. 6d. at two terms in this year. The custody of the coal mines in the bishopric was for the first time made one of the duties pertaining to the office of Master Forester, in the appointment of an individual to that post by Bishop Kellawe (*Regist. Palatin. Dunelm.*, vol. i., p. 562) in 1314; there being no reference to coal mines in a similar appointment, made by the same bishop (*ib.*, p. 114), two years earlier.

At what precise period coal began to be dug on the south bank of the Tyne, at Gateshead and Whickham, is not quite clear. Great difficulty was experienced in shipping coal from the mines there, on account of the strenuous opposition of the merchants of Newcastle, who, in their endeavour to maintain the monopolies to which they laid claim, resisted to the utmost all attempts to carry on an independent trade made by their Durham neighbours across the river. The perpetual dispute with Newcastle regarding the free navigation of the Tyne, and the right of building quays and ballast shores on its banks, was of so prolonged and acute a character as to form, accordiug to Mr. Surtees (*Durham*, ii. 109), perhaps the most important portion of the borough history of Gateshead.

The carriage of coals, among other things, to the lower lands of the bishopric, is referred to in connection with an inquisition regarding navigation rights on the Tyne in 1323. They are again mentioned in a writ issued by Edward III., in 1334 (Brand, ii. 10), prohibiting any interference with the mooring of ships on the south side of the river. Then in 1343-44 (*31st Report of the Deputy Keeper of the Public Records*, p. 61), certain vessels laden with corn, coal, and other merchandise, were seized and carried off from Whickham, clearly indicating that the shipment of coal had begun to be carried on at this point.

Mr. Surtees (*Durham*, ii., p. 239) avers that Bishop Bury granted a lease of the mines under the manors of Whickham and Gateshead, to Sir Thomas Gray, Knt., and John Pulhore, Rector of Whickham, for twelve years, under 500 marks rent; and that the lease was renewed to the same parties by Bishop Hatfield in 1356. While we have evidence that coal was undoubtedly being worked in both of these manors at this time, there is some difficulty in exactly verifying the statement that such a lease was granted by Bishop Bury, particularly in so far as Gateshead is concerned. There appears to be no mention of this lease in the calendar of Bury's rolls (published in the report above mentioned) to which Mr. Surtees gives a general reference. It also seems clear that the mines in Gateshead were held of Bishop Hatfield by other lessees at the period in question.

A notable lease of five mines (*cynk miners*) in Whickham is, however, extant (*Durham Cursitor's Records*, 12 Hatfield, No. 30, m. 11 d') granted by Bishop Hatfield to the above individuals in 1356, for twelve years, at a rent of 500 marks (£333 6s. 8d.) per annum. From the number of mines leased and the unusually large rent paid, it is obvious that the working of coal had already become an industry of much importance at Whickham; the abnormal development and unique value of the mines being perhaps due to the fact that in addition to their favourable situation and exemption from customs, and their being at the time probably the principal if not the only mines on the south side of the river exporting coal, they supplied coal of a quality well suited for smith work, which was in this era one of the most important branches of the trade.

From this Whickham lease, which is the earliest formal Tyneside lease we have, some interesting light is obtained as to the condition of coal mining in this district at this period. Among its stipulations the following are noteworthy :—

The bishop covenants that he will win no new mine on the Tyne, or elsewhere in these parts, nor allow such to be won by any other person, calculated to depreciate the Whickham mines, "save those of the said bishop at Gateshead, which are now going, and the coals from which will not be carried nor sold to ships"; and which the Whickham lessees may take if they choose, on such terms as others are willing to give, as soon as the lease of the present farmers has expired.

The lessees are bound to work the mines for as long (or as far) as they can be wrought by five barrow-men, according to the view and oath of the master forester and the viewers (*veiours*). They are not to draw from each mine more than one keel per day (probably about 20 tons), according to use and wont in times past. They are to make good any damage done to the Whickham tenants by the carriage of coals, or the winning of mines.

The bishop further covenants that none of the workmen will be taken from his work to go anywhere with him against the will of the lessees; nor the carriage of coals be interfered with by him or any of his ministers, so that they may not carry them when occasion requires. Also that the master forester will furnish a reasonable supply of timber for repairing and upholding the mines and the staiths.

A most unusual clause in this early lease providing for due allowance being made to the lessees in the event of the working of the mines being interrupted by war, the "black truth" as to the amount required to be determined by arbitration, bespeaks the unsettled state of the border district in this era.

The limitation of the production, or "output," of coal from each mine to one keel per day is worthy of special remark, as an example of one of the rigid methods adopted in early times for making the quantity of coal worked bear a definite relation to the amount of rent paid. It is also of interest on account of the keel-load having un-doubtedly been the original foundation of the peculiar measure known as the *ten*, which is still used as a unit in leases in this coalfield, and regarding which more will be heard hereafter.

In the adjoining manor of Gateshead the working of coal was evidently already being carried on by other lessees at the date of the granting of the above lease, though the produce of the mines had not yet begun to be exported. Soon afterwards we hear of arrangements being made for the shipment of coal here, not without considerable opposition necessitating the intervention of the king.

In 1364 Bishop Hatfield granted a lease, confirmed by the king

(Pat. 38 Edward III., part 2, m. 26), of one coal-mine, or perhaps seam of coal, in the field, or lea, of Gateshead (*un myne des charbons dedeinz le chaumpe de Gatesheved*), to John Plummer, burgess of New-castle on-Tyne, and Walter de Hesilden, burgess of Gateshead, for twenty-five years, at a rent of 100s. per annum. The lessees were granted timber from the bishop's park at Gateshead for the construc-tion of pits (*puscez*) and a "watergate," or tunnel for draining the mine; and for making staiths for shipping the coal on the Tyne, at their own peril. It was stipulated that they should only work one pit at a time, from which they were to draw a supply of coal from day to day, the same as was being taken from the pit in Whickham; and they were to have a convenient road between their pits and staiths.

This lease contains the first distinct reference to the working of coal on the Tyneside by means of pits and waterdrifts; though, from the complaint of the prior of Tynemouth, such an arrangement would appear to have existed at Elswick a few years earlier. The allusion to the pit in Whickham also points to the same arrangement being now in vogue there. And almost simultaneously we hear of it in another part of this coalfield, as will be seen hereafter.

That the mention of risk in connection with the shipment of coal at Gateshead was no empty phrase, is shown by the fact that the lessees had occasion to appeal to the king for protection from hin-drance and disturbance which they suffered at the hands of certain merchants of Newcastle who themselves had coals to sell. Writs were, in consequence, issued by Edward III. (Pat. 41 Edw. III., part 1, m. 19) in 1368, taking Plummer and Hesilden, and likewise Roger de Fulthorp and John de Britley (Birtley), under his special protection; and commanding the Newcastle authorities, and others, to allow them to lead their sea coals, dug from mines in the fields of Gateshead, across the river to Newcastle, and after paying the customs of the port, to send them to any part of the kingdom, either by land or water, but nowhere out of it except to Calais.

At this time Calais was the only port on the Continent to which the staple commodities of England, including sea coals and grind-stones—the ubiquitous Newcastle grindstone, which, according to the proverb, is to be found all the world over—were allowed to be taken. The foreign export of sea coals (Rymer's *Fœdora*, vol. iii., part 2, p. 683) had been prohibited in 1362; but in 1367 (*ib.*, p. 823) an exception was made in favour of Calais.

The names of Plummer, Hesilden, Fulthorpe, and Brytley figure along with those of William de Menevyll, Allan Lambard, William

de Blaykeston, and Richard de ——— (obliterated) in a recognizance (*Durham Cursitor's Records*, [23] Hatfield, No. 31, m. 1) for the
payment of 1000 marks (£666 13s. 4d.) to Bishop Hatfield, from
which it would appear probable that all these parties were interested
at this date in the working and shipment of coal on the south side
of the Tyne. The name Blaykeston (? black stone) seems to point
very directly towards the digging of coal : a trade in which we find
the Blaykeston family engaged during several succeeding centuries.

King Edward III. was anxious to encourage the coal industry.
In taking the colliery owners of the Gateshead neighbourhood
under his special protection, he expresses his conviction that the
leading of this kind of coals to all places within the kingdom
would be of the greatest benefit to himself and his people.

Though the keel, as we have seen, was already used as a measure
of coals in mine leases, it had not yet been constituted a legal
measure for the sale of coals. In connection with the question of
the shipment of the produce of the mines on the south side of the
Tyne, the attention of the king had been drawn to the fact that
coals were now being loaded into ships at Newcastle in the gross,
or by the keel, without being measured by the standard measure
previously used, which was doubtless the chalder, or chaldron.

Being led to understand that a loss of customs would result to
himself from this unauthorized proceeding—these being paid upon
the chaldron—Edward III. issued a writ (Pat. 41 Edw. III., part 1,
m. 16 d') in 1368, commanding the mayor and bailiffs, and certain
burgesses of Newcastle, to take charge of the measurement of sea
coals, and not to permit them to be loaded into ships before being
measured by the standard measure. But on its being represented
to him by the community of Newcastle, and others, that this writ
had been obtained at the instance of certain lords possessing mines,
and of merchants who bought coals from these lords, for their own
benefit, he withdrew his opposition to the keel measure (*ib.*, m. 11
and 12)—a certain fixed payment from each boat-load of coals sold
to natives of this country being allowed to the town of Newcastle
in aid of the annual rent ; while the king reserved to himself the
usual customs from merchants and strangers who exported coal
abroad.

The abandonment of the standard measure, however, eventually
resulted in a large loss of revenue to the Crown. As we subsequently learn, the amount of the royal duty on coal shipped to
foreign parts was 2d. per chaldron.

How the word " chaldron," signifying a boiler, became the name

of a measure, it is perhaps difficult to explain, unless it was so
named after a boiler-shaped vessel used in measuring. It is the
Latin word *calidarium*, and mediæval Latin *celdra*; the French
chaudron and *chaudière*; the English caldron, or cauldron, and
chalder. In records of the Middle Ages, the word occurs in a
variety of French and English forms, *e.g.* cuedre, schaudre, chaw-
der, etc., which, though identically the same, might almost pass
for being no relations at all.

According to Mr. T. J. Taylor (*Proceed. Archæol. Inst.*, Newcastle,
1852, vol. i., p. 168) the original chaldron of charcoal weighed
2,000 lbs.—that is about 18 cwts. It appears to have been the
largest measure in use at one time ; and was doubtless simply the
load of a four-wheeled wain, which was the largest vehicle employed.
From a contemporary record, dated 1349 (quoted hereafter), we
learn that at this time the chaldron of mineral coal was equal to
three fothers—the term "fother," according to Mr. Taylor (*ib.*,
p. 170), properly signifying as much as could be conveyed in a
cart with one horse.

As the keel carried twenty chaldrons of coal in the fourteenth
century (*ib.*, p. 208) its freight would appear to have weighed about
18 or 20 tons, having in fact been as nearly as possible the same
as the modern keel-load of 21 tons. Though the keel-load became
from this time the principal standard measure used in the Tyne
coal trade, it had not long attained to this position before the
measure of the keel itself began to be a source of difficulty. It
commenced to grow in size, as will presently be seen.

Under the arrangements made by Edward III. for the regulation
of the Tyne coal trade, coals from the mines on the south side of
the river were required to be carried to Newcastle, and to pay the
customs of the port, before being loaded into ships for exportation.
On this occasion the burgesses scored against the bishop.

In 1367, Bishop Hatfield (*Dur. Curs. Rec.*, 23 Hatfield, No. 31,
m. 4 d') appointed one Nicholas Coke, or Cook, of Newcastle,
keeper and vendor of his coals out of Gateshead and Whickham.

The same prelate, in 1373-74 (*ib.*, 29 Hatfield, No. 31, m. 5 d'),
constituted John de Belgrave and Nicholas Cook commissioners
to seize workmen and coal-bearers (*cariours des charbons par lad*) for
the mines of Whickham and Gateshead, wherever they could be
found within his royal liberty, with full power to imprison and
otherwise punish them should they prove rebellious and obstinate—
an instance of the difficulty experienced everywhere with the
labouring classes in the era succeeding the Plague, and which

came to a crisis shortly afterwards in the general insurrection known as the Peasant Revolt.

From the above it is obvious that the workpeople of the north of England collieries at this period were still in a condition of serfdom, or something approaching to it. This seizure of mineworkers was no unique proceeding. Fuller, in his *Worthies of England* (art. Devonshire), states that in 1296-97, 360 miners were impressed out of the Peak of Derby and Wales for the king's silver mines in Devon; and in 1526-28 we hear of a proposal being made to Henry VIII. by Joachim Hochstetter, a German (*Letters and Papers Foreign and Domestic*, Hen. VIII., vol. iv., part 2, 5,110), to levy men for the same mines. Even as late as 1565, in a license to dig for minerals (*State Papers, Dom.*, 1547-80, vol. xxxvii., 44), Queen Elizabeth gave power to impress workmen, wagons and horses; while what was perhaps the last proposal to employ forced labour in the mines of England and Wales was made in the following century by Lord Bacon and his disciple Thomas Bushell, who advocated the employment of felons in recovering and working abandoned metalliferous mines; the latter holding out a prospect of great treasures being thus obtained out of what he quaintly describes as "a promiscuous chaos of drowned minerals and condemned men."

Under Cook's administration the Gateshead and Whickham mines appear to have been carried on with considerable vigour during a lengthened period. The activity of the Whickham mines is evidenced by the references to pits, and allowances made to tenants for ground occupied and damaged in connection with the working of coal there, in Bishop Hatfield's *Survey of the See of Durham* (Surtees Society, vol. xxxii., p. 93), compiled about 1380. And in 1386-87 (*ib.*, Appendix iii.) we find the sum of £23 paid to Nicholas Cook for winning coals in the mine of Gateshead.

While the mines of Gateshead and Whickham were doubtless the most important on the south side of the Tyne, coal was likewise already being worked at a number of other places in the surrounding district.

That the lordship of Winlaton—held of the Bishop of Durham by Lord de Neville—must have been producing a good output of coal, is evidenced by a purchase of the considerable quantity of 576 chaldrons having been made there by order of Edward III. in 1366-67, for the works at Windsor Castle (Pipe Roll, 40 Edw. III., quoted in the *Proceed. Archæol. Inst.*, Newcastle, 1852, vol. i., p. 208).

The manor of Fugerhous, again (Hatfield's *Survey*, p. 93), was held by the Earl of Northumberland, with a coal pit there, for which he paid an annual rent of £26 13s. 4d.; while the circumstance of John de Britley claiming the protection of the king in the shipment of coal, seems to indicate that the mineral was thus early being worked in the cŏmparatively distant Birtley neighbourhood, and carried to the Tyne for exportation.

Though Edward III. sent a special order to the north for the above-mentioned large quantity of coal for the works at Windsor Castle, a regular trade in coal with London had continued to be carried on all along, notices relating to it occurring from time to time. Thus in 1316 we find 60s. paid out of the Exchequer (Devon's *Issues*, Hen. III—Hen. VI., p. 130) to John de Norton, surveyor of works at Westminster Palace, to purchase iron, steel, and sea coal, to make divers heads for the king's lances. Then in 1329, in connection with the prosecution of Hugh de Hecham, we hear of sea coal being the fuel commonly used by the limeburners of the metropolis. In 1337 again (*Fœdera*, vol. iv., p. 730) King Edward III. ordered the Sheriff of London to provide iron, wood, and 100 quarters of sea coal at the Tower, for forging anchors for two of his ships. Measurers, or meters, of sea coal also existed in London. There is a record (Riley's *Memorials*, p. 338) relating to the appointment of four individuals to this office in 1369, who were "sworn that they would well and trustily make measure of coals so coming thither, taking for their trouble as from of old they were wont."

The ascendancy of the burgesses of Newcastle over their neighbours on the Durham side of the Tyne continued till 1383-84, under which date an entry occurs among the records of the bishopric (Raine's *Auckland Castle*, p. 40) of the receipt of 56s. 8d. "from the men of Newcastle for coals sold them by my Lord's letter." The balance of royal favour, however, now swayed to the other side, and the Durham trade was set free. In 1384 (Brand, vol. ii., pp. 12, 258) Richard II. granted a charter to Bishop Fordham, for the mooring of ships, the loading of coals, etc., on the south side of the Tyne, without molestation from the men of Newcastle.

In the same year (Pat. 8 Ric. II., part 1, m. 34 d') the king also appointed the Bishop of Durham, the Earl of Northumberland, and John de Neville, of Raby, commissioners for the supervision and measurement of the keels used in carrying coals at Newcastle. Certain persons had begun to employ keels above the legitimate size, thereby partially evading the king's dues. The commissioners were directed to have these oversized boats amended or destroyed, and to punish those who owned or used them at their discretion. The growth of the keel was thus checked for the time being.

CHAPTER VI.

THE FOURTEENTH CENTURY.—Continued.

Collieries of the Wear and South Durham districts. Northumberland. Pit and adit system of mining. Appliances used. Bearers. Yorkshire. Derbyshire. The Trent exporting. Coal used by Staffordshire metallurgists. Lancashire. Shropshire. Forest of Dean miners. North Wales.

DURING the same time the working of coal had been going on, and numerous collieries had been established, in other parts of the Bishopric of Durham. It cannot be doubted that the freeholders proceeded to open up the coal in their lands immediately after their right to do so had been conceded by Bishop Beck in 1303; and already in the first half of the century mention occurs of the existence of collieries at numerous points.

The earliest notice relating to coal at Lumley, in the valley of the Wear, according to Mr. Surtees (vol. ii., p. 165), is contained in a charter whereby Henry, son of Peter de Lumley, grants to Gilbert de Lumley all his mine (*mineram*) and his part of the sea coals (*carbonum maritimorum*) in the land of Great Lumley. The charter is undated, but was no doubt granted in the early part of the century, inasmuch as the donor was the father of Waleran de Lumley, who was mayor of Newcastle in 1339. The name *carbo maritimus,* or sea-borne coal, also seems to belong to this period; the first instance of its use known to the writer occurring in the accounts of Jarrow Monastery for the year 1313, reference to which has been already made. In thirteenth century records, the mineral is usually termed *carbo maris,* though, after the middle of the century, it is also frequently called *carbo marinus;* either of which names might not inappropriately be rendered as "sea-born" coal.

On the opposite side of the Wear, the digging of coal appears to have commenced in the neighbourhood of Chester-le-Street at the

same period ; one Alan, the collier, of Plawsworth, being mentioned
(*31st Report of the Dep. Keep. of the Pub. Records*, p. 96) in 1343-44.
Numerous instances occur of the application of the term "collier"
to mineral coal workers and, indeed, colliery owners, in the fourteenth century, though it continued to be also applied to charcoal
burners for a long time subsequently.

The Ferryhill neighbourhood in like manner became the seat of
coal mining operations at an early date.   In 1327-28 (Surtees, vol. i.,
p. 70) John de Denhum died, seised of half the vill of Coxhow, with
mines of coal there, held of the bishop by 40s. rent.

At Hett, in the same vicinity (*ib.,* vol. iii., p. 396), the coal mine
of William de Het is mentioned in 1343, as paying tithe to the
vicarage of Merrington.   Another reference to coal mining in the
Ferryhill district, of a few years later date, will be adverted to
hereafter.

An interesting notice occurs (Hatfield's *Survey*, p. 219) of the
opening out of a fresh mine of sea coals at Coundon in 1350—
evidently a new pit.   The cost, inclusive of ropes, scopes, and
windlass, bought and made for the work, only amounted to the
modest total of 5s. 6d.

Coal would also appear to have been receiving attention near
Lanchester.   Mines of coal and iron are stated in the *Picture of
Newcastle* (art. "Coal Trade") to be mentioned in surveys of the
Manor of Collierley, made in 1333 and 1345.   And this is supported
by the fact that about 1370-80 Coldpike Hill is mentioned (Surtees,
vol. ii., p. 319) under the name of Colpit Hill, indicating that now
at all events a coal pit existed in its neighbourhood.

In the middle of this century—a period which was marked by
increased activity in the working and use of coal—we find the
monks of Durham and the monks of Finchale endeavouring to
augment their revenues by means of the coal trade, which they both
continued to prosecute thenceforward till the date of the dissolution
of their houses.

The coal mining operations of the Durham monks are no longer
enveloped in the obscurity and uncertainty of the early "Kolpihill"
charter, but now become matter of clear historical record.   The first
direct notice we have of their commencing to dig coal—though it
must be admitted that it scarcely looks like a maiden attempt—
occurs in 1354 (Surtees, vol. iii., p. 255), when the prior obtained a
lease from Thomas, son of Richard de Fery, of the coal in certain
lands in the north part of the township of Ferry, for thirty years,
with license to dig and work in any place whatever for his pits and

water-gate (water-gage), and with sufficient wayleave (*cheminum*).
And the prior bargains that the lessor and his heirs shall have one-
half cartload (*carrectum*) of coals every week in which coals shall be
worked.

As the above lease contains no mention apparently of any money
rent being paid, it would appear to present an instance of payment
in kind, which, though almost unheard of at English collieries, continued to be practised at some collieries in Wales and Scotland even
at a later period.

Shortly afterwards there is incidental mention of another colliery
belonging to the Durham monks, situated in their estate of Rainton.
By a deed, dated 1361 (*Historiæ Dunelmenis Scriptores Tres*—Surtees
Society, vol. ix., Appendix, p. cxxxvi.), one Thomas Anesley was
confirmed by the prior and convent in the post of forester at
Rainton, with the custody of the coal mine there. For the latter
duty he was to receive a salary of six silver pennies weekly ; but it
was expressly stipulated that if the mine should fail, or even cease
to be worked for a length of time, the said six pennies per week
were on no account to be paid to the said Thomas.

The monks of Finchale, whose house was situated in a beautifully
wooded and romantic spot among the tortuous meanderings of the
Wear, and in the centre of this coal district, had their first
experience of trading in coal in 1348-49 ; an entry in their accounts
(*The Priory of Finchale*, Surtees Society, vol. vi., p. xxxi.) recording
the receipt of " 19s. 5d. from coals sold this year out of our mine of
Lumley." But their permanent connection with colliery enterprises
commenced in 1354 ; and the fact of two coal picks and two iron
wedges (*ij colpikkes ij yeges ferrei*) figuring as items in their inventory
for this year, insignificant in itself, is of interest as being the earliest
mention we have of coal mining implements.

An attempt which they made to find coal at Wyndegates (Win-
gate ?) proved unsuccessful. But another trial made immediately
afterwards at Softley was more fortunate. Though this venture
was a source of expense to them for the first few years, with little
return, a steady paying colliery was eventually established, which
yielded them a rent of about £6 13s. 4d. annually, from 1362 on
into the following century.

The Finchale monks again had a mine at Lumley in 1365, which
produced some profit during the following ten years. But the
proceeds were liable to considerable fluctuations, probably owing
to its depending on an export trade. This mine was worked out
in 1368-69, but was re-established soon afterwards. In 1372-73

they obtained the exceptional return of £26 13s. 4d. from it; and the account for this year contains a notice of the sinking of a new pit at a cost of 46s. 7d. A year or two after, however, from whatever cause, the mine lost all value.

At the end of the century (1398-99) the same monks became owners of a mine at Coken, which had evidently existed previous to this time, as they at once set about repairing its water drain (*aquæductus*). But a law-suit with the landlord supervened regarding it, and they ceased to hold it after a few years.

That a commencement had been made to export coal from the Wear in the latter half of this century, if not indeed earlier, is corroborated by an entry in the rolls of Whitby Abbey (Charlton's *Whitby*, p. 263; Brand, ii. 260), where a purchase of four chaldrons of coal is recorded as having been made in 1394-96, from William Rede, of Sunderland.

With the growth of an inland demand for coal for domestic use, the collieries in the extreme south of the coalfield, though possessing no facilities for exportation, and hence purely what are termed "landsale" collieries, began to rise into importance.

A mine of sea coals in the manor of Cockfield, belonging to the Vavasours, as appears from an inquest held in the year 1375 (*45th Report of the Dep. Keep. Pub. Records*, p. 274; Hutchinson's *Durham*, iii. 282), was then worth 20 marks (£13 6s. 8d.) per annum when let to farm.

A colliery in the barony of Evenwood is heard of in 1383-84 (*32nd Report ut sup.*, p. 312), in connection with the appointment of Roger de Fulthorp, Ralph de Eure, and others, as justices of Oyer and Terminer (hear and end) of the complaint of Walter de Hawyk against the bishop's officers for preventing persons using the highways for the purpose of going to and from his coal mine at Morlay, within the barony of Evenwood.

The decision must have been adverse to Hawyk, as in the same year (Hatfield's *Survey*, Appendix iii.) we hear of the coal mine of Evenwood being leased to John de Merley, William de Blakden, John del Loge, and Alexander Colier, for a term of six years, at a rent of £22 per annum.

At Raylegh (which almost appears to be another form of the name of Lord Neville's estate of Raby), in the same neighbourhood, the working of coal would likewise appear to have been already going on. In the record above quoted reference is made to the fact of Bishop Fordham having assigned a sum within £100 per annum to Lord de Neville, out of the mines of Raylegh and Evenwood.

We have seen that in the early part of this century the custody of coal mines in the Bishopric of Durham was entrusted to the master forester. A special mining agent was now placed over them. In 1384 Bishop Fordham (*32nd Report of the Dep. Keep. Pub. Records*, p. 316 *b*) appointed Thomas Haunsard surveyor, or chief viewer, of all the mines of coal and iron within his royal liberty, and in Norhamshire and Bedlingtonshire.

At this time the northern part of Northumberland formed part of the possessions of the See of Durham, being, in fact, as already mentioned, the original centre of the see, and bore the name of North Durham. The allusion to mines in Norhamshire and Bedlingtonshire, which formed two sections of this tract, is indicative of some activity in mining in the bishop's lands there.

We have an incidental notice of the continued working of coal at Plessey, in the middle of this century. In 1349 Roger de Widdrington bargained to build a house within the site of the manor of Plescys for Margaret, the widow of Richard de Plessis. "The covenant for fuel to be used in this house," says Mr. Hodgson (*Northumberland*, vol. ii., part 2, p. 303), "was that she should yearly have ten wain loads of peat, and liberty to pull as much ling as she pleased on the wastes of Plessys and Schotton; besides two chaldrons (six fothers) of sea coal at the mines of Plescys."

Further north the monks of Holy Island were obtaining supplies of coal for their monastery at Holburn, where coal was now at all events certainly being worked, this house (Raine's *North Durham*, p. 99) owing a small debt to the "collier" there in 1358.

The occupants of the religious houses on the bleak north-east coast were among the earliest to adopt coal as a fuel for domestic purposes. The following statements of the expenses for fuel at the above-mentioned monastery on Holy Island (*ib.*, pp. 86, 89) illustrate the extent to which coal was used at this establishment.

For the year 1344-45 the entries are:

"Fifty-seven and a-half chaldrons of coals for the brew-house, lime-kiln, hall, prior's chamber, kitchen, and infirmary, £4 14s. 5d.
"Brushwood, fewel, and bent bought, 43s. 4d."

For the year 1346-47 the entries are:

"Sixty-six chaldrons and a-quarter of coals, 104s. 3d.
"Twenty-six trusses of 'hather' (heather?) for the bakehouse and brewhouse, for lack of other fuel, 9s. 10d.
"Brushwood bought at Dichard, 53s. 4d.
"To men digging peats at Howeburne Moss, 8s."

From the foregoing records it is evident that in the fourteenth

century the working of coal was being prosecuted at many points
in the great northern coalfield, the collieries for the most part
congregating together in little clusters at the most favourable
centres : as on the Tyne and Wear, where facilities existed for the
exportation of coal, and where also it probably began to be used
at an early date in the manufacture of salt; at Ferryhill, a likely
place for the burning of lime to have been carried on ; and, in the
latter part of the century, after a steady demand for coal for
domestic use had arisen, on the southern frontier of the coalfield,
where they not only commanded the traffic of their own neighbourhood, but of a large district lying beyond the limits of the
coalfield.

The coal mines of early times were doubtless usually opened out
at points where seams, or veins, of the mineral came out to the
surface in ravines and on the sides of hills, and where consequently
it could be both easily discovered and easily worked. They would
consist for the most part of levels, or horizontal galleries, known as
"day holes," which served alike for the extraction of the coal
and the drainage of the workings.

In the middle of the fourteenth century, however, this elementary
arrangement was becoming inadequate in some localities, and coal
mining began to enter upon a more highly developed phase of its
history. In order to command new tracts of coal, the sinking of
vertical pits was resorted to, sites being selected where natural
drainage could be made available ; and to combat the water—the
miner's first great enemy—tunnels, or drifts, were cut horizontally
through the strata from the lower grounds, for the special purpose
of draining the workings.

These waterways, or drains, had various designations in different
parts of the kingdom. In the north of England they were usually
known as "water-gates" (in Latin *aquæductus*) ; the term gate in
early times signifying a road, or passage, as for example in the name
of Gateshead. They were the "surfs" of the Forest of Dean district ; the "soughs" of the lead and coal mines of Derbyshire and
the "sowes" of Yorkshire ; the "avidods," "audits," or "adits," of
the metalliferous mines of the Land's End district, which may perhaps be simply corruptions and contractions of the word "aqueduct."

This mining arrangement, commonly called the "pit and adit"
system, was simple and effective, and continued to be the typical
form so long as coal working was carried on above the level of free-
drainage. It not only provided for raising the coal, and getting rid
of the water, without further expense, but also served to produce a

spontaneous, or natural ventilation, sufficient for the shallow and limited workings of this era.

The mining appliances required must have been few and simple. The services of bondsmen being available, the bulk of all kinds of work was no doubt performed by manual labour. The mention of carriers of coal by the load, points to the "bearing system" having existed in the north of England in early times, as we have indications of its also having done in other districts—a slavish method of conveying coals out of the pits, which continued to be pursued by

FIG. 1.—FEMALE COAL BEARER.

women and girls at the collieries in the east of Scotland down into the present century, and is still followed by boys in the iron mines of the Forest of Dean.

That barrows were also in use, is indicated by the mention of barrow-men. The terms barrow-man, and barrow-way, handed down through succeeding centuries, continue to be used in some of the older mining localities in the north of England even at the present day; though the barrow, which was probably the origin of the "bowle or barrowe" measure—the modern boll—has long been extinct as a mining appliance.

Along with notices of the sinking of pits, the windlass, with its associated ropes, and scopes, makes its appearance in the accounts. Scopes, translated "probably buckets," were used for a variety of ordinary purposes. Thus we find scopes bought (Topham's *Chapel of St. Stephen*, p. 69) for scoping, or scooping water. Brushes and scopes (pails) bought ("Fabric Rolls of York Minster," Surtees Society, vol. xxxv., p. 65) for cleaning purposes. Subsequently they are found in use in the conveyance of coals out of the mines. Perhaps in them we have the original "tubs"—the name still applied in the north of England to the small wheeled carriages employed in the underground conveyance of coal. The term itself may be identical with the modern word "skip," applied in various districts to the vessel employed in bringing the coals to the surface.

Coal was sold in "scoops" in the neighbourhood of Leeds in the present century (*Fossil Fuel*, p. 428); and scopes, or scoops, were still employed in the underground conveyance of coal at some of the Yorkshire collieries in 1842 (*Child Employ. Com.*).

Regarding the methods used at this period in the conveyance of coal from the mines to the place of shipment, we have no very clear data. It would almost appear to have been literally carried by labourers, from mines situated near the loading berths; just as in early times (*Chorographia, or a Survey of Newcastle-upon-Tyne*, 1649, p. 38) the ballast of the coal vessels—also known as "colliers"—was carried to the ballast-heaps in baskets on the heads of women. In the case of more distant mines, pack-horses, and perhaps also vehicles, would doubtless be required.

We know from the rolls of the bailiffs of various manors of the bishopric for the year 1349-50 (Hatfield's *Survey*, Appendix ii.), that the rural population of the inland districts of Durham then commonly employed their carts (*carrectæ*), and wains (*plaustra*), in taking home coals for their own use; they having begun just about this time to utilize coal to a small extent for domestic purposes, in the winter season, to save other fuel. In a roll of the steward of the manor of Auckland for the year 1337-38 (*ib.*, Appendix i.), no coals were so bought, the only purchase recorded being one of twenty-four quarters of sea coals for burning lime.

Already we hear of "viewers" in connection with the control of mining operations, a term seemingly of Norman origin which still continues to be the peculiar appellation of colliery superintendents in the north of England. In early times this word had not acquired its special modern signification. It occurs in the Norman rolls among the State papers in the form of *véeurs*. In the glossary appended to the published calendars of these rolls (*42nd Report of the Dep. Keep. Pub. Records*, p. 471), the term "vejours" is rendered as "persons sent by a court to take a view of any place in question for the better decision of the right thereto"; also "persons appointed to view the result of an offence." It seems not improbable that viewers may have existed in the north of England as forest officials, before they came to be connected with coal mines.

The meagreness of the records available regarding the progress of coal mining in other parts of England during the fourteenth century, presents a marked contrast to the case of the great northern coalfield. No doubt this coalfield was more rapidly developed than others, due to its maritime situation, and the facilities it possessed, by means of its intersecting rivers, for the exportation of coal to unlimited markets. But this district has also been exceptionally fortunate in the elucidation of its early records, owing to the number and excellence of its historians, and the devoted and well-directed labours of the Surtees and other societies.

A few notices exist relative to the working of coal in the Yorkshire, Derbyshire, and Nottinghamshire coalfield.

That coal had begun to receive attention in the neighbourhood of Wakefield is evidenced by the court rolls of this place, where, in 1308 (*Leeds Mercury Supplement*, 9th May, 1885), it is recorded that license was granted by the Lord of the Manor to Richard the Nailer to dig for coals in the greaveship of Hipperholme. On the same rolls, in 1335, Richard Gibson is entered as paying a fine for having dug for coals in the same greaveship. There is also a notice of one John Stra, of Handesworth Woodhous, being drowned in a coal pit in 1378.

The monks of Bolton Abbey, who were buying sea coals for their forge and for burning lime, in the latter part of the thirteenth century (Whitaker's *Craven*, 2nd ed., pp. 384, 392, 401; also his *Whalley and Clitheroe*, 4th ed., vol. i., p. 361), were digging them in their own neighbourhood in 1311, and subsequently.

A dispute between the abbot and convent of St. Jervaulx, and Sir Geoffrey le Scrope, Lord of Masham, "concerning the mine of coals in Colsterdale," was settled by an agreement dated 7, Edw. III., A.D. 1334. By this deed Sir Geoffrey grants the abbot and convent the right to dig for coals within Colsterdale, wheresoever they like, as well without their enclosed ground as within, and make their profit of them at their pleasure ; and the abbot and convent bind themselves to pay Sir Geoffrey eight marks sterling (£5 6s. 8d.) of yearly rent. With a proviso that if the mine by working be so destroyed and reduced that no more coals be left therein, the payment of the rent should cease (Fisher's *History of Mashamshire*, p. 488 ; *Leeds Mercury Supplement*, 30th May, 1885).

Mention occurs in the *Registrum Honoris de Richmond* (p. 100) of a coal mine at Takomtanne, in this honour, as being wont to yield, about 1387-88, 53s. 4d. per annum.

Coal was also receiving attention in the neighbourhood of Sheffield, a town already celebrated for its production of cutlery, as evidenced by the well-known line in Chaucer's description of the accoutrements of the miller—

> "A Sheffield whitel bare he in his hose."

Here a lease of coal mine in the field of Netherhalghe was granted

(Harleian Charters, 55G, 39) by Thomas de Schefeld to Esmond Fitzwilliam in 1396, at an annual rent of 20s.

In Derbyshire we hear of coal being worked at Alfreton, at the commencement of the century. In 1315, Edward II. confirmed a grant made to the monks of Beauchief Abbey by Sir Thomas Chaworth a few years before his death (Pegge's *Beauchief Abbey*, p. 130; Dugdale's *Monasticon*, vol. vi., p. 884), giving them license to get coals for their own use and profit, and that of their tenants, whether bond or free, in their own lands, and in the lands of their tenants, and in the waste grounds lying amongst their lands, in the sokes of Alfreton and Norton.

At a later date a law-suit took place between these monks and Sir Thomas Chaworth's successors regarding coal tithes. It appears that the monks had made a claim for tithes from Sir Thomas for coal got at Swanwicke and other places within their rectory of Alfreton, in lieu of which Sir Thomas agreed to pay the sum of 13s. 4d. yearly for a period of forty years, unless during the term the coal should fail or he should choose to cease working it, in either of which cases the payment was to lapse. The monks seem to have renewed their claim in 1368, when the matter was referred to arbitration; and it was decided that the one party to the suit was bound to pay, and the other to accept, the 13s. 4d. per annum formerly agreed upon.

Coal mines must now have existed at numerous points in this extensive coalfield, notwithstanding the paucity of notices relating to them.

Coal from the Leicestershire, or Staffordshire, coalfield would seem to have been exported by the Trent before the close of the fourteenth century. The rolls of Whitby Abbey for the years 1394-96 (Charlton's *Whitby*, p. 263), record a purchase of four chaldrons of coal from one Baxter de Burton. The Trent is stated by Thoroton (vol. ii., p. 14) to have been navigable before the Conquest.

Some records exist relating to coal at Walsall, in South Stafford-shire, in this era (*Trans. So. Stafford. Inst.*, 1886, president's address): " On the Sunday next after the feast of St. Barnabas the Apostle, in the 19th year of King Edward II. (1326), Robert, son of Henry Bonde, of Walshale, having been enfeoffed by charter by Sir Thomas le Rous, Knight, Lord of Walshale, in three acres of land in his waste at Birchells, conceded that neither he nor his heirs would raise any sea coal nor have any mine there without the consent of the aforesaid Thomas." There are three other deeds of the same date to the same effect.

We have also evidence that the artificers of this county had begun to utilize coal to some extent in their metallurgical operations. A great bell for York Minster, as we learn from the Fabric Rolls, was cast on the spot, in 1371, by John de Stafford and his men, the fuel provided on the occasion consisting of 1,100 peats, two chaldrons of sea coal, and six baskets of charcoal.

Reference occurs to the continued working of coal at Colne, in Lancashire. The monks of Bolton Abbey (Whitaker's *Craven*, 2nd ed., p. 401), while digging coals in their own neighbourhood for ordinary purposes, were sending to Colne for supplies of it for their forge in the time of Edward III.; no doubt on account of the coal obtainable there being of superior quality for this purpose.

In the adjoining county of Cheshire, the sea coal in the Forest of Macclesfield (*36th Report of the Dep. Keep. Pub. Records*, p. 310) was committed to the charge of a forester appointed in 1382.

A remarkable degree of individuality characterizes the conduct of mining operations in the Shropshire coalfield at all periods of its history. The custom of letting coal on lease began here at an early date.

A primitive lease, one of the earliest on record, occurs at Madeley, near Coalbrookdale, in 1322 (Eyton's *Shropshire*, vol. iii., p. 321), when Walter de Caldebrok, for a fine of 6s. paid to Wenlock Priory, was allowed to employ a man for a year digging sea coals in the brook holes (Le Brocholes). In this early lease the output of coal was limited to the quantity which one man could produce.

The same method of restricting the production—the man limit— is observable in an interesting record relating to coal at Benthale, near Brosely, in this county, a few years later. By a deed belonging to the year 1326 (Owen and Blakeway's *History of Shrewsbury*, 1825, i. 347, note), Adam Peyeson, of Buldwas, acknowledges that he holds of Hugh, Lord of Scheynton, certain land at Benthale, etc., paying yearly three marks of silver and a quarter of beans of small measure ; with all the quarries of coal of the sea called "Secoles," together with four labourers to dig the sea coals, and with as many servants as he chooses for carrying the coals to Severn, and thence leading them away : the said Hugh to have coal sufficient for his hearth (*focum*) at Benthale from the quarry of the said Adam.

It is in the military rather than in the mining annals of the kingdom that the miners of the Forest of Dean figure in the fourteenth century. On frequent occasions during the reigns of Edward II. and Edward III. (Nicholls' *Forest of Dean*, p. 17 ; *Fœdera*, vol. iii., part i., pp. 78, 417 ; part ii., pp. 762, 1021) miners were taken from the Forest to assist in military operations; notably at sieges of Berwick-on-Tweed, a town which in this era changed hands with extraordinary frequency. This circumstance of miners being taken to the seat of war may partly serve to explain the clause in the Whickham lease, where, as we have seen, it was stipulated that none of the workmen would be taken from his work, by the Bishop of Durham.

Though coal no doubt continued to be dug in South Wales, we are without information regarding the progress of mining in this great coalfield during this period. In North Wales, however, a few records occur relating to the subject.

The coal mines in the manor of Ewloe, or Ellow (*36th Report of the Dep. Keep. Pub. Records*, Appendix ii., p. 176), were leased along with the forest and mill, etc., in 1322, and from time to time thereafter. In 1358 (*ib.*, p. 259) an individual with the carcinic name of Ithel ap Blethin ap Ithel, obtained a lease of the coal mine which he held of the Prince of Wales, in Eulowe, for as long as it could be worked, at 4 marks (53s. 4d.) yearly ; and also a lease of the sea coal mines in Eulowe (the above mine excepted) for six years, at 6 marks (80s.) yearly.

The coal mines of Hope and Hopedale (*ib.*, p. 441), valued at 53s. 4d. yearly, are mentioned in 1358. While in 1379-80 (3 Rich. II., Otho E. X.) we hear of the Bishop of St. Asaph applying for permission to work his mines of lead, stone, and coal in the township of Vaynol, and elsewhere in the county of Flint. There was evidently some degree of mining activity in North Wales at this early period.

CHAPTER VII.

THE FIFTEENTH CENTURY. 1400—1509 A.D.

Extension of the use of coal for domestic purposes. Manufacture of sea salt with coal. Collieries on the Tyne. Marking of keels. Central and South Durham districts. Importance of water-gates. Northumberland. Raising water by machinery. Leaving pillars in the mines. Mining officials. Yorkshire. Lancashire. Leicestershire. Forest of Dean. North Wales.

IN the fifteenth century coal continued to come into more extended use for domestic purposes in the coalfields and surrounding districts, as it also doubtless did in the maritime towns. Even in London, as early as the reign of Henry IV., a commencement had been made to welcome this once banished fuel into house fires, if we may accept the *ipse dixit* of Shakspeare (*Henry IV.*, part ii., act ii., scene i.) as authoritative on the point, who describes Mrs. Quickly, hostess of the Boar's Head Tavern, in Eastcheap, as reminding Sir John Falstaff of his sworn promise to marry her, made, as she asseverates, "sitting in my dolphin-chamber, at the round table, by a sea coal fire."

But the evidence we have regarding the progress which must have been made in this era in the adoption of coal for domestic use along the coast, as well as in its exportation to the Continent, is supplied by the light thrown upon the subject by later records rather than by contemporary ones, of which there are few.

In the coalfields bordering on the sea an increasing demand for coal was also now springing up, from its employment in the manufacture of salt by the evaporation of sea water. This was a new development of an old industry which had long existed at many points on the coast, reference to which has been already made in connection with the notice taken of it in *Domesday Book*. The maritime saltworks there mentioned, however, were situated in the

more southerly part of the kingdom, particularly on the coast of
Kent, Surrey, and Sussex, the fuel employed doubtless consisting
solely of wood or peat.   Though the manufacture of salt was
probably also going on at this time on the coast of Northumberland and Durham, we learn nothing of it from this source, the four
northernmost counties not being included in the Domesday survey.

But in the following century we begin to hear of salt-making in
Northumberland, the monks of Brinkburn Priory (*Proc. Arch. Inst.*,
Newcastle, 1852, vol. i., p. 246) receiving the grant of a salt pan
at Warkworth, from Henry, Earl of Northumberland, the son of
David, King of Scotland.

Further south, at the mouth of the River Blyth, the monks of
Newminster were engaged in the salt industry in the early part
of the thirteenth century, the covenant made between them and
the family of Camhus, in 1236, having reference to a road to the
saltworks belonging to the monks.   It seems not improbable that
the sea coals on the shore near Blyth, granted about this time to
these monks, may have been intended to be used for fuel at their
saltworks, though we have no direct mention of the systematic
employment of coal in salt-making till a later period.

It cannot be doubted that the monks of Tynemouth, who were
peculiarly well situated for carrying on a salt trade, turned their
attention to this industry very early.   At what date they began
to utilize part of the produce of their collieries for fuel in the
process we have no record.   But in 1463 they obtained a charter
from Edward IV. (Gibson's *History of the Monastery of Tynemouth*,
Appendix cxxxvii., p. cxxxi.) for loading and unloading their own
and other ships, without impediment or imposition from the men
of Newcastle-on-Tyne, the special object in view being to enable
them to trade freely in coals and white salt, which formed great
part of the commodities and profits of their church.   In this era
the stars were unpropitious to Newcastle ; the power of the Church
was in the ascendant.

At North and South Shields numerous saltworks sprung into
existence, this industry, in the course of time, attaining to large
proportions, aud becoming the chief occupation of the inhabitants.
An early reference to the use of *iron* salt pans at South Shields
occurs in 1499 (Surtees, ii. 94), lead being the material of which
they were constructed at the inland saltworks down till a much
later date.

That the manufacture of salt with coal was going on at the
mouth of the Wear is evidenced by a notice in the accounts of

Monkwearmouth Monastery (Surtees Society, vol. xxix., p. 227) of the purchase of a keel, in 1506, to carry coal to the saltwork there. From the saltworks at the mouth of the Wear and elsewhere (*Proc. Arch. Inst.*, Newcastle, 1852, i. 70), a chain of roads known as Salters' Tracks radiated inland, by which the salt was conveyed on pack-horses. Where not paved, these roads were sometimes cut very deep by the wear and tear of ages.

Regarding the progress of coal mining in the Tyne Valley in the fifteenth century, our information is chiefly confined to references relative to the working of coal at a number of new points.

On the north side of the Tyne the townsmen of Newcastle had extended their operations into the manor of Fenham, which lay on the west side of the Town Moor. In March, 1404 (Brand, ii. 260), the Prior of the Hospital of St. John of Jerusalem granted the community of Newcastle-on-Tyne a receipt for £12 10s., being part payment of the sum of £37 10s. due in Michaelmas following for the rent of mines of sea coal in Fenham.

Beyond the fact that the monks of Tynemouth continued to carry on a trade in coal, we have no particulars as to the collieries worked by them at this period, nor do we hear of others on the north side of the river, though doubtless such existed.

On the south side of the Tyne coal continued to be worked in Gateshead, in the early part of this century, by one John de Dolfanby, though apparently not in a very prosperous way, as we find the son of this individual becoming security to Bishop Langley (roll "B," m. 5 d')[1] in 1414-15, for the payment of the rent of 100 marks (£66 13s. 4d.). But very little is heard regarding the bishop's mines in Gateshead for a period of more than a hundred years, after the Durham side of the Tyne was freed from the control of the men of Newcastle, by the charter granted to Bishop Fordham by King Richard II. in 1384. Indeed, so far as records relating to them are concerned, they would almost appear to have been left severely alone. We hear, however, of coal receiving attention at various places in the surrounding district.

In 1441 Bishop Neville—a prelate who seems to have taken an exceptional amount of interest in the working of coal in the bishopric —granted a license (roll 1, m. 13; Brand, i. 472 note; Hutchinson's *Durham*, ii. 461 n.) to Thomas Kirkeby, Master of the Hospital of St. Edmund in Gateshead, to dig coals in the hospital lands, with

[1] The rolls referred to are those of which calendars have been published by the Deputy Keeper of the Public Records in his Annual Reports, commencing with the 31st.

wayleave to carry them over his ground, and power to build staiths for loading them on the Tyne, at a rent of 100s. per annum. That coal was being worked in these lands in 1467-68 is evidenced by a recognizance from William Blaykeston, of Newcastle-on-Tyne, merchant, and Roland Ringthwaite, of Durham, "fleshewer," to Bishop Booth (roll 3, m. 9 d'), for license to carry coals from the hospital to the bishop's staiths.

Bishop Neville likewise, in 1451-52 (roll 3, m. 15), granted license to Geoffrey Middleton, Sheriff of Durham, to obtain sea coal at a place near Gateshead called Camerdikes, and to carry and send away the same for the term of ten years.

The circumstance of the name of John Ravensworth figuring along with that of John de Dolfanby in a recognizance to Bishop Langley (roll "A," m. 9, d') is suggestive of the fact that the owner of the extensive Ravensworth estates was working coal on his lands and sending it to the Tyne for shipment in the early part of this century.

Several notices occur relative to the working of coal in the manor of Whickham. There is mention in 1402 (Neasham's *Hist. and Biog. of West Durham*) of the prosecution of one John del Hall for not carrying coals from the coal pit in Whickham to the Derwent, whereby John de Tyndale sustained damage to the amount of 13s. Hall appears to have been a coal-bearer. The loading of coal on the River Derwent had evidently already commenced. It subsequently became a great *rendezvous* for coal keels.

In 1439-40 we find Robert Rhodes entering into a recognizance (Neville, roll 5, m. 2 and 3) to the Bishop of Durham for the appearance of a certain collier of Whickham before the justices at Durham, to answer to the bishop concerning a trespass in a mine at Whickham.

It was doubtless to coal coming either from Whickham or Gateshead that Bishop Sherwood referred in a letter sent to Sir John Paston, of Norfolk, in 1489 (Fenn's *Paston Letters*, v. 376; Raine's *Auckland Castle*, p. 57), wherein he proposed to barter some of his coals with Sir John in exchange for corn and wine and wax, whereby their familiarity and friendship might be increased.

Shortly after the above date a record of more than ordinary interest occurs relating to a mine at Whickham. It consists of an entry in the roll of the stock-keeper of the bishopric for the year 1492-93 (Raine's *Auckland Castle*, p. 58), recording the payment of 40s. "for two great iron chains for the ordinance of the mine at Whickham, for drawing coals and water out of the coal pit there, by my

Lord's command." This is the earliest mention we have of the employment of machinery at the Tyneside collieries for the purpose of raising water.

In 1444-45 Bishop Neville (roll 2, m. 4) confirmed Thomas Neville in his estate in a close called Gellesfield, in the township of Whickham, with license to work the mines of coal and stone there previously held by Robert Rodes, who had conveyed them to him. This Robert Rodes, or Rhodes, was probably the wealthy Newcastle lawyer of this period, to whose munificence was due the beautiful lantern on the tower of St. Nicholas Church, now the cathedral of the diocese of Northumberland. Gellesfield appears to have formed a portion of the modern estate of Gibside.

We hear of mines in the same neighbourhood—if, indeed, they may not be the same mines—in connection with a law-suit in London (De Banco Roll, Mich. 14, Hen. VI., m. 338) regarding the payment of 160 chaldrons of coal (nominally 80 chaldrons) obtained in 1432 from "the Grothe called Darwent Grothe." Grothe is obviously a corruption of grove, or groove. The coal mines on the Derwent continued to be known as Derwent Grooves down till recent times.

On the west side of the Derwent the working of coal continued to be prosecuted in the manor of Winlaton. Two coal mines here, called Fullay pit and Morlay pit (*Winlawton cum mineris carbonum de fullay pute et morlay pute*) are mentioned in connection with an inquisition taken in 1425-26, at the death of Ralph, Earl of Westmoreland (Hutchinson's *Durham*, ii. 441; iii. 264 note).

Further west notice occurs (Neasham's *Hist. and Biog. of West Durham*) of a pit of sea coal being leased at Ryton in 1402, to John de Tyndale, clerk, and William Carnis, for twelve years, at 40s. rent. It was stipulated that if the place of the said coal should be empty, so that they were unable to get coal thence, the farmers were to be exonerated both of pit and rent. Also that they were to have wood for the construction of the pit, and likewise for making a staith on the Tyne, within the lord's forest, on the lord's soil, to be allowed by the lord's forester, for placing the said coals; and they were to have a sufficient way from the pit to the staith, to be allowed by the council of the lord bishop; and the farmers allowed that if they did damage to the lord's tenants, within the village or without, the trespass should be repaired without impediment.

By a curious coincidence, illustrative of the complete dissociation of the coal and iron industries at this period, other colliers besides the pitmen were at work in Ryton parish a little later. In 1430 a grant was made by Bishop Langley (roll "DD," m. 3 d'; *Proc. Archæological Inst.*, Newcastle, 1852, i. 190) to an ironmaster or "irynbrenner," named Robert Kirkhous, of woods in Crawcrook for converting into charcoal. It was stipulated that the oak, ash, hollin-wood, apple tree, and crab tree, were to be excepted, as also all wood fit for fellyes, or beams; which, it is said, shall always be felled "before the colyers make cole."

Reference has been made to the use of enlarged keels on the Tyne in the reign of Richard II., and to the measures then insti-tuted for bringing them back to the standard size. The check administered to the movement proved only of a temporary character, and in the early part of the fifteenth century the employment of over-sized keels had again become a source of difficulty. From an Act of Parliament passed in 1421 (*Rot. Parl.*, vol. iv., p. 148, n. 35) we learn that whereas two pennies of custom were due to the king on each chaldron of sea coal sold to persons not franchised in the port of Newcastle-on-Tyne, and each keel used for conveying coals to ships ought to carry twenty chaldrons, on which quantity custom was paid, certain persons had made keels to carry twenty-two or twenty-three chaldrons, while only paying duty on twenty, thereby partially evading the king's dues. It was therefore enacted that all keels should have their carrying capacity measured and marked by the king's commissioners before being used to carry coals, on pain of forfeiture to the Crown. (See also *33rd Report of the Deputy Keeper of the Public Records*, p. 186; and Brand, vol. ii., pp. 261, 263.)

This marking, or "signing," of keels—characterized as the earliest instance of the fixing of a load-line in navigation, and effected by driving in nails at the bow and the stern (*1829 Report*, p. 33)—effectually put a stop to the employment of enlarged keels; but, curious to say, it entirely failed in its primary object of preventing the evasion of the king's dues. The ingenuity of the keel owners proved more than a match for the Legislature. While the size of the keel now remained stationary, the size of the chaldron (on which the duty was paid) began to grow; and with such success was this policy pursued during a prolonged period, that when it was finally put a stop to, some two hundred and fifty years later, the chaldron had attained to two and a half times its original size, and the carefully marked keels were only carrying eight instead of the original twenty chaldrons. At the same time it seems not improbable that this continual increase in the size of the chaldron may have been owing to the temptation to give extra measure in order to secure trade, rather than with the direct object of evading the royal duty.

Meanwhile, in the central and southern portions of the Bishopric of Durham, the monks of Durham, the monks of Finchale, and others, were engaged in carrying on the old and opening out new collieries. The frequent references to water-gates, or aqueducts, for draining the pits, and the importance now attached to them, forms a marked feature of the coal mining operations here in this era, and is indicative of the gradual deepening of the mines.

In 1407 an agreement was entered into (Surtees, vol. iii., p. 287) between the Sub-Prior of Durham, the Commoner of the House of Durham, and Sir William Blakeston, to cut a water-way or sub-terranean drain (*aqueductum sive trencheam subterraneam*) at their joint expense, for carrying off the water and winning coal in the lands of Hett, the coal so won to be in common between the three contracting parties. This appears to have been successfully accomplished, inasmuch as in 1415 the Prior and Convent of Durham, Impropriators of the church of Merrington, obtained a decree against Thomas Blakeston, Esq., for tithes of coal in Hett.

Various references occur to the continued working of coal by the Durham monks in their lands of Rainton. Mention is made (*Feodarium Prioratus Dunelmensis*, p. 19—Surtees Society, vol. lviii.) of *le carboner*, or collier, of West Rainton, in 1430; and we find the monks of Finchale purchasing coals there in 1431-32. In 1464 (*Feodarium*, p. 126) the mine at West Rainton yielded the Durham monks a clear profit of £34.

These monks were also working coal in their lands of Aldingrige, or Aldengrange, in the vicinity of Durham. In a record of the year 1446 (Surtees, vol. iv., p. 105) it is stated that "the manors of Aldyngrige, Almershalgh and Beaurepare-moor, are in the hands of the Bursar, etc.; the mine of coal is worth, one year with another, £10; besides twelve score chaldrons delivered for the use of the Convent, and of the manor-house of Beaurepare." In 1464 (*Feodarium*, p. 191) coal was only worked here for the use of the monastery.

In addition to collieries held in their own hands, the Durham monks likewise granted leases of coal in their lands to others. There is extant a curious lease ("Hist. Dunelm. Script. Tres.," Appendix, p. cccxii.—Surtees Society, vol. ix.) made by the prior in 1447 to John Bron of Tudhoe, and five others, of some land and pits at Trillesden and Spennymoor. It is one of the earliest instances of a mining lease in English, all those hitherto quoted

being either in Latin or Norman-French. In this lease, the language
of which is somewhat uncouth according to modern ideas of ortho-
graphy, the prior demises to the above parties "a wast toft and
twenty-eight acres of land with th' appertenantes in Trillesden,
and with a colepit in the same lande, therein to wirke and wyn
cole evere day overable with thre pikkes, and ilk pike to wyn
every day overable sixty scopes"; or, in nineteenth-century
English, "a waste toft and twenty-eight acres of land with the
appurtenants in Trillesden, and with a coal pit in the same land,
therein to work and win coal every working day with three picks,
and each pick to win every working day sixty scopes," for the
term of a year, the rent of the pit being 10 marks (£6 13s 4d.).
The lessees were bound to work the said pit workmanlike and
save the field standing, by the sight of certain viewers assigned
by the said prior.

The prior also grants them a coal pit in the north side of
Spennymoor, on the same conditions, at a rent of £20. In this
case it was stipulated that the lessees shall, at their own cost and
expense, labour and win a water-gate for winning of coal in the
same coal pit of Spennymoor, and the same water-gate like as they
win it they shall leave it in the year end, by sight of the said
viewers.

In the above lease the limitation of the output of coal is very
stringently provided for. The method of restricting the number
of picks allowed to be employed is found still in operation at
collieries in Northumberland in the following century.

Though the Finchale monks were engaged in numerous mining
enterprises, and were at considerable trouble and expense in their
attempts to establish collieries, as appears from their accounts
(Surtees Society, vol. vi.), their operations were not attended with
much success during the first half of the fifteenth century. Their
connection with the mine at Coken had not proved fortunate, and
was discontinued in 1404. During the two following years they
held a mine at a place called Leywode, which yielded them a small
return. Shortly afterwards they opened up mines at Moorhouse-
field and Baxtanfordwood, near Durham. But here they trenched
upon ground already occupied by the monks of Durham, who tried
various expedients to avert competition, by buying their coals,
paying for retaining their mine, and eventually, in 1427-28, purchased the mine in four acres of land near Baxtanfordwood, at a
cost of £40, for the use of the House of Durham only.

The Finchale monks (who had been working coal on a small

scale at Lumley for a year or two) now turned their attention to the neighbourhood of Coxhoe, where they constructed a water-gate at a cost of £60, and obtained a mine which proved profitable for a short period, yielding them £15, £54, and £34 6s. respectively in 1428-29 and the two following years, but failed thereafter.

They next endeavoured to resuscitate their colliery at Softley, which had ceased to be remunerative in 1422, probably owing to a great lease of coal in the south of Durham, which will be referred to hereafter. In 1433-34 they constructed a water-gate for this mine, but without succeeding to re-establish the colliery. At this period they dug supplies of coal for their house at Lumley and Coken Isles.

In 1442-43 they made another attempt to establish a mine at Baxtanfordwood, and expended £26 5s. 9d. in constructing a water-gate. But they again encountered the opposition of the Durham monks; and shortly afterwards the supervisor of the colliery of Aldyngrige offered them sufficient pecuniary inducement to let their pit remain unworked.

In the latter half of the century their connection with the coal trade proved more beneficial to them. After a hiatus in their accounts for some years, we find them in possession of a mine at Moorhouseclose in 1457-58, which yielded them £10 in this year, in addition to eighty chaldrons of coal supplied to their house. This mine—the produce of which was doubtless exported, the monks being owners of a ship and a number of barges—they continued to work until the date of the dissolution of their house, at times deriving an annual profit of £15 or £20 from it, though usually a less amount: the cost of getting the coal being generally about one half of the price obtained for it.

It is at this colliery we first hear of coal being worked under the level of free drainage, and the water being raised by machinery in the Wear district, almost synchronously with the same movement on the Tyne, being one out of many instances of a remarkable parallelism observable in the progress of these two mining centres. In 1486-87 the Finchale monks expended a sum of £9 15s. 6d. on the new ordinance of the pump with the construction of a house and all its fittings, together with horses bought and their requirements; and for some years subsequently, in connection with the cost of winning coals, special mention is made in their accounts of the expenses *de le pompe*.

Several other notices occur relating to coal in various parts of the bishopric. Thus in 1426-27 (Langley, roll "E," m. 13) a law-

suit took place between the Bishop of Durham and the Abbot of
St. Albans regarding messuages, lands, and coal mine at Woodifield.
In 1456-57 Bishop Neville (roll 4, m. 7 and 5 ; see also roll 6,
m. 22 d') granted a lease of a coal mine in Middlewood, near
Beurepark, to Robert Walthewe and Thomas Rycroft, for a term
of thirteen years. And in the following year the same prelate
(roll 4, m. 8) demised the coal and iron mines of Cassop and
Wharyngton—the latter place deriving its name, according to Mr.
Surtees, from the quarries (probably of lime) there—to John
Lound, clerk ; Robert Sotheron, chaplain ; and Richard Raket, for
a term of twenty years.

Reference has been made to a great lease of coal in the south of
Durham, which proved fatal to the mine at Softley, belonging to
the monks of Finchale. This was probably the most important
lease in the bishopric during the fifteenth century, and gave the
various lessees who held it a practical monopoly of the coal trade
of the southern district. It comprised the mines of coal, and of
iron ore under the coal, in Raly, Caldhirst, Hertkeld, Hethere-
clough, otherwise Tollawe and Wollawes, and in the barony of
Evenwood. It was first held by Rauf de Eure—a name redolent
of mining, "eure" being the same word as ore—on whose decease
it was granted by Bishop Langley (roll "E," m. 20 d'), in 1424, to
William de Eure, for a term of nine years, at a rent of £112 13s. 4d.
per annum ; and was renewed to him from time to time (with some
variations) by successive bishops. Among the conditions of the
original lease to W. de Eure, it was stipulated that—

The lessee at his own cost should protect, support, and uphold
the water-gates required for the mines ; and should leave them,
and any others which might be made, in good order at the end of
the lease. He should also, at his own expense, sink the pits
(*puyttes*) required for winning and drawing coals from the mines—
coals only to be drawn on lawful working days.

He was also required to deliver annually on the surface at the
mine of Raly as much coal as the bishop should deem necessary for
his house (Auckland Castle), at the price of 4d. per chaldron.

The bishop grants the timber necessary for the pits and water-
gates from his woods ; and covenants that if the lessee should incur
any great and remarkable expense in making any new water-gate,
he will bear one-half of the cost. Also that he will allow no one to
make any water-gates in his ground, or carry coals out of his ground,
except by the highways, to the injury of the lessee.

Numerous records, consisting of leases and writs of various kinds, exist relative to this important group of mines during the long tenure of them by W. de Eure. This individual appears to have carried on his mining operations with great vigour, and to have driven a considerable trade in coal over a large area. Thus in 1463-64, we find the Sheriff of Durham directed by Bishop Booth (roll 3, m. 6) to arrest and detain certain men of the county of York, of the county of Durham, and of the wapentake of Sadberge, they having been engaged with carts, horses, etc., in taking sea coal from a pit of William de Eure, knight, at "Les Toftes," and thereby injuring the soil and grass of the Lord Bishop.

The strict letter of the lease does not appear to have been invariably adhered to in the working of the mines, and on several occasions investigations were instituted into the proceedings of the lessee. In 1450-51, Bishop Neville (roll 3, m. 9) directed Henry Lescrop and others to inquire concerning offences said to have been committed by W. de Eure and his servants in cutting through the "forbarres" (barriers?) in working the mines. And, again, in 1458-59, Bishop Booth (roll 1, m. 5) assigned Henry Preston and others to make inquiry touching damages and wastes said to be committed by him and his servants and workmen in the coal mines of Rale, etc.

After being held by W. de Eure for a lengthened period, the coal mines of Raly, Calehirst, Toftes and Hartgyll, were leased by Bishop Sherwood (roll 1, m. 1), in 1485, to Robert Walker for a year, at a rent of £150. And three years later the same bishop (roll 1, m. 4 and 5) demised to Thomas Witton, of Newbigging, the mines of coal and of iron ore below the coal in Raley, Toftes, Caldhirst, Hartkeld, Hetherclough, otherwise Tollawe, Morapitt, Ceple and Wollawe, for the term of six years, at a rent of £141 6s. 8d. per annum. Thus this great lease of the South Durham mines continued almost in its original form during the whole of this century, and it is found still in existence in a modified form long subsequently.

Regarding the working of coal in the River Blyth district at this period we have no information, but we hear of it receiving attention at various places in the northern part of Northumberland. The accounts of the church of Norham, for the year 1418-19 (Raine's *North Durham*, p. 269), record the receipt of "13s. 4d. for coals from the pit of sea coals at Shoresworth this year." At Holburn, also, coal continued to be worked. There is mention (*ib.*, p. 119) of the opening out (*in penetracione*) of a pit, or drift, there in 1440-41, at a cost of 46s. 8d. While in 1491-92 a lease of the lands, etc., within and about the town of Tweedmouth, fishing in the water of Tweed,

coal mine belonging to the bishop by reason of Tweedmouth, etc.,
was granted by Bishop Sherwood (roll 1, m. 9) to Sir William Tyler,
for a term of five years.

In this century the collieries in the great northern coalfield were
still almost exclusively planted in situations where natural drainage
was available; though considerable expense was now sometimes
incurred in the cutting of tunnels, or drifts, to accomplish this
desirable object. But towards its close, in order to obtain supplies
of coal at points well situated for its shipment, a commencement, as
we have seen, was already made, both on the Tyne and Wear, to
penetrate into the zone below the level of free drainage, and to raise
the water by means of horse engines—the increased cost of drainage

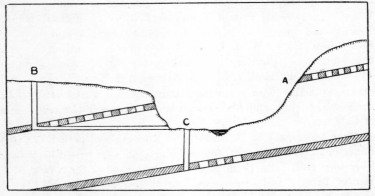

Fig. 2.—Three Stages of Mining. A, Day-hole; no machinery required.
B, Pit and adit; coal raised by machinery, water drained by aqueduct or adit.
C, Pit; coal and water both raised by machinery.

being balanced by the lower cost of conveyance. Coal mining in
this coalfield had begun to enter upon the third stage of its history
—that in which both coals and water were brought to the surface
by machinery. This, however, did not become general till long
subsequently.

The reference to mining in a workmanlike manner so as to keep up
the surface, in the lease of coal at Trillesden and Spennymoor
(while suggestive of the fact that subsidences, termed thrusts or
crushes, had already taken place), points to the leaving of pillars of
coal in the mine : a method of working which seems to have been
pursued in this coalfield since the commencement of coal mining, and
which, in a modified form, continues to be the prevailing system
here at the present day.

Notices regarding the appliances and implements in use are still meagre. The poverty of references to them may be accounted for by the circumstance that in addition to being few and simple, they were manufactured on the spot out of the raw material. Wood could be had anywhere. The iron required usually consisted of Spanish iron bought at Newcastle, or of the home-made Weardale iron, both of which figure in the accounts of the period. Sometimes, though rarely, we find the religious houses having articles made of their own iron, indicating that they were themselves iron manufacturers. Picks, scopes, and wooden shovels, and ropes for raising the coal, are almost the only colliery furnishings of which mention is to be found.

As the mines of the Bishopric of Durham increased in number and importance, the officials entrusted with the charge of them became more numerous and varied. One, Thomas Buk, was appointed by Bishop Neville (roll 5, m.), in 1438-39, to the office of "bankmanship" of the coal mines of Ralifield and Harecrosfeld; and was promoted by Bishop Booth (roll 1, m. 18), in 1464-65, to be surveyor of mines of sea coal, with a yearly fee of 40s.

Bishop Booth likewise (roll 2, m. 9) appointed Ralph Gyllowe to the office of clerk of the mines within the Bishopric of Durham; while in 1496-97 Bishop Fox (roll 2, m. 4) appointed Leonard Forester as surveyor of labourers and workmen in the coal mines within the bishopric, with power to imprison the disobedient.

In addition to the permanent officials, special surveyors, or commissioners, were from time to time appointed to make general surveys of all the bishop's demesnes, castles, forests, mines, etc.

The term surveyor, as used in mining, has altogether degenerated in meaning, and lost its early significance. Originally applied to an official of the highest rank—the overviewer, or chief inspector—it has become the designation of the individual whose special function is to map the progress of the excavations on the plan of the mine, and who occupies a position quite subordinate to the viewer, and even of less responsibility than that of the underviewer.

As to the period when the coal miners of Northumberland and Durham became emancipated from serfdom, no exact information seems to be available. Workers in coal mines had no share in the remarkable franchises enjoyed, as early at least as the twelfth and thirteenth centuries, by the tin miners of Cornwall, the iron miners of the Forest of Dean, and the lead miners of Derbyshire, and elsewhere; but, on the contrary, would appear to have been kept even in somewhat greater subjection than the bulk of the labouring classes. The appointment of Leonard Forester, above referred to, seems to point to the fact that at the end of the fifteenth century the Durham coal miners still continued more or less in a condition of serfdom. A change is observable in the Finchale accounts, commencing about 1460, after which time the cost of getting the coal begins to be recorded. But whether this may have had any connection with the manumission of their miners, or was merely a change in the method of keeping their accounts, is uncertain. We know that serfs existed on some of the royal estates for about a hundred years later, Queen Elizabeth manumitting a number of hers in the western counties in 1574 : the last recorded act of the kind in England. Whether the lifelong bond of the northern coal miners had by this time given place to the Yearly Bond, which survived far down into the present century, does not appear. In Scotland the workers in coal mines and saltworks (not salt mines, as sometimes stated), male and female alike, continued in a condition of pure and simple serfdom—*adscripti glebæ*, or bound to the soil—till the latter part of the eighteenth century ; being the last section of the population of Great Britain to taste the sweets of freedom.[1]

In Yorkshire the digging of coal had become a well-established industry in the neighbourhood of Wakefield at the commencement of the fifteenth century.

In the Wakefield court rolls, under Northowram, in 1401 (*Leeds Mercury Supplement*, May 9, 1885), one Richard of Mekesburgh is charged with having broken the soil of the Lord in Shipden, and acquired sea coals (*carbones marini*) there without license.

In the same rolls (*ib.*, May 30, 1885), under date 1402, it is recorded that "12 pits of sea coals in Horbury lyghtes are sold this year to divers tenants for 31s. 6d."

In presentments made at Court Leets in connection with the same manor, a number of references occur to the digging of coals, and the infliction of fines for selling coal without license :

1404. Wakefield Leet : Stanley—"Presented for coals, 12d."
        Easter Leet—"Penalty for selling coals, 1. each for eight persons."
1461.   Northowram—"Coals digging."
1465.   Wakefield Leet—"For digging coals on the Lord's waste at Alver-
        thorpe and Stanley, 3d. and 4d. each."

---

[1] The writer is disposed to question the hypothesis of Mr. Cosmo Innes that the Scotch colliers and salters, after having been emancipated, were re-enslaved by Act of Parliament in 1606. On the contrary, it would appear from the court records of Dysart, in Fife, that the workpeople employed at the collieries and saltworks there, both men and married women, were in a state of serfdom in 1598.

1475. Wakefield, 30th Sep.—"Presentment for the tenants of the Lord's coal pits on Outwood selling coal to extraneous men" (those living out of the graveship or manor).

1489. Northowram—"Paine for digging coals at Hartishead."

1493. Hipperholme—"Coals taken; fine 2s."

Coals brought up the Ouse, and termed sea coals, had been employed in burning the lime required for the building of the Minster at York, as we learn from the Fabric Rolls (Surtees Society, vol. xxxv.). But the native coal of the county begins to figure in the accounts in 1499, when a payment is recorded of 14s. for 12 quarters of subterranean coals (*carbonum subterrenorum*). We find shortly afterwards that the inland coals came from Wakefield.

In the Lancashire coalfield the mineral continued to be worked in the Colne district, though apparently on a very limited scale. From a record quoted by Whitaker in his *History of the original parish of Whalley and Honour of Clitheroe* (4th ed., vol. i., p. 361), it appears that in 1472-73 the farm of the sea coals in Colne and Trawden was held by Lawrence Lyster, at a rent of 6s. 8d. At the same date the mine of sea coal in Padyham and Brodehede, in the township of Penhull, was held by Roger Cokshote and partners, at a rent of 20s. per annum.

In the name of Coleorton we have the first direct information relating to coal mining in the Leicestershire coalfield. This place, Burton informs us, in his *History of Leicestershire* (2nd ed., p. 198), had previously been known as Overton Quatarmersh, but is mentioned as Colorton, or Cole Overton—the property of Thomas Beaumont Knight—in the early part of the fifteenth century (5 Hen. VI. ; *ib.*, p. 36), indicating that a coal trade of some importance had arisen there.

In the Forest of Dean, apparently in the reign of Henry VI., Mr. Nicholls states (*Forest of Dean*, p. 21) that "the singular perquisite of a bushel of coal, worth twenty pence, from each pit, at the end of every six weeks, was now attached to the office of 'capital forester of all the foresters,' held at this period by Robert Greyndour."

We also begin to meet with notices relating to another official in the forest, known by the peculiar name of the Gawler, or Gaveller ; though this post had doubtless existed long previous to this time, the "gaveler" being frequently referred to in the Laws and Customs of the miners in the forest, which, as already mentioned, are assigned by Mr. Nicholls to the reign of Edward I. In 1484-85 (*9th Report of the Deputy Keeper of the Public Records*, Appendix ii., p. 123), a grant was made "to John Grenehill of the custody of the Gawle of Great and Little Dene, otherwise called the gawle beneath the wood, with the emoluments lately enjoyed therewith by Robert Hiot." Immediately afterwards (1 Henry VII., Rudder's *Gloucestershire*) the mines beneath the wood called "Le Gawle" were granted to John Motten for his life without rent.

The term gaveller (*gabeleur*) was originally applied to an official of the excise who collected the king's duty on salt. It was doubtless given to this mining official in the Forest of Dean from his supervising and collecting the tribute (*gavel*) due to the king from the miners for the privilege of working the mines.

Such information as is available regarding the progress of coal mining in Wales at this period still relates only to the North Wales coalfields. From records cited in the *36th Report of the Deputy Keeper of the Public Records* (Appendix ii.), we learn that a lease of the mines in Ewloe (with the exception of those held by the heirs of Ithel ap Blethin ap Ithel) was granted to David de Ewloe in 1408, for a term of ten years, at a rent of five marks (£3 6s. 8d.) for the first two years, and £4 yearly thereafter, the mines there during the remainder of the century being included in leases of the lordship and town. By a charter granted to them by the Earl of Arundel in 1410 (Pennant's *Tours in Wales*, ed. 1810, vol. i., p. 404) the inhabitants of Holt, in Denbigh, were allowed to dig coal and turf at Brymbo, near Wrexham. Mention also occurs (Ormerod's *Cheshire*, ii. 60) in 1425-26, of the existence of a mine of sea coal at Hawarden.

CHAPTER VIII.

THE SIXTEENTH CENTURY. 1509—1603 A.D.

The failure of the wood supply causes coal to begin to come into general use for domestic purposes. Foreign export of coal. Collieries and coal trade of the Tyne.

NOTWITHSTANDING the extent to which coal had come into use, England was still essentially a wood-consuming country. As late as the middle of the sixteenth century, the bulk of the populace continued to burn wood in their fires, and looked upon sea coal as of all kinds of fuel about the very worst. Such we can well conceive it to have been when used under the same conditions as wood, in open fire-places in the centre of the floor.

But the supply of wood was beginning to fail. Already in the time of Henry VIII. this accustomed and favourite fuel was becoming sensibly scarcer and dearer; so much so as to necessitate a revisal of the legislation affecting its sale (34 and 35 Hen. VIII., c. 3). Acts of Parliament passed at various times during this century (*e.g.* 35 Hen. VIII., c. 17; 1 Eliz., c. 15; 13 Eliz., c. 25; 23 Eliz., c. 5; 27 Eliz., c. 19; 28 Eliz., cc. 3, 5) for preserving woods and restraining the erection of ironworks, the manufacture of charcoal for which was so destructive to the forests in their neighbourhood, proved of little avail. The wood resources were fast becoming inadequate for the requirements of the kingdom: a fact not belonging to the order of ills "which laws and kings can cause or cure."

At the same time, and possibly owing to the necessity felt of having recourse to cheaper kinds of fuel, the primitive arrangements of the fire-hearth which had continued to prevail, particularly in inland districts, down till the era of the reformation—previous to which time, according to a MS. of Aubrey's in the Ashmolean collection, ordinary men's houses and copyholders and the like had no chimneys, but flues like beaver holes—began to be generally discarded, and to give place to the improved modern fashion of fireplaces having proper chimney-flues attached to carry off the smoke.

What with the failing wood supply, and the removal of the great obstacle to its use brought about by this revolution in house-firing arrangements, the strong objections hitherto entertained against coal began to abate, and a wider field to open up for its employment. The demand for coal for domestic purposes now gradually became the most important branch of the trade, followed by a great increase in the quantity of coal consumed. So marked was the advance in the use of coal which was taking place about 1570 that Grey, the earliest historian of Newcastle, characterizes this period as the real commencement of the coal trade. In his *Chorographia, or a survey of Newcastle-upon-Tine*, published in 1649 under the initials W. G., he avers that "the coale trade began not past four score years since; coales in former times was only used by smiths and for burning of lime."

In addition to the growing demand for coal at home, the exportation of it to the Continent had also attained to some importance in the middle of the sixteenth century. Brand (ii. 265) mentions a notable order being sent by Henry VIII. in 1546, to the Mayor of Newcastle, Robert Brandling, and Henry Anderson, to forward 3,000 chaldrons of coal to the town of Bullein (Boulogne) with all possible despatch. But, on account of the scarcity of fuel in England, the drain upon the resources of the country due to the export of coal was viewed with some degree of disquietude ; and it appears from the *Commons Journal* (vol. i., p. 19*b*) that the question of prohibiting it was under the consideration of Parliament in 1549.

A few years later (1552) it was proposed to suppress the foreign export of coal with another object in view—that of distressing the French (Ellis's *Original Letters*, vol. ii., p. 195), whose artificers, it was stated, could no more live without Newcastle coal than fish without water. At this time coal was still a very low-priced commodity on the Tyne, while it brought a high price in France. It is mentioned as having been purchased at Newcastle at 2s. 2d. per chaldron, and sold in France at thirteen nobles (£4 6s. 8d.), from which this trade would appear to have been of a very profitable character. Though the subject was agitated on numerous occasions, both in and out of Parliament, no actual steps were taken to put a stop to the shipment of coal from Newcastle to the Continent.

In this era information regarding coal and collieries is obtainable from a greater variety of sources. Hitherto they were of such little interest to the community at large as to be scarcely ever referred to outside of their own immediate records. Now they begin to make some figure in general literature, various writers of the period commenting on the decay of the woods, and the spread of the adoption of coal for fuel, which they observed to be going on around them.

On this subject Harrison makes some interesting and informing remarks in his Description of England (book iii., c. 16), prefixed to Holinshed's *Chronicle*, published in 1577. "Of cole mines," says this author, "we have such plentie in the north and westerne partes of our Islande as may suffice for all the Realme of Englande. And so must they doe hereafter indeede, if woode be not better cherished than it is at this present. And to say the truth, notwithstanding that very many of them are caryed into other countryes of the maine, yet theyr greatest trade beginneth nowe to growe from the forge into ye Kitchin and Hall, as maye appeare already in most cities and townes that lye about the cost."

The same writer (book ii., c. 10) refers to the great increase which took place in the number of house chimneys as a marked feature of the middle of the sixteenth century. "There are olde men," he says, "yet dwelling in the village where I remayne, which hauve noted three things to be marueylously altered in Englande within their sound remembraunce. One is the multitude of chimnies lately erected, whereas in their yoong dayes there were not above two or three if so many in most uplandish townes of the realme (the religious houses and mannour places of their Lordes alwayes excepted, and peradventure some great personages), but eache one made his fire against a reredosse in the hall where he dined and dressed his meate."

Harrison did not think much of chimneys, however, and imagined that people had become less hardy since their extended employment. "Now," he observes, "we have many chimnyes, and yet our tenderlings complaine of rewmes, catarres, and poses; then had we none but reredoses, and our heads did never ake. For as the smoke in those days was supposed to be a sufficient hardning for the timber of the house, so it was reputed a far better medicine to keep the good man and his family from the quacke or pose, wherewith, as then, very few were acquainted."

One of the last surviving halls in England with the fire-place in the centre of the floor, was that of Penshurst, in Kent, which

was still in existence at the time of William Howitt's visit about
1840.

Though all the coalfields doubtless participated in the benefits
accruing from the increasing consumption of coal, the lion's share
fell to the River Tyne, with its exceptional natural advantages for
obtaining and shipping the mineral. Here, too, the export trade
was almost exclusively confined to mines situated in close proximity
to the river ; the cost of conveying coal even a short distance by the
elementary methods at this time in use, being sufficient to prevent
outlying collieries from sharing in the trade to any extent, and
reducing their value to a mere trifle ; though towards the close of the
century some of the more distant mines attained to greater importance.

In the district to the west of Newcastle and Gateshead, where the
coal seams approached the surface, the working of the mineral was
now being carried on in all the lands situated within a radius of
some miles from the navigable part of the Tyne.

The mines of Gateshead and Whickham rose into special prominence in this century, particularly towards its close ; but the
working of coal was being carried on in this neighbourhood with
considerable activity in the early part of the century as well, as
appears from the following notices relating to it.

The coal mines and pits of Gateshead were leased by Bishop
Ruthall (roll 2, m. 2 d'), in 1513-14, to William Inskip, of Gateshead, Robert Athe, the elder, of Durham, and William Thomlynson,
of Gateshead, for sixteen years, at £66 13s. 4d. per annum. An
indirect reference to the working of the coal is met with shortly
afterwards in the accounts of the receiver-general of the bishopric
(Raine's *Auckland Castle*, p. 63), where under date 1519-20, an entry
occurs :—" Paid to the rector of Gateshead for tithe coals of my
lord's pit there 31s. 6d."

At a subsequent date we hear of a dispute between the parson of
Gateshead and the lessees of the mines regarding the question of
tithes, which was settled after a singular fashion, as set forth in the
following agreement (Hutchinson's *Durham*, ii. 468) :

" An order for the tithe coles of Gateshead.

" M^d that the xth day of October, in the year of o'r Lord God
MVCXXXIX.

" Whereas discord, clame, and suyt, haith been dependinge
betwixt Sir John Brown, clerk, p'son of Gateshead of th' one p'tie,
and Will'm Thomlyngson and Will'm Inskip fermers of my lord of
Duresme cole mynes, wt'in the township and p'ishe of Gateshed, on
th' oder p'te, of, for, and upon the detynewe of the tiethe coles of

the said cole mynes, for the appeasing of all such discord and suyt had and maid betwixt the said p'ties, it is agreade and ordered by the consent of bothe p'ties in the presence of Mr. Doctor Hyndmer, chauncelor of Duresme, the daye and yeare above written in maner and forme followyng, that is to saye, the said W. Tomlyngson and W. Inskip and either of them confessythe and grauntythe that the said p'son shall have in recompence of his said tiethe coles for every pyt thre holl days work in the year wt'in the said cole myne, to work and drawe coles at the costs of the said p'son or his assignes. And the said W. and W. to fynd the said p'son cole rope, corff, shoile, and barrowe, ev'ry daye of the said thre days ; and the said p'son to be no further charget, but only what workmens wags for the said thre dais, etc." The parson's workmen to be allowed to work and draw at each pit as many chalders of coal as were daily drawn by the lessees.

The above document contains the earliest reference we have met with to the corf (Latin, *corbis* ; Danish, *korf*), or circular basket, which was subsequently so extensively employed in the drawing of coals out of the pits. The corves were made of hazel twigs, and were provided with a wooden bow for suspending them to the hook at the end of the rope. They were in use in the metalliferous mines of Germany at this period, being figured in the pages of Agricola. The *nom de plume* of Georgius Agricola, adopted by this able writer on Mediæval Mining and Metallurgy, appears to have been a Latin form of his own name. In some accounts (*Trans. Manchester Geolog. Soc.*, xix., p. 278 ; *Trans. Midland Inst.*, xi. 222), this is stated to have been Landmann ; but according to what is perhaps more reliable authority his real patronymic was Bauer (*i.e. boor*, or husbandman). He is said to have been a doctor of medicine, and an intimate friend of Erasmus.

Wheelbarrows were evidently still used in the north of England mines. It seems not improbable that the coals may have been wheeled to the pit bottom in barrows, and there emptied into the corves to be drawn up the shaft.

Leland, the royal antiquary to Henry VIII., whose *Itinerary* extends from about 1538 to 1545, travelling from Durham northwards, tells us in his quaint style (vol. i., p. 78, ed. 1768) that "a litle a this side Getehed is a great cole pitt."

During the short period Cardinal Wolsey presided over the See of Durham (1523-29), which he never visited, the minerals of the bishopric were on several occasions the subject of correspondence between him and his agents in the north. The following interesting letter (Cotton MS.—*Darlington Reprints*) regarding the coal mines at Whickham, and the vexed question of the free shipment of coal and other merchandise on the south side of the Tyne, was addressed to Wolsey by Franklyne, the Chancellor of the Bishopric :

"Please it your grace to be advertisid that ther be thre cole pytts at a township of yours callid Whikam, thre mylis from New castell, where be alreddy gotyn a gret substance of colis to the nombre of 25 score kele, every kele contayning 20 chald', for the whiche colis I have taken suche ordre withe fermers of the same that your grace maye have clearly fyve hundreth marks, your rent accustomyd, and all other charges borne, so that we maye shippe the said colis on the bishopriche side accordingly to the liberties and privilegis heretofore grauntyd. . . . The marchaunts of New castell will be lothe taplie thereunto howbeit your privilegis and graunts be clere inow, and it is no reason that they shuld enforce your grace to sell your colis only unto theym at their own prices, and they to utter the same at their own libertie bothe to Englishmen and straungers at prises onreasonable as they have done heretofore. And sewerly the shipping of colis on the bishopriche syde should be muche beneficiall and p'fitable to all this realme, for than the marchaunts of New-castel, and other, wold make cost and labor to get moo cole pytts going in Northumberland, wherby gret plenty of colis and so by reson of this gret habundance on bothe sydes this and other realmes myghte be myche better servid and easiar pricis ; if your grace will stik to your liberties (as in conscience your grace is bownde to do), the bishopriche wilbe better than it is by a 1,000 marks a yere only in cole and led."

Wolsey wrote to Franklyne in 1528 (Raine's *Auckland Castle*, p. 63), regarding a supply of coals for burning lime at his college of Ipswich, in the following words :

"Ryght welbeloved, we great you well : and forasmoche as the maister of oure werks, by us appointet for the erection of oure colege at Ipeswyche, is mynded, for the mor spedy advauncement of the same, to brenne great quantyte of lyme in places lymyttede nere unto oure sayed college, for whiche purpose it is requisit that a good quantite of see coolis be provyded fore by fore hand, and sent thydder w[t] spede, we therfor woll that ymmedyatly upon the syght of thes oure letters, ye doo ship and send thydder, to and for the use aforsayd, two hundred chaldre of oure owne coolis, and that the sayde coolis be shipped of the best and largest measure used at Newcastell upon tyne. Fayle ye not thus to doo as we trust you. From Rychmonte, the 29th day of Septembre.   T. Car[lis], Ebor.

" For as moche as the spedy provysyon and sending of the sayde coolis shalbe greatly to the advanciment of the intendyd byldyng at oure sayde college, we therfor hartly pray you to use dyllygence in the premysis, wherby ye shall deserve oure especyall thanks. *Manu propria.*"

Wolsey's Gateway at Ipswich, bearing date 1528, is still in existence. A view of it was given in the *Penny Illustrated Paper*, September 14, 1895, on the occasion of the visit of the British Association to the town.

Wolsey also sent instructions to Dr. Strangwysshe, surveyor of Durham, and Richard Bellysis, Esq. (*Letters and Papers Foreign and Domestic*, Hen. VIII., vol. iv., part ii., 5,111, 3), directing them to survey all lead, coal, and other mines, and to make them as profitable as possible.

By a deed given at length by Bourne in his *History of Newcastle* (p. 223), the Cardinal, in 1529, appointed William Thomlyngson, of Gateshead, and Thomas Thomlyngson, his son, to the office of clerk of all his mines in the Bishopric of Durham, whether of lead, iron, or coal. In return for this service they were to receive 10 marks (£6 13s. 4d.) yearly, and one chaldron of coals per day out of each coal mine in the demesnes of Gateshead, Whickham, and Lynnedean. From a payment subsequently recorded (Raine's *Auckland Castle*, p. 68), it appears that William Tomlynson was still receiving the above salary of 10 marks in 1542, under the title of " overseer of all the Bishop's coal mines."

A project which Wolsey attempted to carry out of smelting the lead ore from his mines in Weardale, at Gateshead, with the coal from his mines on the Tyne—the earliest proposal to employ coal in smelting metalliferous ores—will be referred to hereafter.

Of other notices relating to coal in the Gateshead and Whickham neighbourhood in the early part of the sixteenth century, there is mention (Wolsey, roll 2, m. 3) of a lease of the coal mines of Chester, from the Blackburn to the Team, being granted, in 1528-29, to Robert Adhee, of Durham, for forty years, at 26s. 8d. per annum; and of a grant of wayleave (Surtees, ii. 209) from Bishop Ruthall (Tunstall ?) in 1530, to Thomas Boynton, of York, Esq., for " carriages by wayne, cowpe, or horses, from the cole mynes and pitts now opened, or which shall be opened, in Ravensall and Eighton (the inheritance of Richard Gascoigne, Esq.), through all the groundes, waistes, and mores of the said Rev. Father " for twenty-one years, at 5s. rent. Confirmed by the Dean and Chapter of Durham, 6th September, 1530.

At this period an event occurred which exercised a potent influence over the future of the Tyne coal trade. It is clear from the letter of Franklyne to Wolsey above-quoted that the merchants of Newcastle were again enjoying a domination over the shipment of coal on the south side of the river, though without possessing any legal title thereto. Whether Wolsey made any attempt to revive the rights of the See of Durham, at the instigation of Franklyne, does not appear. But with the downfall of this great prelate came Newcastle's opportunity, and in 1530 (Brand, ii. 17) the burgesses succeeded in obtaining an Act of Parliament, securing to themselves the conservatorship of the Tyne from Sparhawk (or Sparrow Hawk), a rock at the mouth of the river, to Hedwin Streams, the furthest limit of the tidal influence, seventeen miles inland, together with a monopoly of the trade in coals and other merchandise, which were to be sold only at the town of Newcastle. Though these exclusive privileges were temporarily withdrawn by Queen Mary, who restored the south side of the river to the palatinate, the result nevertheless was that in the course of time all the principal collieries on both sides of the Tyne fell into the hands of Newcastle merchants.

An allusion to active mining operations being carried on in the town lands of Newcastle occurs in the pages of Leland (vol. viii., part ii., page 7, ed. 1768), who speaks of coal pits existing at Cowhill, or Cowmore, half-a-mile out of the town.

The records we have regarding the working of coal on the north side of the Tyne in this era, however, chiefly relate to mines situated in the lands of Tynemouth Priory.

The collieries in Elswick were now of considerable importance, and were leased under different conditions from what they were exactly two centuries before. In 1530 (Gibson's *History of the Monastery of Tynemouth*, vol. i., p. 197), the prior and convent leased a mine of coal within the fields of Elswick to Christopher Mitford, of New-castle-upon-Tyne, gentleman, with all the profits and advantages of the coals and coal mine, or mines, there to be won and digged, for twenty-five years, at the yearly rent of £20. The lessee was empowered to make and sink pits at his own cost, and was granted sufficient wayleave and staithleave ("lyve" and "statlyve") over the ground, and liberty to cut timber in the woods of Elswick for timbering and upholding the pits, and maintaining the staiths and houses thereto belonging, "with a proviso that he should not dig or draw more than 20 chaldrons, reckoning 16 bolls to the chaldron, for every working day in the year"—equal to about 40 tons.

In 1538 (the year before the dissolution of the monastery) the same lessee also obtained a lease from the prior and convent (*ib.*, p. 203) of two pits sunk in the fields of Elswick in addition to the one above-mentioned, for eight years, at a yearly rent of £50. The lessee was granted similar powers as to "way leve" and "staith leve," cutting timber, etc., and "was not to dig or draw from the pits demised more than 40 chaldrons in any working day, reckoning 16 bolls to the chaldron."

By this deed the prior and convent covenant—That the farmers of their four salt-pans at North Shields shall purchase all the coals used by them during the term from Mitford, at the rate of 15s. for every ten chaldrons; that the tenants of Elswick and Benwell shall at all convenient times be ready with their furnished carriages to serve the lessee in conveying his coals; and that they will make no lease of coal from the east side of Benwell to the west side of Elswick, or occupy any pit within these bounds : Reserving to themselves the right of digging and drawing weekly, at their own cost, 10 chaldrons of coal to be applied solely for the necessary fuel of the monastery.

From a statement of arrears due to the Crown in the following year (*ib.*, p. 211), it appears that Henry Anderson, another merchant of Newcastle, was associated with Mitford in the lease of the Elswick mines.

Brand, in referring to the above records (ii. 264), by some oversight, states the size of the chaldron in the case of the first lease to have consisted of " *six* boulls," though quoting it correctly enough as 16 bolls in the second lease in a foot-note which he appends. The erroneous 6 bolls has found its way into the pages of Dunn, Taylor, and other writers on the coal trade.

While the chaldron measure used on the Durham side of the Tyne continued to be maintained at its original size—20 forming a keel-load, as we have seen from Franklyne's letter to Wolsey—it is obvious that the Newcastle chaldron was now double its original proportions; 10 chaldrons of 16 bolls being just equal to 20 chaldrons of 2,000 lbs.

It seems clear from the above Elswick leases, with their references to ten chaldrons and multiples of ten, that the quantity of ten chaldrons was now used as a measure of coals at Newcastle, and also that it constituted the load of a keel. It cannot be doubted that in this we have the origin of the Newcastle "ten" measure— the foundation of the tentale rents still used in leases in this coal-field—the keel and the ten having been originally synonymous, as pointed out by Mr. T. J. Taylor in his memoir on the "Archæology of the Coal Trade," already referred to (*Proceedings Archæological Inst.*, Newcastle, 1852, vol. i., p. 169), and the outputs of the pits limited to a certain number of keel loads, or tens, per day : an arrangement which we have seen to have existed on the Tyne as early as the middle of the fourteenth century. At a later period we hear of a "five" measure in the southern coal trade, consisting of five chaldrons and a quarter (*Report on the Coal Trade*, 1830, p. 86).

Queen Mary, in 1554 (Brand, vol. ii., p. 265), in consideration of a fine of £13 13s. 4d., granted a lease of all the coal mines within the fields and bounds of Elswick to Bertram Anderson, for twenty-one years, at the annual rent of £68. This lessee still held them in 1577-78, as appears from extracts from the accounts of the Ministers of the Crown, quoted by Gibson in his *History of Tynemouth Monastery* (vol. ii., Appendix No. cliii.).

While the Elswick collieries, on account of their advantageous situation, were the most important, coal mines likewise existed on several of the other estates belonging to the monks of Tynemouth at the date of the dissolution of their house.

In their manor of Denton they had a mine let on lease at a rent of £20 per annum, and worked at the rate of 20 chaldrons for every working day. In 1577-78 Launcelot Errington and William Dent held the Denton mines under lease from the Crown. In the case of this royalty, as in that of a number of others, a practice begins to be observable towards the end of this century of charging a rent for each working pit. In the *Minister's Account* for the year 1593-94 (36 Eliz.) it is noted that "Christopher Errington is to paye xli. for every pitt to be gotten in Denton."

A coal mine likewise existed in Benwell, near the (Roman) wall, which at the dissolution of the monastery was valued at 106s. 8d. per annum, and was leased by the Crown (Gibson's *Tynemouth*, vol. i., p. 217) to Sir Thomas Hilton for twenty-one years at that rent. In the latter part of the century the Benwell mines, like a number of others situated a similar distance from Newcastle, had risen to more importance, being leased by Queen Elizabeth in 1578 to Richard Hodgeson, for twenty-one years, at £20 rent. In 1594 there is mention (*Cal. State Papers, Dom.*, Eliz., 1591-94, p. 523) of a "lease on surrender of Roger Lawson" of three coal mines in Benwell; but this individual is found still occupying them at a later period.

A statement made by Horsley in his *Britannia Romana*, to the effect of there being "a coalry not far from Benwell, a part of which is judged by those best skilled in such affairs to have been wrought by the Romans," has been very frequently quoted. This supposition, however, is purely conjectural and rests upon no evidence. Dr. Bruce tells us in the *Roman Wall* (3rd edition, p. 93) that "when the lower reservoir of the Newcastle Water Company, in the neighbourhood of South Benwell, was formed in 1858, some ancient coal workings were exposed. The author examined them, and though he and those whom he consulted saw no reason to suppose they were not Roman, no coin, lamp, or shred of Samian was discovered to give authority to the conjecture. The seam of coal was 2 feet thick. It was wrought by shafts sunk to the depth of 12 or 15 feet, and at a distance of 40 or 45 yards from one another. Lines of excavation radiated in every direction from the bottom of the shaft. The coal crops out on the bank between the workings and the river, so that the mines could be drained by means of an adit." There is nothing in the above account to indicate that the workings explored were of any more ancient date than the sixteenth century.

Coal would appear to have now begun to receive attention in the lands of Kenton. In 1580 depositions were taken by special commissioners on behalf of the Crown (*38th Report of the Dep. Keep. Pub. Records*, p. 188) regarding waste grounds, coal mines, etc., in the manors of Kenton, or Kyneton, and Benwell.

Further west at Newburn, bordering on the Tyne, we first hear of coal being worked in this era, though it had probably commenced here at an early period. At the end of this century the mine of the lordship of Newburn is named among the collieries of the Tyne.

Though coal had been dug, as we have seen, in the manor of Wylam, on the western edge of the coalfield, in the infancy of coal mining on the Tyne, the mines here being situated far from the centre of the export trade, continued to be worth little or nothing. The rent of a coal pit in Wylam in 1577-78 (*Ministers' Accounts*) only amounted to 13s. 4d. ; and its working appears to have been discontinued soon afterwards.

The mines at Tynemouth in like manner, lying equally distant from Newcastle on its opposite side, and, owing to the Newcastle monopolies, possessing no facilities for the export of coal, were also of insignificant value. At the dissolution of the Monastery a mine here was leased by the Crown (Gibson's *Tynemouth*, vol. i., p. 217) to Sir John Hilton—the lessee of the mine in Benwell, and also of four salt-pans at North Shields in the tenure of John Robinson and others—for twenty-one years, at £2 6s. 8d. per annum. In 1560-61 the Tynemouth mines and salt-pans were granted by the Crown (*Cal. State Papers, Dom.* Addenda, Eliz., 1566-79, p. 335) to Sir Henry Percy.

Later in the century a commencement was made to open up the coal at some new points in the Tynemouth neighbourhood. In 1584 (*Ministers' Accounts*, 26 Eliz.) Queen Elizabeth granted a lease of the coal in Preston to John Robinson, for twenty-one years, at £6 13s. 4d. per annum ; and also a lease of the coal in Monkseaton, East Chirton, and Middle Chirton, for the same period, at a rent of 20s.

Meanwhile, the working of coal was proceeding with equal, if not greater vigour, on the south side of the Tyne. Here also the more outlying collieries were still of surprisingly little value as late as the middle of the sixteenth century.

In 1554-55 Bishop Tunstall (roll 3, m. 6) granted John Broune, of North Auckland, yeoman, a lease of the water-mill of Swalwell for twenty-one years, at £5 6s. 8d. per annum ; and a similar lease of the coal mines of Ryton at £1 6s. 8d.—the mill being worth just four times as much as the coal at this period.

The same bishop (*ibid.*) in 1558-59 also granted a twenty-one years' lease of the above premises to Thomas Hedworth, yeoman, to begin in 1572, or as soon as Broune's lease should become void. In his will dated 1572 (*Trans. North of England Inst.*, vol. xv., p. 184) John Killinghall, Esq., mentions his leased "cole pittes" at Wyndleston and Ryton.

Proceedings were instituted about 1561 (Bishop Pilkington, roll 1, m. 2) against John Swynburne, of Chopwell, for having entered into the common of the Lord Bishop at Ryton, without any title thereto, having sunk pits there and taken out and sold large quantities of sea coal therefrom. In an award relative to the boundaries of the manors of Ryton and Chopwell dated 1563 (Surtees, vol ii., p. 281), it is stated that "If John Swinburn durynge his lyffe shall maike cole-pytts upon his mores or grounds of Chopwell, and shall require passage, or way-leve, over the waystes of the Bishopp in Ryton, the said R^t Rev^d, in consideracon of ye faithfull friendshipp of ye said John hereafter to him to be hadde, shall grant the way-leave, Swinburne paying 20s. per ann. so long as his yearly gain does not exceed £20 ; and if above £20 then he shall pay 40s. and no more."

The above arrangement illustrates the movement towards the adoption of a more elastic system of rents, which begins to be observable in the leases of this period, in lieu of the absolutely rigid methods heretofore in use. In connection with this agreement it may be mentioned that in the *Ministers' Accounts* relating to Monkseyton, in 1583-84 (26 Eliz.), notice occurs of a coal pit in Chopwell.

The working of coal was likewise going on in Stella, a freehold estate bordering on the Tyne, which had belonged to the nuns of Newcastle previous to the dissolution; but here, as in the adjoining lands of Ryton, the mines were of insignificant value in the middle of the sixteenth century. In an inventory of Thomas Swinburn, of Haughton, dated 1566 (Surtees, vol. ii., p. 281), the rent of Stelling —so named from being the seat of a fishery—is set down at 26s. 8d., and "the rent of the colle pitts 5s."

A lease of the coal mines in Stella (called Stelley or Stellingley) was granted by Queen Elizabeth to Sir Nicholas Tempest, of New-castle (*Proc. Arch. Inst.*, Newcastle, 1852, vol. i., p. 167), of whose family this estate became the property and residence soon after the dissolution. In this deed sufficient wayleave and stayleave are granted, with power to lead away the coals by all kinds of carriages. Liberty is also given to drive "sougheads" for draining the coal; and it is stipulated that sufficient pillars (*columnæ vel pillers*) shall be left to support the roof. After coming into the possession of the Tempests, Stella soon became one of the important collieries of the Tyne.

The principal group of collieries on the south side of the Tyne, however, were situated in the lands of Winlaton, Whickham, and Gateshead, with their exceptional advantages for obtaining coal and loading it into keels on the Tyne for transportation to Newcastle; and in the estates immediately adjoining, which participated in these benefits.

Pardon for the acquisition of the manor of "Wyndlaton" without license, from Charles, late Earl of Westmoreland, was granted by Bishop Barnes (roll 1, m. 6), in 1578-79, to Richard Hodgeson, Robert Anderson, William Selbie, and Umfrey Scrivener. Depositions were taken by special commissioners, in 1587 (*38th Report of the Dep. Keep. of the Pub. Records*, p. 237), touching a lease of the coal mines in Winlaton granted to Cuthbert Blunt, late of the town of Newcastle-on-Tyne, merchant and alderman, by Henry, late Earl of Westmoreland, and grant of same by Blunt to Christopher Cooke. The suit appears to have chiefly referred to the interference of the new proprietors with Cook's mining operations, particularly between Martinmas 1581 and Martinmas 1582. It is worthy of remark that in these depositions mention is made of the employ-ment of women in working the mines "for lack of men."

On the other side of the Derwent the working of coal continued to be pursued in Gellesfield. In 1578 (Surtees, vol. ii., p. 251) William Blaxton, Esq., leased to Cuthbert Hunter, of Newcastle, merchant, "all his coal pytts and mynes in Gellesfeld, with a convenient way through the said field to the water of Darwen," for fifteen years, at £10 rent; reserving the fourth of every pit sunk to be let at will; "doing all neighborhode as is accustomed at the working of coles."

The above reservation is peculiar and points to its having some-times been the practice for different parties to work simultaneously in the same pit, and even in the same seam of coal. The arrangement must have been attended with difficulties. Even when working in different seams, as was sometimes the custom subse-quently, the conflict of interests was conducive to litigation. The doing of neighbourhood doubtless refers to rendering assistance when necessary in the conveyance of coal for shipment, in the same manner as we have already seen bargained for in the case of the mines in Elswick.

In the adjoining lands of Whickham notices occur of leases of mines being granted to various parties about the middle of the century.

Bishop Tunstall (roll 4, m. 14), in 1548-49, leased a particular mine at Whickham to John Sotheron, of Whickham, yeoman, and Stephen Sotheron, of Newcastle, merchant, for twenty-one years, at £20 per annum.

The same prelate (ib., m. 13), in 1550, granted the above parties a lease of all his coal mines in Whickham, of which they and Anthony Thomlynson have had a previous lease (they having pur-chased, Mr. Surtees tells us, vol. ii., p. 239, Thomlynson's remaining interest) for twenty-one years, with a condition for payment of £10 on opening every new pit.

Bishop Pilkington, in 1570 (Surtees, ib.; Brand, vol. ii., p. 265), leased the mines within the Cross Moor, in Whickham (adjoining the Whagges and Newfield on the north, Gellesfield and Greenley-field south, the Cross Moor west, and the road from Newcastle to the Streat Yate east), to Bertram Anderson, of Newcastle, merchant adventurer; three pits only to be opened at once, for twenty-one years, at £30 rent.

The same bishop, in 1575 (Brand, ii. 266), granted Henry Smith, gentleman, his servant, a lease of coal mines within the south field of Whickham, with sufficient way-leave to the Tyne, where he was to have a staith to lay the coals on, for twenty-one years, at £18 rent.

CHAPTER IX.

THE SIXTEENTH CENTURY.—Continued.

The Grand Lease. Combination of coal owners and great advance in the price of coal. Taxation of coal. The Newcastle hostmen. Marking of wains. The coal fleet. Lighthouses at the mouth of the Tyne.

A LEASE of the mines of Gateshead and Whickham combined, made in the latter part of this century, may be said to have constituted an epoch in the history of the Tyne coal trade. From its importance it obtained the mame of the "Grand Lease." It eventually came into the possession of the town of Newcastle, and formed the nucleus of a gigantic monopoly of the coal production on the Tyne. To it was ascribed a great and rapid advance which took place in the price of coal.

It is difficult to reconcile the statements made by various writers regarding this lease, or to understand the purport of some of the negotiations, and several other matters, connected with it. The commonly-received version is that furnished by Gardiner, in his book already referred to entitled *England's Grievance Discovered in Relation to the Coal Trade,* published in 1655. According to this author (chap. viii.), it began with a lease of the manors of Gateshead and Whickham obtained by Queen Elizabeth from the Bishop of Durham in April 1582. This, he states, was procured from the Queen by the Earl of Leicester, who sold or gave it to Sutton of the Charterhouse, who again for £12,000, as was reported, sold it to the mayor and burgesses of Newcastle. Gardiner's account, however, is obviously inaccurate in some respects. Sutton's connection with the lease appears to have begun and ended previous to 1582.

The Grand Lease would seem to have originated with Sutton. Regarding this gentleman we are told that about 1562, being then about thirty years of age and highly accomplished, he was retained by the Duke of Norfolk, and after some time became secretary to the Earl of Warwick, and occasionally also to his brother, the Earl of Leicester. The former of these two noblemen, being Master-General of the Ordnance, appointed Sutton Master of the Ordnance at Berwick in 1569.

Sutton's sojourn in the north proved a brilliant success. He not only acquired glory in his military capacity, in connection with the suppression of a rebellion which broke out, but at the same time rapidly amassed wealth as a merchant. Soon after his arrival in the north, by the assistance of his noble patrons, and on no other security than his own word (Wilford's *Memorials*, p. 617 ; Brand, vol. ii., p. 266), he was enabled to farm the coal mines in Whickham and Gateshead. According to one of his biographies (*Biog. Britan.*, vol. vi., p. 3,851) he purchased these manors from the Bishop of Durham (a statement, however, which can scarcely be literally correct), and in 1570 obtained a lease from the Crown for the term of seventy-nine years. Be this as it may, Sutton's connection with the coal trade took place just at the time assigned by Grey to its commencement as an important industry—the period when coal began to come into general use for domestic purposes. The rising tide of the coal trade bore Sutton rapidly on to fortune. On his return to London in 1580, he took with him two horse loads of money, and was reputed to be worth £50,000.

The following memoranda relating to the Grand Lease were obtained by Brand from the archives of Newcastle, and are given by him in vol. i., pp. 480-2. It would appear that a certain amount of rivalry existed at one time for the possession of this lease between Queen Elizabeth and the Earl of Leicester.

"February 1, 1578, a lease of the manors of Gateshead and Whickham, which had been granted to Queen Elizabeth for seventy-nine years by Richard Barnes, Bishop of Durham, was confirmed by the dean and chapter of that church.

"June 20, 1581, the above Bishop Barnes granted a lease of the manors aforesaid to Robert, Earl of Leicester: this must have been done by permission of the Queen, who is said to have given this lease to her favourite courtier. A declaration from the bishop, upon what terms he had granted the lease, occurs, dated June 23 following.

"January 4, 1582, Richard, Bishop of Durham, granted a lease of the manors of Gateshead and Whickham to Queen Elizabeth for seventy-nine years : this term must have been thought too short, for we find, on the 26th of April following, the same bishop granting a lease of the above manors, confirmed also by the dean and chapter, to the said Queen for ninety-nine years, from the day of the date, under an annual rent of £117 15s. 8d. This grant included all the coal pits and coal mines, and all the common wastes and parks belonging to the said manors."

This was in a special sense the Grand Lease. Mr. Surtees (vol. ii., pp. 112, 239) attaches considerable blame both to Queen Elizabeth and Bishop Barnes in connection with this lease, which he characterises as one of the spoliations of the See of Durham made by this bishop in favour of the Crown. According to Strype (*Annals of Reform.*, vol. iii., Append. 30, p. 182), there was lost to the bishopric in this lease "£110 reserved in leases in Esse which were for colemines to three persons, viz., Anderson, Lewen, and White, and to one named Blackston for wayleave £10 per annum."

The Queen did not long retain possession of the lease:

"November 12, 1583, Queen Elizabeth made an assignment to Henry Anderson and William Selby, magistrates of Newcastle, of two terms of the above manors granted to her by the Bishop of Durham.

One colliery after another had been coming into the hands of the merchants of Newcastle, but this great lease of the mines of Gateshead and Whickham was the crowning acquisition of all. Soon afterwards we begin to hear of arrangements being made for the regulation of the coal trade, accompanied by a large advance in the price of coal, so much so as to give occasion to the Lord Mayor of London to complain to Lord Burghley in 1590 (Lansdowne MSS., No. 65, 11), "of the monopoly and extortion of the owners of the Newcastle coals."

The rise in the price of coal was probably, in some measure at all events, due to natural causes; but it was ascribed at the time wholly to the policy of the Newcastle merchants, who suffered a considerable amount of obloquy in consequence. An interesting account of the matter is furnished in Strype's edition of Stow's *Survey of London* (vol. ii., p. 391, ed. 1720) to the following effect :—

"About the year 1590 and odd, sea coal began to advance its price far higher than ever before, being enhanced by sinister ways and means of some at Newcastle, a few engrossing the whole commodity to themselves. And besides, the coals were not so good as they used to be, by their sending out the best into foreign parts, and sending the worst to be spent in the realm. The price of sea coal of the best sort went at 4s. the chaldron many and many a year before now. Then there happened a leasing of the mines, which was called the Grand Lease; which Grand Lease was assigned to one Mr. Sutton, and then the price came to 6s. the chaldron, and so continued during the time that Sutton enjoyed the lease. Then it was assigned over to the town of Newcastle, and then the price began to increase to an excessive rate, first to 7s., then to 8s., and was now grown to 9s. Neither could be so had unless the buyer would be content to take of both sorts, viz., the good and the bad together.

"Of this the Lord Maior made complaint to the Lord Treasurer Burghley against the town of Newcastle, setting forth the causes of these abuses, and then the remedies for the reformation of them. The chief causes were certain inhabitants of Newcastle called Free Hosts, to whom the Grand Leases were first made over to the use of that town, being to the number of sixty persons or thereabouts, these, of later times, had compounded and made over their whole right to a far less number, viz., eighteen or twenty men, who having before coal pits of their own, engrossed the whole commodity, and reduced the trade into a few men's hands, combining together to sell the sea coal at their own prices, and so advanced the price, as was said before, to 9s. the chaldron, one with the other. The said few persons, being men of great wealth, had, besides the Grand Lease, taken and engrossed all the coal mines about the said town, viz., the mine of Stella, the Bishop's mine, sometime farmed by one Mr. Tempest and others, the mine of the lordship of Ravensworth, the mine of Mr. Gascoin, the mine of the lordship of Newborne, and divers others; of these mines or pits they opened or shut up such and so many as they thought good, for the advancing of their private gain. Whereby the free hosts, who were wont to make suit for the sale of their coals, and offer the same unto the shipmasters (which made a cheapness) were now sued unto, and made it a matter of favour and preferment whom first they should serve, ordering the prices at their own pleasures.

"The remedies propounded were that the Lords of the Privy Council would take order that all owners and farmers of coal mines might open them, and make sale of their coals at reasonable rates, not exceeding the price of 7s. the chaldron, and to lade the same at the most opportune places without any restraint."

In reference to this complaint (Reprint by M. A. Richardson), Henry Mytforde and Henry Chapman, aldermen and coal owners of Newcastle, were called upon for themselves and other coal owners "to explain the causes of the excessive pryces of coles inhanced at New-castell aforesaid."

We hear, however, of no steps being taken, unless the new

arrangement referred to in the following record was made in connection with this matter :

"August 4, 1591, Henry Anderson and William Selby granted to thirteen of the principal burgesses of Newcastle-upon-Tyne, in trust, the reversion of the above manors of Gateshead and Whickham, which had been demised as aforesaid to the Queen, and assigned by the Queen to them as before related."

For some years longer, nevertheless, Anderson and Selby continued to exercise a sway, seemingly of a somewhat despotic kind, over the Tyne coal trade. In 1597, we find Robert Dudley and fourteen other aldermen and burgesses of Newcastle, for themselves and many more, addressing a complaint to Lord Burghley (*State Papers*, Dom., 1595 97, vol. cclxiii. 72) against these two individuals, charging them among other things, with letting trust leases to private persons instead of to the town, and at low rents, especially grand leases of coal mines ; engrossing all the coal mines in grand leases, and refusing at any price to renew them to the former tenants ; unfair dealing in the price and mixture of coals, etc., etc. From this time nothing more is heard of Anderson and Selby in connection with the Grand Lease.

In 1598 the Crown authorities (*ib.*, 1598-1601, vol. cclxvi. 91) granted a lease of a coal mine in Gateshead to William Riddell, for twenty-one years, at £16 rent and £10 fine.

But immediately afterwards a general surrender of interests in the manors of Gateshead and Whickham was made to the town of Newcastle.

"September 8, 1599, Henry Chapman, George Farnaby, William Hodgshon, George Selby, Lyonell Maddison, Ralph Jennison, and Nicholas Hedley, assigned their right and title to the manors of Gateshead and Whickham to the mayor and burgesses of Newcastle."

By a clause in her great charter granted to Newcastle in 1600 (Brand, vol. ii., p. 617, *et seq.* ; Gardiner's *Grievance*, ch. xi.), Queen Elizabeth gave license to William Riddell and the parties above enumerated, as well as to all others whatsoever of her tenants in Gateshead and Whickham, to assign to the mayor and burgesses of Newcastle ; and to the mayor and burgesses she gave special license to hold the manors of Gateshead and Whickham during the residue of the years then to come, notwithstanding the Statute of Mortmain or any other statute.

Newcastle was now supreme mistress of the trade of the Tyne, and likewise of the production of the coal shipped upon its waters ; having achieved a vastly greater triumph than could ever have been hoped for by her aspiring sons, in the days of her early struggles as a royal burgh. Well suited to her case was now the legend graven on her arms, " *Fortiter defendit triumphans.*"

Up till the closing years of Queen Elizabeth's reign coal had remained almost wholly exempt from taxation, but from this time it began to be burdened with many impositions.

We have seen that King Edward III., in regulating the Tyne coal trade in 1368, allowed a charge to be made by the burgesses of Newcastle on all coal sold to natives of this country in aid of the payment of their £100 rent. With the growth of the coal trade this had in the course of time become a fruitful source of revenue to the town. Brand tells us (vol. ii., p. 269) that towards the close of Queen Elizabeth's reign the duty of the town at 4d. per chaldron appears to have brought in £10,000 per annum to the corporation.

Edward III. on the same occasion reserved to himself a tax on all coal sold to foreigners. From whatever cause—possibly in connection with Sutton obtaining the sway over the coal trade—the payment of this Crown duty had been discontinued in 1578 (*Cal. State Papers*, Dom., 1619-23, p. 61; *Commons Journal*, vol. i., p. 769); and, according to Gardiner (*England's Grievance*, ch. ix.), on the arrears being demanded by Queen Elizabeth from the mayor and burgesses of Newcastle in 1599, they professed themselves unable to satisfy the claim, but offered instead to pay a duty of 1s. per chaldron for the future on all coal sold to the free people of England. This compromise was accepted by the Queen, and was the origin of the coal tax known as the "Richmond Shilling," which was peculiar to the Tyne, and continued to be levied down into the present century. In early documents relating to this tax it is usually spoken of as the *composition*.

Queen Elizabeth at the same time (*Proc. Arch. Inst.*, Newcastle, 1852, vol. i., pp. 210-211) imposed a duty of 5s. per chaldron on all coal transported over sea. This tax was common to all the ports of the kingdom. A protest occurs (Lansdowne MSS., numbers 156, 102, fo. 413) in the form of a letter from Lord Deputy Mountjoy, and the Council of Ireland, against the imposition on sea coal, dated Dublin, 26th March, 1600. Another (*ib.*, 106, fo. 421) came from the Mayor of Liverpool in June following; also others from Wales, Guernsey and Jersey; in consequence of which, relief from this foreign duty was forthwith extended to these parts. In early documents this tax was usually spoken of as the *imposition*.

The sale of coals on the Tyne had from time immemorial been in the hands of a guild, or fraternity, of persons known as hostmen, or ostemen, otherwise fitters, who acted as middlemen between the owners of coal mines and the merchants frequenting the port; and who provided the keels employed in conveying coals from the staiths to the ships. These agents are supposed to have originated in a statute passed in 1404 (5 Hen. IV., c. 9), by which it was ordained that in every town and sea-port to which foreign merchants repaired, sufficient "hoostes" should be appointed with whom only such merchants might dwell during their stay. Curiously they only shared the name in common with the foreign merchants, who were also known as hosts, or oastes. These are so termed in a record of the time of Henry VIII. (Brand, ii. 270 n.), as well as in the early books of the hostmen's company; while the seal of this company represents a hostman grasping the hand of the newly-arrived stranger, and at the same time exclaiming, "Welcome, mine oaste." It was perhaps this circumstance that led Camden to suppose the word hostman to be derived from *oustmanni*, or eastmen, *i.e.* persons trading with the eastern parts of Europe. But a simple and satisfactory explanation of the apparent anomaly (kindly pointed out to the writer by Dr. C. Le Neve Foster) is no doubt to be found in the fact that the English word host—like the Latin *hospes* and the French *hôte*—retained at this time the dual meaning of both host and guest. The hostmen of Newcastle are stated by the author of *Fossil Fuel* (1835, p. 362 note) to have greatly resembled a class of agents known as "hostelers," in the port of Yarmouth.

Coincidently with the rapid growth of the coal trade in the latter part of the sixteenth century, the Newcastle hostmen rose to a position of much influence and importance, many of them being, indeed, themselves owners of collieries.

By a clause in her charter above-mentioned, Queen Elizabeth incorporated the Society of Hoastmen, confirming to them the sole privilege of loading coals, etc., on any part of the Tyne between Sparhawk and Hedwin streams, but as near as possible to the town of Newcastle. The incorporated hostmen undertook to pay to the Queen the shilling tax previously referred to, and to sell coal at a price not exceeding 10s. per chaldron for the best sort, and 9s. for the worst.

Though the names of forty-eight hostmen are enumerated in the Queen's charter, more than a third of these appear to have taken no active part in the sale of coals. From the books of the society (Brand, vol. ii., p. 273) we learn that in 1602 there were twenty-eight acting fitters, or hostmen, who were to vend this year 9,080 tens of coal, and to find eighty-five keels for the purpose. Assuming the ten of this period to have been equal to a modern keel-load of 21 tons, Mr. T. J. Taylor (*Proc. Arch. Inst.*, Newcastle, 1852, vol. i., p. 168) estimated the above quantity at about 190,600 tons. The prices fixed for this year were for the best sort not above 10s., for the second best not above 9s., and for the poorer sorts, called "meane coles," not above 8s. per chaldron. The details of the arrangement were fixed by "an order and agreement of partnership for the vente of coalles proportioned by quarters" dated February 26, 1602, viz. :—

	Tens of coals.	And to find for the vent thereof. Keels.
For the first quarter :—		
Mr. William Selbie	600	5
Mr. George Selbie	150	1
Mrs. Barbara Riddell } Mr. Peter Riddell }	700	4 or 6
Mr. Wm. Hodgshon	450	5
Mr. Robert Anderson	300	2½
Isaack Anderson	150	1½
	2,350	19
For the second quarter :—		
Mr. Henry Chapman	900	9
Mr. Henry Anderson	200	1
Matthew Chapman	400	4
Mr. Nicholas and Rowland Tempest	250	1½
Mr. Francis Anderson	300	2
Bertram Anderson	100	1
John Strangwiche	150	2
	2,300	20½
For the third quarter :—		
Mr. Lyonel Maddison and Henrye Maddison	700	9
Mr. John Barker	550	5
Robert Shafto	260	2½
Ralph Atkinson	420	4
Thomas Hall	300	3
	2,230	23½
For the fourth quarter :—		
Mr. Thomas Lyddell and Francis Lyddell	500	5½
William Bonner	400	4
William Jenyson, jun.	400	5
Mr. Timothie Draper	420	5
Margaret Grey, widow	180	1½
Edward Crome and Thomas Crome	300	2
	2,200	23

From the books of the Society of Hoastmen, we also learn that the conveyance of coals from the pits to the staiths was chiefly carried on at this time by means of wains. The standard size of the wain, "tyme out of mynde," is stated to have been eight bolls; but some having of late brought only or scarce seven bolls, an order was issued by the society in 1600, that all coal wains should be measured and marked. "Foothers" (*i.e.* fothers, or cart loads) are likewise mentioned; and also small panniers, or "maunds," holding two or three pecks apiece, carried by pack-horses.

In connection with a proposal, made in 1596 (*State Papers*, Dom., 1595-7, vol. cclvii. 63), to provide an armed convoy for the coal fleet, which had now become an institution of vital importance to the Metropolis, we hear that at this date there were 200 "Newcastle coalhoys" engaged in the coal trade.

Though two lighthouses—the high and the low lights—had been established at the mouth of the Tyne (Brand, vol. ii., p. 324) in the reign of Henry VIII., little or nothing had yet been done in the way of placing lights along the coast. But in this era, and indeed for a long time subsequently, the shipment of coal and other merchandise was only carried on during the lightest and best part of the year, between the spring and autumn equinoxes, and ceased altogether in the winter months; when the mariners, we are told, lay up with their boats on whatever shore the end of summer happened to find them.

CHAPTER X.

THE SIXTEENTH CENTURY.—Continued.

Collieries of the Wear district. South Durham. Northumberland.
Noxious gases in coal pits.

In the river Wear district the monks of Durham, and of Finchale, continued to carry on their mining operations in the early part of the sixteenth century.

A variety of details regarding the working of a small. and evidently very shallow colliery, belonging to the monks of Durham, and situated in the vicinity of the city, are preserved in the *Durham Household Book* (published by the Surtees Society, vol. xviii.), which contains the accounts of the bursar of the monastery during the years 1530-34. At this sixteenth-century colliery five men were employed, who were paid an aggregate sum of 21d., or about 4d. each per day. A man clearing away rubbish, or "ridding," was paid 3d. per day. The pits worked a very small area, lasting only about a year, or less; but the cost of sinking new ones was a mere nothing, ranging from 2s. 6d. to 5s. Among incidental charges connected with the operations, are payments for coal ropes, at 2s. to 2s. 6d. each; for scopes, at 4d. each; for "wyndyngs," or windlasses, at 2d. each; for candles and pick-sharpening, the latter costing 12d. per annum. Small allowances were made to the colliers for drawing water. The coals were conveyed to Durham both in wains (*plaustra*), and on pack-horses; in the former case at 6d. per wain-load, and in the latter at 6d. per dozen loads.

In the above accounts reference is made to other pits at work in the neighbourhood of Durham; one of these belonging to the bursar of the monastery, and another to a person named Christopher Ricerson. Regarding the collieries belonging to the monks of Durham situated elsewhere we have no information at this period.

The monks of Finchale continued to work and derive a small

annual revenue (£10 to £18) from their colliery at Moorhouseclose down till 1528-29, when their accounts cease, doubtless owing to the suppression of the monastery.   At this date, and, indeed, for a long time previously, their collieries at Lumley, Baxtanford, and Softley, all lay unworked.   The history of the collieries of the above-mentioned religious houses, after the confiscation of their possessions to the Crown, is doubtless preserved in the *Ministers' Accounts*; but, so far as the writer is aware, these have not been published.

In the latter part of the century we have evidence of some industrial activity in the Wear district, particularly in the lands immediately adjacent to the navigable part of the river.

The coal pits at Rainton were now in the hands of the Dean of Durham, as appears from a letter (*State Papers*, Dom., 1591-94, vol. ccxxxviii. 148) from one Ralph Corby to his son at Maynooth, dated Hett 1591, wherein he informs him that he "has the friend-ship of the dean, being a doer for him at Ranton coal pits and Spenmore."

Several members of the house of Bowes—a house which had previously been and still continued to be connected with the prosecution of metalliferous mining—are found engaging in the coal and salt industries of the Wear.

In 1587-88 (Surtees, vol. i., p. 205) Ralph Bowes, of Barnes, held the Panne-hole, at Bishopwearmouth ; and in 1601 had a new grant from Queen Elizabeth, of the waste on the south side of the Wear from the high- to the low-water mark.

Robert Bowes, likewise, had become owner of collieries and salt pans.   In 1591 we find one Christopher Sheperson addressing a petition to Lord Burghley (*State Papers*, Dom. Addenda, 1580-1625, vol. xxxii. 21) regarding the coal mines and salt works of his master, Robert Bowes, treasurer of Berwick, in the following terms :

"Pray consider the losses falling upon my master by want of the occupation of the coal mines at Ufferton, and the salt pans at Sunderland, which have been waste since they were seized and taken from him.   The salt pans are consumed with rust, and the houses and premises decayed, so that great charge must be bestowed in repairing them before the salt works can be set forward.   The earth has fallen within the coal pits ; the water-gate, which cost £2,000, is stopped, and new shafts must be sunk, which cannot be done until the water-gate is cleared.   This work will expend much money and time ; and must be done before winter and the great floods, or the whole field or coal mine will be in danger of being lost.

"I beseech order that these things may be enjoyed by such as shall bestow the charge thereon, and pay Her Majesty the yearly rent of £800 as has been offered.

"Also pray move Her Majesty to call my master from the service in Scotland, where he cannot perform his duties without better maintenance, that he may perfect assurances to be made to her satisfaction, and repair and put in order the coal pits and salt pans, and provide that Her Majesty may have as large a payment as possible."

At the same date one John Smythe made an offer to Lord Burghley (*ib.*, 1591-94, vol. ccxl. 13) to lease the above coal mines and salt pans with Mr. Bowes' consent, and to pay an annual rent of £800, on condition that the salt made at Sunderland might have free sale.

What transpired with regard to the matter above mentioned we are not informed, but we hear subsequently (Surtees, vol. i., p. 200 note ; and vol. iv., p. 105) that Robert Bowes was accidentally killed in the Keswick lead mines, by a falling in of the roof there, in 1606.

The word "shaft," which now makes its appearance in coal mining records, was no doubt borrowed from the metalliferous miners, among whom it appears to have been already long in use. According to Fuller (*Worthies of England*, art. Wales) the Danes and Saxons worked the silver mines in Cardiganshire by the means of "sheafts"; a term applied by them to anything long and narrow, whether rising into the air like the shaft of a column, or penetrating into the earth like the shaft of a mine.

George Bowes, the elder brother of the above Robert, had also made a commencement to open out the coal in the Biddick estate, which had been purchased by him. In an account of this property, dated 1595 (Surtees, vol. i., p. 199), he states that "there is a navigable river running along the domaine, and there is coles gotten in five severall places, the furthest place therof is not three miles from the house ; and I have sonke a shafte within the domaine, having only bestowed 4*l.* charges, and have already gotten some coles, which, if the seame of coles proves to be 3 quarters of a yeard thicke, the same with 200*l.* stocke will yeald 200*l.* per ann. clean benefit." He further states that the parties who have taken the grounds have for the last four years supplied him with sixty wain-loads of coal, at the price of 15d. per wain-load at the coal pits.

A few years later we find George Bowes holding a lease of Lumley Colliery. In his will (*ib.*, p. 200), made in 1603, previous to his leaving for Scotland to superintend the working of some royal mines in Crawford Moor and other places—a kind of work, in which, according to his own account, he had already experienced considerable hazards—he values his lease of Lumley Colliery, together with his keels, at £800.

In connection with this colliery, as indicative of the development which it was now receiving, it may be mentioned that in 1600, John, Lord Lumley, is stated (*ib.*, p. 226) to have received from Queen Elizabeth a grant of ground for the construction of a staith. But at this time the export of coal from the River Wear was still very inconsiderable.

In the southern portion of the coalfield the great lease of coal which had existed throughout the fifteenth century continued to be of equal, or, indeed, more importance in the early part of the sixteenth. The coal mines and pits of Grewborn and Raile were leased in 1525-26 (Wolsey, roll 2, m. 4) to Margaret Symson, of Henknoll, widow, Richard Bellasys, of Walworth, and Bartholomew Harwode, of Barnard Castle, for thirty years, at £180 per annum.

These mines appear to have attained to the zenith of their importance at this period, supplying coal to a large district of North Yorkshire. Leland (vol. viii., part ii., p. 19)[1] mentions that most of the coal consumed about the town of Richmond was brought from the Rayle pits, near Auckland.

The above lease was not wholly completed, and the mines began to decrease in value, probably owing to increasing competition. Bishop Tunstall (roll 4, m. 8), in 1551-52, leased the coal mines of Grewburne and Railee to Anthony Tydeman, for twenty-six years, at £150 per ann. ; but this lease, like the preceding one, terminated prematurely.

Tydeman's mining operations were made the subject of various inquiries. In 1553-54 (*ib.*, roll 3, m. 15), he and two others were charged by the king and queen's Attorney General with intruding on the manor of Softley, part of the possessions of the dissolved "cell of Fynkelowe"; but they maintained that the lands belonged to the Bishop of Durham, and in his right they had entered and carried away coals ; a plea which was eventually admitted.

Again, in 1560-61 (Pilkington, roll 1, m. 8), the Dean of Durham, and others, were appointed commissioners by Queen Elizabeth to inquire how much sea coal had been won by Tydeman in the bishop's mines of Raley, Grewburn, Toft', Hargyll, and their members, and its value.

After having existed for about a century and a half this lease

[1] This and the subjoined references are to the 1768 edition of Leland's *Itinerary*.

seems now to have lost its importance. In 1568-69, Bishop Pilkington (roll 2, m. 12) granted a lease of the coal mines of Rayley
to Henry Smythe—doubtless the same individual who, as we have
seen, obtained a lease of coal mines in Whickham from this bishop
—for twenty-one years, at £10 per annum (*37th Report of the Dep.
Keep. Pub. Rec.*, p. 81). Among the covenants is one that if coals
cease to be found, the rent shall no longer be paid.

These mines are again heard of in 1580 (*38th Report of the Dep.
Keep. Pub. Rec.*, p. 186), in connection with depositions taken by
special commissioners regarding the dissolved deanery of Auckland ;
" and tythes of coals of Raly pitts, and other tythes, Ralyfell, Hard-
gill, Grewborne, coal pits in the same deanery." And in the
following year (*ib.*, p. 189) a similar inquiry was again made, in
which mention occurs of the coal pits of Ralifell and Carterthorne.
At this date they were still in the occupation of Henry Smythe.
By his will dated 20th July, 1598 (*Industrial Resources of the Tyne,
Wear, and Tees*, 2nd ed., p. 233), Mr. Henry Smith granted all his
coal mines, then of the clear yearly value of £100, to the city of
Durham.

Mines were included (*37th Report ut sup.*, p. 130) in the sale of " a
messuage and farm called Pontopp, in the parish of Lanchester," in
1602-3 ; but we have no direct reference to the working of coal
going on there at this time.

On the River Blyth, in Northumberland, a number of little
collieries existed in this era, the produce of which was probably
almost wholly consumed in the neighbourhood, notably in the
manufacture of salt at the mouth of the river.

The monks of Tynemouth were owners of coal mines and salt
pans here as well as on the Tyne. In 1530 (Gibson, vol. i., p. 197)
the prior and convent leased a coal pit, with two picks (*les pigges*),
lying in the fields of Bebside and Cowpon, to John Preston and
Nicholas Mitford, for seven years, at the annual rent of 22s. 8d. ;
and the same lessees, in 1535, were granted a new lease for a term
of seven years, at 26s. 8d. per ann. Another pit was leased to
Richard Benson.

In the *Ministers' Accounts* for 1539-40, the bailiff of Cowpon
township answers for the above 26s. 8d. from Preston and Mitford,
and for £4 10s. for the farm of two salt pans, with a coal pit,
leased to Richard Benson, and for £4 10s. for the farm of two
salt pans, and a coal pit, held by Cuthbert Robynson at the King's
pleasure.

From the statement of the collector of Crown rents at Cowpon for

the year 1577-78, it would appear that the pits were then in some
cases shared by different tenants.   In this year (20th Eliz.) he
accounts, For the farm of a coal mine and a windmill, £3 ; and for
the farm of four salt pans with a coal pit, viz., two in the tenure of
Thomas Bates, gentleman, and two in the tenure of Gavin Milborne,
£9.   For any profit from the farm of a pit lately occupied by
Robert Maune, *nil*.   For a new rent of four picks leased by the
supervisor, William Pryce, to Gavin Milborne and Thomas Preston,
and two coal picks leased to Cuthbert Redhedde and James Redhedde, £4.   For a new rent of two picks in the coal mine in the
tenure of Cuthbert Redhead, 26s. 8d.

The coal pits and salt pans in Bebside and Cowpen were leased
by the Queen's Commissioners in 1595 (*State Papers*, Dom., 1595-97,
vol. ccli. 50), to Peter Delavall and Ambrose Dudley, for twenty-
one years at £22 13s. 8d. per annum.

The monks of Newminster likewise, at the dissolution of their
house, were engaged in the manufacture of salt, and also in the
working of coal in this neighbourhood, in lands belonging to the
Bishop of Durham—a general reference to whose coal and iron
mines in Norhamshire and Bedlingtonshire, was met with towards
the close of the fourteenth century.   In the accounts of the Crown
agents for the year 1536-37 (*Newminster Chartulary*, p. 307, Surtees
Society, vol. 66) there is recorded the receipt of £14 from the farm
of seven salt pans at Blithesnook, with a granary, and mine of coals,
which the late abbot and convent of Newminster held in perpetual
lease from the Bishop of Durham, under an annual rent of five
marks (£3 7s. 8d.).   At this date they were farmed by one Oswald
Willesthrop.   Ten years later (*ib.*, p. 311), along with the other
Newminster possessions, they were leased by the Crown to Richard
Tyrrell, by whom they were assigned to Sir Thomas Grey.

An incidental reference to the coal and salt industry of this
neighbourhood is met with in a letter from one John Mount to
Cecill (*State Papers*, Dom., 1547-80, vol. xli. 13), dated 1566,
wherein he informs him that he "has been in Northumberland, at
a small village called Blithe, near Newcastle, and set up certain
salt works there.   Is about to take a coal pit on lease."

We now hear of collieries existing at West Sleekburn.   In 1551-52
Bishop Tunstall (roll 4, m. 8) leased the demesnes of Bedlington,
together with tenements and coal mines at " Westlikeburne," nigh
Bedlington, to Henry Kirkeby, yeoman, for twenty-one years ; at
£3 14s. 4d. per annum for the demesnes, and £2 per annum for
every mine sunk and producing coal.

Coal was likewise being got on Coquet Island. Regarding it, Leland observes (vol. vi., p. 64) that "the isle of Coquet standith apon a very good vayne of se coles, and at the ebbe men digge in the shore by the clives (*i.e.* cliffs) and finde very good."

At Amble, on the mainland nearly opposite to Coquet Island, a salt pan and coal mine are mentioned in the *Ministers' Accounts*, 20 Elizabeth (Gibson's *Tynemouth*), as held in lease from the Crown by Robert Bullock; the former at 4s. and the latter at 12s. per annum.

In the extreme north of Northumberland the mines and pits of Tweedmouth were leased by Bishop Ruthall (roll 2, m. 1, d') in 1514-15, to Thomas Strangwysshe, master porter of Berwick, and William Gardyner, of Berwick, for thirty years, at £6 13s. 4d. per annum. While Leland (vol. vii., p. 67) speaks of coal being dug on the opposite side of the Tweed, at the village of Morton, two miles from Berwick.

Regarding the getting of coal in general, the above writer remarks (vol. viii., part ii., p. 19) that the craft is to come at it with least pain in deep digging; and he proceeds to say that some veins of coal are under rocks and heads of stone, "as some suppose that coales ly under the very rokks that the minstar close of Duresme standithe on." From this it would appear that the continuity of coal seams under overlying strata was now to some extent becoming understood.

While it seems clear that mineral coal originally obtained the name of "sea coal" from having been gathered on the Northumberland coast, and having consequently been supposed in early times to be a product of the "mysterious main," this term had now for a long period been also applied to it in the sense of coal carried over sea—as, for example, by the meters of sea coal appointed in London, as already referred to, in 1369—and the meaning of the name had now become uncertain and a matter of controversy.

On this question Leland observes (vol. viii., part ii., p. 19) that "The vaynes of the se coles lye sometyme open apon clives of the se, as round about Coket Island and othar shores; and they as some will, be properly caullyd se coall; but they be not so good as the coles that are diggyd in the inner parte of the lande."

On the other hand, Dr. Kaye, or Keys, a contemporary of Leland (founder of Caius College, Cambridge) advocates the opposite view. In an interesting passage relating to coal, which contains the earliest notice we have regarding noxious gases in coal mines, this writer observes :—

"We also have in the northern parts of Britain certain coal pits, the unwholesome vapour whereof is so pernicious to the hired labourers, that it would immediately destroy them, if they did not get out of the way as soon as the flame of their lamps becomes blue, and is consumed. These mines are of a bituminous nature, and the proof of the presence of bitumen is a certain stone, black, hard, scaly, which we thence derive for the service and fuel of our fires. Pliny calls it obsidian; we term it sea coal, or Newcastle, or smithy coal, names borrowed either from the mode of its carriage, from the situation in which it is found, or from the use to which it is applied; for it is dug up in places near to New Castle, a famous city of England, and it is carried thence by ships to other parts of the kingdom, and it is used by smiths to soften their iron."[1]

Whether the unwholesome vapour referred to by Dr Kaye consisted of explosive gas, the *firedamp* of the miners, or of suffocating gas, the *chokedamp* of the miners, is perhaps not altogether certain; though the latter would seem to answer the description best. But it can scarcely be doubted that at this time the distinction between different kinds of noxious gases was as yet little understood.

Scarcely indeed had these gases emerged from the region of supposed supernatural mystery in which they had ever lain. It was an emanation of this character which gave rise to the once world-famed oracle of Apollo, at Delphi; the noxious gas issuing from a fissure at the surface constituting the "vapour of prophecy" which inspired the sibyl seated on the sacred tripod, to whose hysterical ravings under the influence of the gaseous intoxication the priests vouchsafed such interpretation as to them seemed good, usually of a more or less ambiguous tenor.

The burning fountains of natural gas in the neighbourhood of the Caspian Sea, known as "The Holy Fires of Baku," are stated (*Min. Jour.*, xviii. 167) to have continued to be worshipped by some of the more savage tribes of the district down to the present century.

In the Middle Ages the noxious gases encountered in the mines of Germany were ascribed to the agency of subterranean *dæmons*, one of whom, according to Agricola (*De animantibus subterraneis*), destroyed more than twelve men in the mine called the Rosy Crown, by the blast of his breath.

In Scotland, in this era, noxious gases appear to have been

[1] *Joannis Caii Britanni de Ephemera, Liber unus non ante æditus*, Dedication dated London, 1555.—*A History of Shrewsbury*, London, 1825, vol. i., p. 346.

thought to come into the mines from the surface. In the records
of Dysart, in Fife (*Notices from the Local Records of Dysart*, p. 25
—Maitland Club), under date 1578, it is stated that "ane evill
air enterit into the main heuche, the dur (door) beane than at the
wast entrie of the toun." The Dysart mines were much infested
with noxious gases, probably owing to an underground fire existing
there, to which reference is made by Agricola in his treatise *De
Natura Fossilium*. This author died in 1555. George Buchanan,
also, from this circumstance, fixed upon the neighbourhood of
Dysart for the scene of the exorcism in his *Franciscanus et Fratres*,
written in the reign of James V., and describes the place as it
appeared under one of those violent eruptions which are stated to
have occurred periodically.

From this time, however, more enlightened notions regarding
noxious gases began to prevail. The day of natural science was
beginning to dawn.

CHAPTER XI.

THE SIXTEENTH CENTURY.—Continued.

Collieries of Yorkshire, Derbyshire and Nottinghamshire, Lancashire, Staffordshire, Shropshire, Warwickshire, Leicestershire, Somersetshire, Cumberland, South Wales, North Wales.

In the Yorkshire, Derbyshire, and Nottinghamshire coalfield numerous collieries were now at work.

That the use of coal for domestic purposes was already quite fashionable in Yorkshire, is evidenced by the fact of the Earl of Northumberland employing it as the chief fuel at his castles of Wresill and Lekinfield in this county. In the *Northumberland Household Book*, compiled for the regulation of these residences by the fifth Earl of Northumberland, and begun in 1512, the supply of fuel for one whole year is particularized (pp. 20, 21) as follows :

Eighty chawders of "seecolys," viz., twenty at 4s. 2d., and sixty at 5s.

Twenty quarters of "charcolys," at 12d. the quarter, to serve in the time of Christmas. "Which ys bicause the smook of the seecolys wold hurt myne arras when it ys hunge."

Three thousand four hundred and sixty "fagotts, which ys for bakynge and brewynge."

Sixty-four loads of "great wodd," at 12d. the load, "which ys bicause colys will not byrne withowte wodd."

It would appear from the above account that the arrangements for getting rid of smoke were not yet of a very perfect description, even in castles, though chimney-flues, as we have seen, had begun to be introduced into the thick walls of these buildings in the Norman period. It would also appear to have still been customary to burn wood and coal together ; the coal alone perhaps not burning sufficiently briskly in comparison with fires of wood.

In records of Court Leets in connection with the Manor of Wakefield (*Leeds Mercury Supplement*, 30th May, 1885), reference occurs to the digging of coal at Flockton in 1515.

Wakefield had become a busy centre of the coal industry, and the produce of its mines competed at York with Newcastle coal brought up the Ouse. The Fabric Rolls of York Minster record a payment, made in 1527-28, of £5 5s. 8d. for divers sacks of coals from Waikfeld, and sacks of coals called "charcool," and chawders of coals from Newcastle. The probability that the charcoal mentioned in this passage is an early reference to charred mineral coal, will be adverted to hereafter.

This is no doubt the district alluded to by Fuller in his *Worthies of England* (art. Yorkshire), where he tells us that when King Henry VIII. made his progress to York, in 1548, at a point some few miles north of Doncaster, Dr. Tunstall, Bishop of Durham, then attending him—the bishop who is said to have burnt at Paul's Cross the first edition of Tindall's *New Testament* in English—showed the king a valley which he avowed to be the richest that ever he found in all his travels through Europe ; for within ten miles of Hasslewood, the seat of the Vavasors, there were, among other things, 120 rivers and brooks whereof five were navigable ; twenty-five coal mines, which yielded abundance of fuel for the whole county; three forges for the making of iron, and stone enough for the same.

Leland also refers (vol. i., p. 44) to the plentifulness of veins of sea coal in the quarters about Wakefield; and makes various comments on the collieries and the use of coal for domestic purposes in this county. About half-way between Wakefield and Pontefract he observed coal pits a little way off on the right hand. He likewise mentions (vol. v., p. 102) very good coal pits a mile from Rotherham; and states that though wood was plentiful between Cawood and Rotherham, yet the people burnt much "yerth cole," because it was found plentifully there and sold good cheap. In Halamshire also much sea coal was burnt (*ib.*, p. 108), though there was plenty of wood. That people should burn coal when they might have wood, was regarded as something remarkable by this casual visitor to the coal districts.

The same writer (vol. viii., part ii., p. 19) speaks of veins of coal found in the upper part of the west mountains of "Richemontshire," but not used, on account of incommodity of carriage to the lower parts.

From records of the Duchy of Lancaster (quoted in the *Leeds Mercury Supplement*, 30th May, 1885) a considerable amount of information is obtained relating to the mines in the Wakefield neighbourhood, in the reign of Queen Elizabeth.

The following leases are recorded to have been made at this period :

The coal mines on the waste called Lofthouse Moore and Roodesmoore to Jo. Mallett.

In 1578-79 (21st Eliz.) the coal mines in Wakefield to Edward Carye, at an annual rent of 26s. 8d.

In the same year a license to John Nutter to dig for sea coals in a close called Ingclose, in Rothwell, at a rent of 3s. 4d.

In the same year the mines and pits of sea coals, within the extra-manorial wood of Wakefield, in the graveship of Stanley, to Ferdinand Lee, at a rent of 26s. 8d.

In the same year a license to Christopher Mather, jun., to dig coals in a common or waste ground, in the manor of Berwick, called Brownemoor, at a rent of 12s.

In 1579-80 (22nd Eliz.) the mines of slate stones within the wastes of Northowram, and the mines of "sea cole" upon the waste within the manor of Bradford, to Edward Cary, Esq.

Various law-suits relating to coal-digging also occurred during this reign.

In the court of the Duchy of Lancaster, in 1560-61, a bill was filed by William Fornes, of Shelf, yeoman, who held a lease of that manor from the Queen, against Robert Sunderland and others, complaining that they had broken and dug the orator's ground in his manor of Shelf, and "there do make colle pittes and gett colles," refusing to pay any consideration for the same.

Another bill of complaint relating to coal belonging to the manor of Bradford, was filed by the Attorney-General in the same court, against Walter Cawverley (Calverley), John Hunter, and Thomas Hunter, who, some time prior to 1591, "had intruded into the said cole mynes upon the waste of Bradford, and the same have filled and stopped upp with earth."

A few years later (1595-96) a suit occurred relating to coal poaching in the township of Northowram, manor of Wakefield. From this it appears that on or about the 9th February, 1582, the plaintiff, Henry Farrer, took of Her Majesty in the manor court of Wakefield, all the said mines of coals, with free liberty from time to time to make and dig the "soughes and newe pitts to every parcel and member of the same several coal beddes, for the wynding and geating of the same coales, and the same coales soe theare had and gotten to carry awaie, sell and converte to the proper use of your said orator, his heirs and assigns." The defendants were charged with having intruded into the mine, and "in the most forcible and violent manner, felled and cut down all the heads, pillars, and other works, being placed and made within the grounds of your orator's said mine, at your orator's great charges, for bearing up the ground there, and the same being by them so forcibly cut down, all the earth and ground thereof did presently, thereupon, by the space of forty yards, sink and fall into the same soughs and pits so suddenly that the cutters of the same works hardly escaped away alive."

Among other notices relating to coal in this county, we find Sir Thomas Gargrave writing to Cecil in 1570 (*Cal. State Papers, Domestic*, 1566-79, p. 181) regarding the lease of a coal mine at Beeston, near Leeds. In 1578 (*38th Report of the Dep. Keep. Pub. Records*, p. 176), depositions were taken by special commissioners regarding coal pits in the manor of Houghton. And from the time of Queen Elizabeth downwards leases continued to be made of the coal in the Shibden Hall estate, near Halifax (*Leeds Mercury Supplement*, 9th May, 1885).

Leland (vol. vii., p. 49) refers to cannel and coal pits existing in various parts of "Darbyshire," but mentions no particular localities. We hear, however, in the records report above-quoted, of coal being worked in the Denby neighbourhood. In 1580 two inquiries were made by special commissioners; the first (p. 183) regarding the lordships of Codnor and Heynor, and the lordships of Smalley, Kiddesley, and Morley, and Loscowe highway or carriage road through Kiddesley Park and Denby lordship, for coals, etc., and coals obtained near Ollercarre Park. The second inquiry (p. 188) had reference to the manors of Codnor and Kiddesley Park, and a piece of ground called Egreve, and the coal pits of Heynour, and a highway from Selston to Derby.

Among the possessions of Beauvale Monastery, Nottinghamshire (*Monasticon*, vol. vi., p. 14), the estate of Kimbleye figures, in 1540-41, as yielding from coal mines, etc., £13.

With reference to the fuel used by the inhabitants of the town of Nottingham, Camden, writing in 1586 (*Britannia*, first edition, p. 309), remarks that Sherwood—the classical forest of "Ivanhoe"—supplied them with great store of wood for fire; adding parenthetically "though many use the offensively-smelling dug-up coal."

While this writer, in the above passage, designates mineral coal as *carbo fossilis*, in a later edition, published in 1607 (p. 658), he applies the name of *Lithancraces* to it. This is obviously a slightly incorrect form of *Lithanthraces* (*i.e.* stone coals): a word which is ascribed by several writers to Theophrastus, but which appears to be of no greater antiquity than the time of Camden. According to Gough, one of his translators (ed. 1789, vol. iii., p. 232), no other authority for the term is known.

In the Lancashire coalfield the cannel coal of Wigan was already famed. The great mine of it was situated at Hawe, or Haigh, where lived a Mr. Bradshaw, of whom Leland remarks (vol. vii., pp. 47-49) that "he hath founde moche canal like se coole in his grounde very profitable to hym."

From the same authority we learn that the inhabitants of Bolton burned some cannel, but more sea coal, obtained from pits not far off. They also used turf.

Regarding the coal at Cliviger, in this county, Mr. T. D. Whitaker, in his *History of the Original Parish of Whalley and Honor of Clitheroe* (4th ed., vol. ii., p. 237), makes the following personal remarks:— "How long the coal so abundant in this rocky district has been wrought for sale does not appear from any document which I have seen. I only know that in the 3rd and 4th of Philip and Mary (1556-57) those sovereigns granted to my ancestor Thomas Whitaker, of Holme, gentleman, his heirs and assigns for ever, all their 'coole-mynes and coole-pitts in Clyvecher,' which in the year 1567 this improvident grantee transferred to John Townley, Esq., for the trifling sum of £20, and by this bargain his descendants have, during the last forty years, been deprived of at least £1,000 per annum."

That the collieries in the western part of this coalfield were sending coal to Liverpool for shipment in the latter part of the sixteenth century, is evidenced by the mayor of that town writing to Lord Brockhurst in 1600, as we have seen, "concerning the payment of the imposition on sea coal."

References occur to the working of coal at various points in the Staffordshire coalfield.

Leland (vol. vii., p. 29) speaks of sea coals at Wednesbury, and of sea coal pits at Walsall; and notes (vol. iv., p. 114) that the smiths of Birmingham drew their supplies of sea coal and iron out of this county. The coal mine belonging to Hulton, or Hilton Abbey, is mentioned in the *Monasticon* (vol. v., p. 716) as worth £1 6s. 8d. per ann. in 1539-40. And in a rental of Sir William Paget's estate at Longdon for the year 1549-50 (Shaw's *Staffordshire*, vol. i., p. 212), a coal mine in the manor of Beaudesert, below the park, is valued at £4 per ann.

During the time that the unfortunate Mary Queen of Scots

remained at Tutbury, a supply of coal for the Castle was obtained from the Beaudesert mine. In the correspondence in connection with the intended removal of the Queen here (*ib.*, Append. to Tutbury, p. 7 *b*), Sir Rafe Sadler wrote to Secretary Walsingham, under date 15th November, 1584, regarding a supply of fuel, in the following terms :—

"As touching wood and cole mentioned in your letter; the queenes ma^te hath woods good harde joining to Tutbury whereof cole may be made. As for sea coal, which is much used in this contrey, and compted their best fewell, there ys none nearer than six miles from Tutbury, and order is already this day sent to make ready wood and cole there."

Among the charges of the diet of Queen Mary (Hunter's *Sheffield*, p. 172) is an item for "getting 188 rooks of sea cole in Bewdeserte parke, with the chardges incidente to the same, £12 5s. 5d."[1]—a curious illustration of the change which had taken place in the employment of coal for fuel, since the time when Queen Eleanor removed from Nottingham to Tutbury three centuries before. The queens of Scotland had already, however, for a long period, been accustomed to use coal in their northern homes.

In Queen Elizabeth's reign (*Trans. So. Stafford. Inst.*, president's address, 1886) the tenants of the manor of Wednesbury had a lawsuit as to their right to dig coals for their own use. In 1577 deaths are recorded of men killed in the pits at Wednesbury (*Proc. Inst. Mechan. Eng.*, 1860, p. 95).

The following deed belonging to the year 1597 (2nd Dec., anno 40, Eliz.) has reference to a supply of coal for the town of Walsall :—

"Sale for 100 marks, by William Webbe, mayor of Walsall, John Wollaston, gent., Thomas Webbe, Thomas Stone, and Thomas Gorway, of the same, yeoman, to George Whithall, of Great Bloxwich, gent., of a messuage or tenement, with buildings, in tenure of John Madeley, in Great Bloxwich, and three acres of land there. The said George covenanting to serve all the inhabitants of Walsall with coals, called 'dassell coalles' at the rate of 3d. for each horse, mare, or gelding load, and with others, called 'bagge coals' at 2d. per like load, and to refuse none so long as there be any coals 'upon the bancke'" (*Trans. So. Stafford. Inst.*, 1886).

In the Shropshire coalfield records exist of coal being dug at various places.

[1] Another account for coal supplied for the use of Queen Mary, by Messrs. Nadin & Co., is stated never to have been paid (*Trans. Fed. Inst.*, vol. v., p. 461 ; *Col. Guard.*, Aug. 21, 1896, p. 353).

In 1536-37 the farm of a coal mine belonging to Wombridge Priory (*Monasticon*, vol. vi., p. 391; see also Leland, vol. vii., p. 25) yielded an annual rent of £5. Coal also continued to be worked in the lands of Wenlock Priory, but apparently on an extremely small scale. The rent of a coal pit called "a cole delffe" at Burwardesleye, or Broseley (*Monasticon*, vol. v., p. 81), in 1541-42, only reached the exceptionally insignificant amount of 1s. 4d.

The digging of coal was likewise still pursued on the Clee Hills, where, as we have seen, it was commenced at a very early date, and where it seems to have been chiefly used for burning lime. Leland remarks (vol. viii., part ii., p. 62) upon the "plenty of cole yerth stone nether, exceedinge good for lyme, whereof there they make muche and serve the contre about."

There is a notice of a vigorous search being made for coal in the vicinity of Shrewsbury with a successful result. It is recorded (Owen and Blakeway's *History of Shrewsbury*, London, 1825, i. 348 note) that "This yeare (1571) and the X. of Marche, Mr. Richard Gardner, of the towne of Shrewsbury, dyer, and free of the drapers' company, attemptyd and put in proof to fynde owt coles about the towne in soondry placys, and in one place in especiall, called Emsterie haye, hard by the sayd towne, he found by hys great dyligence and travell great store of secole; the which is lyke to come to sutche commoditie bothe for riche and poore, that he ys not only woorthy of commendacon and mayntenance, but also to be had in remembrance for ever."

A paucity of records exists relating to the mediæval coal mines of the Warwickshire coalfield, though from the tenor of subsequent references it cannot be doubted that the digging of coal must now have been going on for a considerable time. The early history of the collieries of this county may perhaps be obscured by the circumstance of their passing (like Griff) by the name of "groves." Sir William Dugdale throws little light upon the subject in his *Antiquities of Warwickshire*. We there find mention (p. 91, ed. 1765) of "a certain Grove called Fowlesmore," in the time of Henry III.; also of Hawkesbury Grove (*ib.*, p. 84 *b*) in the time of Henry VIII.; and in records relating to the possessions of Coventry Priory, quoted by the same author in the *Monasticon*, the terms "grova" and "grava" likewise occur; but whether these are referable to peateries, or collieries, or groves of wood, cannot be determined without additional evidence. The only reference this author seems to make to the coal mines of the county relates to those in Bedworth—a place, he remarks, very well known in regard of the coal mines there—which he incidentally mentions (*Antiquities*, pp. 83 *a*, 84 *a*) in connection with a change in the ownership of this estate in 1601-2.

The colliery owners of the Leicestershire coalfield had their first recorded experience of an underground fire in this era—it being, indeed, one of the earliest we hear of anywhere : the pits at Coleorton (Burton's *Leicestershire*, second edition, p. 198) having burned for many years in the beginning of the reign of Henry VIII.

In the Somersetshire coalfield mention occurs of coals being worked at one or two points.

Leland observes (vol. vii., part ii., p. 106) that there cometh a brook from the coal pits in Mendip and striketh by south into the bottom of Mells, and then runneth into Frome River. It is probably the same pits to which Camden refers in 1607 (Gibson's translation, ed. 1695, p. 69), who speaks of the Frome as rising in the mineral mountains of Mendip, and "hastening eastwards by these pits of coal made use of by smiths as most proper to soften iron."

Coal was also being dug in the neighbourhood of Bristol. A letter to Cecill, dated 1566 (Ricart's *Kalendar*, p. 84—Camden Society), states that "at Bristoll all manner of fewell is good cheap, a myne of sea cole being also within iiij^{or} myle of Bristoll." In the *Calendar of State Papers* (Dom., 1547-80, vol. xl. 17) the mine is stated to be within a mile of Bristol.

Little is heard at this period of the mines in the Forest of Dean. There is a notice (*Letters and Papers*, Hen. VIII., i. 183) of the appointment of one Philip Cachemay, in the time of Henry VIII., to be keeper during pleasure of the Gawle, called "The Gawle above the wood," in Dean Forest.

In the Cumberland coalfield the working of coal for local requirements was probably commenced near Whitehaven at an early date, in the lands belonging to the Monastery of St. Bees. But the records hitherto adduced only begin from the time when the lands passed into private hands in the reign of Edward VI., who granted them to Sir Thomas Chaloner in 1553.

It is stated (*Trans. Fed. Inst.*, vii. 613) that Sir Thomas, in granting leases, about 1560, reserved the right to dig for coal, giving liberty to his tenants to take coal for their own use at his pits, by the delivery of his officer, as they had been accustomed, "so always that they pay therefor and labour from time to time in the lord's coal pits according as they ought to do by the custom of the said lordship."

A free grammar school was erected at St. Bees about 1587 (Hutchinson's *Cumberland*, ii. 34, 39 note; *State Papers*, Dom.,

Addenda, 1580-1625, vol. xxxvi. 33), by the executors of Arch-
bishop Grundall, who was a native of the locality, on a site granted
by Thomas Chaloner, Esq., son of the above, who also gave forty
loads of sea coal yearly out of his coal mines for the use of the school.

In the sixteenth century Whitehaven was merely a small hamlet
(*Cal. State Papers*, Dom. Add. Eliz., 1566-79, p. 7) containing in 1566
six householders. Its subsequent rise was wholly due to the
development of the coal mines of the neighbourhood.

Regarding the progress of coal digging in the great South Wales
coalfield at this period some information is obtainable from various
sources.

A number of pits were now working in the neighbourhood of
Neath, in Glamorganshire. Among the receipts from Neath Abbey
lands, in 1541-42 (*Monasticon*, v. 261), the Crown agent acknowledges
20s. for the rent of a coal pit lately in the hands of Leysan Thomas,
the abbot, and now in the occupation of Richard Crumwell. Leland
also mentions (iv. 50) that coals were found half-a-mile above the
town of Neath in a moor, and likewise a little below the town;
and states that boats came up from the Severn to the timber bridge
situated somewhat lower than the town.

Records are extant (*State Papers*, Dom., 1581-90, clxxii. 16, 60;
cxcix. 18) relating to a smelting-house established at Neath in 1584,
for smelting copper ores brought from mines in Cornwall. After it
had existed for a few years the working of the mines was from some
cause suddenly discontinued. What the fuel used consisted of does
not appear to be specified in the published calendars of these records,
though it is reported (*Trans. N.E. Inst.*, xxiii. 197) to have been pit
coal.

Leland informs us (v. 23) that there were coal pits along each
side of Wendreth or Vendreth Vaur, where sea coals were dug; and
that coals of a different quality were obtained at Llanelly. "Ther
be ii manner of thes coles," he observes, "ring coles for smiths be
blowid and waterid, stone coles be sometime waterid but never
blowen, for blowing extinguishit them. So that Vendreth Vaur
coles be stone colis, Llanethle coles ring colis."

He also speaks (*ib.*, 79) of the ground in divers parts of Pembrokeshire bearing sea coals, wherewith commonly the people made fires,
as they also did with firs, wood being scarce; but coal was likewise
commonly used for fuel about Carmarthen, though there was plenty
of wood there. He passed coal pits when three miles from Llan-
feth; and went from Tenbigh to pits on a hilltop two miles off,
not far from the shore.

Later in the century incidental reference occurs (*Cal. State Papers*, Dom., 1591-94, p. 12) to lime kilns and lime coals at Milford Haven.

But the most interesting account of the South Wales coal industry in this era is contained in a History of Pembrokeshire, left in manuscript by George Owen, and published in the *Cambrian Register* for the year 1796. The memoir is undated, and has been variously assigned to 1570 and 1595, but neither of these dates appears to the writer to accord with the internal evidence which it contains. Thus reference is made (p. 177) to 20th July, anno Reg. Eliz. 44. It is also mentioned (p. 108) that "about three years past there was a generall and new imposition or custom raysed upon the coles throwout the realme, which was that for every chaudron transported her Majestie shall have of custome at the rate of 4d. for every barrell"—a duty which we know to have been imposed by Queen Elizabeth in 1599. Owen's history would thus clearly appear to have been written in 1602. It has been characterized (*Trans. Nat. Hist. Soc., Northumberland and Durham*, i. 83) as a work of the highest merit, being the earliest example extant of what can properly be called geological investigation.

Owen has been charged (*Fossil Fuel*, 125 n.) with improperly designating coal beds as veins; but this was one of the terms most widely applied to seams of coal, and still is the prevailing one in this coalfield. Like Leland, he speaks of two kinds of coal, viz., Stone coal, and Ring or Running coal (*Trans. N.E. Inst.*, xxiii. 197); describing the former as "Hard coal which is burned in chimnies and grates of iron, and delighteth to burn in dark places"; while he says that "Running coal melteth and runneth as wax, and groweth into one clodd."

Coal-bearing had now ceased in Pembrokeshire, except that the coals were still carried in baskets underground by boys. It had, however, been practised previously. "In former tyme," Owen states, "they used not engins for lifting up of the coles out of the pitt, but made theire entrance slope, soe as the people carried the coales uppon theire backes along stayers, which they called landwayes; whereas nowe they sinke theire pittes downe right foure square, about six or seaven foote square, and with a wyndles turned by foure men, they drawe upp the coles, a barrell full at once by a rope; this they call a downright dore (door)."

Pits were now sunk from 70 to 120 feet deep, whereas in former times 25 feet was counted a great labour. They were drained by water-levels, or adits, which are spoken of as "very chargeable, and may cost sometimes £20, and oftentimes more."

Noxious gas (obviously chokedamp) was already a source of trouble in the mines, and the connection between its appearance and the state of the weather had been thus early remarked upon. "All tymes of the yeare," says Owen, "are indifferent for working, but the hett weather worst, by reason of sodaine dampes that happen, which oftentymes cause the workmen to found, and will not suffer the candells to burne, but the flame waxing blew of collor, will of themselves go out."

Even at this period payment in kind still survived among the collieries of this district. The lords of the land, it is stated, "have eyther rent, or the third barrel, after all charges of the worke deducted."

As regards the question of using coal or wood for fuel, South Wales was in the same transition state as other parts of the kingdom in this era. Cardiff, at the time of Leland's visit, about 1540, appears to have still been a wood-consuming town, as he speaks (iv. 38) of it being partly served with wood from Kiven On, in Kibworth. At that period, as we have seen, coal was already becoming commonly used in Pembrokeshire, and about Caermarthen. But even when Owen wrote, wood appears still to have retained its sway in Pembrokeshire in the more private apartments, and among the better classes, though coal was used to a considerable extent by those who could obtain supplies with facility. Speaking of certain woods, the above writer remarks that with these, "the gentlemen of the sheere are well servid with wood for theire fuell; but for the most parte, those that dwell neere the cole, or that may have it caried by water with ease, use most cole fiers in theire kitchings, and some in theire halles, because it is a ready fiere, and very good and sweete to rost and boyle meate, and voyd of smoake, where yll chymnies are."

In North Wales coal continued to be worked at Ewlowe. The town and lordship, with the coal mines (*29th Report of the Dep. Keep. of Pub. Records*, p. 244), were leased to Peter Stanley in 1509-10, for four years, at £20 10s. rent; and a lease of lands and a coal pit in the same manor was granted by Queen Elizabeth's commissioners in 1594 (*State Papers*, Dom., 1591-94, vol. ccxlix. 37) to John Cordrey and Wm. Combe, for twenty-one years, at £20 10s. rent and £5 fine.

In the district of Bromfield, Leland mentions (vol. v., p. 33) sea coals at Harwood and a place called the Mines (Minera?). He also speaks (*ib.*, p. 37) of coal pits three-quarters of a mile from Molesdale town.

CHAPTER XII.

THE SIXTEENTH CENTURY.—Continued.

*Coal still obnoxious to the upper classes.   The charring or coking of coal.
Attempts to smelt minerals with coal.*

WHILE the general adoption of chimneys had removed the great
material obstacle to the use of coal in house fires, and considerations
of economy had turned the scale in its favour with people in general,
strong æsthetic objections to its use continued to be entertained by
a section of the community who were uninfluenced by the question
of comparative cost.

A notable illustration of the lingering dislike to coal fuel occurs
in a letter sent by Sir Henry Sidney, when residing at Ludlow
Castle as Lord President of the Marches (*Archæologia Cambrensis*, 4th
series, vol. ii., p. 49), wherein he requests permission to cut wood in
the forest of Deerfold for the use of the garrison, because the supply
of wood in the neighbourhood of Ludlow was so reduced that they
were compelled to burn that noxious mineral pit coal.

Queen Elizabeth herself, though the owner of numerous collieries,
objected strongly to coal smoke ; and in her reign the use of coal in
London is said to have been stringently restricted during the
sessions. A petition presented to the Government by the London
brewers in 1578 (*Cal. State Papers*, Dom. Eliz., cxxvii. 68), evidences
that coal had again obtained a footing among them, though at the
same time they were anxious not to offend the Queen. In this they
offer to burn wood only, in the brew-houses nearest Westminster
Palace, as they understand that "Her Majesty findeth hersealfe
greatly greved and anoyed with the taste and smoke of the se cooles."

Coal was doubtless now coming into extended use for domestic
purposes in the metropolis. In referring to the decay of wood
Harrison enumerates various kinds of inferior fuel, including sea
coal, as likely in the course of time to become "good merchandise

even in the City of London, whereunto," he says, "some of them have alreadie gotten readie passage and taken up their innes in the greatest merchants' parlours." And in a note of the revenues of the Bishop of London dated 1598 (*State Papers*, Dom. Eliz., vol. cclxvi. 119), it is set forth that whereas his lordship's predecessors had derived no small income from sales of wood, the present bishop had to buy timber for repairs, and he "has to burn sea coals."

Up till this time the London ladies continued to maintain their opposition to the use of coal apparently unabated. Writing in 1632, Howes states (Stow's *Annals*, edited by Howes, 1632, p. 1025) that "within these thirty years last," or, in other words, up till the very end of Queen Elizabeth's reign, "the nice dams of London would not come into any house or roome when sea coal was burned, or willingly eate of meate that had been either sod or roasted with sea coale fire." But a great change was at hand.

In this century we hear of a commencement being made to char, or coke, coal in order to free it from smoke and sulphur.

Smokeless fuel had been obtained from wood by this process from a remote period—the original *coal*, in fact. Peat, too, which was largely used in the smelting of minerals in the Middle Ages, had been treated in this way for at least one or two centuries previous to this era; considerably earlier than Beckman supposes. Moor coal was used at the silver mines at Byrland, in Devon, in 1301-2. This may perhaps be regarded as not wholly conclusive on the point; but another record occurs which is sufficiently decisive. In 1465-66 (Jones' *Index to the Originalia*, vol. ii., Addenda, *Cornubia*, 5 Edw. IV., rot. 49) Edward IV. granted license to the tin smelters of Cornwall to dig peats in the Forest of Dartmoor, and make them into coals (*et carbones inde facere*) for the smelting of tin.

At what period the charring process was first applied to mineral coal we have no record; but there is evidence that it was practised in Yorkshire in the sixteenth century. Allusion has been made to what appears to be an early reference to charred coal in the Fabric Rolls of York Minster. Baskets of charcoal figure in these accounts, as we have seen, in 1371, and occasionally thereafter. But in 1527-1528 a purchase of some sacks of coals *called* "charcool" is made along with sacks of Wakefield coals and chalders of Newcastle coals. The qualification of the name, and the fact of its being bought as part of a purchase of mineral coal, seems to point to this being something different from the usual charcoal, and is suggestive of its being an early reference to coke. Apart from this, however, we have other proof of attention having been given to the coking of coal in this county at the period under consideration; a patent having been granted in 1590 (*Cal. State Papers,* Dom., 1581-90, p. 692) to John Thornborough, Dean of York, for refining sea coals ; or, as it is otherwise expressed, "to purify pit coal and free it from its offensive smell"; evidently with a view to the employment of the product in house fires.

In a draft of this license preserved among the Lansdowne MSS. at the British Museum (No. 67, pencil folio 56 *b*), it is set forth that by reason of the scarcity of wood in England of late years, pit coals, commonly called sea coals, are in great use, and "do serve for a very necessarie supply for commen fuell . . . and would be brought to serve to farre greater comodite and use for the sparing and saving of wood, were yt not for the noysomnes and unsavery qualitie which is founde in the burning of the same for fuell"; and proceeds to say that the licensee has found out a method to correct the "sulphury nature" of these coals by refining them in such perfect sort, that thereby they shall burn as sweet and clear as charcoals. The patent was granted for a term of seven years, on the condition that the same process had not been previously practised by anyone else.

This Elizabethan dean, Mr. John Thornburgh, must have taken considerable interest in coal. In the same collection are three letters addressed by him to the Government in 1591, on the prevention of the exportation of "our best pit coal." He seems to have been of opinion that there was not the same objection to our sharing the inferior qualities with foreign nations !

The idea of employing coal in the smelting of minerals, in lieu of wood and charcoal, had also already begun to be entertained in the sixteenth century.

Cardinal Wolsey's scheme for smelting his Durham lead ore with his Durham coal, is the earliest project of the kind on record. This prelate had a large house and furnace built at Gateshead-on-Tyne for the purpose. In his instructions, already referred to, sent to Dr. Strangwysshe, surveyor of Durham, and Richard Belysis, Esq., in 1526-28, he directs them to finish the new house and furnace for melting and trying lead with sea coals, and to urge the finers who have undertaken the task to proceed as diligently as possible, and not to allow them to lack any ore or other thing which they might allege as an excuse. But regarding the experiments themselves we are left without any information, and can only conjecture that the results were unsatisfactory, inasmuch as lead continued to be smelted with wood for 150 years subsequently. In 1528-29 Wolsey (roll 2, m. 2) granted to farm to one Thomas Wynter, a great house and furnace near Gateshead, and all mines of metals and minerals within the bishopric, and the country called Wardell, for the term of thirty years, at the rent of £5 per annum.

For a long interval no further notice occurs of any attempt to employ coal in smelting, except, perhaps, in the case of the copper works at Neath, as already mentioned.   But in 1589 a patent was granted by Queen Elizabeth (Lansdowne MSS., No. 59, pencil folio 196) to Thomas Proctor, of Warsell (?) (or Narsell, perhaps Nosthill), in the county of York, Esq., in conjunction with one Wm. Peterson, "to make iron, steel, or leade, by using of earthe coale, sea coale, turffe, peate, or some of them." The patentees were not wholly restricted to the above kinds of fuel, but claimed that by using them they could smelt with one-fourth part of the charcoal hitherto required.   The scheme, however, appears to have turned out a signal commercial failure.   While coal continued to steadily oust wood from house fires, wood and charcoal held their ground in smelting furnaces, for a prolonged period, against all attempts to supersede them.

With the close of the reign of Queen Elizabeth the first great period in the history alike of the coal trade and of coal mining may be said to have come to an end.

During this period it was chiefly by artisans that coal had been used for fuel.   From this time forward, for a long interval, it was as a fuel for domestic purposes that it was most largely employed.

The mining operations of this period likewise had a character of their own.   The coal was almost all obtained from shallow collieries above the level of free-drainage, by the pit and adit system of mining—the mines being opened out in elevated situations affording natural facilities for this desirable arrangement.   But the halcyon era of natural drainage was now passing away.   Though adits continued to be driven under special circumstances, they were becoming so long and costly in the districts where the mining of coal had been most actively carried on as to be getting out of date; and this method of mining no longer sufficed to meet the enlarged demand for coal which had sprung up.   The miners were coming face to face with the necessity of winning supplies of the mineral from the region below the level of the water; though the combating of this formidable enemy to any distance downwards seemed at this time almost an impracticable project; as, indeed, it would have been but for the splendid aid subsequently afforded to mining art by the discoveries of modern science.

CHAPTER XIII.

THE SEVENTEENTH CENTURY.

King James I. accustomed to coal.   Smallness of the production.   Fears of the exhaustion of the coal supply.   Collieries of the Tyne: Elswick, Benwell, Denton, etc.   Inundation of a colliery on Newcastle Town Moor.   The Tyne basin.   Sliding rents.   The collieries of Gateshead and Whickham.   First recorded fatal accident from fire-damp.   Other accidents.   Ravensworth, Gellesfield, Winlaton, and other collieries on the south side of the Tyne.

On the accession of King James to the throne of England, in 1603, coal was elevated to a higher status than it had hitherto held. With the hostility to the use of mineral fuel King James had little or no sympathy.   For generations back his ancestors had been using coal in Scotland; and it was doubtless owing to the coal smoke which pervaded the atmosphere of their picturesque metropolis, that it obtained the well known *sobriquet* of "Auld Reeky" (*i.e.* Old Smoky).

We hear of King James burning cannel coal in his private apartments at the palace of Falkland, in Fifeshire.   "An account is to be seen in Largo House," says a writer in the old *Statistical Account of Scotland* (vol. ix., p. 299), of so many loads of parret coal driven yearly from Fatfield to Falkland, a distance not less than ten miles, for the use of King James VI. his own chamber."

It is not, therefore, surprising that after his arrival in England coal began to be substituted for wood fuel in his new residences. There is a record (Devon's *Extracts from the Issues of the Exchequer*, James I., p. 84) of the purchase of "coals for his Majestie's house" in 1608.   From its humble beginning as the peculiar fuel of obscure artisans, coal had won its way upwards, step by step, until its triumph as a fuel for domestic purposes had now been consummated by its admission into the royal palaces of England.   The Westminster brewers, however, were not allowed to use coal in the reign of Charles I. (*Cal. State Papers*, Dom., 1635-36, p. 161), one of them being fined 500 marks, and committed to the Fleet, for brewing with sea coal; but being pardoned on giving security not to brew any more in Westminster with coal.

Being now a fashionable as well as an economical fuel, the use of coal spread apace. The rapidity with which it was being adopted is well illustrated by the following remarks of a contemporary writer: "At this day," says Howes (Stow's *Annals*, ed. 1615, p. 210), "viz., in the yeere 1612, and the 10 yeere of the raigne of King James, at which time I wrote this booke, the fore-said sea cole and pitt cole is become the generale fuell of this Britaine Island, used in the houses of the nobilitie, cleargy, and gentrie, in London and in all the other cityes and shires of the kingdome, as well for dressing of meate, washing, brewing, dying, as otherwise."

In some of the more inland districts, where supplies of coal were less easily obtainable, wood held its ground longer; but even here the wholesale use of wood fuel was regarded as an extravagance. Among the instances of misconduct enumerated by Wood in his *Athenæ Oxonienses* against the warden of Merton College, he specifies his "burning in one year £60 worth of the choicest billet that could be had, not only in all his roomes, but in the kitchin among his servants: without any regard had to cole; which usually, to save charges, is burnt in kitchens, and sometimes also in parlours."

While still applied to a considerable extent, the older name of sea coal, with its associations of unpopularity and even odium (though interesting from a historical point of view), began to gradually drop out of fashion in the course of this century, and the simple name of coal to be more commonly attached to the mineral. The question of the origin of the term "sea coal" still continued to be debated, Fuller in 1662 (*Worthies of England*, art. Shropshire) ascribing it to the fact of its being "brought from Newcastle"; while Sir John Pettus in 1686 (*Fleta Minor, Essays on Words Metallick*, art. Coal) ascribes it to the circumstance of its being "dig'd out of coal mines near the sea at Tinmuth, by Newcastle." Already also it had begun to be employed in the new sense attached to it at the present day; being first applied by Taylor, the water poet, in 1618 (*Pennyles Pilgrimage*), to coal dug *under the sea*, at Culross, in Scotland.

Though now so largely used for domestic purposes, the total production of coal was as yet very inconsiderable, according to modern ideas. The quantity exported from the Tyne in 1609 (*Proceed. Arch. Inst.*, Newcastle, 1852, vol. i., p. 178), only amounted to 239,261 tons, of which 24,956 tons, or about a tenth part, was sent abroad. The export from the Wear at this time was merely a small fraction of that from the Tyne, amounting in the same year to 11,648 tons, of which 2,383 tons were sent abroad. While Blyth, at this date, had only a coast export of 855 tons. Total vend of the northern ports 251,764 tons.

The accounts of the farmers of the coal taxes show that in the early part of this century a small foreign export of coal (in addition to that shipped coastwise, as well as to Ireland and the Channel Islands, which was duty free) had commenced at a number of points on the west coast.[1] In a balance-sheet of these parties for the year 1617 (*ib.*, p. 220), shipments abroad, though of a diminutive character, are recorded as having been made from Bristol, Swansea, Milford Haven, the port of Chester and Liverpool, and Cumberland.

Small as the production of coal at this time appears to our eyes, the possibility of its being able to be maintained for any lengthened period was already beginning to be feared. Indeed, the exhaustion of the Newcastle coal supply was supposed to be within easy measurable distance. In 1610, we are told (*ib.*, p. 186), Sir George Selby informed Parliament that " the coal mines at Newcastle would not hold out the term of their lease of twenty-one years." This was based upon the supposition that water presented an insuperable obstacle to the progress of the mines downwards to any depth, and that the water limit of working had been already nearly reached.

The prediction of this seventeenth-century prophet is merely calculated to provoke a smile ; but that the fears entertained at the time were not without some reasonable foundation is amply attested by the course of subsequent events. Throughout the whole of this century, the task of obtaining supplies of coal for the northern coal trade, was only achieved by carrying on a continuous and severe, and at times ruinous and unsuccessful struggle, with the water that ceaselessly sought to fill up the excavations ; and, in the first half of the century at least, the colliery owners appear to have been in deep water financially as well as literally.

Indications of the changed conditions under which coal mining was now being carried on soon become apparent, in notices of drowned coal pits, of colliery inundations, and of debts and losses being incurred in connection with the working of coal, all of which

[1] The coal is said to be "transported," and the duty appears to have been 5s. per chaldron. The figures given (to be referred to hereafter) must be taken to represent only from one-fifth to one-tenth of the total shipments from the various ports.

begin to be heard of for the first time in the history of coal mining. A place has also now to be found for the catalogue of accidents, accompanied by loss of life, with which the working of coal has been attended; inevitable, doubtless, to a great extent, on account of the dangerous surroundings under which it is carried on, but at the same time sad and deplorable.

So far from the coal trade being, as formerly, an almost unknown industry, it had, in a comparatively short space of time, risen into such prominence as to begin to rank as one of the most important industries of the kingdom.

Almost a plethora of information is available regarding the coal trade of the Tyne in this era, but the collieries themselves lie somewhat in the background. A number of records exist, however, which furnish us with a tolerably clear idea of the situation of the mines and of the character of the mining operations of this period.

On the north side of the Tyne, the coal mines in the fields of Elswick were leased by the Crown to Robert Errington and Timothy Draper, in 1612 (Gibson's *Tynemouth*, i. 242), at a yearly rent of £30. An attempt made to open out a colliery in Elswick about 1680, evidently in one of the deeper seams, proved a failure (Brand, ii. 686 note), the undertaker being unable to contend with the water encountered in sinking the pit.

In the adjoining lands of Benwell notice occurs (*Cal. State Papers, Dom.*, 1603-10, p. 512) of a prolongation of a lease of the mines there being granted by the Crown to Roger Lawson in 1609. These mines are again mentioned in 1631 (*ib.*, 1631-33, vol. ccvi. 76; also p. 282 of *Cal.*), at which date the rent appears to have been in arrears; while in 1637-38 (*ib.*, 1637-38, pp. 247, 419) notice occurs of an intrusion being made upon them. Benwell was the scene of a great underground fire in the latter part of the century, to which reference will be made hereafter.

The working of coal in Denton is heard of in 1610 (*ib.*, 1603-10, p. 642), when we find Anthony and Roger Errington petitioning Salisbury for continuance of their lease of a coal mine there, alleged to have been bought over their heads on false pretences by Wm. Court and [John] Lyons, Receiver of Northumberland. This appears to have been conceded, as immediately afterwards notice occurs (*ib.*, p. 651) of a warrant to pay to Robert Chapman £197, disbursed on certain coal mines at Denton, the lease whereof has been surrendered to His Majesty.

The coal mines at Newbiggin (*Cal. State Papers*, Dom., 1663-64,

p. 76) were forfeited by confiscation to Sir Arthur Hazlerigg, Governor of Newcastle; and were leased in 1655, for twenty-one years, at £100 per annum.

Coal was doubtless also being actively worked at a number of points in the surrounding district, though information on the subject is extremely meagre. In 1638-39 mention occurs (*State Papers*, Dom., Chas. I., vol. cccx. 142) of a staith at Newburn and another at Lemeden (Lemington), in connection with an inquiry about coals affirmed to have been bought from Mr. R. Anderson; while there is incidental reference in 1701 (Sykes's *Loc. Rec.*, i. 128) to collieries in Kenton and the neighbourhood.

Brand, under date November 6, 1646 (ii. 290 note), speaks of a colliery about to be wrought on Newcastle Town Moor. In connection with the working of coal here at this period, we meet with the earliest instance on record of a colliery being inundated by the bursting in of water from an ancient abandoned working, or "waste.' The accident occurred in 1658; the recovery of the bodies of two of the victims long subsequently, being thus referred to in the burial register of St. Andrew's Church, Newcastle (Richardson's *Table Book*, H.D., i. 327):—"April 24, 1695, were buried James Archer and his son Stephen, who, in the moneth of May, 1658, were drowned in a coal pitt in the Galla Flat, by the breaking in of water from an old waste. The bodys were found intyre, after they had lyen in the water thirty-six years and eleven months." Coal had been worked, as we have seen, in Elswick Moor, adjoining the Gallow Flat, upwards of two hundred years before.

On the east side of Newcastle the coal seams sloped downwards, or "dipped," till they passed under the village of Wallsend—the point where the Roman wall terminated on the Tyne—shortly beyond which they rose again towards the surface at Tynemouth, forming what is termed by geologists a synclinal trough, which was locally known as the "Tyne basin." In the deeper part of this tract the coal lay as yet beyond the reach of the miners, but in this era some progress was made in the opening out of collieries round the edges of the depression.

On the side next Newcastle the working of coal is stated by Mr. Dunn (*Coal Trade*, p. 20), to have been going on in the latter part of this century in the lands of Heaton, Jesmond, Byker, and St. Lawrence, but of direct records relating to these collieries at this period, few, if any, seem to exist.

In the Tynemouth neighbourhood, however, on the opposite side of the basin, we hear of various leases of coal being made; an outlet for the produce of the collieries of this district having been found by the construction of a shipping place on the sea shore.

The mines of coal dug, or to be dug, in the fields of Moreton (Murton), Billimore, and Billimill Moor, otherwise Shiremoor, valued at 5s. per ann., were granted by the Crown, in fee-farm, to Henry, Earl of Northumberland, in 1624, at that rent. (Gibson's *Tynemouth,* vol. i., p. 242; *Cal. State Papers,* Dom., 1623-25, p. 181).

All the pits or mines of coal in the fields of Tynemouth, and the mines and veins of coal discovered in Flatworthfield, were granted by the Crown in 1631 to William Collins and Edward Fenn, of London, Gentlemen (Gibson, *ib.,* p. 244).

The pits or mines of coal in Preston, lately demised to John Robinson, and valued at 66s. 8d. per annum, and the pits and mines of coal in East Chirton and Middle Chirton, lately demised to John Robinson, and valued at 20s. per ann., were granted by the Crown in 1633 to William Scriven and William Eden, of London, Esquires, at a yearly rent (*ib.,* p. 245).

Mention occurs in 1656 (Richardson's *Table Book,* i. 288) of "cole pitts" about two miles from the Castle of Tynemouth, supposed to have been at Whitley. In 1675 the mines in the township of Whitley were leased for a term of eleven years, at a rent of 7s. 6d. per ten for the first year, and for the residue of the term £50 a year, and 7s. 6d. for every ten over 134 tens (Gibson, vol i., p. 245 note)— an instance of the abandonment of the ancient system of rigid rents and the substitution of the modern arrangement of having both a fixed and sliding or optional rent, which makes the quantity of coal worked bear an exact relation to the amount of rent paid, however it may vary from year to year. This improved system begins to be commonly met with in colliery leases after the middle of the seventeenth century.

A lease of coal mines in the township of Earsdon was granted in 1685 (*ib.*).

It is observable that the merchants of Newcastle had little or no share in this small cluster of collieries. Their produce, even such as came from pits situated at North Shields, in close proximity to the Tyne (Charleton's *Newcastle Town,* p. 239), was shipped on the open coast, at the village of Cullercoats. We are told (*Transactions, North of England Inst.,* vol. xv., p. 196) that the activity of the coal trade carried on about 1683 at this little independent port of "Color Coats" (?collier cots), just beyond the bounds of their jurisdiction, excited the jealousy of the hostmen of Newcastle.

On the south side of the Tyne the Grand Lease, as we have seen, was now vested in the Corporation of Newcastle; but certain portions of the manor of Whickham, at least, must have been retained in the possession of the Crown, inasmuch as we still find leases of coal being granted here independently of the authorities at Newcastle.

Thus in 1610 (*Cal. State Papers*, Dom., 1603-10, p. 589) certain chancery lands and coal pits in the parish of Whickham, valued at £5 per annum, were granted by the Crown to Robert Chapman and Thos. Walford; and in 1623 (*ib.*, 1619-23, p. 543) a lease of a coal mine in Whickham was granted to Alex. Stephenson, page of the bed-chamber, during the lives of Robt. Anderson, of Newcastle, and Fras. Anderson, of Jesmond, and Thos. Sanderson, of Hedley Hope.

If the Grand Lease was ever worth the amount of £50,000 a year, as stated by Gardiner (*England's Grievance*, ch. viii.), its value must have subsequently become greatly reduced. In 1658 (Brand, i. 484) the mayor and burgesses of Newcastle demised all their lands and coal mines in Gateshead and Whickham to George Dawson, mayor, Thomas Bonner, Mark Milbank, and Henry Rawling, to procure the sum of £2,000 to prosecute the building of the new town court.

The Grand Lease expired in 1681 or 1682, when the manors reverted to the See of Durham. The reversion of the Grand Lease, says Mr. Surtees (*Durham*, ii. 239), had been granted by Bishop Cosin to his son-in-law, Sir Gilbert Gerard. Bishop Crewe afterwards leased to Colonel Liddell and his partners, and the Manor of Whickham has been since held by their successors, Sir Thomas Henry Liddell & Co., commonly called the Grand Allies.

In no part of the great northern coalfield, or indeed of the kingdom, had the working of coal been so long and extensively carried on as in the manors of Gateshead and Whickham. It is not, therefore, surprising that a number of the earliest known accidents in coal mines should have occurred here.

The earliest accident occasioned by firedamp, or explosive gas, which we hear of (brought to light by a writer in the *Newcastle Chronicle*, 10th September, 1880, p. 2) took place in a pit in Gateshead. In the register of St. Mary's Church here, under date 14th October, 1621, is recorded the interment of "Richard Backas burn'd in a pit."

In the same record, under date 16th February, 1692, there is registered the burial of "Michael Laurin, slain in a pit."

In the Whickham register, in like manner, a few notices of casualties of various kinds have been recorded (Surtees, ii. 242):—

Jeffrey, son to Jeffrey Morice, slain with the start at a pit of Mr. Henry Liddell's, in Jacks leezes, the 15th November, 1636.

Man and child drowned in a pit on the fell, 1647.

Ralphe Harrison slaine in a grand lease pitt in the leigh, 19th Sept., 1650. John Harrison slain in a pitt, 18th Oct., 1650.

Accidents from people falling into old unfenced coal pits, particularly when the ground was covered with snow, appear to have been somewhat common (Gardiner's *Grievance*, ch. viii.) in the Tyne district in this era. We also have accounts of these old pits being utilized for murderous purposes. One of these, mentioned in a letter of Bishop Cosins (Raine's *Auckland Castle*, p. 131), relates to the case of a young woman who, under pretence of courtship, was enticed by a villain to the edge of an old pit, where he proceeded to strip her, with the intention of pushing her in. But being ready-witted, the young woman contrived to push him in instead. On her story being told and search being made, truly enough the man's body was found at the bottom of the pit, and beside it the naked bodies of three women whom he had pushed in previously. The bishop, however, did not credit the story.

A stratum of burnt earth at Whickham was occasioned, according to tradition (Surtees, ii. 239; Edington's *Coal Trade*, p. 139), by the king's army firing their tents so precipitantly when the Scots, under Lesley, crossed the Tyne to attack them, that the flame communicated with a small seam of coal, which burned for several years, and at night flames issued from different parts of the village and grounds adjoining.

The tendency of colliery owners to place their produce on the market under some well-known name, has long been a marked feature of the coal trade. Perhaps this may serve to explain how it is that the name of Grand Lease is found applied to one or two other collieries in the seventeenth century, as well as the original lease of Gateshead and Whickham.

Thus we hear of a lawsuit (*Trans. North of Eng. Inst.*, vol. xv., p. 266) being instituted in 1663, by George Vane, soldier, and others, lessees under the Bishop of Durham, of seams of coal (in a colliery called the Grand Lease Colliery) lying under the copyhold lands, wastes, moors, and commons, within the manors of Whickham and Gateshead, against John Marley and others, proprietors of an estate called Brenkburn freehold, in which they had sunk three shafts, by means of which it was alleged they had wrought great quantities of coal out of the complainant's liberty—with a prayer for relief and the appointment of a commission to go down defendants' pits, to view and measure the coal mines wrought by the defendants.

"The decree empowered William Lyddell, Trystram Fenwick, John Emerson, and Ralph Haggerston, to view the defendants' workings, and from time to time to ryde the shafts of the pits wrought by the defendants, and to go into and return out of their coal works until they had perfected the view ; and in order thereunto to make use of the standard rowler, wayes, and other like instruments, and also to carry with them spades, shovels, hacks, picks, and other towles and instruments, to remove all such lettes, obstructions, and impediments, above or underground, as should hinder of viewing the said defendants' collieries and their doings therein," and to certify the result.

It is obvious that the Bishop of Durham had coal let on lease in Gateshead and Whickham, independently of that held by the Corporation of Newcastle ; and also that the Bishop's lessees made use of the name of Grand Lease. And in the case of Stella Colliery further west, the name of Stella Grand Lease is retained till the present day.

The extensive Ravensworth estates changed hands early in the seventeenth century, becoming the property of the Liddell family at this period. In 1607-8 the Bishop of Durham granted pardon to Thomas Liddell (*40th Report of the Dep. Keep. Pub. Rec.*, p. 500), for entry without license into these estates, acquired from William Gascoigne, Knt., and Barbara his wife.

Reference has already been made to the working of the coal which abounded in this property, and in the seventeenth century the Ravensworth collieries were perhaps the most extensive and important on the Tyne.

Sir Thomas Liddell was one of several[1] "malignant coalowners" who on the capture of Newcastle by the Parliament forces in 1644, were "wholly excluded from intermeddling with any share or parts of collieries, or interest in any coals wharsomever that formerly they had laid claims to "—Bourne's *Newcastle*, p. 234.

The following record, dated 1650 (*Cal. State Papers*, Dom., 1650, p. 613), doubtless relates to the restitution to him of his lands and rights :—" Injunction by the Keepers of the Liberty of England to Ralph Cole and all who under him claim the manors, lands, coal mines and collieries, lately extended on the suit of Sir Henry Vane and others, on behalf of Thomas Liddle and Anne his wife, to yield

---

[1] The others were Sir Thomas Marley, Sir Thomas Riddell, Sir Alexander Davison, Sir John Minns, and Sir Francis Anderson.

obedience to an order made after hearing the facts in the said suit requiring them to deliver up possession of the said manors, lands, coal mines and collieries, to Sir Henry Vane—to which order they have refused obedience—under penalty of £2,000 to be levied on their lands and chattels if they still refuse or delay."

By the will of Sir Thomas Liddle, 1661 (Edington's *Coal Trade*, p. 136), it is set forth that he received the sum of £600 from Sir George Tonge, of Denton, as the filial portion of his daughter Elizabeth, on her intermarriage with his son Sir Francis Liddle; in consideration of which he granted to Sir Francis the working of one coal pit within the lordship of Ravensworth. The prominent position of the Ravensworth collieries in the latter part of the century will be adverted to hereafter.

One or two notices occur relative to the continued working of coal in Gellesfield. In 1617 (Surtees, ii. 251) William and Ralph Blakiston, of Gibside, Esqs., settled half the close of Gellesfield and half the mines, on the marriage of Nicholas Blakiston, second son of William, with Jane Porter, of Shield-row; and in 1645, Sir Ralph Blakiston, Bart., granted a fourth of Gellesfield Colliery to his brother, John Blakiston, Gent.

The owners of the lordship of Winlaton, Sir William Selby, Sir Robert Hodgson, and Mr. Robert Anderson, who had hitherto enjoyed it in common, came to a division of it in 1632, but collieries, quarries, etc., were not divided. The mines in Winlaton appear not to have been carried on with success at this period. William, son of Sir William Selby, is stated (*Cal. State Papers*, Dom., 1637, p. 159) to have incurred a large debt in their management.

A record relating to coal in Swalwell, etc., is quoted by Hutchinson (*Durham*, ii. 443 note), which he describes as, "Pardon of alienation to Sir John Lumley, Lord Lumley, and Catherine his wife, by fine to Geo. Smith, and Thomas Kimraston, of a coal mine in Swalwell, Tugerfield, and Lyngfield, in Whickham, 1st August, 1607." It is doubtless connected with the sale of the Lumley estates, made in this year, to be hereafter referred to. A slightly different version of the record is given by Edington (*Coal Trade*, p. 133). Tugerfield is a misprint for Fugerfield. We have seen that coal was worked in the manor of Fugerhous in the fourteenth century.

Incidental mention occurs of coal mines in the Axwell lands, near Blaydon, in 1604 (Surtees, ii., p. 247); and according to Edington (*Coal Trade*, p. 131) pits were open on Stella Grand Lease during the civil wars, and many thousand dead bodies were thrown into them.

In the middle of the seventeenth century a colliery was working at Crawcrook, in Ryton parish, a lawsuit having taken place in 1665 (*Trans. North of Eng. Inst.*, vol. xv., p. 267) regarding the delivery of twenty tens of coal. The matters in dispute were referred to Sir Francis Anderson and Sir Nicholas Cole. The ten in this case is specified to have consisted of "good merchantable ship coles accompting twenty wagons to a tenn, every wagon to contain fifteen bowles usual cole measure." This is 300 bolls.

No collieries appear to have existed in Chopwell lands in 1607 ; a grant of this manor being made at this date to Sir William Constable (*Cal. State Papers*, Dom., 1603-10, p. 384) with a proviso for coal mines if discovered. It is probable, however, that collieries may have been subsequently opened out, as the coal in outlying districts was beginning to receive a greater amount of attention in the latter part of the century.

In 1693 the Bishop of Durham let Blackburn Fell to Sir J. Clavering and Thomas Liddell (Edington's *Coal Trade*, p. 133), for three lives, at £40 per annum ; and from a law-suit already referred to, it would seem that coal was now being worked at Marley Hill, if it had not likewise commenced in the still more distant districts of Tanfield and Pontop.

On the east side of Gateshead, where, as at Newcastle, the coal seams sloped downwards and became deeper, comparatively little extension had as yet taken place; but at this period we begin to hear of collieries in this part of the Tyneside.

In 1623 (*Cal. State Papers*, 1619-23, vol. cxxxvii. 34) Sir Hen. Wodrington, Sir Geo. Selby, and Sir John Fenwick, wrote to the Council to the effect that they had caused the coal mines of the Earl of Northumberland called Bird's Nest—doubtless situated at what is now known as "the Nest," on the Tyne, below Gateshead—to be surveyed as ordered, and finding that they are in danger of being drowned, if the farmers of them continue to work them as they have begun, have stayed the works.

At this period, the working of coal must have been carried on at some points in very close proximity to the Tyne, inasmnch as it was found necessary (Gardiner's *Grievance*, ch. xii., E. 7) to make an order, in 1613, that no coal should be dug within sixty yards of the river.

Further east, a colliery, from 90 ft. to 96 ft. in depth, is stated to have been working at Hebburn about the time of King James I.[1]

---

[1] Said to be noticed in a rent deed of Durham Cathedral, dated 1618 (Hair's *Sketches of the Coal Mines*, p. 30).

(Edington's *Coal Trade*, p. 139), in a seam of coal high up in the series, known as the Monkton seam, being so named after Monkton, near Jarrow; a village which claims to have been the birthplace of the Venerable Bede. The produce of the colliery was shipped at a staith at Hebburn, shown on Gardiner's map of the Tyne in 1655, under the name of the "Black Steath."

Before the close of this century, according to Mr. Dunn (*Coal Trade*, p. 20) collieries had also been opened out at Heworth, Felling, and Tyne Main, but we have met with no contemporary notices relating to them.

CHAPTER XIV.

THE SEVENTEENTH CENTURY.—CONTINUED.

The Tyne coal trade. Complaints against the hostmen. King Charles I. attempts to monopolize the coal trade. Interruptions occasioned by the Civil Wars. A strike of the coal owners. The size of the chaldron fixed. The keel-load and the ten. Manufacture of glass with coal.

WHAT with coal ships, English and foreign, arriving and departing, the Tyne must have been a scene of considerable stir, during the shipping months, already in the early part of the seventeenth century. In 1615 the coal fleet numbered 400 vessels, one-half of which were required for the supply of London, and the remainder for other parts of the kingdom. "Besides our own ships," says a writer of the period (Anderson's *Commerce*, i. 494), "hither, even to the mine's mouth, come all our neighbouring nations with their ships continually. The French sail thither in whole fleets of fifty sail together, serving all the parts of Picardie, Normandie, Bretagne, etc., even as far as Rochelle and Bourdeaux; and the ships of Bremen, Embden, Holland, and Zealand, supply Flanders, etc., with our coals."

During the seventeenth century the authorities at Newcastle continued to hold the monopoly they had secured to themselves of the coal trade and general navigation of the Tyne, notwithstanding the vehement complaints which their policy evoked from time to time from many quarters.

In 1620 we find Robert Brandling, surveyor of coal mines, petitioning the king (*State Papers* 1619-23, vol. cxvi. 74) for examination into the abuses of Sir Peter Riddell, Mayor of Newcastle, and others, who lay heavy impositions on coals, engross the ballast wharfs, and rent the king's coal mines at less than a thirtieth of their value, to the loss both of His Majesty and his subjects.

Two years later (1622) a petition was presented to the council (*ib.*, vol. cxxix. 8) by the Masters, Wardens, Assistants, and Company of Woodmongers, Chandlers, and others, traders in coals in London, to take cognizance of their former petitions relative to the frauds committed by the oastmen of Newcastle in mixing their coals, and to grant them speedy redress, the answers of the oastmen tending only to delay, for their own private enrichment.

Other complaints came from the collectors of the coal taxes regarding the covert lading of great quantities of coals, and false and short entries of the same, as well as of the lading of ships by the bulk and not by the due measure of keels and lighters.

Enjoined by Government, the hostmen bestirred themselves, and held a court May 20, 1622, at which they passed a series of orders for the reformation of the abuses which had crept into the trade (*Proc. Arch. Inst.*, Newcastle, 1852, i. 212); and appointed a few of the principal members—consisting of Sir Peter Riddell, Mr. Thomas Tempest, Mr. Thos. Liddell, Mr. Robert Shaftoe, Mr. Alex. Davison, Mr. Wm. Bonner, and Mr. Robert Anderson—to superintend the loading of all the coals.

The total quantity of coal to be vended was 14,420 tens, or about 300,000 tons, distributed among the various members according to the subjoined list :

"The number of coals which every brother of the fellowshipp hath to vent this year as follows :

1622.	Tens.		Tens.
Sir George Selby,	750	Mrs. Barbara Riddell,	450
Sir Thomas Riddell,	900	Mr. Robt. Anderson,	350
Sir Peter Riddle,	300	Mr. Wm. Bonner,	600
Sir Fra. Brandlyn,	500	Mr. Robt. Bewick,	500
Sir Nichs. Tempest,	600	Mr. Nichs. Blaxton,	550
Mr. Thos. Tempest,	900	Mrs. Barbara Milburne,	60
Mr. Henry Liddall,	700	Mr. Robt. Gray,	500
Mr. Thos. Liddall,	800	Mr. Jos. Clavering,	400
Mr. Fra. Burrell,	150	Mr. Lyonell Madison,	300
Mr. Henry Madison,	700	Mr. Ra. Madison,	300
Mr. Robert Shaftoe,	550	Mr. Henry Anderson,	125
Mr. Alex. Davison,	450	Mr. Thos. Crome,	400
Mrs. Mary Hall,	450	Mr. Thomas Hall,	120
Mr. Robt. Hodgson,	600	Mr. Henry Eden,	350
Mr. Henry Chapman,	700	Mr. Wm. Sherwood,	225
		Mr. Chas. Tempest,	140
	9,050		3,370

The total of the tens is, 14,420 "

During the reign of Charles I. the Tyne coal trade passed through some remarkable vicissitudes.   The taxation of coal, commenced, as we have seen, by Queen Elizabeth at the close of her reign, was perpetuated and augmented by her successors, and in the course of time became a prolific source of revenue to the Crown.   In March, 1634-35 (*Cal. State Papers*, Dom., 1634-35, p. 595) the farm of sea coals is characterized as "the bravest farm the King has"; though the revenue derived from the pre-emption of tin amounted at this date to £12,000 per annum.

But so far from the king, or his advisers, being satisfied with the result, it seems only to have served to excite further cupidity.   In May following we find (*Cal. State Papers*, Dom., 1635, p. 90), a "Note by Sec. Windebank of business to be transacted by the Lords of the Treasury : To remember the proposition concerning sea coal, how his Majesty may be made the sole merchant of it."   That this was determined upon is shown by a record dated March 12, 1635-36 (*ib.*, 1635-36, p. 292).   "Coals : his Majesty to be the sole merchant of them, if the prices rise his Majesty will suffer in the people's clamour."

It was doubtless in connection with this new project that a "Society of Cole Merchants" was incorporated at Newcastle at this time (Jones' *Index to the Originalia*, 11, Chas. I.) ; but a delay of some three years took place before the arrangements were completed.   In August in the thirteenth year of his reign, according to Gardiner (*England's Grievance*, chap. xxi.), King Charles created a new corporation of free hostmen[1] in Newcastle, and granted a lease to Sir Thomas Tempest and others, for the selling of all coals exported from the Tyne; who were to receive 11s. 4d. per chaldron custom, and 12s. from all strangers, and to have 2d. per chaldron towards their charge, and were empowered to seize all coals sold by the owners of such coals.   The chaldron to consist of twenty-one bolls (47 cwt.).   The lease to continue for twenty-one years from January then last past.

An agreement was likewise entered into for the same length of time (*Proc. Arch. Inst.*, Newcastle, 1852, vol. i., p. 222) in 1638, between the King on the first part, the Governor, Stewards, and Brethren of the Hoastmen of the second part, and the Coal Owners of the third part, for all coals to be sold only to his Majesty, his heirs and successors, at the price, in the first instance, of 11s. per chaldron for coals loaded into English, and 12s. per chaldron for coals loaded into foreign ships, with a clause providing for an

[1] Fifty hostmen were appointed (*Cal. State Papers*, Dom., 1638-39, p. 250).

advance of price, if necessary, at the end of any seven years of the term. To this agreement the following colliery owners subscribed their names :

Thos. Lyddell	Toby Dudley
Sir Thos. Tempest	Lanc. Errington
Sir Thos. Riddell, Knt.	Michl. Baxton [1]
Sir Wm. Selby, Knt.	Peter Maddison
Sir Peter Riddell, Knt.	Fra. Lyddell
Sir Rich. Tempest, Knt.	Thos. Lyddell
Sir Robt. Hodgson, Knt.	Frances Cole
Sir J. Middleton, Knt.	Robert Anderson
Sir Lionel Madison, Knt.	Ralph Anderson
Alex. Dobinson	Ralph Cole
Robt. Bewick	John Morley [2]
John Clavering	Thos. Crome
Henry Lyddell	Rich. Hodgson
Sir Robt. Shaftoe	F. Fowler
P. Cole	Henry Heyden [3]
Leo Carr	Edw. Pearson
Ra. Maddison	

In June, in the fourteenth year of his reign, according to Gardiner (ch. xxii.), King Charles incorporated a company of coal buyers, consisting of Thomas Horth and other masters of ships, to buy all coals exported from Sunderland, Newcastle, Blyth, and Berwick, paying to the king 1s. per chaldron custom, and to sell them again in London at a price not exceeding 17s. per chaldron in summer, and 19s. in winter, these prices having been fixed in the metropolis by an order of council (*Cal. State Papers*, Dom., 1638-39, p. 327).

The above arrangements were seemingly intended to secure to the Crown a pre-emption of coal, similar to that already enjoyed by it in the case of the tin production of Cornwall. This has been characterized as one of those attempts at monopoly which contributed so largely to overturn the throne. The covenants had scarcely been completed before the civil wars began, and broke up the whole organization.

The great crop of chimneys which had sprung up throughout the kingdom did not escape the notice of the collectors of taxes, and they, in common with the coal consumed in them, were brought under taxation. The hearth-money, or chimney tax—the representative of the smoke-pennies of earlier times—was one of the most unpopular of taxes. It pressed heavily on the poor and lightly on the rich. Macaulay tells us that "The collectors were empowered

---

[1] Nicholas Blaxton. [2] John Marley. [3] Henry Eden.

to examine the interior of every house in the realm, to disturb
families at meals, to force the doors of bed-rooms, and, if the sum
demanded were not punctually paid, to sell the trencher on which
the barley-loaf was divided among the poor children, and the pillow
from under the head of the lying-in woman. Nor could the Treasury
effectually restrain the chimney-man from using his powers with
harshness; for the tax was farmed, and the Government was consequently forced to connive at outrages and exactions such as have, in
every age, made the name of publican a proverb for all that is most
hateful":

> "The good old dames whenever they the chimney-man espied,
> Unto their works they haste away, the pots and pipkins hide,
> There is not one old dame in ten, search all the nation through,
> But if you talk of chimney-men will spare a curse or two."

The wars occasioned great interruption to the Tyne coal trade.
When Newcastle was taken by the Covenanters in 1640 (Brand, ii.
284), the coal trade, which before that event is said to have employed
10,000 people, sustained an immense loss: everyone fled, thinking
the Scots would give no quarter, and more than a hundred vessels
that arrived off Tinmouth Bar the day after the fight returned
empty.

In January, 1642, an ordinance of Parliament prohibited ships
from bringing coals from Newcastle (Gardiner, p. 193, ed. 1796;
ordinance reprinted at Newcastle, 1843). An extreme scarcity of
fuel resulted, the price of coal rising to £4 per chaldron. In
October, 1643, Parliament ordered the poor and others to be supplied with wood in default of coal; and in the following year
another ordinance was made to provide London with peat and turf
(*Proc. Arch. Inst.*, Newcastle, 1852, i. 179; Brand, ii. 287).

"It's an ill wind that blows nobody good," however, and during
the temporary paralysis of the northern coal trade, new life was
inspired for the nonce into the decaying wood and charcoal industries
in the outskirts of the metropolis. In 1643 a small tract was published, entitled "Sea-coale, Char-coale, and Small-coale; or a Discourse between a New-Castle Collier, a Small-Coale-Man, and a
Collier of Croydon, concerning the prohibition of trade with Newcastle. And the fearful complaint of the poore of the Citie of
London, for the enhancing of the price of Sea-coales."

To the Croydon collier this prohibition of the sea-coal trade was
the best news he had heard, he tells us, for twenty years; and he had
made his way to London to verify it, thinking it too good to be true.

But his momentary elation soon passed away. Sea-coal speedily regained its sway; and from this time little more is heard of the once well-known colliers of Croydon. A small village in Essex still bears the name of Collier-row.

The coal trade of the Tyne seems to have narrowly escaped at this time from a more serious calamity than a mere temporary stoppage. In 1643, during the hostilities, the Marquis of New-castle ordered the coal mines to be fired to prevent them from falling into the hands of the enemy (Wallis's *Northumberland*, i. 133), which is said to have been only averted by the vigilance of Lesley, the Scotch general, who captured the parties destined for the purpose.

The coal trade with Sunderland and Blyth was set free in May 1643, and that with the Tyne in November 1644, on the recapture of Newcastle (Gardiner, p. 194, ed. 1796).

To the inhabitants of the district lying between Newcastle and the sea-coast, the monopolies enjoyed by that town were in a special manner galling. Fleets of ships passed their doors, but they could not even bake bread or brew beer for sale; the carrying on of trade of all kinds being claimed by the burgesses of Newcastle as belonging to themselves exclusively.

In this district, and in the village of Chirton, near North Shields, was situated the home of Ralph Gardiner, Gent., a sturdy brewer of that place. Hampered and opposed in his business, Gardiner seems to have endeavoured to defy the Newcastle monopolists, with the result that he was imprisoned in the Castle of Newcastle. Smarting under his sufferings, and what he regarded as the curtail-ment of his natural rights, he addressed himself to the herculean task of overthrowing the ascendency of Newcastle, and breaking up the combination for regulating the sale of coal. The town of New-castle proved too strong for him; but his book, entitled *England's Grievance Discovered in Relation to the Coal Trade*, first published in 1655, and to which frequent reference has already been made, sets forth in a strong light how oppressive and unfair to neigh-bouring communities became the exclusive privileges granted to the burghs in the Middle Ages.

Time after time, in the course of the seventeenth century, attempts were made by the Legislature to fix the prices of coal in the metropolis, but invariably with transitory results. Such an attempt brought about a singular episode in the history of the Tyne coal trade in the summer of 1665.

It began with a proposal, made apparently in 1664 (*Cal. State*

Papers, Dom., 1664-65, p. 154), to pass an Act of Parliament to fix the prices of coal the same as in 1638, these having been interrupted by the late wars. In 1657 many poor people are stated to have been starved to death by the unreasonable price of fuel.

Though this was not exactly carried out, an act was evidently passed relating to the matter, as in a record dated March 6, 1664-65 (*ib.*, p. 242), we hear of proclamation being made enforcing the late Act for regulating the measures and prices of coals. The chaldron to be 36 bushels; the cwt. 112 lb. The prices to be set by the Lord Mayor and justices of the peace for London.

This was followed by an order, issued at a meeting of the Lord Mayor and justices held at Guildhall, 20th March, 1664-65 (*ib.*, p. 262), that from March 22nd the price of coals shall not be more than 30s. a chaldron.

The authorities in London, however, had reckoned without their hosts, or in this case it might perhaps more appropriately be said without the "free hosts" at Newcastle. How the news of this arrangement was received in the north is shown by the following letter, dated Newcastle, 25th April, 1665, and received in London three days later :

"The people say they shall be great losers by the Lord Mayor's proceedings about coals; the coalworks have ceased, and many thousands will go begging."

This turned out to be only too true. The Tyne coal owners had resolved upon a total suspension of operations at their collieries, so far as the working of coal for shipment was concerned, during the whole of the ensuing summer.

The engagement was formally entered into among the coal owners at a meeting held at Newcastle, 27th April, 1665 (*Proc. Arch. Inst.*, Newcastle, 1852, i. 216), when the following document was agreed to and signed:

"At a meeting of several of the principal traders in coals at the said town, upon a serious debate and consideration, that there is a great quantity of coals now wrought and lying at pits and staiths, which, if it should please God trade should be open and free in a short time, cannot be vended in the ensuing summer, and that if more coals be wrought it will not only bring such necessity upon the owners of the mines as that they will not have money to keep on their water charge and other necessary charges for preserving the collieries from being utterly ruined and rendered useless to themselves and the people in general, but the coals that are, and may be wrought, will become unfit for fuel. They have, for the

causes aforesaid, unanimously agreed and concluded that from the
first day of May next no coals shall be wrought at all on any of
the collieries at the River Tyne for ship coals, until the coals now
at the pits and staiths that are merchantable be so near vended that
the trade may be supplied with-fresh and merchantable coals.

"I am content that my colliery, wherein I am concerned, shall
lye until the 29th day of September next.—Fran. Liddell.

"For want of money, I cannot carry on work, and therefore I
am content to let mine stand till the 29th of September.—Jas.
Clavering."

And so in succession the coal owners subscribe their names, each
with his little prefatory remark, one because he has too many coals,
another for reasons best known to himself, etc., etc., but unanimously omitting to allude either to London or the price of coals, the
following additional signatures being appended:—Fras. Anderson,
Willm Riddell, Wm Blackett, Robt. Ellison, J. Watson, Jer. Col-
herst, Robt. Carr, Cuth^t Dikes, Ra. Gray, junr., for his father,
Henry Maddison, Ra. Carr, Ra. Johnson, Henry Marley, Peter
Maddison, John Fletcher, Thos. Harrison, Thos. Belley, Geo. Bead-
nell, Ja. Baird for Sir Thos. Liddell, John Rogers, John Varey.

During the next year or two the coal market was in a very
sensitive state, and the price of coal underwent severe fluctuations;
the state of matters being aggravated by, if not chiefly due to
the presence of hostile Dutch men-of-war off the English coasts.
Pepys makes many comments in his diary on the scarcity and
dearness of coals in London in 1666 and 1667. On June 15,
1667, the price reached £6 per chaldron (*Cal. State Papers*, Dom.,
1667, p. 190), and complaints of the dearness of coal are described
(*ib.*, p. 294) as "great and unspeakable."

In the middle of this century an idea got abroad which, had
it proved correct, would have been sufficiently alarming to the
northern coal owners. This was that supplies of coal could be got
by sinking pits in Windsor Forest (*Cal. State Papers*, Dom., 1664-65,
p. 472, 1665-66, p. 227), or Blackheath, just as well as at Newcastle,
and that the sole object for bringing it from the north in preference
was in order to maintain the coal fleet for rearing seamen for the
navy; the coal fleet having now attained to such large proportions
(900 sail) that it was regarded as a boon to the kingdom, on account
of being "a great nursery for seamen." A lease of coal in Windsor
Forest was actually granted, but nothing more is heard about it;
the lessees doubtless learning a lesson in geology in the dear school
of experience.

Duties were put on coal imported into London to assist in rebuilding St. Paul's and fifty parish churches after the great fire in 1666.[1] The coal taxes underwent many changes from time to time, too numerous to specify.

It was near the close of the seventeenth century that the growth of the Newcastle chaldron measure was at length finally put to an end. We have seen that in 1530 the chaldron used at Elswick consisted of sixteen bolls, and ten of these chaldrons constituted a keel load. In 1638, just a century later, the chaldron had become twenty-one bolls; this being the size specified in the arrangements made at this date between King Charles I. and the hostmen and coal owners.

The chaldron again was fixed at twenty-one bolls, heaped measure, by statute (30 Chas. II., c. 8). By the same Act the size of the wain was fixed at seven bolls, and of the cart, three bolls and one bushel, heaped measure; and three wains, or six carts, were to be a chaldron (*Proc. Arch. Inst.*, Newcastle, 1852, i. 169).

As long as the chaldron remained merely a measure, however, it continued to increase in size. It was only when the radical change was made from measure to weight that its size was finally determined. This was effected by statute in 1695 (6 and 7 Will. III., c. 10). The Newcastle chaldron was then declared to be of its modern weight of 53 cwt.; the weight carried by wains, $17\frac{1}{2}$ cwt.; and by carts, $8\frac{3}{4}$ cwt.; and three wains, or six carts, were to be a chaldron. The Newcastle chaldron was now almost exactly double the size of the London chaldron; curiously in the above Act it is made to consist both of $52\frac{1}{2}$ cwt. and 53 cwt., but the latter was always accepted as the correct weight.

By the same Act the freight of the keel was fixed at not more than ten such chaldrons; and immediately afterwards a Commission was issued to the Duke of Somerset (Jones's *Index*, 7 of Will. and Mary) to measure and mark the keels used for carrying coals in the port of Newcastle.

Notwithstanding that 10 chaldrons are mentioned in the above Act as the limit of the keel load, it seems improbable that the keel was ever permitted to carry this, inasmuch as 8 chaldrons of 53 cwt., or about twenty-one tons, continued to be its legal freight down to the present century (*1829 Report*, p. 33).

As a measure employed in the sale of coal the ten gradually

[1] An account of moneys collected is given in the *Antiquarian Repository*, vol. i., p. 140.

dropped out of use. The term ceased to be appropriate after the freight of the keel came to consist of 8 chaldrons instead of 10 chaldrons. But as the unit commonly employed in leases in this coalfield it has survived to the present day.

It is obvious that, as used in Elswick Colliery leases about 1530, when the keel and the ten were synonymous, the ten measure must then have consisted of not more than 160 bolls. But in the course of time the ten of colliery leases ceased to bear any relationship either to the keel load or to the chaldron, and being free from any check either of measure or weight, it advanced rapidly in size; the larger the ten obtained from the landowner, the smaller being the rent charge paid by colliery lessee.

By the middle of the seventeenth century the size of the ten had become doubled; it being specified in a lawsuit already referred to relating to Crawcrook Colliery, in 1665, to consist of "twenty waggons of fifteen bolls each usual cole measure," or 300 bolls. The same result is arrived at somewhat differently in a lease from Tempest to Emerson in 1684 (*Proc. Arch. Inst.*, Newcastle, 1852, vol. i., p. 169). In this case the ten is specified to be "forty fothers, each fother a wain load containing seven bolls and one bushel of coals at the pits Newcastle usual coal measure," or in other words 300 bolls. Subsequently, however, its size increased greatly. In an undertaking by Albert Silvertop in 1703 (*ib.*, p. 170) the ten is declared to consist of "twenty-five waggons of fifteen bolls to the waggon," or 375 bolls; and still later, as will appear hereafter, it attained to quantities of 440 and 450, and in some instances even to 550 bolls (*1830 Report*, p. 271).

In the foregoing instances the calculation of the quantity of coal produced was based upon the vehicles employed in conveying it away from the pits. This was sufficiently suitable when all the output was transported in wagons, or wains, of uniform size.

But, in the case of collieries carrying on a landsale or miscellaneous trade, a different arrangement had to be devised, and on this account, with the general adoption of sliding rents now taking place, a new measure called the *score* begins to be heard of. This was based on the vessels employed in drawing the coals out of the pits, which were required to be made and kept of a definite size, usually containing a specified number of pecks, and twenty-one of these were held as constituting a score. But more is heard of this new rent basis in other parts of the coalfield.

In referring to the Newcastle coal trade, Grey remarks that "this great trade hath made this part to flourish in all trades." A notable example of this is afforded by the migration of the glass trade to the Tyne in the early part of the seventeenth century.

The same causes which led to the adoption of coal as a substitute for wood fuel in house fires, led in like manner to its gradual adoption in the arts and manufactures. But in some branches of trade much difficulty was experienced in making the change—involving as it did the invention of new arrangements and different processes, or even the removal of the industry altogether to new localities. No doubt coal was as unsuitable a fuel in many cases as it had been for house fires in the earlier period of its history.

From the beginning of the seventeenth century numerous schemes (usually protected by royal letters patent) were brought forward for the substitution of coal for wood and charcoal in manufacturing processes.

One of the earliest of these related to glass-making, which had hitherto been carried on in the south of England, principally in Sussex, where wood fuel abounded. It is first heard of in 1610-11, when there is a mention of a patent for newly-invented furnaces for making glass with sea coal. (See *Cal. State Papers*, Dom., 1603-10, p. 625; 1611-18, p. 13.)

The patent was purchased from the original patentees by Sir Robert Mansell, Vice-Admiral of England, in 1614-15; and immediately afterwards (*Cal. State Papers*, Dom., 1611-18, p. 287) a royal proclamation was issued prohibiting the manufacture of glass with wood, and also the importation of glass from abroad. King James was himself interested in Mansell's monopoly, having been promised £1,000 per annum from it (*ib.*, vol. civ. 21). The king at the same time was amused at his admiral taking to glass-making. He wondered, he said (Brand, vol. ii., p. 43 note), "that Robin Mansell, being a seaman, whereby he had got much honour, should fall from water to tamper with fire, which are two contrary elements."

The making of glass with coal is said by Dud Dudley (*Metallum Martis*, reprint 1854, p. 35) to have been first effected near his dwelling, in the neighbourhood of Stourbridge. Sturtevant, however, in his *Metallica*, published in 1612, tells us (reprint 1854, p. 8) that "very lately by a wind-furnace, greene glass for windows is made as well by pit-coale at Winchester House, in Southwark, as it is done in other places with much wast and consuming of infinite stores of billets and other wood-fuell." Be this as it may, Mansell experienced considerable difficulty in bringing the process to a successful issue. He erected works successively at London, the

Isle of Purbeck, Milford Haven, and on the Trent (*Cal. State Papers*, Dom., 1623-25, vol. clxii. 63) without accomplishing anything beyond melting vast sums of money in this glass business. But at last his indomitable perseverance was rewarded. About 1619, he tried works near Newcastle-on-Tyne, which proved a success, and here the manufacture of glass with coal took root and flourished, already employing 4,000 work-people in 1624. The works established by Mansell were carried on uninterruptedly for over two hundred years. They were long presided over by three families of Hugue-not glassmakers, natives of Lorraine, named Henzell, Tytory, and Tyzack (the latter a form of the name Isaac), some of whose descendants remain in the district at the present day. It appears that the Henzells, or Henzes, established themselves in England as glassmakers in the reign of Queen Elizabeth. (See *Extracts from the Letter Book of William Scott*, Newcastle, 1848, p. 41 note ; see also *The Pottery Gazette*, December 1, 1880, p. 808.)

Grey in his *Chorographia* (1649) informs us that the Glass Houses at Newcastle served most part of the kingdom with plain glass for windows. It cannot be doubted that it was the abundance of glass, resulting from the adoption of coal fuel in its manufacture, that caused glass windows—which had been bequeathed by will as late as 1590—to become as common a feature of domestic architecture as doors and chimneys.

In the reign of William III. the chimney tax was repealed and a tax on windows substituted for it. This obviated the objectionable internal examination of houses on the part of the collectors. The Window Tax was continued down till 1851, when it was at length repealed.

It was about the end of the seventeenth century that the salt industry of the Tyne, which was so intimately connected with its coal trade, attained to its greatest development. Inferior, or " course coles," were used in the manufacture, and for these it furnished a ready market.

The number of salt pans at North and South Shields to-gether in 1636 (*Cal. State Papers*, Dom., 1636-37, p. 304) was about 200. In 1667 (Surtees, ii., p. 95) the number at South Shields is set down at 123. When Lord Guildford was entertained by the magistrates of Newcastle to a trip down the Tyne in 1676, Roger North refers to the saltmaking operations as the most interesting sight they saw. In 1696 the number of pans at South Shields had reached 143. In this thriving condition the Tyne salt trade con-tinued for about half-a-century, the pans at South Shields in 1740

numbering 130 (*Proc. Archæol. Inst.*, Newcastle, 1852, i. 208) ; but
the zenith of the industry had now been passed.

In the course of a hundred years from 1609 the quantity of coal
exported from the Tyne was exactly doubled, advancing from
239,261 tons (*ib.*, p. 178) to 475,000, which it averaged for some
years previous to 1710 (*ib.*, p. 191).

CHAPTER XV.

THE SEVENTEENTH CENTURY.—Continued.

Improvements in mining machinery and appliances at the Tyneside collieries. Boring; railways; chain pumps. Damps, or noxious gases. Long water levels. Seaton Delaval. Fire in Benwell.

THE condition of the colliery owners on the Tyne would appear to have been anything but an enviable one in the first half of the seventeenth century. Between long adits, and wet pits, and hostmen's monopolies, not to speak of the primitive methods of conveying coal both underground and on the surface then in vogue, the lessees of collieries seem to have been in quite a sorry plight. None but the free oastmen, we are told (*Cal. State Papers*, Dom., 1637-38, p. 387), could make gain out of coals.

Grey, writing on the spot, gives a lugubrious account of the state of the coal industry. In his *Chorographia, or a Survey of Newcastle-upon-Tine*, published in 1649 (pp. 24, 25), he tells us that "many thousand people are imployed in this trade of coales : many live by working of them in the pits : many live by conveying them in waggons and waines to the river Tine : many men are employed in conveying the coales in keeles from the stathes aboard the ships ; one coal merchant imployeth five hundred or a thousand in his works of coals : yet for all his labour, care, and cost, can scarce live by his trade : nay many of them hath consumed and spent great estates and dyed beggars. I can remember one of many that raysed his estate by coale trade : many I remember that hath wasted great estates.

"Some south gentlemen hath upon great hope of benefit come into this country to hazard their monies in coale pits. Master Beamont, a gentleman of great ingenuity and rare parts, adventured into our mines with his thirty thousand pounds ; who brought with him many rare engines not known then in these parts ; as the art to

boore with iron rodds to try the deepnesse and thicknesse of the
coale; rare engines to draw water out of the pits; waggons with
one horse to carry down coales from the pits to the stathes, to the
river, etc.   Within few years he consumed all his money, and rode
home upon his light horse."

Regarding the progress of the art of coal mining on the Tyne,
during the first half of the seventeenth century, we have no information beyond that furnished by Grey in the above account of the
improved appliances introduced into the district by Master Beamont, or Beaumont.   We should have liked to have heard more about
this ingenious gentleman, who came from the south with his considerable fortune, and his skill in mining appliances so far ahead of
his contemporaries on the Tyneside, and whose brief career in the
north ended so differently from that of Sutton.   There were wealthy
families of Beaumonts both in the Yorkshire and Leicestershire coalfields, and it seems probable that he may have been a scion of one
or other of these houses.

The arrival of this gentleman in the Newcastle district has usually
been supposed to have taken place shortly before Grey wrote
(1649); but foremost among the novelties which this author gives
him the credit of introducing here is "the art to boore with iron
rodds"; and as there is a payment in the "Household Books of
Naworth Castle" (Surtees Society, vol. lxviii., p. 94), under date
July 2, 1618, "for a sett of boaring rods bought at Newcastle, vli.
xvis. ixd."; and another dated February 20, 1618 (ib., p. 101) "Too
men's charges carrying the bowring rodds xijd.," it is evident that
he must have arrived on the Tyne in the early part of the century.

As to the source from which he obtained some at least of his
superior mining knowledge, it is perhaps not difficult to conjecture.
Even as early as the middle of the sixteenth century, the metalliferous mines in Germany were well equipped with engines of various
kinds for raising water, and other appliances (described and figured
by Georgius Agricola in his excellent treatise, *De Re Metallica*, first
published about 1550), such as are found in use in the coal mines of
England in the following century.   It can scarcely be doubted that
this gentleman had either seen or read of these useful contrivances,
the want of which was now becoming so keenly felt in the prosecution of coal mining as the mines increased in depth.   Beaumont is
supposed to have discovered and worked a new seam of coal at
Montague Main Colliery (Hair's *Sketches of the Coal Mines*, p. 26
note), which bears the name of the Beaumont, or Engine seam,
in the Elswick and Newburn neighbourhood to this day.

The useful art of boring begins to be first heard of about the commencement of the seventeenth century. What appears to be an early reference to a boring apparatus occurs in Rovenzon's *Treatise of Metallica*, published in 1613 (republished 1854, p. 14), where we read of "a new devised engine, which will either with augors bore holes under the clampes of sea cole, or pit cole, or any other mineral; or with a rapping-wheele make such rigals that they may fall the easier, and with less charge and toyle of men, and will serve for many other uses."

Whether the art of boring was known in Germany before it came into use in England we are not informed. Among the hard rocks and almost vertical veins of metalliferous mines, it could have been of little or no service for exploring purposes. But in perforating the horizontal strata of the coal measures, in order to ascertain the depth and thickness of seams of coal, it was destined to render invaluable aid. The boring apparatus became the true "divining rod" of the coal miners, vastly more reliable than the supposed magical hazel wand employed by the metalliferous miners of the Middle Ages in their quest for veins of ore. By this means the rocky strata could be examined to depths of many fathoms, by merely cutting a small hole a few inches diameter through them, without the necessity of resorting to the tedious, and costly, and problematical sinking of shafts.

The boring process was rapidly adopted by the coal miners. That it was known in the Newcastle-on-Tyne district, and as far out as Naworth, in 1618, we have already seen; and soon afterwards we hear of borings being made in one coalfield after another. In 1628 Lord William Howard, of Naworth Castle (*Household Books*, p. 249), sent a coal borer to the Forest of Dean to assist his son-in-law, Sir John Winter, in searching for coal there.

A family of borers of the name of Wake long practised the art on the Tyneside. One Thomas Wake executed various boreholes in the neighbourhood of Ryton, and in Stella Grand Lease Colliery, in 1692-96. Another borer named Andrew Wake made various borings at Blaydon and Winlaton in 1779-89; while still another — Wake is found boring at Blaydon in 1840. That this family of borers originally came from Yorkshire, seems evidenced by the circumstance that there is a record (*Phil. Trans.*, No. 250, p. 73) of one Thomas Waike making a series of coal borings near Leeds in 1639. Possibly their name might be supposed to connect them with Wakefield.

Another notable improvement which begins to be heard of at the Tyneside collieries at this period, was the commencement to con-

struct railways for the better conveyance of coal between the pits
and the staiths. With the great and incessant traffic of wains and
carts laden and empty—some of the more important collieries
employing several hundreds of these vehicles in the shipment of their
produce—the wear and tear of roads must have been excessive, and
the task of keeping them in anything like tolerable condition
attended with great difficulty and cost. It was to overcome this
inconvenience that the earliest railways—or as they were originally
called in the coal districts, *wagonways*—were formed, which from their
humble commencement as a mining appliance, have since risen to
such world-wide importance.

At what precise date railways were first used on the Tyneside we
have no definite record. From references already made to the books
of the Hoastmen's Company, it is clear that they had not come into
existence here in 1600. It has been frequently asserted that they
were among the improvements introduced into the district by Beaumont, but the only foundation for this statement is contained in
Grey's allusion to his bringing with him " waggons with one horse to
carry down coals from the pits to the stathes." Of railways this
author makes no mention, nor are they otherwise heard of in the
district until after the period when he wrote (1649). It is thus
somewhat uncertain whether they were at all in use on the Tyneside
previous to the middle of the seventeenth century, but immediately
afterwards we begin to meet with references to them.

The railway can scarcely be considered as altogether indigenous
to this country ; having, in fact, been used at the metalliferous
mines in Germany, though in an elementary form, a hundred years
before.

The germ of the railway is no doubt to be found in the barrow-
way, consisting of a single plank. An important step in advance
was made in the early German railways, which consisted of two
planks, thus forming a road suitable for four-wheeled wagons. The
planks were placed parallel to each other, with a narrow space
between. Agricola in his treatise, *De Re Metallica* (L vi.), figures a
small four-wheeled wagon, provided with an iron pin projecting
downwards to run between the beams, or rails, and guide the vehicle
on the track : the wheels and rails being both plain. The axles of
the wagons were of iron ; the wheels, which ran loosely upon them,
were of solid wood. The wheels, owing to the narrowness of the
road, were placed beneath the wagon. One pair of wheels were of
somewhat larger diameter than the other (as in the coal wagons of
later date). The wagon, according to Agricola, obtained the name

of dog (*canis*) from the noise which it made. It still survives in the German mines under the name of the *Hund*, or hound.

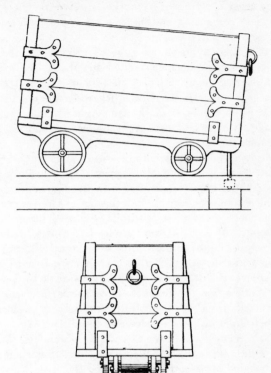

FIG. 3.—HUND AND RAILWAY.

The early railways on the Tyneside, however, were of a more advanced form, the wheels of the wagons being provided with flanges; this being the little secret which guides the modern railway train upon the track, which is not accomplished by the skill of the engine-driver, as some simple-minded people imagine. Unfortunately neither the date of its first application, nor the name of the inventor with whom the happy thought of the wheel and rail adapted to each other originated, has been handed down to us. This great improvement enabled the rails to be placed as far apart as was desired, and laid the foundation of the railway system as now existing.

The early railways were originally, and for a long period, wholly constructed of wood; consisting of wooden rails, fastened to wooden sleepers, by wooden pins; while the wheels of the wagons were of the same material: iron being at this time too scarce and costly to be employed for such purposes.

The first distinct allusion we have to railways at the northern collieries occurs in a document cited by Mr. T. J. Taylor (*Proc. Arch. Inst.*, Newcastle, 1852, vol. i., p. 180), and dated 1660, regarding "a bargain and sale from Sir Richard Tempest and others to William Carr and others, of ten keels or lighters, and a quarter part of the wood or timber laid upon trenches, bridges, and waggon ways, or unlaid upon the same."

Other evidence of the existence of wagon-ways in the Stella and Ryton district at this time also, appears to be afforded by the information obtained in connection with the law-suit already mentioned, which took place in 1665, relating to Crawcrook Colliery. The wagons used here are stated to have carried fifteen bolls each, equal to about 33½ cwt., or two wain-loads, a size of vehicle which it can scarcely be doubted must have been run upon a railway.

Then we hear (Surtees, ii. 209) of coals being conveyed in wagons from Sir Thomas Liddell's colliery at Ravensworth to Team Staith in 1671. While a few years later we have the earliest description of a railway itself, from the pen of Roger North, who accompanied Lord Keeper Guildford on the northern circuit in 1676. "Another thing that is remarkable," says this writer (*Life of the Lord Keeper Guildford*, i. 281, ed. 1826), "is their wayleaves; for when men have a piece of ground between the colliery and the river, they sell leave to lead coals over their grounds, and so dear that the owner of a rood of ground will expect 20*l.* per annum for this leave. The manner of the carriage is by laying rails of timber, from the colliery down to the river, exactly straight and parallel, and bulky carts are made with four rowlets fitting these rails; whereby the carriage is so easy that one horse will draw down four or five chaldron of coals, and is an immense benefit to coal merchants."

This was, however, only the commencement of railways, and their use did not become general till long subsequently, some of the large collieries near the Tyne still adhering to the ancient methods of conveyance. Whickham Colliery, according to Edington (*Coal Trade*, p. 133), employed upwards of 700 wains and carts in leading coals to Derwent Gut; and in 1693 the coals from Blackburn Fell were led in carts to Swalwell. Jesmond Colliery in like manner employed upwards of 700 carts and wains in leading coals to the Ouseburn (*ib.*, p. 116). While at a still later period the collieries of Elswick, Benwell, and Fenham employed upwards of 600 or 700 carts and wains leading their coals to Scotswood Quay (*ib.*, p. 118).

In no department of mining was the need for improved appliances more urgently felt than in the raising of water from the collieries. This was what presented the most formidable obstacle to the prosecution of coal mining : the principal pits at this period being situated in the belt of watery strata which usually extends from the surface downwards to a depth varying from 300 to 600 feet. This was in a special sense the wet period of coal mining. The drainage of the mines was a work of the greatest difficulty ; the invention of a machine to effectually accomplish it was the great engineering problem of the age, as is amply attested by a reference to the patent records, where a long list is found of appliances of all kinds designed for the purpose, the wide field presented for the application of engines for effecting the drainage of mines attracting the attention of a host of inventors at this period.

Though the systematic raising of water by machinery was a comparatively new feature in coal mining in this era, it had been long practised in the older metalliferous mines on the Continent. Many engines for the purpose, consisting of various forms of chain pumps, and common lifting pumps, worked either by water-wheels or by horses, were in common use in the mines of Germany as already adverted to. These were doubtless the "rare engines to draw water out of the pits," a knowledge of which, as Grey informs us, was communicated to the northern miners by Beaumont.

About 1670 chain pumps were most in favour in the north of England, particularly where water power could be had to drive them ; and the most important pumping establishments at this period were planted in such situations. These chain pumps were of two kinds—viz., the chain of buckets, and the chain with plates and pipes.

The chain of buckets—or, as it was sometimes called, the Egyptian wheel—had been known and used in the East for ages, for raising water from deep wells for domestic use and irrigation purposes. As used in mines it consisted of an endless chain with oblong wooden buckets attached at regular intervals, suspended from an axletree extending across the mouth of the pit. As the axletree revolved, the buckets arrived at the top full of water, discharging their contents into a trough as they passed over the axletree, and so down the other side to fill themselves again in the well at the bottom of the pit; precisely in the same way as the modern river dredging machine

performs its operations, it being, indeed, a present-day representative
of the chain of buckets, as also is the apparatus known as a "Jacob's
ladder," used for raising small coals at collieries.

FIG. 4.--WATER-WHEEL AND CHAIN OF BUCKETS.[1]

The chain of plates, on the other hand, consisted of a similarly-
worked endless chain, which carried circular discs inserted at regular
intervals.   In ascending, the chain passed up through a column of
tubes or pipes, which the discs exactly fitted like so many pistons,
thus carrying the water above them to the surface.   Small machines
of this antique type may still be seen in use, as, for example, in raising
liquid manure in farmyards.

To raise water by means of chain pumps from a depth of 240 ft.
was at this period considered to be a great performance.   To accomplish this all at once was quite beyond the power of the appliances
in use.   The total depth was therefore divided into several stages,
or stories, and several separate pits and engines were required.

In the earliest account of coal mining in Scotland, which was communicated at his request to Professor Sinclair by a person conversant

---

[1] This figure, as also 5 and 21, are from blocks prepared for an article by
the writer on " The Progressive Improvement of Mining in Scotland," prefixed
to the Catalogue of the Mining Exhibition, held at Glasgow in 1885, which
have been kindly lent by the Council of the Mining Institute of Scotland,
per Mr. James Barrowman.

with the subject, and published in his treatise on *Hydrostaticks* in 1672, some interesting information is afforded regarding the methods of raising water practised in the north of England at this period.

After referring to the processes of draining collieries in Scotland— viz., by men drawing with buckets, or by horse engines, or water-wheels, driving either chains with plates or chains of buckets, all of which he tells us were in common use, but in Scotland were capable of drawing water from small depths only, making use merely of one pit for the purpose—this writer proceeds to state that there were to be seen in the north of England, in the Bishopric of Durham, waterworks by which water was drawn above 40 fathoms (240 ft.) perpendicular, though not all in one "sink," or shaft; and these water-engines being placed in low situations, pits situated on the high ground above were drained to depths of 60 or 70 fathoms (360 or 420 feet).

He then describes how one pit was sunk to the full depth from which the water was to be drawn; another a little way off, about two-thirds of the depth; and still another sunk only to one-third of the depth; all three pits being provided with engines. In the first, or deep pit, the water was raised up to the level of the bottom of the second pit, into which it was discharged by a communicating drift, or passage; in the second pit it was raised to the level of the bottom of the third pit, and so by the third pit to the point of discharge at the surface; the power to work the lower lifts being carried down the pits by means of vertical shafting and wheelwork actuated by water-wheels at the surface.

"The most curious of these engines that are to be seen," says this writer, "are at Ravensworth, near Newcastle, which belongs to Sir Thomas Liddell, a most ingenious gentleman, who, for procuring a fall of water which may serve the wheels of all the three sinks, hath erected the first upon pillars like a wind-mill, pretty high above ground, from which the water falling makes the second go close above ground. And to make the water fall to the third, the whole wheel is made go within the surface of the ground [from which the water passes into a mine] which terminates at a river under the works, which mine is of considerable length."

The collieries of Heaton and Jesmond, on the north side of the Tyne, are also stated (Dunn's *Win and Work*, 2nd ed., p. 11) to have been drained by chain pumps, worked by water-wheels.

Professor Sinclair's informant mentions that when water could not be had to drive these engines, horses were used, but not with such good success, on account of the greater cost. He thought that windmills might be employed with advantage, having seen these machines at work in Holland, which might be replaced by horses when there was an insufficiency of wind; a suggestion which appears to have been acted upon, as we subsequently hear of attempts being made to utilize the force of the wind in the drainage of collieries.

Reference has been made to Roger North's visit to the north of England in 1676. Besides being the first to leave us a description of the early railways, this writer furnishes us with a considerable amount of information of various kinds relative to mining in the Newcastle district at this period.

Regarding the art of coal mining in general, he gives the following neat and pithy little epitome :

" Coal lies under the stone, and they are twelve months in sinking a pit. Damps or foul air kill insensibly ; sinking another pit, that the air may not stagnate, is an infallible remedy. They are most in very hot weather. An infallible trial is by a dog ; and the candles show it. They seem to be heavy sulphurous air not fit for breath : and I have heard some say that they would sometime lie in the midst of a shaft, and the bottom be clear. The flame of a candle will not kindle them so soon as the snuff ; but they have been kindled by the striking fire with a tool. The blast is mighty violent, but men have been saved by lying flat on their bellies.

"When they are by the side of a hill, they drain by a level carried a mile underground, and cut through rock to the value of 5 or 6,000l; and where there is no rock it is supported with timber."

The term "damp," as applied to a noxious mine gas (from the German *dampf*, vapour, fog), was doubtless introduced by the German miners who came over to work in the metalliferous mines of this country. It occurs in the names chokedamp or blackdamp (carbonic acid gas) ; firedamp or whitedamp (carburetted hydrogen gas) ; also afterdamp, applied to the gases resulting from an explosion.

The sinking of air shafts was the only means practised in the north of England at this period for producing a circulation of air through the mines. The nature of noxious gases was evidently as yet but imperfectly understood, though the connection between them and the weather is remarked upon by nearly all the early writers who touch upon the subject. The allusion to the mighty violent blasts shows that explosions of some severity had already occurred in the north, just as they began to do in several of the other coal-fields in the course of the seventeenth century, as will be seen hereafter. It is stated that here the gas was known to have been kindled by striking fire with a tool. Elsewhere at this period we hear of firedamp being ignited by accidental sparks, caused by the motion of the sled used in drawing coals.

The employment of dogs for the purpose of testing whether deleterious gases were present was probably suggested by the practice pursued at the famous Grotto del Cane, near Naples, which obtained its name from these animals being used to demonstrate to visitors the effects of the noxious gases in the cavern (see Bradley's *New Improvements of Planting and Gardening*, 1718, part iii., p. 82). Professor Sinclair in his *Hydrostaticks* (p. 197) gives an account of experiments made with a dog, etc., in a coal pit at Tranent, in Scotland, in May, 1669.

The great length and cost of the water levels, or adits, is again referred to by Roger North in his account of the *al fresco* supper to which the magistrates of Newcastle entertained Lord Guildford, on a small island, known as the King's Meadows, which then existed in the Tyne opposite to Elswick, where are now situated the vast engineering and shipbuilding works of Sir W. G. Armstrong, Mitchell & Co. Among the strange histories of their coal works told on this occasion by the aldermen, "one was by Sir William Blackett, who cut into a hill in order to drain the water, and conquered all difficulties of stone and the like till he came to clay, and that was too hard for him, for no means of timber or walls would assist, but all was crowded together; and this was by the weight of the hill pressing upon a clay that yielded. In this work he lost 20,000*l.*" The inability of the miners in Spain to penetrate horizontally through clay though they could perforate hard rock is remarked upon by Pliny. It is probably to this era that the first of the long water levels driven on the north side of the Tyne may be assigned. It commenced (Edington's *Coal Trade*, p. 118) at a place called Delaval Drift, on the Benwell Estate, and was continued through the 90-fathom dyke to Whorlton, Newbiggin, and West Kenton.

The long water levels of this period were executed solely by means of pick work, and were made as narrow as possible. Mr. Greenwell (*Mine Engineering*, 2nd ed., p. 195) speaks of instances of levels in various places "driven sometimes in stone and sometimes in coal, the width of which does not exceed 18 in."; and remarks that "it is truly a wonder how the work has been performed, the sides of the drift being as smooth and straight as though they had been chiselled." Sometimes a rut, or groove, was cut along one side for the ventilation of the drift (*Trans. North of Eng. Inst.*, vol. xv., p. 201 note), which was probably accomplished by means of bellows and tubes. This method of ventilating had long been practised by metalliferous miners on the Continent, though Bushel claims the invention of the system of mining by way of adits, ventilated by bellows, and tubes, and thus dispensing with air shafts, as the masterpiece of Lord Bacon.

In his account of the visit paid by Lord Guildford to Seaton Delaval, where his lordship went by invitation to dine with Sir Ralph Delaval, Roger North gives a description of a little independent port there, constructed on the open coast by Sir Ralph, for the shipment of his coal and salt. The situation being a very exposed one, Sir Ralph had built, or rather often rebuilt, a stone pier to fend off the heavy north-east surge. The vessels entered at high water, and at low water lay dry on a hard flat rock. As the harbour was liable to silt up, Sir Ralph had constructed a sluice which he closed at high tide, thus retaining a large volume of water behind ; and on the sluice being opened at low water the rush of the imprisoned torrent scoured the rock "as clean as a marble table." This novel method of dredging the harbour obtained for it the name of Seaton Sluice.

At the beginning of the dinner a servant brought a letter inform-ing Sir Ralph that a bag of water had burst into his greatest colliery. "Folding up the letter, he remarked, 'My lord, here I have advice sent me of a loss in a colliery which I cannot estimate at less than £7,000, and now ye shall see if I alter my countenance or behaviour from which ye have seen me already.' And so fell to discoursing of these bags of water, and the methods to clear them, as if the case had been another's and not his own. He said his only apprehension was that the water might come from the sea, and 'then,' said he, 'the whole colliery is utterly lost : else with charge it will be recovered.' Whereupon he sent for a bottle of the water, and finding it not saline, as from the sea, was well satisfied. Afterwards we enquired if the water was conquered, and we were told it proved not so bad as he expected. For it seems that although £1,700 was spent upon engines, and they could not sink it an inch, yet £600 more emptied it, so that it had no more than the ordinary springs; and in about six weeks he raised coal again. He said that chain pumps were the best engines, for they draw constant and even ; but they can have but two stories of them, the second being with an axletree of 7 or 8 fathoms ;

and the deepest story is wrought by buckets, and a wheel and ropes, with the force at the top." This last observation is somewhat difficult to explain, as we hear of the existence of engines of three stories elsewhere at this period.

An underground fire, which occurred in the lands of Benwell in the seventeenth century, attracted a considerable amount of attention ; being a phenomenon of comparatively rare occurrence in the great northern coalfield. Regarding the date when it originated we have no exact information, but it would seem to have been about 1643. It is incidentally referred to by Gardiner in 1655 (*England's Grievance*, p. 205, ed. 1796), who, in his bitterness against the town of Newcastle, observes that "some owners of coal pits will rather let their pits be fired, like those at Benwell, and consumed, than let their coals to the magistrates of Newcastle." [1]

An account of it was communicated to Mr. Boyle by Mr. Durant, of Newcastle, in a letter dated Feb. 9, 1673-74 (*Phil. Trans.*, No. 480, p. 221). From this we learn that it had then been burning about thirty years, and that it had been commenced by a pitman's candle being carelessly placed against the coal. It was at first so small that a person who offered to extinguish it for half-a-crown was refused the trivial sum. Subsequently it gained great strength and marched northward, "sometimes preying on the coals nearer the surface of the earth, and then subverting houses and grounds lying over it, sometimes on the deeper mines, and was conspicuous only by its smoke and fire in the night. Now," says this writer, "it rages, and has already caused great devastation, in grounds belonging to a village called Fenham, near a mile northward from the place where it first was kindled."

"Its eruptions at present are in many places, and various depths. I have, both last winter and this, in frosty nights, for then it burns most furiously, occasionally riding by, in near twenty places, seen its flames and pillars of smoke."

It was made the subject of another communication to the Royal Society, in 1676, by Dr. Lucas Hodgson, of Newcastle (*Phil. Trans.*, No. 130, p. 762), who treats chiefly of the chemical products deposited by it at the surface, such as flour of sulphur and sal ammoniac. It was remarked as singular that a substance so black as coal should furnish products which were perfectly white.

The seat of the fire was pointed out to Lord Guildford when passing on his way from Newcastle to Hexham, but Roger North remarks

[1] Regarding the selling of coal to the magistrates at Newcastle, see Anderson's *Commerce*, ii. 95.

that they could discover nothing of it beyond the deadness of all plants there.   Gibson (*Britannia*, p. 872, ed. 1695) alludes to it as actively burning at Fenham in 1695, and states that the flames were visible by night, and that the track of it could be followed in the daytime by the brimstone lying on the surface of the ground.   After having burned for a period of over fifty years the fire appears at length to have died out.

CHAPTER XVI.

THE SEVENTEENTH CENTURY.—Continued.

The collieries of the Wear district.   South Durham.   Northumberland.

THOUGH the River Wear was shipping away coal, as has been seen, as early as the fourteenth century, so little progress had been made in developing the mineral wealth of the estates bordering on the navigable part of the river, that its coal trade may almost be said to have only commenced in the beginning of the seventeenth century.   Unhampered, however, by the restrictions imposed on the Tyne coal owners, in connection with the exclusive privileges of the hostmen, and the regulation of the coal trade in force there, and furnishing coal excellently adapted for domestic requirements, the Wear collieries now advanced their production at an extraordinary rate for the period.

Nothing is heard here, as on the Tyne, of impoverishment and beggary arising from the coal trade; but, on the contrary, large profits are mentioned as being reaped, and the general annals of the district indicate a condition of great prosperity and progress.

The town of Sunderland received a charter of incorporation from Bishop Morton, of Durham, in 1634 (Surtees, i. 256).

Shortly after this the Wear collieries became objects of much importance, during the temporary closing of those on the Tyne occasioned by the civil wars, and Sunderland received a garrison from the Parliament.

About 1654 the port of Sunderland began to rise into great consequence.   In 1661 a petition was sent from the hostmen of Newcastle (Dunn's *Coal Trade*, p. 17) to impose a duty of 1s. per chaldron on coals exported from Sunderland, which town was fast growing into rivalry.   Bishop Cosin, in 1663, issued a commission for measuring the keels and coal boats of Sunderland, and in 1669 a lighthouse was erected there.

The collieries of Harraton, on the north side of the Wear, acquired great notoriety, and were worked with considerable profit, during the time of the Commonwealth.   Their history is some-what intricate.   They had been partly leased, for a very trifling consideration, by Sir John Hedworth to Sir William Wray, of Beamish (Surtees, ii. 178), but were among those sequestered on the success of the Parliamentary forces in 1644, Wray being described as "a papist and recusant convict."   At this date they were valued at £3,000 per annum, though then drowned up.

Another lease appears likewise to have been granted by Sir John Hedworth (who died in 1642) to one Robert Conyers, and to have been transferred by him to Josiah Primat, of London, leather-seller. On the strength of this, Primat proceeded to recover and open out the five-quarter and nine-quarter seams in 1647, which had lain lost and drowned since 1642,[1] and this he accomplished after an expenditure of near £2,000.   Primat then granted a sub-lease to George Grey and George Lilburn, who had acquired some interest in the collieries under the State, and who carried them on for a year or two with great profit, Lilburn being said to have cleared £15 per day.

This arrangement, however, was anything but satisfactory to Wray, who seems to have invoked the aid of Sir Arthur Hazlerigg, Governor of Newcastle, against the Lilburn party.   But, instead of taking Wray's part, Sir Arthur swooped down upon the colliery in 1649, under the State's title, on Wray's delinquency, and turned out Lilburn, and let both land and colliery to Colonel Hacker, Colonel Mayers, Major Tolhurst, and Colonel John Jackson.

Primat made unavailing efforts to obtain the restitution of his two seams of coal, both in the local courts and finally by addressing a petition to Parliament.   But Hazlerigg's influence was extremely strong; Primat's petition was ordered to be burnt by the common hangman, and he was fined and imprisoned.   Lilburn was banished by Act of Parliament in 1651 (Baker's *Chronicle*, p. 613, ed. 1684). The colliery was admitted by Sir Arthur Hazlerigg to be worth £5,000 per annum.

Though coal had been worked at Lumley, on the south side of the Wear, for a period of three centuries, only now did the great mineral resources of this well-situated estate begin to receive a due measure of development.   This important property changed hands in 1606-7 (*40th Report of the Dep. Keep. Pub. Rec.*, p. 509), being

[1] Some of the coal mines on the Wear are stated to have been flooded by the Republican army (*1829 Report*, p. 141).

then acquired from John, Lord Lumley, by George Smith, Thomas Kynnaston, Robert Cooper, and Richard Matthewes, gentlemen. In the course of the seventeenth century the Lumley mines became the most important on the Wear, if not in the north of England.

An interesting notice of these mines in 1676 is furnished by Roger North, who tells us that Lord Guildford "was curious to visit the coal mines in Lumly Park, which are the greatest in the north and produce the best coal, and, being exported at Sunderland, are distinguished as of that place. These collieries had but one drain of water drawn by two engines, one of three stories, the other of two. All the pits, for two or three miles together, were drained into these drains. The engines are placed in the lowest places, that there may be the less way for the water to rise; and, if there be a running stream to work the engines, it is happy."

This large pumping establishment, which we can well conceive to have formed one of the chief features of the collieries, doubtless consisted of chain pumps. They were usually worked by water-wheels, the drains being carried to this point for the sake of the water power. A traveller who visited Lumley in the following year (*Journeyings through Northumberland and Durham,* 1677) informs us that when this water failed "they wrought it out with horses as in a horse mill."

In connection with a law-suit at Sunderland—Conyers *v.* Rogers —in 1664 (*Trans. North of Eng. Inst.,* vol. xv., p. 267), we hear of coal from Lumley Park being then shipped there at 14s. per chaldron.

Another law case—Watson *v.* Ayton—in 1667 (*ib.,* p. 269) furnishes some interesting information regarding another colliery in the Lumley neighbourhood. The complainant, Mrs. Watson, averred that about three years before, Ayton had demised to her late husband "all those mynes and seames of coles, usually called the Maine cole seame or myne," within the townfields of Great Lumley, for a term of three years, at a rent of 15d. yearly for every twenty-one corves of coal wrought, each corve not to exceed ten pecks (3 cwts.). It was covenanted that during the first year Watson should win 2,000 scores of coals, and in the second 3,000; the defendant to find such gins, and engines, as then were upon the land, on condition, by Watson, that he should leave them in as good repair as he found them, and that for working the five-quarter coal the defendant was to have one of the gins, or engines, during the last two years—the two parties working simultaneously, in different seams, in the same colliery. Ayton was also to find sufficient horses and drivers for drawing the coals to bank.

Ayton admitted the agreement, but insisted that Watson had not kept it, and had drawn coals in corves containing more than ten pecks each; also that he did not deliver gins for him to work the five-quarter coal at the end of the first year; and by irregular working had occasioned divers "thrusts of cole" which hindered him from working.

From such incidental references as we have to the style of horse gin, or engine, employed at this period in raising the coals in the pits, that known as the "cog and rung gin" appears to have been the form in common use. In this machine—the horizontal gin—which was the earliest known form of horse-engine used in drawing coals, the drum or barrel, which formed the rope-roll, was placed immediately over the pit as the windlass had been, it being, indeed, simply an enlarged windlass, adapted by means of wheelwork to be actuated by a lever drawn by horses. The horse-track, or "gin race," was round the mouth of the pit. The teeth or "cogs" of a horizontal wheel, fixed on a vertical axis which was turned by the horse lever, worked in the bars, or "rungs," of a small vertical wheel on the drum shaft, causing it to revolve in the required direction. On account of the position of the drum directly over the pit, it was frequently blown off in early colliery explosions.

FIG. 5.—COG AND RUNG GIN.

The "thrusts" of coal (also called crushes), to which reference is made above, occurred when the pillars left were of insufficient size to carry the weight of the superincumbent strata resting upon them. They were, in consequence, crushed down till a bed was formed affording adequate support. occasioning the collapse and loss of all the working-places affected, and at times damaging the surface.

In this era, after a long interval, we again hear of the working of coal being carried on at Coken, in the neighbourhood of Lumley. In 1662 (Surtees, i. 206) Francis Carr, of Coken, Esq., mortgaged

Coken to Ralph Carr, of Newcastle-upon-Tyne, reserving the colliery and seams of coal. In 1671 the mines were conveyed to Joseph Carr, of Coxlodge, on trust for Ralph Carr, to whom he immediately assigned them.

"The colliery is stated (*ib.*, p. 207 note) to consist of 2,500 score of coales computed to be wrought yearly, each score 21 corfes, each corfe 11 pecks; and Francis Carr, Esq., received from his lessee sevenpence upon every score, which was estimated at half the net value of the colliery."

Among other matters connected with the Wear district at this period, there is mention (Brand, ii. 290 note) of two of the best collieries having been drowned in 1648 by an extraordinary flood.

The first railway in the Wear district was constructed in 1693 (*ib.*, p. 125), by Thomas Allan, Esq., of Newcastle-on-Tyne, proprietor of Allan's Flats Colliery, near Chester-le-Street.

At the collieries of the Tyne and Wear together, there were estimated, in 1696 (Charleton's *Newcastle Town*, p. 61), to be 20,000 carriages and cart horses employed in conveying away the produce of the mines.

The extraordinary rate of progress made in developing the Wear coal trade during the seventeenth century is exhibited by the fact that the average annual export of coal for some years up to 1710 amounted to 175,000 tons. While the export from the Tyne was only doubled in the preceding hundred years, that of the Wear had increased fifteen-fold. Total vend of Tyne and Wear about 1710 (*Proc. Arch. Inst.*, Newcastle, 1852, i. 191), 650,000 tons.

Though numerous collieries doubtless existed throughout central and south Durham, comparatively few notices relating to particular mines in the inland districts are to be met with.

A petition was presented to the King in 1634, by Lord Arundel of Wardour (*Cal. State Papers*, Dom., 1634-35, vol. cclxxii. 79), relating to a lease of the coal mines of Raley-fell, *alias* Carter Thorne, which had been granted by the late Bishop of Durham to Lord Eure and others.

Records exist of a law suit in 1667 relating to Edderley Colliery (*Trans. North of Eng. Inst.*, vol. xv., pp. 268, 269), a lease of which had been granted by the Bishop of Durham for three lives, in consideration of a fine of £1,100. The relators had been put to great charges in winning and working the colliery and clearing it from water. The defendants, who were owners of a freehold colliery adjoining, had sunk pits very near the boundary of the bishop's colliery, and had secretly worked great quantities of coal from it

which they had brought out at their own pits, and had also worked
great part of the walls (or barriers) purposely left by the relators
for the purpose of keeping the water from coming into the bishop's
colliery ; they had also driven drifts into Edderley Colliery, whereby
the water ran in and would inevitably drown it. A first commission, appointed to ascertain the damage which had been done,
found the working-places stopped up. The defendants were ordered
to remove the rubbish, and to allow the commissioners "with
instruments, lights, lynes, compasses, and utensils, as well to
remove obstructions without endangering or drowning defendants'
colliery, as to view and measure the workings"; and an attachment
was further ordered to issue against such of the defendants as
should obstruct the execution of the commission.

A proposal was laid before Bishop Cosin, in 1670 (Raine's
Auckland Castle, p. 124), to grant a lease of coal mines in Auckland
Park, Coundon, and Coundon Grange. This the bishop declined to
sanction, alleging that he might be blamed by his successors in the
see for establishing collieries in such close proximity to their
residence, and remarking further that "Robert Morley hath the
lease of Coundon Grange already."

In the lease of Greenfield Colliery, near West Auckland, made by
Bishop Crewe in 1687 (*Trans. N.E. Inst.*, xv. 196), the score is
described as consisting of twenty-one corves of twenty pecks each.

We again hear of coal being worked in the Barony of Evenwood.
There is mention in 1646 (Hutchinson's *Durham*, iii. 338) of a great
colliery within the manor of Evenwood, called Thorne, on lease
from the bishop for lives at the rent of £70, let to one Mr. Drake,
assigned to Mr. Charles Vane and Mr. Thomas Rowe for £350 a
year.

The following particulars extracted from a lease of the coal in
this barony granted by Bishop Crewe in 1688 (*Trans. N.E. Inst.*,
xv. 196) to Thomas Langley, the elder, of York, are not without
interest : The "Bishop demises all his 'cole mynes, cole pitts, and
seams of cole' within ye parks of Eavenwood, and within all and
singular ye coppyhold lands of Eavenwood, towne, and townships,
and within all and singular the townships, hamlets, places, and
villages of Ramshaw, Gordon, Morley, and Toft Hill, according to
their antient moots and courts within ye barony of Eavenwood, in
the county of Durham, and within all ye coppyhold and coppyhold
lands whatsoever within ye sd. barony of Eavenwood, together with
full power and authority to break ye ground and soyle, and digg
and sinke within ye said parks, and within all and singular the sd.

coppyhold land and premises, as well as for the digging of so many
cole pitts as shall please him, ye sd. Thomas Langley, to digg and
sinke for ye winning and getting of coal there, as for drawing and
conveying away of water and styhe,[1] etc.

"Together with all and singular liberties, priviledges for carriage
with free way, liberty of passage, egresse and regresse for all
manner of persons, carts, carriages, horses, oxen, to or from those
cole mynes through all wastes, commons, demesnes, and coppyholds,
belonging to the said Lord Bishop of Durham, for carrying away of
the coles.

"And the said Thomas Langley shall have and take sufficient
and convenient wood for the making, timbering, maintaining and
upholding of the shafts, pitts, water-gates, hovils, and lodges, as
also wattels and wands for the curves (i.e. corves) fit and necessary
to be used and occupied in and about the cole mynes, pitt or pitts,
there to be had and taken in ye woods of ye said reverend father
next adjoining to the sd. cole mynes.

"To have and to hold for the longest of three lives, yielding and
paying 20s. yearly for the time being, and for every pitt 33s. 4d.
yearly, from which coals shall be wrought."

There is a record, dated 1611 (Lansdowne MSS., Nos. 156, 109),
of orders concerning the titles of certain lands and coal mines at
Branspeth (Brancepeth) and Greenlaw.

An undated record relating to liberties claimed within the manors
of Barnard Castle, Raby, and Brancepeth, has been supposed (ib.,
p. 177 note) to belong to about the thirteenth century, but the
document contains no internal evidences of any such antiquity.
Had it been so old as the thirteenth or fourteenth century it would
doubtless have been written either in Latin or Norman French. It
would seem to belong more probably to about the seventeenth
century. The ipsissima verba are as follows :

"Tennants of Raby clayme to have theire coles at 0·6 a corfe
lode, and the one rope till they be served.

"Tennants of Tudhoe to have theire coles at 0·6 the corfe, and
the corfe to conteyn 6 peckes upheaved Durham measure, which
now is but 3, and they pay 0·6. Everie pitt ought to be filled and
rayled or else well covered.

"And to have theire coles at Hargill pitts for 1d. a wayne lode
and 0·6 a corfe, and at Brandon pitts at 0·6 a corfe, and at Thorne-
ley pitts 6d. a wayne lode."

The port of Stockton is mentioned (Proc. Arch. Inst., Newcastle,

[1] Stythe or chokedamp.

1852, i. 179) as exporting ten chaldrons of coal in 1622; but whether this came from the inland collieries, or was brought there by sea is doubtful. London, Lynn, Aldborough, and Barnstaple, were likewise exporting small quantities at this period, which were doubtless merely re-shipments abroad of coal previously imported into these places.

The coal trade of the Blyth district appears to have been insignificant in the seventeenth century. The coal produced here was less adapted for household purposes than that of the Tyne and Wear. While the Wear was rapidly waxing in importance, the coal and salt industries of the Blyth seem to have been on the wane.

In the "Booke of Rates" of Northumberland for the year 1615 (Raine's *North Durham*, Appendix, p. 157), Bedlington coal mines are set down at £2 per annum. Under Bedlingtonshire improved rents, 1655 (*ib.*, p. 158), there is entered "Camboyes and ye salt panns lying wast"—in the margin £110. "The colliery £12." And in an account of the yearly value of Bedlington for 1670-71 there is given, under East Sleekburne :

	£	s.	D.
Edw. Millburne, for salt pans,	30	0	0
Chr. Reah, for colliery,	10	0	0

All the coal pits in Bebside and Cowpon, with four salt pans there, were leased by the Crown (*Cal. State Papers*, Dom., 1635-36, p. 305), in 1635-36, to David Errington, for twenty-one years, at the yearly rent of £16 1s. 3d.

The coal mines at Amble, valued at 41s. per annum, were granted in fee farm by the Crown (Gibson's *Tynemouth*, vol. i., p. 243) to Edward Ditchfield, of London, and others in 1628.

While further north there is mention (Raine's *North Durham*, Appendix, pp. 159-61) of Sir William Forster's Shoreswood Colliery (Felkington ?) ; of Kyloe Colliery ; Scremerston Colliery ; and Unthank Colliery, Tweedmouth.

CHAPTER XVII.

THE SEVENTEENTH CENTURY.—Continued.

Coal mining in the great northern coalfield at the close of the seventeenth century. Bord and pillar system of working coal.

WHILE various works relating to the metalliferous mines of England made their appearance in the course of the seventeenth century— among others a small one entitled " *Rara avis in terris*, or The Compleat Miner," having been issued in 1681—no publication devoted to the subject of coal mining had yet been produced. But a good picture of the condition of the mines of the north of England about the end of this century is furnished by a little treatise which came from the press a few years after its close. It is entitled " *The Compleat Collier* : or the whole art of sinking, getting, and working, the Coal Mines, etc., as is now used in the Northern Parts, especially about Sunderland and Newcastle." By F. C. It was printed at London, for G. Conyers, at the Ring in Little Brittain, 1708. A reprint was issued by M. A. Richardson, Newcastle, in 1846.

This pioneer of coal mining literature in England evidently resided in the Wear district. From one or two references to *pour boires* in his able little brochure, he appears to have been a person of a somewhat convivial disposition. He speaks of having had personal experience both in the working and selling of coal. His connection with the coal trade does not seem to have been altogether fortunate, as some of the advice he gives on the subject of selling coal, is stated to be based upon "woful experience in my late business." Like Grey, the earliest historian of Newcastle, he only subscribes his initials ; but in his case tradition has failed to hand down the name.

The Compleat Collier is in the form of an imaginary dialogue, first between a coal owner and a sinker, and afterwards between the same individual and a colliery viewer. It sheds considerable light upon almost every branch of mining, as carried on in the north at this early period.

After describing "the way of boreing"—an art which (unlike his Scotch predecessor) he held in high estimation—the author proceeds to speak of sinking pits. These, he tells us, were commenced of a square form, and were timbered with oak spars, or fir balks (usually the latter), and backing deals. But on nearing the rock an octagonal form was adopted to incline to the form of the stonework, which was invariably circular.

Quicksands, when not too thick, were penetrated by using choke deals, which were put in as fast as the sand or earth was dug out. He had heard of iron frames being used for the purpose, at Harraton (probably the work of the military coal owners there), made square and deeper than the thickness of the quicksand, but thought they must be dear to be so cast or wrought.

When the upper part of the sinking pit was burdened with water, an auxiliary, or half shaft, was sunk close at hand, and the top feeders diverted into it, to be there drawn independently to the surface.

The work of sinking through the rocky strata was wholly executed by manual labour, the heavy stone pick, or "hack," being the only implement mentioned as used in the operation; though doubtless the wedge, and probably also the stook and feathers, were employed.

The invaluable process of damming out water from shafts by means of watertight frames formed of wooden staves like the sides of a tub, and hence termed in the north of England "tubbing," was already commonly practised. The author had known whole wastes of water stopped back by this means. The introduction of this important improvement may be regarded as a fourth stage in the history of mining. But for this system of keeping the water out of the shafts, the working of deep seams of coal would in many cases be altogether impracticable.

Even in sinking pits, accidents from suffocation by chokedamp, as well as severe explosions of firedamp, now sometimes occurred ; to guard against which he urges the necessity of employing none but experienced workmen. If the workman, he says, be altogether unacquainted with this sort of sinking labour, he may lose his life by styth (chokedamp), which cheats an ignorant man of his life insensibly, or "by his ignorance he may be burnt to death by the surfet (firedamp), which is another dangerous sort of bad air, but of a fiery nature like lightning, which blasts and tears all before it, if it takes hold of the candle, which an experienced labourer will discover and extinguish though it be going to take at his candle, and can sometimes smell to be dangerous or hurtful; therefore all sinkers should be skilled in these matters, for their own security sake, as also for the benefit of the master of the colliery. For if £1,000, or more, be spent in carrying down a pit or shaft, almost to the coal expected, and then by an ignorant man should be blasted by a strong blast, by surfeit, so that it may (as has been known) tear up your timber work and shatter the gins, and shake the stone work or frame work, so as to let in feeders of water, besides the destruction of the persons in the shaft, this would be a dismal accident with a witness."

It was water, however, that presented the greatest obstacle to mining operations, alike in the sinking of pits and working the collieries at this period. "Were it not for water," he observes, "a colliery in these parts might be termed a golden mine to purpose, for dry collieries would save several thousand pounds per ann., which is expended in drawing water hereabouts."

With regard to the machines in use for draining mines, he passes lightly over water wheels as of limited application, and windmills as too inconstant, and characterizes the common horse engine, or gin, as the most serviceable machine of all; being applicable everywhere and at all times, and serving alike to sink the pit and to draw both coals and water afterwards. He admits at the same time the want of some more powerful draining apparatus, in the following passage, the interest of which is heightened by its containing an allusion to the engine for raising water by fire, which Captain Savery was then endeavouring to induce the miners to adopt; if not, indeed, even to rumours of the coming steam engine itself, which was on the point of being presented to the world:

"If it would be made apparent," he observes, "that, as we have it noised abroad, there is this and that invention found out to draw out all great old waists, or drowned collieries, of what depth soever, I dare assure such artists may have such encouragement as would keep them their coach and six, for we cannot do it by our engines, and there are several good collieries which lye unwrought and drowned for want of such noble engines or methods as are talk'd of or pretended to. Yet there is one invention of drawing water by fire, which we hear of, and perhaps doth to purpose in many places and circumstances, but in these collieries here-away I am afraid there are not many dare venture of it, because *nature* doth generally afford us too much sulpherous matter to bring more fire within these our deep bowels of the earth, so that we judge cool inventions of suction

or force would be safest for this our concern, if any such could
be found that would do so much better, and with more expedition
than what is done generally here." Little did our author imagine
how near this was of realization.

The pits, or shafts, of this period were of small size. The author
speaks of the diameter of the square, at breaking away ground,
being nine quarters, or 6 feet 9 inches; but if from this we deduct
the breadth of the timbering, it only leaves a diameter of about
6 feet for the finished pit. This tallies with what he tells us of the
cost of sinking through a bed of whin, which, he states, amounted to
£30, though only 22 inches thick and 2 yards diameter.

Pits were now sunk to depths of 300 and 400 feet, the cost of
sinking them amounting, as we have seen, at times to £1,000 or
more; but the great bulk of the pits were much less deep, and sunk
at small cost. According to the report of the manager of the
collieries belonging to the Earl of Mar, in Clackmannanshire, Scotland, who was sent to visit the Newcastle coalfield in 1709 (Bald's
Coal Trade of Scotland, p. 8), the common depth of the pits was from
120 to 180 feet, and the cost of sinking £55.[1]

Small and shallow as were the pits of this era, judged by modern
ideas, they were really capacious and deep compared with some
other mine shafts which we hear of. Thus, Agricola (*De Re
Metallica*, L. v.) speaks of a pit as being for the most part two paces
long, two thirds of a pace broad, and thirteen paces deep. Even in
1668 (*Phil. Trans.*, No. 39, p. 767) the grooves, or shafts, of the
Mendip lead mines, in Somersetshire, were made 4 feet in length by
2½ feet in breadth. Some old coal pits found in quarrying in the
neighbourhood of Stella-on-Tyne were only 4 feet in diameter.
Others at Pelsall, in South Staffordshire, were as little as 3 feet
6 inches in diameter, and some of them square, the depth being 36
feet (*Trans. Fed. Inst.*, ii. 133).

The underground workings consisted of two sets of excavations,
driven in the seam of coal, at right angles to each other. The
boards (now usually spelt bords), or wide workings, were the main
excavations from which the supply of coal was obtained, and were
driven across the cleat, or cleavage, of the coal, this natural geological feature affording assistance to the coal hewer in digging the
mineral. They are supposed to have been so named, according to
one view (Phillip's *Report on the Ventilation of Mines*, p. 4 note), on

---

[1] This visitor to the north of England comments on the system of raising
water in two or three stages or stories, by means of two or three separate
pits and engines, as the method in use where necessary.

account of the board-like structure of the coal in this direction. A more probable etymology, however, recently suggested—and brought under the writer's notice by Mr. M. Walton Brown—is that *bord* is an old word signifying "a house" (Jamieson's *Dictionary*, ed. 1867, *sub* bordel); and this receives support from the circumstance that the rock overhead is known as the *roof*, and that underneath as the *floor*, while the coal forming the sides constitutes the *walls*. In Scotland the collier's working place is called his *room*; in other districts his *stall*, etc.

The headways, being passages intended for haulage and ventilation, were driven narrow, and on the head, or end, of the cleavage. The effect of the two sets of excavations was to cut up the coal seam into a series of square or oblong masses—the pillars or walls—which were at this period permanently allowed to remain to support the weight of the superincumbent strata.

From the bottom of the pit the workings were opened out by a main or winning headway (either single or double), driven very narrow, a yard and a-quarter being described as full sufficient. For a pit 360 feet in depth, 7 yards was taken as a suitable breadth to allow for a pillar and working-place—together termed a "winning"—4 yards for the pillar, and 3 yards for the board or working-place of a hewer. Three yards of coal being taken and 4 yards left, it is obvious that at the depth of 360 feet less than one-half of the coal seam was obtained.

The length of the pillars, or distance between the headways, is not specified by our author, who merely remarks that single persons carry their workings, or boards, a pretty long way; but frequently hole, or cut through, from one board to another to carry their air forward with their works.

The underground haulage of the coal was entirely performed by manual labour, by persons known as barrow-men, or coal-putters. Whether wheeled vehicles were at all in use in the northern mines at this period is not altogether certain. Mr. T. J. Taylor thought not. There were then no underground railways, or horses, he says (*Proc. Arch. Inst.*, Newcastle, 1852, i. 182), the coals being dragged to the bottom of the pit, by one or two persons, in corves placed on sledges. On this point our author is not altogether definite. It is true that he speaks of the corfe as "set when empty upon a sledge of wood," and, after being filled, being "so halled all along the barrow-way to the pit-shaft, by two or three persons, one before and the other behind the corfe." But he also makes use of the term *tram*, which would almost seem to imply a frame upon wheels;

though it must be admitted that there is no distinct reference to the employment of wheeled vehicles in the north of England mines till about sixty years later, and sledges without wheels continued to be used long after that period.

The word tram, as pointed out by Brand (vol. ii., p. 681), is of some antiquity : the line

"Beat on with barrow trams"

occurring in an old poem entitled "Christ's Kirk on the Green."[1] The supposition that tram-roads took their name from having been first constructed by Outram, about 1800, is clearly a popular fallacy.

At the pit bottom the corves were attached by the corf-bow to the hook at the end of the rope, by the barrowmen or putters, to be swung up the shaft to the surface.

To draw twenty one scores of corves, containing 14 or 15 pecks (about $4\frac{1}{2}$ cwt.) each, or altogether from 90 to 100 tons, was considered a good day's work for a pit 360 feet deep; and to accomplish this eight horses were required to work the gin—viz., in four shifts, or relays, of two at a time. The drawing ropes were of hemp, and 3 inches in circumference.

Fig. 6.—Whim Gin.

The "whim gin"—or vertical gin—was probably now in use. This was much superior to the cog and rung gin for the deeper and more important pits. The drum, or rope-roll, was built on a vertical axis placed some distance from the pit, the ropes being carried to pulleys placed on a timber frame directly over the pit's mouth. The diameter of the drum could thus be increased without inconvenience. The levers to which the horses were yoked were attached directly to the axis of the drum, and the horses moved round it in a

[1] Ascribed to James I. of Scotland (1395-1437) (Scrymgeour's *Class Book of English Poetry*, part i., p. 25). Ascribed by others to James V., but authorship quite uncertain.

circle, altogether clear of the pit. The number of levers, and the number of horses, could thus be added to as required, without at all obstructing the operations at the top of the pit.

As in the fourteenth century, the question of the number of barrowmen, or putters, required, still limited the distance to which a pit's workings were extended; the cost of underground conveyance increasing rapidly with distance. It was usual, we are told, to begin with six trams—this term including both the vehicle and its attendants—and to add another tram about every thirtieth day, till the total number reached sixteen trams. This was equal to wasting the pit all round for a distance of about 200 yards, and would obviously occupy about a year. It was then considered time to have a new shaft ready for another pit; which, says the author, "if happily done by the dayly care, prudence, and orders of the viewer, and his drift to the new pit carried on exactly so as to hit the new shaft and supply her with air, then has he evidenc'd both his care and parts, in the respects I have mention'd, and well deserved his 15s. or 20s. per week, or more as he has pits to look after; and he has an under-overman always allowed for every pit, whilst one viewer serves for three or four working pits, and the overman's wages is about 8s. a week." The underground workpeople—putters and hewers—were already usually paid by piece-work, in the great northern coalfield.

The ventilation of the mines was entirely dependent on the natural circulation of air between the shafts; but checks, or partitions, termed "stoppings," were placed in the excavated passages where necessary, to carry the current of air forward to the extremities, or "faces," of the boards actually being driven, and prevent it from dispersing itself too much, "for the brisker it ranges in the works the sweeter and safer it is for the miners." This primitive arrangement of ventilating is known as "face-airing."

Regarding noxious gases in the underground workings, the author speaks of a great explosion of firedamp (to be hereafter referred to) which occurred in a pit at Gateshead shortly before he wrote, and remarks that, "this is known by woful experience and which I myself have seen and narrowly (by good providence) escaped, that some collieries are very subject to this fatal surfeit, and therefore it behoves the viewers and overmen to be experienc'd in guiding the air to good purpose, as also to order prudently, for styth, which I before spoke of, doth destroy the ignorant and unwary."

He likewise recommends coal owners to keep on good terms with the fitters, or hostmen; and also to have a good stock of coal provided beforehand for the season of sale, which he says "is chiefly in summer, by reason of the weather, which makes it hazardous for ships to sail in winter on these coasts."

The mode of working coal described by the author of this little treatise—the only one evidently with which he was acquainted—is one of the two great cardinal systems of coal mining, and may be referred to generally as the pillar system. It is variously known as bord-and-pillar, or bord-and-wall, post-and-stall, stoop-and-room, etc., names all having reference to the alternating working-places and coal supports.

The pillars in early times were probably made very small and square, being in reality mere pillars of coal measuring one or two yards each way. The working places were probably also all of small width. "The dimensions of the pillars found in old workings at Butterknowle, near the south-west outcrop of the lowest seam of the Newcastle coalfield," says Mr. Greenwell (*Mine Engineering*, 2nd ed., p. 195), "where the depth is not more than 7 or 8 fathoms (42 to 48 feet), are about 3 yards square; the width of the excavations being about 3 yards, and the whole driven beneath 8 or 10 inches of top coal, and accurately arched, the object of the arching being to prevent the use of props." In some old workings in the neighbourhood of Stella, in like manner, at a depth of 50 or 60 feet, the dimensions of the pillars left were 4 yards square.

The system of forming square pillars, and keeping the working-places almost of uniform width, has continued common at Whitehaven, and in Scotland, down to the present day. In the north of England the pillars were more usually oblong. Here, at some early period, in order to obtain the greatest aid from the cleavage of the coal, the bords began to be lengthened, and the narrow cross-holings between them reduced in number, thus forming the pillars into long narrow ribs, or mere walls of coal. This old method of working is described by Professor Phillips (*Ventilation of Mines*, p. 6), who states that "the ancient practice is still to be seen in operation at Derwent Main, a colliery of early date west of Newcastle. The headway courses, along which the coal is transported from the working bords, are thirty yards apart. The bords are four yards wide, and are separated by pillars of only one yard across, except at the side of the headways, where they are left much stouter to secure the road." A considerable extent of ground was formerly worked in this way at Mickley, and other collieries of small depth in the district west of Newcastle.

This lengthening of the pillars attained to its greatest development in South Wales, where cross-holings were so little resorted to as scarcely to form a part of the system of working at all.

FIG. 7.—STOOP AND ROOM (Scotland).

The pillar system of working coal under some circumstances is the only method admissible. The system was manifestly originally designed for the purpose of upholding the surface; and as the depth of the mines increased, pillars of larger dimensions required to be left to preserve the mine itself from thrusts, or crushes—the pillars, as we have seen, being made 4 yards broad, and the bords 3 yards broad, in the deeper collieries at this period. But, theoretically speaking, the bord-and-pillar system can scarcely be regarded as the most perfect method of working coal. (*Proc. Arch. Inst.*, Newcastle, 1852, i. 199.) Great modifications of the system were subsequently introduced. Its defects, as practised about the end of the seventeenth century, were strikingly apparent in the fact that already, at a depth of

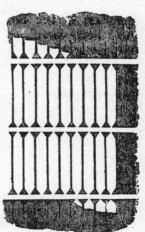

FIG. 8.—BORD AND PILLAR (Derwent Main, Newcastle).

360 ft., more than one-half of the coal was being permanently left in the mine. To the removal of any portion of the pillars,

the author of the *Compleat Collier* makes no allusion, indicating
that this had not yet begun to be entertained at the time when
he wrote in 1708.

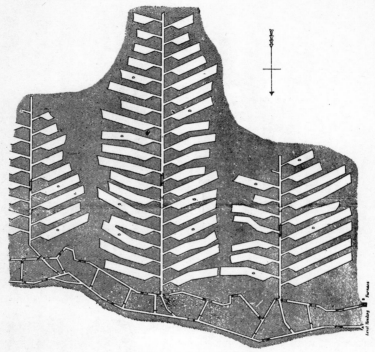

FIG. 9.—POST AND STALL (South Wales).

It is to a colliery worked on the bord-and-pillar system that the
simile first made use of by Dr. Dalton, in his poem on the Whitehaven mines, published in 1755 (and subsequently by Jago and
others), is peculiarly appropriate, where it is spoken of as a

City of subterraneous streets.

CHAPTER XVIII.

THE SEVENTEENTH CENTURY.—Continued.

The Yorkshire, Derbyshire, and Nottinghamshire coalfield. Account of coal mines near Derby in 1693 ; and of an attempt to monopolize the coal trade. Descent into a mine at Smaley. Coking of coal. Damps or noxious gases. Explosions of firedamp near Chesterfield. Employment of fire to produce ventilation. Export of coal from the Trent. The Lancashire coalfield. The cannel coal of Wigan. The burning well. Export of coal from Liverpool. Early projects for smelting iron with coal.

The amount of information available regarding the progress of coal mining in the other coalfields varies greatly in different cases ; a considerable amount of light beating upon some of them, while others lie enveloped in much obscurity. The day of mediæval monastic records was over. The modern tourist had scarcely yet begun to set out upon his travels. Though, in the latter half of the century, some assistance is afforded us by the information collected by the early disciples of the " new philosophy," as modern inductive science was at first called, preserved for the most part in the *Transactions* of the Royal Society of London for improving natural knowledge, which was incorporated by Royal charter in 1662.

Among matters connected with mines which began to receive a considerable amount of attention at this period, was the subject of noxious gases which were now becoming so prevalent and troublesome. The great discovery of the pressure of the atmosphere had lent a new interest to the subject of air and gases generally, and the singular phenomena connected with noxious gases in mines received a share of investigation from men of science. Numerous papers relating to them, both as occurring in the mines of this country and on the Continent, as also of the methods employed to combat them, were brought before the Royal Society soon after its institution, as will appear forthwith.

A dearth of records is felt in the case of the Yorkshire, Derbyshire, and Nottinghamshire coalfield.   Calmly and peacefully the coal trade of this district seems to have held on the even tenor of its way, little if at all affected by wars civil or naval, or the price of coal in the metropolis.   Even the attempts at monopolies in coal, which occasioned so much contention in other parts, are almost unheard of here.   And though the project of smelting iron with coal was entertained here earlier than anywhere else, this coalfield does not appear to have participated in the multitudinous attempts to accomplish this great desideratum, the accounts of the continuous struggles in connection with which, during this century, serve to illumine for us to some extent the mining history of the districts in which they were made.

Among the meagre records relating to Yorkshire there is mention, in 1624 (*Cal. State Papers*, Dom., 1623-25, vol. clxxi., No. 67), of a lease from Wm. Rolfe, vintner, of London, to Lancelot Gledhill and Thos. Brackenbury of certain coal mines near Wakefield.

The art of boring appears to have been well known in this district early in the seventeenth century.   It is referred to in a document relating to the Halifax neighbourhood, bearing date 1633 (*Leeds Mercury Supplement*, 9th May, 1885).   A series of borings, to which reference has been already made, were also executed near Leeds, in 1639, an account of which is published in the *Philosophical Transactions* (No. 250, p. 73), the depths explored ranging from 24 to 126 feet.

Collieries no doubt now existed in large numbers, though they were probably for the most part small and shallow.   In the Halifax district, even subsequent to the close of this century (*Leeds Mercury Supplement*, May 16 and 23, 1885), sixty yards all round was considered to be a sufficient distance to carry the workings of a pit from the shaft or "eye," on account of the expense connected with the laborious method of hauling, or "hurrying," the coal underground, which was performed in *scoops* shod with iron.

Camden, in 1607, speaks of the western parts of Derbyshire as being rich in lead, iron, and coal.   But while numerous records exist relating to the lead mines, or groves as they were still commonly called, of the coal mines much less is heard, and almost nothing in the early part of this century.   There is mention, however (MS. records relating to mines in Derbyshire, *Brit. Mus.*, 1687, p. 193), of a grant of coal mines at Ripley being made in 1612-13.

An interesting notice of the coal mines in the neighbourhood of Derby, with an account of a descent made into one of them, is contained in a letter of Houghton's, dated 1693 (*Collection*, ed. 1727, vol. i., p. 105).

"The chiefest coal mines thereabouts," he says, "are at Smaly, four miles, at Heaner, six miles, and at Denby, five miles from Derby; thro' which abundance in summer are carried as far as Northamptonshire, from whence is brought back barley. These coals at Smaley and Heaner, are in the hands of one, Mr. Samuel Richardson, who finding that Derby consumed annually about 3,000 loads, besides what was fetch'd into Leicestershire and Northamptonshire, design'd to sell his coal for three pence the hundred; and had got them to six shillings and six pence the load; but the worshipful John Lowe, of Denby, Esq., after an expense of between nine hundred and one thousand pounds in perfecting a sough to lay his delf dry, the last spring accomplisht the same, and has laid as many coal dry as will be got this forty years; and before the sale came he had got above one thousand loads upon the bank, any of which he upholds to be at least five and thirty hundred weight, and sells them for five shillings six pence, so that this year we bought coals delivered for three pence half penny the hundred.

"These coals are drawn up by a horse, as in a malt mill, where there is a barrel, on which a rope winds, so that while one end winds up, the other goes down through the pulley, and so contrary, the particular description whereof I have, but 'tis not easy to those who are not artists therein without a cut [a whim gin].

"At Smaley my friend went down the pit 20 fathom, by ladders of twelve staves each, set across the pit one by another: when he was so deep, he went underground (he believes as far as from my house to St. Paul's Church, which is well near half a mile) in a mine or vein, which was about six foot, where were coals over head and under foot, the workmen knew not how thick: from this place he was led twenty yards through a narrow passage, upon hands and feet, till he came into a large space, which was the head of a sough (a place to carry away water) which laid all the pits dry that were on that level, and presently he came to a pit twenty yards deeper than before [an underground staple, or blind pit], out of which they drew water brought from another pit twenty yards deeper, with two vessels, which would hold above sixty gallons each: they were hoopt with iron and biggest in the midst: when one of these came to the top a boy with a hoop drew them to him, and easily did throw the water down, which in that concave made a noise like thunder."

The coking of coal, and the employment of coke in drying malt, had now been practised in Derbyshire for a period of fifty years; and the change to this mineral fuel was considered to have effected a decided improvement in the quality of the brewings. "The reason of Derby malt being so fine and sweet," says Houghton (*ib.*, p. 109), "my friend thinks is the drying of it with cowks, which is a sort of coal (so call'd there)"; and he proceeds to describe how the collier "cowkefied" the coal in large round heaps, of six or eight waggon loads, built in as pyramidal a form as they would stand.

He further states (*ib.*, p. 127) that cowkes and coals appeared to be cheaper in Derbyshire than in any part of England, Newcastle not excepted; and adds that "'Tis not above half-a-century of years since they dryed their malt with straw (as other places now [1693] do), before they used cowkes, which has made that alteration since, that all England admires."[1]

In Derbyshire, as in a number of other parts of the kingdom, explosions of firedamp began to become alarmingly violent about 1675. An account of the various kinds of damps with which mines are infested, with remarks regarding them, from the pen of Mr. Jessop, of Broomhall, Yorkshire, was communicated to the Royal Society, in two parts, and published in the *Philosophical Transactions*.

In the first of these, sent by Mr. Lister in a letter dated July 28, 1675 (No. 117, p. 391), four sorts of damp are described as common in these parts, viz. :

The ordinary, or smothering damp, the remedy for which, he says, is to dig a hole in the earth and lay them on their bellies with their mouths in it; if that fail they tun them full of good ale; but if that fail they conclude them desperate.

Pease-bloom damp, a variety known by its pleasant smell, and supposed by some to be derived from flowers.

The third sort, to which no name is given and which appears to have been somewhat imaginary, is described as assuming the form of a globe about the size of a football, and as being very destructive if accidentally broken, suffocating all near. The miners dealt with it by breaking it from a distance by means of a long pole; after which they purified the place well by fire before they durst venture in—seemingly an early reference to artificial ventilation by means of fire.

---

[1] Illustrative of the connection between fuel and flavour, it may be mentioned that peat continues to be employed to some extent even at the present day in drying the malt used in the manufacture of whisky; the smoke of this antique fuel, known in Scotland as *peat reek*, being supposed to impart a piquancy and gusto to the "barley-bree."

"The fourth," he says, "which they also call a damp, is that vapour, which being touched by their candle presently takes fire, and giving a crack like a gun produceth the like effects, or rather those of lightning. A fellow they commonly call Dobby Leech is at this day a sad example of the force of one of those blasts in Hasleberg Hills, having his arms and legs broken and his body strangely distorted. Captain Wain told me he saw one of them in a bloomery near Peniston. But I shall say no more of them, because I have just now such an opportunity of informing my self about this matter as I am never like to have again as long as I live. For at Wingersworth, two miles beyond Chesterfield, within this month or five weeks, a cole pit of Sir F. Humblocks hath been fired four times by this vapour and hath hurt four several men."

From the continuation of the account (No. 119, p. 450) we learn that the pit in which the explosions occurred was 45 feet deep, and was in communication with some other pits from which it drew a supply of air. There were four "binks," or working-places (also called banks and benks), 4 yards wide and 40 yards long, except the one in which they met the fiery or fulminating damp, which wanted 4 or 5 yards of its due length. This bink was the furthest removed from the air. When the firedamp ignited the colliers found themselves environed with flames; their faces, hands, hair, and clothes being very much burnt; while one of the blasts issued from the mouth of the pit like a clap of thunder, shooting off the turn, or windlass, and carrying small coals and rubbish a considerable height into the air; shaking the very earth so much that a workman in another bink hard by feared the roof would have fallen in upon him and buried him.

Mr. Jessop remarks that "damps are most generally observed to come about the latter end of May, and to continue during the heat of summer. I never heard of damps that kindled of themselves, although I have been told that in some places they have been kindled by the motion of the sled in which they draw their coals. Damps generally are considered to be heavier than air, but this was manifestly lighter, for it lay towards the top of the bink."

Some damps will quite extinguish all those fires that are let down into them, he says, but fire often creates damp in places not subject to them; and those grooves in which they are forced to break the rock by the help of great fires, are seldom free from damps. At the same time, fire was known to be a present remedy, if by means of it a circulation of air could be produced through the infected place.

The collieries of Nottinghamshire are scarcely heard of at this period. It is singular that the Trent does not figure as exporting coal abroad in the balance sheet of the farmers of the coal revenues for the year 1617, as a trade of this description is found existing there immediately after this date. In 1620 (*Cal. State Papers*, Dom., 1619-23, vol. cxiii. 22), the justices of the peace of Nottinghamshire inform the justices of assize that they have no need of a storehouse for corn, the prices not being extraordinarily low, "nor is future scarcity to be feared, as other countries who send up the Trent for coals, bring in corn whenever it is needed."

In the Lancashire coalfield, almost the only topics touched upon are the cannel coal of Wigan, and the once famous "burning well" of the same neighbourhood, of both of which accounts are furnished by several contemporary writers.

In the course of his visit to Lancashire, when on the northern circuit in 1676, Lord Guildford stayed some days, Roger North tells us, with Sir Roger Bradshaw, "whose lordship is famous for yielding the cannel (or candle) coal. It is so termed, as I guess, because the manufacturers of that country use no candle, but work by the light of their coal fire. The property of it is to burn and flame till it is all consumed, without leaving any cinder. It is lighted by a candle like amber; and the grate stands not against the back of a large chimney, as common coal grates, but in the middle, where ballads are pasted round; and the folk sit about it, working or merry-making. His lordship saw the pits where vast piles of that coal were raised; and it is pity the place wants water carriage [a subject receiving some attention at this time], else London would be in the better part served with it."

Bishop Gibson, in like manner (*Britannia*, ed. 1695, p. 802), refers to the very plentiful and profitable mines of extraordinary coal, found at "Haigh, near Wiggin," and mentions its being "curiously polished into the appearance of black marble, and fram'd into long candlesticks, sugar-boxes, spoons, with many other such sorts of vessels."

At a subsequent period we hear of a dinner being given at Wigan, served upon dishes made of cannel coal, at which the guests, after consuming the viands, proceeded to amuse themselves by consuming the plates, which they did by piling them on the fire.

The other "lion" of this neighbourhood, the burning well, was situated within a mile and a half of Wigan, and in close proximity to a coal pit. The water in the well seemed to boil like water in a pot on the fire, and yet remained quite cold. On the application of a light it burned like oil, or brandy, and by the heat of the flame eggs and meat could be boiled ; but when taken out of the well it would not burn any more than ordinary water.

A scientific examination of this mysterious phenomenon was made by Thos. Shirley, Esq., in 1667, and the results communicated to the Royal Society (*Phil. Trans.*, No. 26, p. 482). The cause of the mystery was discovered to be a continuous discharge, or "blower," of firedamp coming from a fissure in the strata at the bottom of the well, and making its escape up through the water.

The firedamp issued at the surface at many points in this neighbourhood, which was all underlaid with coal, and the people found out the art of making burning wells, for the amusement and astonishment of visitors. This they did by digging up a turf at a place where gas issued and then clapping it down again. "When the show company are come," says Roger North, "a man takes up the turf, and after a little puffing and blowing of a brown paper match, gives fire, and instantly the hole is filled with a blue spirituous flame like brandy. While it was burning they put water in the hole, and the flame continued upon the water as if it had been spirits." The greatest wonder his lordship saw, this writer remarks, was that which they call the burning well.

Firedamp was thus already familiarly known in the Lancashire coalfield, though fortunately, as far as we know, only as making its escape harmlessly to the surface.

Little or no information appears to be available regarding the collieries of this district, and the progress of coal mining. There is a notice of a boring having been made for coal in the adjoining county of Cheshire in 1670 (*Phil. Trans.*, No. 66, p. 2,105), which failed in its primary object of finding coal, but led to the discovery of valuable deposits of rock salt.

A small, but very small, foreign export of coal had commenced from Liverpool in the early part of the seventeenth century ; the port of Chester and Liverpool figuring in the balance sheet of the collectors of the coal taxes for the year 1617, as having sent 1,879½ chaldrons of coal abroad.

We have no accounts of attempts being made in this coalfield to smelt iron with coal ; but it may be mentioned that Leigh, in his *Natural History of Lancashire*, published in 1700 (p. 81), speaks of his having been informed "that lately by the cakes of pit coal those ores may be run into a malleable iron." The success achieved, however, as in some other cases, was probably of a partial character. We have no clear records of any decided and permanent progress having been made in this direction till a later period, not-withstanding the numerous patents taken out for the process in the course of the seventeenth century; commencing with a grant to Robert Chantrell in 1607 (*Cal. State Papers*, Dom., 1603-10, p. 346); others to Simon Sturtevant in 1611, and John Rovenzon in 1612-13; followed by many others, to some of which reference will be made hereafter; the extraordinary number of unsuccessful attempts to utilize coal in the smelting of metalliferous ores, particularly of iron, forming a remarkable feature of the industrial history of this era.

CHAPTER XIX.

THE SEVENTEENTH CENTURY—Continued.

The Staffordshire coalfield. Collieries near Dudley Castle. Spontaneous combustion. Damps. Use of fire lamps to produce ventilation. Dud Dudley's attempt to smelt iron with coal. Raising water by fire. Captain Savery's fire engine—the Miner's Friend. The Warwickshire coalfield. Attempt to monopolize the coal trade. The Leicestershire coalfield. Coleorton. Measham.

STAFFORDSHIRE was now famed for its abundance of pit coal and iron mines (Camden's *Britannia*, ed. 1607), but in the seventeenth century a barrier, seemingly insurmountable, separated the two industries. Charcoal was the fuel universally employed at the iron works ; which had originally taken root and flourished here, not on account of the existence of so much coal, but—as in the similarly famous early iron-producing districts of Sussex and the Forest of Dean—owing to its having been a mighty woodland country.

In the manipulation of the iron, however, coal was of invaluable service to the multitude of smiths who swarmed in the district ; the number of these artizans located in the South Staffordshire coalfield being estimated, in 1665 (Dudley's *Metallum Martis*, reprint 1854, p. 39), to be at least twenty thousand. Wednesbury, in particular, and also Dudley, and Sedgley, were celebrated (Plot's *Staffordshire*, p. 127) for the excellence of the coal which they supplied.

Within a circuit of ten miles from Dudley Castle (partly in Staffordshire and partly in Worcestershire), noted for possessing the magnificent stratum of coal, from ten to twelve yards in thickness, distinguished by the name of the Ten Yard or Thick Coal, there were at the same period (*Metallum Martis*, p. 26) twelve or fourteen collieries at work, besides twice as many out of work. But the production of individual collieries was small, only averaging about two thousand tons per annum, though some obtained from three to five thousand tons.

This was probably the last district in which coal was worked to any extent by means of surface, or "open-cast," workings. A number of these existed in the middle of the seventeenth century, and were known by the name of " foot-rids." But workings of this kind— resembling quarries more than coal mines—were gradually becoming rare. In the majority of cases pits had to be resorted to which, however, were still very shallow, ranging from 24 to 60, and in some instances nearly 120 feet in depth.

In working this extraordinarily thick seam of coal in the pits, the colliers are described (*ib.*, p. 27) as beginning at the bottom and carrying working-places (crutes or staules), about two yards in height, as far forward and of such a breadth as was deemed expedient; then taking slice after slice of the coal upwards till they reached the top ; making use of the small coals (which were left underground as of no value) as a platform for raising themselves to the upper parts of the seam. According to Mr. Bald, when this coal first began to be worked by means of pits, a distance of twenty yards all round was considered a sufficient area to be worked, after which a new pit was sunk (*Edinburgh Encyclopædia*, art. Mine).

A remarkable feature connected with coal mining in South Staffordshire and Worcestershire thus early, was the numerous underground fires which occurred. Holland, the first translator of Camden's *Britannia* (eds. 1610, 1637), was told of a fire burning in Pesneth Chace, Worcestershire, which was said to have been "begun by a candle long since, by the negligence of a certain grover, or digger. The smoak, and sometimes the flame, was seen, but the scent oftener smelt, and in other places not far off the like was shewed to him." (Gough's *Camden*, ed. 1789, vol. ii., p. 382.)

Burton, writing in 1622 (*Leicestershire*, 2nd ed., p. 198), speaks of a fire then burning near Willingsworth and Wednesbury ; at the latter of which places in 1686 (Plot's *Staffordshire*, p. 141) the coal works on fire extended over eleven acres. Dud Dudley also refers (p. 8) to the frequent ignition of the small coals left underground, by spontaneous combustion, stating that the fire often flamed out of the pits and continued burning "like Ætna in Cicily, or Hecla in the Indies,"—the latter word being doubtless a *lapsus linguæ* for Iceland. He also tells us that in connection with these fires water issued from some of the soughs, or adits, as hot as the bath at Bath, and possessed of similar curative properties.

Fires from spontaneous combustion had also already occurred above ground, both on the staiths at Newcastle-on-Tyne (*Cal. State Papers*, Dom., 1639, p. 157), and on the wharves at London (Plot's

Staffordshire, p. 142). Coals containing pyrites (termed metal coals) were at this time supposed to be peculiarly liable to ignition in this way ; and Dr. Plot quotes an instance, mentioned by Dr. Powers, which occurred at Ealand, in Yorkshire, where a person had collected many cartloads of pyrites for some private purpose of his own ; but the roof of the place being faulty and admitting rain water to fall copiously in among them, they began to smoke and then took fire and burnt like red-hot coals, so that the town was in an uproar about the quenching of them. This idea is, however, now maintained not to be scientifically correct ; and the Staffordshire Thick coal, which is so peculiarly liable to spontaneous combustion, is stated to be exceptionally free from pyrites.

Though underground fires were so common in the South Stafford-shire coalfield that Dr. Plot tells us they were little dreaded, they gave rise to a system of working the Thick Coal specially designed to afford facilities for their extinction. In allusion to them in his *Worthies of England* (art. Staffordshire), Dr. Fuller remarks, "I wish that the pit coal (wherewith it aboundeth) may seasonably and safely be burnt in their chimnies, and not have their burning antedated, before they be digg'd out of the bowels of the earth."

The coal mines at Beaudesert were probably now the deepest in the county. Here in 1686 cannel coal was dug 120, 180, 240 feet deep. It could be carved like stone; and the choir of Lichfield Cathedral was floored with this coal and alabaster in alternate squares (Plot's *Staffordshire*, pp. 125-26).

We hear (*Report of Royal Coal Commission*, iii. 30) of coal being found at Talke at this period. "Mr. Thomas Pool, in a little piece of land in this parish, left him by his father (who had, twenty years before, dug for a coal mine with no success), found one which, in the years 1674 and 1675, yielded him £800 clear profit."

Dr. Plot enters at some length into the question of damps in mines. He cites no case of firedamp having as yet been encountered in the Staffordshire mines, which were still for the most part very shallow, though he refers to a number of instances of this gas being met with in other districts. But chokedamp was prevalent, especially in the mines in the northern part of the county. He speaks of having entered a drift, or "footerill," at Apedale, for a distance of two hundred yards, by which time, two of his candles having become extinguished and the third in danger of being so, he deemed it prudent to retreat.

Chokedamp was specially troublesome, he tells us (p. 134), in mines drained by adits, where there was "no laveing, drawing, or pumping of water, all which kept the air in motion"; also in mines where fire was used to break the rocks (as at Cheadle), which were seldom free from damps. He also remarks (p. 138) on the connection between damps and the weather, and to the circumstance that "a prudent collier minds the wind."

His account of the methods of combating noxious gases is of special interest, as containing one of the earliest notices we have, in England, of the employment of fire to produce an artificial circulation of air in mines. "Damps occasioned by smoke" (*i.e.* fire-setting), he says, "they expel either by water, where they have no air pits, and in winter time; but chiefly by fire, which they let down in an iron cradle they call their lamp. Which very way they use about Chedle." The employment of the fire-lamp would appear to have been spasmodic as yet.

This was the initial stage of ventilating by means of an underground furnace—a system which the author of the *Compleat Collier* regarded as too dangerous to introduce into the fiery mines of the north. Fire had already begun to be employed to ventilate coal mines in Belgium. An account of a method of working adits and mines at Liége without air shafts, was communicated to the Royal Society, by Sir R. Moray, in 1665 (*Phil. Trans.*, No. 5, p. 79). In this case the furnace was placed at the surface, in connection with a chimney 28 or 30 feet high and about 5 feet square; and from this, tubes, 8 or 9 inches square, were carried into the mine.

The saltmakers of Nantwich had now begun to draw their supplies of fuel from Staffordshire (Houghton's *Collection*, vol. ii., p. 88, ed. 1727; *Phil. Trans.*, 1669), having adopted coal in lieu of wood in the seething of the salt brine about the middle of the seventeenth century. The use of coal in saltmaking is spoken of as a novelty at Nantwich in 1656 (*Chambers' Journal*, January, 1879). At Droitwich, coal, brought from the Forest of Dean, first began to be used about 1678 (*Phil. Trans.*, No. 142, p. 1,059).

It was in the South Staffordshire coalfield that Dud Dudley made his repeated, but disastrous efforts to wed together the coal and iron industries, which he may be said to have made the object of his life. The unending opposition which he encountered from the charcoal iron masters is recounted in his *Metallum Martis*, first published in 1665. His earliest experiments in substituting coal for charcoal in the blast furnace, were made at Pesneth Chase, Worcestershire, about the close of the year 1619; and a patent for the process having been obtained by Lord Dudley in 1621, he persevered with it for a few years, when his progress was arrested by his being ousted from his works somehow by the iron masters and others.

He made a fresh start at Himley Furnace, Staffordshire, only to have it soon afterwards taken from him to be let to charcoal iron masters. He then built a new furnace after his own design at Hasco Bridge, in the parish of Sedgley, provided with extra large bellows, and proceeded to work coal and ironstone there (to which, however, it is doubtful whether he possessed any proper title), but was in a short time ejected from the works, "and the bellows of his new furnace and invention by riotous persons cut in pieces."

What with the persecution of the iron masters, lawsuits, and riots, the patent (granted at first for thirty-one years, but afterwards curtailed to fourteen) expired in 1635 without Dudley having derived anything but losses and disappointment from his schemes.[1] Then the civil wars came on ; and though he subsequently renewed his attempts to set up iron works, he never got the length of actually smelting iron again.

Though Dudley's efforts were partially successful, he failed altogether to establish the manufacture of iron with coal. That the iron which he produced was not equal to charcoal iron in quality, may be taken for granted : this fuel, on account of its freedom from sulphur, being pre-eminently adapted for iron smelting. Then as to quantity, even in his specially-designed furnace, with its extra large bellows, he could only produce seven tons of iron per week, or in other words, from one-half to one-third of the production of a charcoal furnace. So far as Dudley's performances were concerned the charcoal iron interests had no great cause for alarm.

A subsequent attempt to smelt iron with coal made in this coalfield by one Dr. Frederic de Blewstone, who obtained a patent in 1677, proved a still more dismal failure. He built his furnace at Wednesbury (Plot's *Staffordshire*, p. 128), "so ingeniously contrived (that only the flame of the coal should come to the ore, with several other conveniences) that many were of opinion he would succeed in it. But experience, that great baffler of speculation, showed that it would not be ; the sulphureous vitriolic steams that issue from the pyrites which frequently, if not always, accompanies pit coal,

[1] Even previous to the expiration of Lord Dudley's patent, other patents for employing coal in smelting had been granted. Thus, in 1627 a patent for making iron with coal was granted to William Astell, John Copley, and Francis Croft ; and in 1632 another to Dr. Jorden, of Bath, for melting tin, iron, lead, and copper, with pit coal, sea coal, peat, and turf (see published lists of patents).

ascending with the flame and poisoning the ore." Dr. Plot speaks of the use of coal for house purposes (in kitchens, parlours, bed-chambers), in glass houses, saltworks, brickmaking and malting; but

he says "for melting, fineing and refining iron, it cannot be brought to do." The process of coking coal was already well known in this county, as we learn from the same writer.

Whether the familiarity of the people of Staffordshire with fire may have had anything to do with the circumstance we do not know, but the miners of this county were not only among the first to employ this agent in the ventilation of mines, but were likewise foremost to apply it to the raising of water.

The project of raising water by fire is first mentioned in a petition to the king by David Ramsay, dated 15th November, 1630 (*Cal. State Papers*, Dom., 1629-31, p. 382), praying for a patent for a new invention "to raise water from low pits by fire"; which was granted 17th January, 1631 (*ib.*, p. 483). Nothing more is heard of the idea till the publication of his *Century of Inventions*, by the Marquis of Worcester, in 1663, wherein (No. lxviii.) he speaks of "a new and most forcible way to raise water by fire," on which is based the extravagant claim put forward on his behalf as the inventor of the steam engine. Then, on the 25th of July, 1698, a

FIG. 10.—SAVERY'S ENGINE FOR RAISING WATER BY FIRE, 1702.

patent was granted to Captain Savery for a new invention for raising water "by the impellent force of fire, which will be of great use for draining mines, etc." Originally granted for fourteen years, Savery in the following year (25th April, 1699) obtained a private Act of Parliament extending the patent privilege twenty-one years further, or for a total term of thirty-five years. In this machine the water was raised to the engine by suction obtained by the condensation of steam, and forced above it by means of high-pressure steam acting directly on the water.

Savery was convinced that he had hit upon the very engine for the miners. Not only was his engine to free the mines from water, the one great enemy of miners, but it was at the same time to dispel the damps, or noxious gases, their other great enemy. To apply his engine in a mine it was necessary that it should be placed in a recess in the shaft, within 26 or 28 feet of the level of the water to be raised; and Savery proposed to utilize the furnace and chimney of the engine to ventilate the mine, by means of a tube carried into the workings, after the manner referred to as practised at Liége.

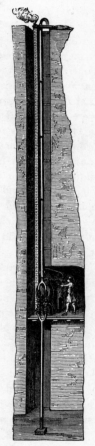

So confident was Savery that his engine would prove a brilliant success in this direction, that he expected it would be the means of doubling if not trebling the mining trade of the kingdom in a few years. But Savery vastly over-estimated the capabilities of his engine, and under-rated the drawbacks to its use. He erected several which raised water very well for gentlemen's seats; but as an engine for draining mines it proved an absolute failure. " The only situation in which this machine could be employed with perfect safety," says Dr. Robison (*Mechanical Philosophy*, vol. ii., p. 54, ed. 1822), "and with some effect, was where the whole lift did not exceed 30 or 35 feet. In this case the greatest part of it was performed by the suction-pipe, and a very manageable pressure was sufficient for the rest."

Under these circumstances, to drain one of the deeper mines by means of this machine, from five to ten engines would have been required, one above the other, which was not to be thought of. When higher lifts were attempted there was great

FIG. 11.—SAVERY'S
ENGINE IN A MINE.

danger of the boiler bursting, it not being provided with any safety valve. It is not therefore surprising that the miners did not hasten to adopt Savery's steam fountain. "Savery," says M. Arago (*Life of James Watt*, 2nd ed., p. 36) "entitled his work The Miner's Friend, but the miners seemed scarcely to appreciate the compliment he paid them. With one solitary exception, none of them ordered his engines."

Where the mine above referred to was situated, we are not informed; but we have an account (Shaw's *Staffordshire*, vol. ii., part i., p. 85) of an attempt being made by Savery to recover a colliery in South Staffordshire which had been inundated by a sudden irruption of water :

"Mr. Thomas Savary (the original inventor of the steam engine) set one of these engines down about 17— in the liberty of Wednesbury, near a place called then the broad-waters, which is now dry land again. For this place being low ground, the water rose so hastily many years ago, and in such quantities, from the coal pit, that it covered some acres of land, buried many stacks of coals that were on the bank, and so continued till drained again about fifteen or twenty years ago. . . . The engine thus erected could not be brought to perfection, as the old pond of water was very great, and the springs very many and strong that kept up the body of it ; and the steam, when too strong, tore it all to pieces, so that after much time, labour, and expense, Mr. Savary was forced to give up the undertaking, and the engine was laid aside as useless ; so that he may be said to have discovered a power sufficient to drain any kind of mine, but could not form an engine capable of working and making it useful."

Savery's apparatus being dangerous as well as weak, the miners preferred waiting for "cool inventions of suction or force," and they had not long to wait. The pulsometer pump of the present day is to some extent a representative of Savery's fire engine.

The collieries of the Warwickshire coalfield come into prominence in the first half of the seventeenth century, through a determined attempt to establish a monopoly of the coal trade there made by one John Briggs and his partners, which was the occasion of a succession of petitions and counter-petitions being addressed to the Privy Council by the contending factions, as well as of the appointment of several commissions to arbitrate between them.

There are, first, two petitions against Briggs and his party, dated October [31] 1622. One of these is described (*Cal. State Papers*, Dom., 1619-23, vol. cxxxiii. 67) as "Petition of the inhabitants and colliers in Griffe and Bedworth, co. Warwick, against John Briggs and his two sons, John and Anthony, and Thos. and Ant. Robinson, who, having coal mines in Bedworth, and wishing to sell the coal at their own prices, endeavour to frustrate the working of the coal mines in the lordship of Griffe, by turning water into the pits, etc."

The other was from Mat. Collins and John Potter, citizens of Coventry, for themselves and others, and set forth that "John Briggs and his partners, wishing to sell their coals at 5s. 1d. per load, bought out several parties who were working for coal near the petitioners; they leased several coal mines near Coventry, covenanting to sell at 3s. 5d. the load, and refused to be bought out, on which John Briggs and his partners tried to ruin them by letting the water into their pits. Entreat redress." (*Ib.*, 68.)

About the same date a counter-petition was presented by "the poor colliers of Bedworth, Exhall, and Folshull, tenants of John Briggs and Thos. Robinson, farmers of the great coal mine at Bedworth." This sets forth that "the mine at Bedworth, after being long unworked, was undertaken by Briggs and Robinson, who thereby employ 500 persons, giving houses rent free, and coals to many poor workmen, and to the orphans and widows of others. The mine is sufficient to serve the country forty miles round, but will be stopped if Matt. Collins and others of Coventry are permitted to work another coal mine near. Entreat favour therein." (*Ib.*, 69.)

By a communication, dated Warwick, 26th November, 1622 (*ib.*, vol. cxxxiv. 31), Sir Thos. Leigh, Bart., Sir Rich. Verney, and Sir Thos. Lucy, inform the council that they "have examined the complaint preferred by Matt. Collins and others, citizens of Coventry, against John Briggs and his partners in a coal delve, at Bedworth, taking information voluntarily offered, not that of witnesses on oath. Briggs takes exceptions to the witnesses : have bound him to appear before their lordships."

At the above inquiry, one Hum. Saunders, of Bedworth, and ten others, gave evidence substantiating the charges against Briggs and his partners, of endeavouring to buy off all who attempted to dig coal in the neighbourhood, and turning the water into the pits belonging to Matt. Collins and others (*ib.*, 32, i.). Briggs and Robinson, on the other hand, denied or explained the accusations, and accused Collins and his party of poisoning their water, whereby many of their horses died (*ib.*, 32, ii.).

On October 8, 1623 (*Cal. State Papers*, Dom., 1623-25, vol. cliii. 23), Sir Clement Throckmorton, Sir Barth. Hale, and Rich. Chamberlain, inform the council that they "have examined the differences between Matthew Collins and other citizens of Norwich (Coventry), and John Briggs and others, farmers of Bedworth coal mines, and decided that the farmers should not bore any holes which might endanger flooding the mines of the citizens, but shall be paid for damages incurred by the citizens running coal water through their mowing grounds." An early reference to boring operations.

So ended the coal war between the Warwickshire coal owners on this occasion, but in November, 1631, the Griff mines were drowned ; a catastrophe which was ascribed to the malicious contrivance of Robinson and Briggs, who had dammed and turned the land water out of its ancient course during certain recent floods (*Cal. State Papers*, Dom., 1631-33, vols. cciii. 92, 93, 94 ; cciv. 82). Robinson and Briggs, "farmers of the ancient coal mine at Bedworth," entirely denied that the dams were the cause of the drowning out of the Griff mines, and ascribed it to a great and sudden flood which occasioned great store of water to run into both their mines. (*Ib.*, vol. cciv. 83-87.)

A way was eventually found to turn the water by Eaton's Close, so that it should not be prejudicial to either party ; an arrangement which was sanctioned by the Council in February, 1632. (*Ib.*, vols. ccx. 68 ; ccxi. 43, 44.)

About the middle of this century the mines at Bedworth appear to have been in a somewhat backward condition. Fuller, writing in 1662 (*Worthies of England*, Warwickshire), who in his usual facetious way speaks of the mines here as the most southward of all coal mines north of the Thames, remarks that he is sorry to hear that these Black Indies, both in quantity and quality, "fall short of their former fruitfulness, and wishes they may recover their lost credit, being confident the earth there will *bleed* profit as plentifully as any, had the miners but the good hap to hit the right *vein* thereof."

When we again hear of the Griff mines in the early part of the following century, we find them very heavily burdened with water.

Of the coalfield of Leicestershire but little is heard.

Camden in 1607 (*Britannia*, Gibson's translation, ed. 1695, p. 445) speaks of Cole Overton as the residence of Henry de Beaumont, of the same famous family with the Viscounts Beaumont, and remarks that "it hath a name of distinction from pit-coles, being a bituminous earth hardened by nature, and here (to the Lord of the Manour's great profit) digg'd up in such plenty as to supply the neighbouring country all about with firing."

Fuller also alludes to the plentiful supply of coal here, and speaks of another village called Cold Orton in the same county, observing that this prefix might be applied to most of the towns in Leicestershire "if not warmed in winter with this under ground fewell, that above ground is so much decayed."

We now hear of coal being worked at Measham in this coalfield, but evidently not with the same satisfactory pecuniary results as at Coleorton. A record belonging to about 1623 (*Cal. State Papers*, Dom., 1623-25, vol. clvii. 51) contains a statement of losses sustained by Lord Beaumont on Measham coal mine. Thus others of this name appear to have suffered from their connection with the coal trade at this period, besides our quondam friend the ingenious Master Beaumont.

CHAPTER XX.

THE SEVENTEENTH CENTURY.—Continued.

The Shropshire coalfield: Railways. The Long Wall, or Shropshire method, of working coal. Manufacture of pitch, tar, and oil, from coal and shale. Forest of Dean coalfield. Curtailment of the rights claimed by the Free Miners. Regulations with regard to surfs; fencing abandoned pits; weighing coals. Attempts to smelt iron with coal. Use of coal in the copper works at Redbrook.

Of information regarding individual collieries in the Shropshire coalfield there is little or none, but we have evidence that in the method of digging coal pursued here, and other allied matters, this district was as far, if not further, advanced than any other part of the kingdom.

Its mines were doubtless not so large and deep as those in the north of England, nor had it probably any great establishments for raising water like those which existed there, but in the matters of getting and conveying coal it may almost be said to have led the van.

It contests with the north of England the honour of being the first to employ railways at its mines. At what date these were introduced we have no record. Professor Pepper (*Playbook of Metals*, p. 23) speaks of Coalbrookdale, in this county, being celebrated as the place where railways formed of wood were first used in the year 1620 and 1650, though without adducing any authority in support of the statement. There seems, however, to be no reason to doubt the fact, inasmuch as we have independent evidence that this method of conveying coal was in common use in various parts of the coal-field about the end of the seventeenth century. The railways appear also to have been thus early carried into the underground workings; and the same small wagons conveyed the coals direct from the working-places of the colliers to the point of shipment on the Severn.

The following extract from a letter of the Rev. Francis Brokesby, dated 1711 (Leland's *Itinerary*, vol. vi., p. 100, ed. 1768), furnishes some interesting information on this matter :

" I observed the like [mineral waters] near Shifnall, in Shropshire, and at Madeley, not far from thence, adjoining to Severn. Where (pardon my digression) are considerable cole mines into which they descend not, as in other places, into pitts ; but go in at the side of a hill, into which are long passages, both strait forward, and from thence on each side ; from whence they have dug the coles : which, by small carriages, with four wheels of above a foot diameter, thrust by men, they convey not only out of the long underground passages, but even to the boats which lye in the Severn ready to receive them : a sight with which, some years ago, I was not a little pleased."

While the letter above quoted enters into no details as to the method pursued in the actual digging, or getting, of the coal, the allusion to underground passages " from whence they have dug the coles," strikes the key-note of the mode of mining coal practised in this coalfield, and said to have been so for centuries (*Trans. Min. Inst. of Scotland*, vol. vii., p. 221). Far distant from the great northern coalfield, and situated on the opposite side of England, the way of mining coal adopted here was the direct antithesis of that which sprung up in the north. It forms the other great cardinal system of coal mining, which may be spoken of generally as the no-pillar system, and which was formerly known as "the long way,"[1] or Shropshire method, but is now usually called the "long wall" system, the latter name being applied to it by Mr. Bald in 1820 (see *Edinburgh Encyclopædia*, vol. xiv., pp. 348, 352), the earliest instance of the use of the term known to the writer.

Under this system, in its ordinary or typical form, the seam, or vein, of coal is entirely excavated as the workings advance, the space previously occupied by the coal, now called the *gob*, or *goaf*—a term derived (Richardson, *Accidents in Mines*, p. 31 ; Professor Phillips, *Ventilation of Mines*, p. 5 note), from a Cymraic word *ogof*, a cave or hollow—being partially or wholly packed or plugged up with stones and refuse, upon which the superincumbent strata settle down. Through the excavated part of the mine the necessary roads, called *gob-roads*, are maintained by strong packs of stone, some yards in thickness, built on both sides ; and when these become so crushed

---

[1] The designations "long way" and "long work," however, were not confined to true long wall, but likewise applied to other systems of working with broad faces.

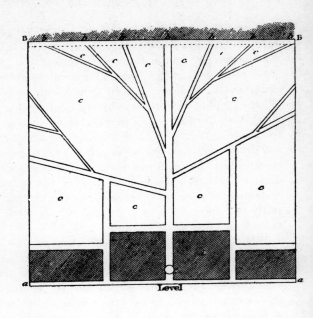

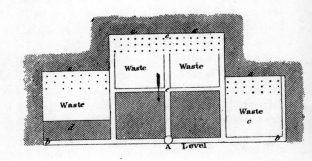

LONG WALL, O▮

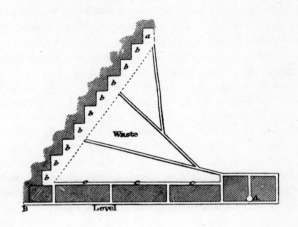

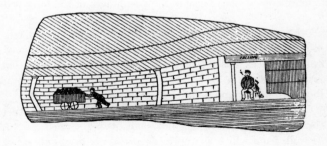

SHIRE METHOD OF WORKING.

down by the subsidence as to reduce the roads below the height required, additional height is obtained by cuttings made in the roof or floor ; so that frequently, in the course of time, almost the full height of the road has been cut out of the solid strata.

This bold and trenchant mode of mining coal bears a considerable likeness to the process pursued in working metalliferous mines, from which it was probably derived. It also savours much of the same spirit. The getting of the mineral is the paramount consideration ; the upholding of the surface goes for nothing.

This system of working possesses the great merit of simplicity. The whole of the coal seam is obtained at a single operation, and with the least expenditure of labour ; the weight of the super-incumbent strata rendering great assistance in bringing down the coal after it has been undermined by the miner's pick. The ventilation of the workings is also of the simplest character, the air-current sweeping along the face of the coal where the miners are at work.

Needless to remark that in cases where it is absolutely necessary to maintain the strata above unbroken, as for example to avoid damage to objects on the surface, and at moderate depths under rivers, etc., where the safety of the mine might be imperilled by the letting down of water, a portion of the coal must perforce be sacrificed, and the long wall system of working is under such conditions inadmissible. But otherwise, in one or other of its various forms, it may almost be said to be limited by no considerations of thickness or inclination of the coal seam, or depth from the surface. The more adverse the circumstances in point of thinness of seam, as well as of depth, the more conspicuous become the advantages of the long wall system.

In some other coalfields (notably in Yorkshire) modes of working sprung up, in which pillars of coal were more or less made use of, and the working faces formed of such a variety of breadths, that they almost constitute a complete bridge between the extreme types of bord-and-pillar and long wall.

It is in the Shropshire coalfield we first hear of the manufacture of pitch, tar, and oil, out of coal and shale, being carried on. A remarkable well, from which a supply of natural pitch was obtained, existed here, and had given the name of Pitchford to the place where it was situated. Camden, referring to this place in 1607, informs us (*Britannia*, Gough's translation, ed. 1789, vol. ii., p. 396) that on the surface of the well bitumen floated every day, and was most carefully scummed off, and used by the inhabitants as pitch. Fuller also gives an account of it in 1662 (*Worthies*, art. Shropshire).

Whether this well had anything to do with the establishment of the manufacture of pitch, etc., from minerals in this district, we are unable to say, though it seems not improbable. The subject began to attract attention in the latter part of the seventeenth century, the first direct notice relating to it being contained in a patent granted to Becher and Searle in 1681, for making pitch and tar out of pit coal ; and the matter is referred to in a work published by Becher in 1683 (*Fossil Fuel*, p. 404). In 1694 another patent was obtained by one Ele, and others, for making pitch, tar, and oil, out of a sort of stone ; and in 1697 a communication was sent to the Royal Society (*Phil. Trans.*, No. 228, p. 544) "On making pitch, tar, and oil, out of a blackish stone in Shropshire," by Martin Ele, the inventor of it.

That the distillation of coal had become an established industry in this coalfield is evidenced by the account given by the Rev. F. Brokesby in his letter dated 1711, to which reference has already been made. "Opposite to Madeley, on the other side of Severn," he says, "lies Broseley, where there is a pitch made, which as 'tis in time of war afforded cheaper than the ordinary pitch, so is as serviceable for ships and boats, and hence is sent down the Severn to Bewdley, Worcester, Gloucester, and Bristol, for that service. 'Tis by fire extracted out of their coles, which consist much of a resinous substance."

It is somewhat singular that it is when speaking of the coal in Shropshire, Fuller should give vent to his earnest wish that this fuel could be made available in the manufacture of iron, as well as his expectation that it would eventually be achieved. "Oh," he exclaims, "if this coale could be so charcked as to make iron melt out of the stone, as it maketh it in smiths' forges to be wrought in the bars. But 'Rome was not built all in one day,' and a new world of experiments is left to the discovery of posterity." May not this passage have stimulated those experiments made in this very coalfield in the following century, which carried the smelting of iron with coal to a triumphant consummation ?

During the long period which had elapsed since the free miners of the Forest of Dean became possessed of their peculiar mediæval franchises, changes of various kinds had been slowly but steadily going on. The small forges in which malleable iron was manufactured in early times direct from the ore, had become out of date, and were being superseded by the manufacture of *cast iron* in enlarged furnaces provided with a more powerful blast. The custom of digging minerals from small holes, opened up here, there, and everywhere, had likewise fallen behind the age.

A curious account of the Forest and its iron industry in this era is given by Dr. Parsons (Nicholls's *Forest of Dean*, p. 56):

"It abounds," this writer informs us, "with springs for the most part of a brownish or umber colour, occasioned by their passage through the veynes of oker, of which there is a great plenty, or else through the rushy tincture of the mineralls of the ore. The ground of the Forest is more inclined to wood and cole than corn, yet they have enough of it too. The inhabitants are, some of them, a sort of robustic wild people, that must be civilized by good discipline and government. The ore and cinder wherewith they make their iron (which is the great imployment of the poorer sort of inhabitants) 'tis dug in most parts of ye Forest, one in the bowells and the other towards the surface of the earth. But whether it be by virtue of the Forrest laws, or other custom, the head gaviler of the Forrest, or others deputed by him, provided they were born in the Hundred of St. Briavel's, may go into any man's grounds whatsoever within the limitation of the Forrest, and dig or delve for ore and cinders without any molestation. There are two sorts of ore: the best ore is your brush ore, of a blewish colour, very ponderous and full of shining specks like grains of silver; this affordeth the greatest quantity of iron, but being melted alone produceth a mettal very short and brittle. To remedy this inconvenience they make use of another material which they call cinder, it being nothing else but the refuse of the ore after the melting hath been extracted, which, being melted with the other in due quantity, gives it that excellent temper of toughness for which this iron is preferred before any other that is brought from foreign parts. But it is to be noted that in former times, when their works were few and their vents small, they made use of no other bellows but such as were moved by the strength of men, by reason whereof their fires were much less intense than in the furnaces they now employ; so that having in them only melted downe the principal part of the ore, they rejected the rest as useless and not worth their charge; this they call their cinder, and is found in an inexhaustible quantity throughout all the parts of the country where any glomerys formerly stood, for so they were then called."

In the reign of James I. we begin to hear of the introduction of innovations into this ancient royal demesne; not without difficulties being experienced in connection with the privileges which the free miners claimed as belonging to them by immemorial usage.

In February, 1612 (*ib.*, p. 24), the Earl of Pembroke obtained a grant for twenty-one years of a large annual supply of wood, together with liberty to dig for and take within any part of the Forest, or its precincts, such and so much mine ore, cinders, earth, sand, stone, breaks, moss, sea coal, and marle, as should be necessary for carrying on the ironworks let to him, or which he should erect; no person whatsoever, other than the earl, to be permitted during the term to take or carry out of the Forest any wood, timber, mine ore, or cinders, without the earl's consent, except such timber as should be used for his Majesty's shipping. And in June following the earl obtained a grant of all the Forest of Dean, including lands, mines, and quarries, for a term of forty years.

Notwithstanding the above grants the miners continued to dig for ore as before, without having obtained the earl's consent, and an information was in consequence filed against some of them by the attorney-general. Upon this an order was made by the court in January, 1613, that "those miners, and such others as had been accustomed to dig ore in the forest, upon the humble submission for their offences and acknowledgment that the soil was the king's, and that they had no interest therein, and upon their motion by counsel that they were poor and had no other means of support, and praying to be continued in their employment, should be permitted, *out of charity and grace and not of right*, to dig for mine ore, and cinders, to be carried to his Majesty's ironworks, and not to any other place, at the accustomed rates; and if the farmers of the king's ironworks should refuse to give those rates which, as well as the number of diggers, were to be ascertained by commissioners to be named by the court, that then they might sell the ore to others; but no new diggers were to be allowed, but only such poor men as were inhabitants of the said Forest."

No further steps were taken, the miners having seemingly acquiesced in this arrangement. Thus were their ancient privileges to some extent curtailed, and the original title of the crown to the minerals in a manner re-established.

The project for the employment of coal in the smelting of iron, which had been entertained when the grants were made to the Earl of Pembroke in 1612, having come to nothing, a proposal to farm the coal mines in the Forest was made to the council in 1635 (*Cal. State Papers*, Dom., 1635, vol. ccciii. 61) by one, Edward Tyringham (or Terringham). The king's surveyor was accordingly instructed to confer with the auditor of the county as to what profit came to his Majesty from these coal mines, and what parties made profit out of them and by what warrant. It was ascertained that the auditor had no record touching them, and that they had yielded

small or no benefit to his Majesty, "for the miners pretend a custom
to dig coals, paying a small duty for every pit opened by the hands
of an officer called the Gawler or Gavelour of the Forest.   The Lord
Chamberlain claimed the coal mines under a lease granted 13th
June, 9th James, to the late Earl of Pembroke.   It was conceived
that the mines open at the making of that lease were granted
thereby, but that no new mines might be opened without the license
of the lessor " (see also *ut supra*, vol. cccvii. 8).

The claims of the miners, and of the Lord Chamberlain, appear to
have been alike set aside, and in 1637 (Nicholls's *Forest of Dean*, p.
27) a grant was made to Terringham of "all the mines of coal and
quarries of grindstones within the Forest of Dean, and in all places
within the limits and perambulations thereof, as well those within his
Majesty's demesne lands, and the waste and soil there, as also all
such as lay within the lands of any of his Majesty's subjects within
the perambulation of the said Forest, to his Majesty reserved or
lawfully belonging, to hold for thirty-one years at the yearly rent
of £30."

This lease, however, seems to have brought Terringham nothing
but trouble and expense, probably owing to difficulties with the free
miners.   He is stated to have spent £2,500 in defending his rights,
and in the end was granted an annuity of £300 out of the fee-farm
rents of the Forest in lieu of the lease.

This arrangement would no doubt be subverted shortly afterwards
by the civil wars; but at the Restoration, in 1660, we find Francis,
eldest son of Edward Terringham, petitioning the Crown regarding
the coal mines in the Forest (*Cal. State Papers*, Dom., 1660-61, p.
295), the annuity granted to his father having still about eight years
to run.   Whether they were then restored to him does not appear.
But in 1668 an important Act of Parliament was passed relating to
the Forest (Nicholls, pp. 42, 43, 231), providing, among other things,
that all lawful rights and privileges relating to minerals in the Forest
were to continue, with permission to the Crown to lease coal mines
and stone quarries for periods not exceeding thirty-one years; and
this latter provision was immediately acted upon, the coal mines and
quarries of grindstones being granted to Francis Tyringham, Esq.,
for thirty-one years, at a rental of £30 per annum.

Notices of the appointment of gavellers by the Crown recommence
immediately after the Restoration.   The office of the Gawle, called
"le Gawle above the wood," was granted (Jones's *Index to the
Originalia*, 12 Chas. II.) to Baynham Throgmorton, jun., in 1660.
One Ryley was appointed Master, or Keeper, of the Gawle in

1692-93 (4 Will. and Mary); and one Howe to the same post in 1702-3 (1 Queen Anne).

From the proceedings of a local tribunal known as the Mine Law Court, the earliest extant records of which belong to the year 1668 (Nicholls, pp. 45, 232), though references to it occur previous to this period, we obtain some insight into the state of mining in the Forest. The court consisted of a jury of forty-eight free miners, who met periodically and regulated all matters relating to the coal and iron industries of the Forest.

As late as 1668, pack-horses alone appear to have been employed by the miners in the conveyance of minerals. In an order relating to the western half of the district, made in this year by the Mine Law Court (Nicholls, p. 45—said to be 1663, but see p. 232), it was set down that no manner of carriage was to be used in transporting minerals out of the Forest, nor more than four horses to be kept by any one party.

The increasing length and cost of the adits, or "surfs," for draining the pits, rendered it necessary to introduce modifications into the ancient Laws and Customs of the miners. In early times, as already adverted to, the bounds of a mine had been fixed at the distance to which the miner could throw the rubbish from his pit. Taking advantage of this ancient custom, when an adit was driven by any party, other miners came and sunk pits quite near, in order to secure a share of the benefit of free drainage. To put a stop to this unfair proceeding the following order (Nicholls, p. 232) was issued by the Mine Law Court in 1678 :

" Whereas the myners within this Forest are at a very great charge to make surffes for the dreyning of their pitts to get cole, wch when they have finished others sincke pitts so near them that they are deprived of the benefit of their labour and charge, to their very great loss and damage : To remedie whereof it is now ordered that after a surffe is made, noe myner shall come to work within 100 yards of that surffe to the prejudice of the undertakers without their consents, and without being contributory to the making of the said surffe, upon payne of forfeiting 100 dozen of good fire coal, the one moiety to the king's Matie, and the other to the myner that shall sue for the same."

The miners in the Forest were evidently still only in the pit and adit stage of mining. By a subsequent order made in 1692 (ib., p. 233), the distance of 100 yards was further extended to 300 yards.

Among other enactments made by the Mine Law Court it may be mentioned that in 1687 it was ordered that all coal pits, and dangerous mine pits when not in working, should be securely fenced, under a penalty of ten shillings; a salutary regulation which was repeated in 1707, under a penalty of twenty shillings. And by an order in 1701, miners were required to keep a pair of scales at their pits for weighing their coal, none of which was to be sent away unweighed. Curiously in the rules laid down by the Mine Law Court, people living outside of the Forest are denominated "foreigners."

The question of preserving wood *versus* making iron, was much agitated in the Forest of Dean in the course of the seventeenth century; ironworks having been built and again demolished several times during this period, as the one interest or the other prevailed for the time being. It is therefore not surprising that this locality should have been the scene of some of the early attempts to substitute coal for wood in the making of iron.

A reference to the projected use of coal in the ironworks occurs, as we have seen, in the lease made to the Earl of Pembroke in 1612. Again in 1636-37 (*Cal. State Papers*, Dom., 1636-37, vol. cccxli. 105) we find Sir Philiberto Vernatti and Captain Thomas Whitmore petitioning the king for the use of certain deserted furnaces in the Forest, together with a supply of ironstone, for putting their invention of making iron with sea coal into practice—a patent for which process was granted to Vernatti in 1636. They were opposed, however, by the iron masters in the Forest, and whether the suit was granted does not appear.

During the time of the Commonwealth, about 1651-56, a powerful company, consisting of Captain Birch, Major Wildman, and many others—Cromwell himself being interested—were at great cost in their attempts to smelt iron with coal in the Forest, in wind furnaces, and in pots for keeping the ore separate from the coal (Dudley's *Metallum Martis*, reprint 1854, pp. 16-18; Nicholls, p. 220), but all to no purpose, their efforts, like those of so many others, ending in disastrous failure.

In an account of the ironworks in the Forest, communicated to the Royal Society by Henry Powle, in 1677-78 (*Phil. Trans.*, No. 137, p. 931), allusion is made to the attempts to smelt with coal, and to this fuel having proved ineffectual for the purpose.

In the latter half of the century, however, coal was being conveyed from the Forest of Dean to copper works at Redbrook—a name suggestive of the Rio Tinto in Spain—where this fuel had probably begun to be used in the smelting of the copper ore. Coal was taken to Redbrook in 1668 (Nicholls, p. 232); and is mentioned in 1694 (*ib.*, p. 233), as intended for the copper works there. If coal had already come to be so used at Redbrook at the former of these two dates, it is somewhat earlier than Sir John Pettus would have us believe ; who, writing in 1686 (*Fleta Minor : Essays on Words Metallic*), says of sea coal and pit coal, "these are not useful to metals "—a statement which began to be abundantly disproved almost as soon as uttered, as will be seen hereafter.

CHAPTER XXI.

THE SEVENTEENTH CENTURY.--Continued.

The Somersetshire coalfield : Attempt to monopolize the Bristol coal trade. Export of coal from Bristol. Firedamp in the mines of the Mendip district. Attempts to smelt iron with coal. The Cumberland coalfield : Export of coal. Whitehaven collieries. Collieries at Workington, etc. The North Wales coalfield : Export of coal. Various notices of collieries. Difficulties with firedamp, and severe explosion at Mostyn. The South Wales coalfield : Export of coal from Swansea and Milford. Collieries at Neath. Sir Humphry Mackworth's copper works and coal mines. Coffering of shafts. Sailing wagons, and engines. Smelting copper with coal. Railways.

AN attempt to secure a monopoly of the coal trade of the Bristol neighbourhood, made by a person of the name of Player, was the occasion of a petition being addressed by the citizens to the Privy Council. The document (Harleian MSS., Brit. Mus., No. 368, pencil fo. 11) bears no date. It is considered at the British Museum (see also Ricart's *Kalendar*, p. 84, Camden Society), to belong to the reign of James I. It is as follows :

"The humble petition of the Mayor and Commonaltye of the cytie of Bristoll.

"To the right honorable the Lordes of His Maties moste honorable Pryvie Counsell.

"That whereas the poorer sorte of thinhabitantes in Bristoll doe vse to burne stone coale *alias* sea coale in their howses, wch coale they have had from Kinges Woode and other places adioyninge to the sayd cytie, payenge for the same not above three pence halfe penye for a bushell beinge broughte home to theire howses, wch hath bin a verye great benefytt vnto them, not beinge hable to buye woodde wch ys verye deere and scarse to be had.

"Soe yt ys that one Arthur Player, nowe inhabitinge in the castle of Bristoll, of a greidye desyer of gayne to him selfe hath to the greate grievaunce of all the poore people of the sayd cytie and places adioyninge engrossed and taken into his handes all the coale pyttes in Kingeswood afore sayde and other places in the countye of Gloucester neere adioyninge to the sayd cytie, and geveth yerelye rentes to have them all shutte vppe and not wroughte, savinge only some fewe at his pleasure, whereby the pryse of the sayd coale ys much enhaunsed, and hath cutte and dimished [1] the sackes of such as vse to bringe coale to the said cytie and broughte euery sacke from twoe bushells to conteyne but one bushell and three peckes for some speciall gayne to him selfe.

"Your supplyantes doe therefore moste humblye beseeche your good Lordshippes to take such order herein for the relieffe of the sayd poore people as to your honorable wysdomes shall seeme moste expediente. And your supplyantes shall ever praye, etc.

to directe your honorable lettres to Sr George Grigge, knight, etc., aucthorisynge . . . . to heare examyne and ende the same or otherwise to certyfye your honours."

The following regulation as to the sale of coal at Bristol (Egerton MSS., Brit. Mus., No. 2,044, fo. 12) was made in the time of John Barker, Mayor, 20th Oct., 1606:

"Item it is ordained that the colliers which bring stone coale to this cittie to be sould shall bring and sell the same either in sacks which containe just one bushell or two bushells in every sack, and to sell their cole in such sacks filled and none other, or otherwise shall sell their cole by bushell by heape, the bushell to be made according to the statute."

In 1609 the king granted to Captain Edward Fitzgerald (*Cal. State Papers*, Dom., 1603-10, p. 499), a lease of all coal mines, stone, and slate, in the Forest of Kingswood, in counties Gloucester and Somerset. Fitzgerald, however, does not appear to have obtained possession of the mines, as in the following year we find him writing to Salisbury (*ib.*, p. 606) informing him that he is ill and cannot attend him, and begging favour for his petition concerning the coal mines in the Forest of Kingswood, granted him by the king, but kept from him by the defendants. Whether anything further transpired in the matter does not appear.

In 1679 the coal pits at Kingswood are referred to as a sight worth seeing by visitors to the district (*Life of Locke*, p. 134), indicating that the working of coal was being prosecuted on a considerable scale.

[1] Diminished.

That some quantity of coal was being exported from Bristol in the early part of this century is shown by the fact that in 1617 the farmers of the coal taxes received a sum of £108 15s. for coal transported from that port (*Proc. Arch. Inst.*, Newcastle, 1852, vol. i., p. 220); which at the foreign duty of 5s. per chaldron equals 435 chaldrons; this being apparently independent of the coasting trade, which would no doubt be considerable.

Bristleton was likewise the scene of active mining operations. Gibson, in 1695 (*Britannia*, p. 82), speaks of this place as abounding in the same sort of coals that are brought from Newcastle; and adds that in several places of the adjacent country as far as Stratton and Mendip Hills, as also northward in Gloucestershire, are found veins of this coal, which afford a strong and cheap firing to all these parts.

Mention occurs (Jones's *Index to the Originalia*, 12 Chas. II.), of a coal mine in the manor of Faringdon Gurney being demised to one Hugh Tint in 1660.

The collieries of the Mendip district are heard of in this era in connection with the prevalence of firedamp there. In a paper on Firy Damps in Mines, communicated to the Royal Society, in 1681, by Mr. J. Beaumont (*Philosophical Collections*, No. 1, p. 6), this writer informs us that in the middle and more easterly coal works there these damps are so very frequent that scarce a pit fails of them. "Many men of late years have been there killed, many others maimed and burnt; some have been blown up at the work's mouth, the turn-beam which hangs over the shaft has been thrown off its frame by the force of it." To combat the firedamp the miners endeavoured to "keep their air very quick," and made use of very thin candles.

The phenomenon of people being shot out of pits, alluded to in the above passage, was a frequent, indeed almost regular concomitant of early colliery explosions of any magnitude, as will be seen hereafter. It may possibly have been due to the limited extent of the workings, the narrowness of the main underground roads, and the small size and comparative shallowness of the shafts at the time. Somersetshire and Gloucestershire in particular were remarkable for the small size of their shafts, which as late as the middle of the present century continued to be made only four or five feet in diameter.

Some of the numerous unsuccessful attempts to utilize coal in smelting minerals were made in this coalfield.

As already mentioned, Dr. Jorden, of Bath, obtained a patent in

1632 for melting tin, iron, lead, and copper, with pit coal, sea coal, peat, and turf. His efforts were specially directed to the smelting of tin with coal ; and though he failed to carry his experiments to a successful conclusion, in a commercial sense at least, he was confident that it was quite practicable to do so.—Fuller's *Worthies*, art. Devonshire ; Jorden's *Discourse of Natural Bathes.*

Various schemes for smelting iron with coal in the neighbourhood of Bristol were entered into during the time of the Commonwealth. Dud Dudley appears to have been the first to project a work of the kind here in 1651 (*Metallum Martis*, reprint 1854, p. 16), but he became involved in a law-suit with his partners, which led to the abandonment of the scheme.

After their failure in the Forest of Dean, Captain Birch and his partners erected new works at Bristol (*ib.*, p. 18) ; but succeeding no better than before, they desisted in 1656. And Captain John Copley, who obtained a patent from Cromwell, and set up works near the Forest of Kingswood, immediately afterwards, though he had the assistance of Dud Dudley to make his bellows blow, who accomplished the task so successfully "that one man may blow them with pleasure the space of an hour or two," nevertheless soon tired of his experiments, and desisted in 1657 ; after which the flames and the smoke of the blast furnace were no more seen in the Bristol neighbourhood.

The circumstance of the Cumberland coalfield transporting 1155 chaldrons of coal abroad in 1617, may be taken to indicate some degree of activity in the coal trade here, already in the early part of the seventeenth century.

A print is in existence giving "a south-east view of Whitehaven in 1642," which shows a small pier and six or eight three-masted ships behind it. It also shows a string of pack-horses conveying what is surmised to be coals to the ships, though Mr. Fletcher, in his memoir on the Archæology of the West Cumberland Coal Trade (*Trans. of the Cumberland and Westmoreland Antiq. and Archæol. Society,* iii. 271), expresses doubts on the subject. But he seems to have been of opinion that the exportation of coal from Whitehaven commenced at a later period than it really did.

One of the earliest leases of coal in this coalfield, of which there is mention, was made by the governors of St. Bees Grammar School in 1650 (*Trans. Fed. Inst.*, vii. 614). In this they demised "all that pit of Coalgrove, or Bearmouth, already sunk within the closes called Stephen Ridding, in the parish of St. Bees, holden of the

school under the rent of 4s.," with liberty to dig for coal therein for
the term of four years, at the yearly rent of £3.

The origin of the term "coalgrove" we have already seen. The
term "bearmouth" was applied to level or sloping roads into the
mines of this district, on account of the coals having been carried up
these roads by coal-bearers.

In the course of the seventeenth century the Whitehaven coal
trade underwent considerable development at the hands of the
Lowther family, into whose possession the lands passed under a
foreclosed mortgage in the reign of Charles I. When Sir Christopher
Lowther died, in 1644, his son John (afterwards Sir John Lowther),
who succeeded to the estate, was only an infant about eighteen
months old.

On growing up, Sir John set himself to improve his property, and
particularly to promote a trade in coal, with which it abounded.
And in order to further his projects and anticipate competition
(Hutchinson's *Cumberland*, ii. 48), he obtained from Charles II., in
1666, all the ungranted lands in the neighbourhood ; and in 1678 a
further grant of all the lands for two miles northwards between high
and low water mark.

At the commencement to work coal near Whitehaven, a level or
watercourse was driven from the bottom of the valley near the
Powbeck to the south of the town, starting from near the copperas
works. This was for the purpose of draining a seam of coal known
as the Bannock band, which it cut at a distance of about 900 yards.
The driving of this level is spoken of as Sir John Lowther's first
great engineering performance. The date at which it was carried
out is somewhat uncertain, but is supposed to have been about
1660.

This level drained a considerable area of coal, which was drawn out
of pits from 60 to 180 feet deep. The coals were at this period
drawn by men with jack-rolls, or windlasses, and were carried from
the pits to the harbour on the backs of small pack-horses (Hutchinson's *Cumberland*, ii. 66).

A little later we find Sir John working another and superior
seam of coal known as the Prior or Main band, near Greenbank,
where it cropped out to the surface. The wages book of this
colliery is still extant at Whitehaven Castle (R. W. Moore, *Trans.
Fed. Inst.*, vii. 618). It dates from the beginning of the year 1675.
The following curious little pay-bill is extracted from it, and is
entitled "An accompt of all wages and disbursements upon Greenbank Colliery in ye week ended ye 14th April, 1675":

Tons	Bur.		Days.	£	s.	d.
47	2	Three haggers, 42 burthens, 8½d., . .	6	00	12	09
26	2	Two haggers, ...	5	00	07	01
73	4	2 bearers, 7½d. per day, . . .	6	00	11	03
		2 bearers, ...	5	00	06	03
		3 wattermen and bankman, . . .	6	00	16	03
		4 men in a dike 6 days, and 2 men 7 days,.		01	05	04
		John Gilliat using a stone,. . . .		00	00	06
		Pᵈ for one spoutch and 3 swills, . . .		,,	,,	,,9
		Pᵈ item : meales smith's note, . ⸱ .		00	19	04
		Pᵈ leadings, 22 tons, ...		01	02	00
		Sum pᵈ		06	01	06

From the above bill the coal appears to have been still carried on the backs of coal-bearers, at the collieries working on the outcrops of the coal seams. Mr. Moore is disposed to question this, but there seems to be no valid reason for not accepting the fact as stated, even granting that corves were introduced at Greenbank not long subsequently. Bearers continued to be employed at collieries in the east of Scotland for about 180 years later. Eight burthens formed a ton, and the Cumberland ton from the earliest times has (according to Mr. Fletcher) been 22 cwt.

This is probably the colliery referred to by Sir John Lowther in a document dated 1680, where he states that "he has thought fitt to cease working where he formerly gott coals, and has opened a new mine where coals are had much cheaper than in the said old works," though these were not by any means exhausted (Mr. Fletcher's *Memoir*, Appendix II.).

From the same document it appears that Whitehaven had now got the large share of the Dublin coal trade (formerly held by the collieries of the Dee) ; also that a number of other parties were shipping coal at Whitehaven, in addition to Sir John Lowther.

An event of some importance in the history of this district was the discovery of the Main band in the vicinity of Whitehaven, about the end of the century, at a depth of about 120 feet. The coal being under level, pits were sunk to win it, and horse gins erected for drawing the water as well as the coals—the neighbourhood taking the name of "The Gins," doubtless from the fact of these machines being first seen there.

In 1698 the output of coal at the Howgill Colliery, as this group of pits were termed, amounted to 350 tons weekly, drawn out of several pits by means of horse gins, partly from the Main and partly from the Bannock band (*Trans. Fed. Inst.*, vii. 620). The coals were

now led to the harbour in carts.   Greenbank Colliery was still
working and producing 35 tons weekly ; and Sir John Lowther was
also working another small colliery situated between Whitehaven
and Parton.

During the time of Sir John (who died in 1705) mining at Whitehaven passed from the first into the second or pit and adit stage,
and finally into the third stage, in which both water and coals were
drawn by machinery.   His achievements in this direction are thus
referred to in a document assigned by Mr. Fletcher to about the
year 1706 :

"The country adjacent afforded coals sufficient for a staple export,
but a great part of them were in the hands of small freeholders, and
could not be wrought without great and expensive levels, which must
go through several people's lands, and, draining all upon the rise,
would enable such as have none of the charge to under sell and ruine
those who did, so that the working of them under these circumstances was impracticable, and they were lost as well to the owners
as to the country, until Sir John Lowther, at his own cost, introduced
the art of carrying on levels, and of working what was under level
by engines, a thing unknown in that country before."

From this time the Whitehaven coal trade underwent rapid
development.   From colliery pay-bills, quoted by Mr. Fletcher, it
appears that in the year 1709 there were seven pits at work
producing in the aggregate from 700 to 800 tons weekly, or about
38,000 tons per annum.   The colliery workpeople were still all paid
by day's wages, viz., haggers (coal hewers), 10d. per day ; trailers
(putters), 8d. ; winders, 8d. ; corvers (basket makers), 1s.

As yet the pits were extremely shallow, but the rapid deepening
of them which ensued, combined with the introduction of the newest
improvements, as well as the invention of others, caused the Whitehaven mines to rise subsequently to a foremost place among the
collieries of the kingdom.

Coal was likewise being worked and exported by the Curwen
family at Workington in the middle of the seventeenth century.   In
1661 we find Sir Pat. Curwen writing to one Jos. Williamson (*Cal.
State Papers*, Dom., 1660-61, p. 472), regarding the customs of coal
on the west coast.   Sandford, describing Workington in 1676 (Mr.
Fletcher, *ut sup.*, p. 297), speaks of their being "a fair haven but not
so much now frequented by ships, the coleyery being decayed there-
about."   And Denton (Thomas), who wrote in 1688,[1] states that

---

[1] Date and Christian name kindly furnished to the writer by R. S.
Ferguson, Esq.

there is "a salt pan and colliery worth £20 per annum within the demesne."

Collieries also existed at this period in various other parts of Cumberland (Mr. Fletcher, *ut sup.*, p. 305), as at Gilcrux, Oughterside, Bolton, and Sebergham.   In 1681, William Orfeur, Esq., of High Close, Plumbland, made his will, by which he bequeathed to his eldest son, among other things, "all manner of geare belonging to my colliery at Outersyde."

That the working of coal below the level of free-drainage, by means of pits, was going on in Wales in the beginning of the seventeenth century, is shown by the circumstance that in 1618 (*Cal. State Papers*, Dom., Addenda, 1580-1625, vol. xli. 85) the fact of coal having advanced in price from 3s. to 6s. 8d. per chaldron is alleged to have been due to many of the pits being drowned.

Little coal appears to have been exported abroad from the collieries on the Dee in 1617, the port of Chester and Liverpool combined, as we have seen, only sending away 1,879½ chaldrons. But an active trade with Ireland was going on in this era (Pennant's *Tours in Wales*, vol. i., p. 23, ed. 1810).   The following are a few records relating to the collieries of this district.

Mention occurs in 1614 (*Cal. State Papers*, Dom., 1611-18, p. 241) of a grant to Sir John Wynn, Bart., of purchase of the lease of lands, coal mines, etc., cos. Carnarvon, Anglesea, and Flint, value £34 17s. 6d. per annum.

The collieries at Mostyn would appear to have been inactive about 1630, as in an account of the "revenue of the Earldom of Chester as they stand charged to the Crown" (Sir J. Doddridge's account of the *Stannaries*, p. 92), "the mines of coal and wood within the Mannor of Mostyn," are set down at the small sum of 10s.   Soon afterwards, however, we hear of a colliery being opened up, in which firedamp was found to be a source of difficulty and danger, as will be adverted to forthwith.

By letters patent, in 1636-37 (Bainbridge's *Law of Mines*, 4th ed., p. 137), the crown made a grant of coal within the commons, waste grounds, or marshes, of the manor of Englefield, in Flint.   A law-suit supervened as to whether this grant included the coal underneath the land lying between high and low water marks, called the "White Sands," part of the foreshore of the estuary of the Dee.   The claim of the Crown was dismissed.

Yarranton, writing in 1677 (*England's Improvement*, p. 192), speaks of coal being brought to Chester from a colliery at Aston, in Flint ; and Gibson, in 1695 (*Britannia*, p. 692), refers to the sinking of new coal pits in the township of Leeswood, in the parish of Mold.

In Denbigh, the remaining term of years in a lease of all the mines of coal, stone, and lead, and the materials to make lead, within the whole lordship of Bromfield and Yale, which had been granted to Richard Grosvenor, of Eaton, Esq., deceased, was assigned to John Wich, citizen of London, by William Colly, Mr. Grosvenor's executor, 10th March, 1633, but two days later was reassigned by Wich to Colly (Harleian MSS, 2,002, 7, 253; 10, 274).

In 1667 Sir Cyril Wyche obtained a grant (*Cal. State Papers*, Dom., 1667, p. 497), for thirty-one years, of all the lead and coal mines in the lordship of Denbigh, at 20s. a year, and one-tenth of the ore and coals that shall be found.

To a paper prepared for the Royal Society, by Mr. Roger Mostyn, in 1677 (*Phil. Trans.*, No. 136, p. 895), we are indebted for the only account which has been preserved, giving a description of the early difficulties of coal miners occasioned by firedamp; as well as a graphic relation of the phenomena connected with an explosion of great violence which took place at Mostyn in 1675.

It was in opening out a new colliery here, about 1640, on a seam of coal 5 yards in thickness, that firedamp is first heard of in this district. The coal, when first sunk to, was so full of water that it could not be pierced down to the bottom, but an excavation (witchet or cave) was driven out in the middle of the seam for gaining room to work, and draining the water to the bottom of the shaft, or eye of the pit.

After they had gone a considerable distance underground, and were in want of fresh air, the firedamp gradually began to "breed." At first the workmen made but a sport of it, toying with it with their lighted candles, till one morning "the first collier that went down, going forward in the witchet with his candle in his hand, the damp presently darted out violently at his candle that it struck the man clean down, singed all his hair and clothes, and disabled him from working hereafter."

In consequence of some warnings of this sort, the colliers selected one of their number more resolute than the rest—a man of purpose —to go down into the mine some time before them every morning to fire, or explode, the small accumulations of the gas. Clothing himself with the worst rags he had, saturated with water, this individual—subsequently known as the "fireman"—advanced towards the places where firedamp was supposed to exist, and crawling

forward held a long pole before him with one or more lighted candles
at its end. This ignited the firedamp if present, and produced an
explosion of more or less violence, according to the quantity of gas
accumulated. As the flame ran along the roof the fireman lay flat on
the floor of the mine till it passed over him. When his operations
had been completed the rest of the colliers entered the pit, and the
motion of the air caused by their working prevented the gas from
collecting during the day.

This is the earliest account we have of this primitive method of
dealing with firedamp, which may be termed the firing system, and
which was subsequently practised in many of the coalfields when
difficulties with the gas had become more general. It is spoken of
as "the ordinary way" by Professor Sinclair in 1672 (*Hydrostaticks*,
p. 294), and we have records of its being pursued at a later date
in Shropshire, Staffordshire, Leicestershire, Lancashire, Yorkshire,
Cumberland, and South Wales.

After the workings of the pit at Mostyn above referred to had
been fully opened out, firedamp ceased to annoy the miners, and was
not further seen or heard of till the latter end of the year 1675. At
this time it was encountered in sinking a pit to a seam of coal which
had been discovered at a depth of 14 yards below the former seam,
though not in such quantity as to occasion much inconvenience.

But shortly afterwards a commencement was made to sink an
underground pit (staple, or blind pit), below the workings made in
this new seam, at a distance of 16 to 17 yards from the bottom of the
pit communicating with the surface ; and in this operation the miners
were greatly harassed by firedamp, which annoyed them the more
the deeper they sank, "whereby they saw that the want of air was the
great encourager of this damp." By continuous working, however,
they carried this underground pit down a distance of fifteen yards.

Leaving off at this depth at the end of a week, on returning on
Monday so much firedamp had accumulated in the sinking that it
was deemed necessary to fire it. This was accordingly done by
means of a long pole and lighted candles ; but the explosion which
resulted was so alarmingly violent as to deter the sinkers from
resuming work. This was, however, merely the precursor of an
explosion of much greater severity which followed, the account of
which is given in the words of the original paper :

"In this juncture there was a cessation of work for three days,
and then the steward, thinking to fetch a compass about from the
eye of the pit that came from the day, and to bring wind by a
secure way along with him, that if it burst again it might be done

without danger to men's lives, went down and took two men along
with him, which served his turn for this time. He was no sooner
down but the rest of the workmen that had wrought there, disdain-
ing to be left behind in such a time of danger, hastened down after
them, and one of them, more indiscreet than the rest, went headlong
with his candle over the eye of the damp pit, at which the damp
immediately catched, and flew over all the hollows of the work, with
a great wind and a continual fire, and a prodigious roaring noise.
The men, at first appearance of it, had most of them fallen on their
faces, and hid themselves as well as they could in the loose slack or
small coal, and under the shelter of posts ; yet, nevertheless, the
damp returning out of the hollows, and drawing towards the eye of
the pit, it came up with incredible force, the wind and fire tore most
of their clothes off their backs, and singed what was left, burning
their hair, faces, and hands, the blast falling so sharp on their skin
as if they had been whipped with rods ; some that had least shelter
were carried 15 or 16 yards from their first station, and beaten
against the roof of the coal and sides of the posts, and lay afterwards
a good while senseless, so that it was long before they could hear or
find each other.   As it drew up to the day pit, it caught one of the
men along with it that was next the eye, and ascended with such a
terrible crack, not unlike, but more shrill than a cannon, so that it
was heard 15 miles off along with the wind, and such a pillar of
smoke as darkened all the sky for a great while.   The brow of the
hill above the pit was 18 yards high, and on it grew trees 14 or 15
yards long, yet the man's body and other things from the pit were
seen above the tops of the highest trees, at least 100 yards.   On
this pit stood a horse engine of substantial timber and strong ironwork, on which lay a trunk or barrel for winding the rope up and
down, of above 1,000 lb. weight ; it was then in motion, one bucket
going down and the other coming up full of water.   This trunk was
fastened to the frame with locks and bolts of iron ; yet it was
thrown up and carried a good way from the pit, and pieces of it,
though bound with iron hoops and strong nails, blown into the
neighbouring woods, as were also the two buckets, and the ends of
the rope, after the buckets were blown from them, stood awhile
upright in the air like pikes, and then came leisurely down.   The
whole frame of the engine was moved out of its place, and the
clothes, caps, and hats, of those men that escaped, were afterwards
found shattered to pieces, and thrown into the woods a great way
from the pit.   This happened the beginning of February, 1675,
being a time when other damps are scarcely felt or heard of."

According to the above account, the body of the man blown up the pit was carried to a height of at least 35 yards into the air.

Little information seems to be obtainable regarding the collieries and coal trade of the great coalfield of South Wales in this era. The foreign export of coal was still small, however, in the beginning of the century ; the balance-sheet of the farmers of the coal taxes for the year 1617, showing that 1,245 chaldrons were shipped abroad from Swansea, and 747½ from Milford in this year.

Various references to the coasting trade occur in the *State Papers* in 1666-67, when the trade of the east coast was interrupted owing to the Dutch War. In 1666 the Welsh coal trade is noticed, and there is mention of a vessel coming to Swansea port for coal (*Cal. State Papers*, Dom., 1666-67, pp. 23, 290). In 1667, in a communication from Plymouth (*ib.*, p. 567), it is stated that "several colliers have come in from Wales, which it is hoped will allay the high price of 40s. a quarter now paid for coals."

In the same year (*Cal. State Papers*, Dom., 1667, p. 107), in a communication from Pembroke, it is stated that "The 'Garland' has sailed for Plymouth with twenty laden colliers "; and reference also occurs to coals from Swansea in a small bark (*ib.*, p. 480).

There appears to have been considerable industrial activity in the Neath district in the latter part of the seventeenth century.

Coal pits belonging to the demesne of Eagle's Bush, in the vicinity of this place, are incidentally mentioned by Bishop Gibson in 1695 (*Britannia*, p. 693).

From the account furnished by Waller (in his *Essay on the Value of the Mines late of Sir Carberry Price*, published in 1698) of the collieries and copper works of Sir Humphry Mackworth, it is evident that mining and metallurgy were both well up to date in this neighbourhood, due in large measure to this gentleman, who appears to have belonged to Shropshire.

Regarding the sagacity and ingenuity of Sir Humphry, Waller observes as follows :

" His new method of coffering out the water from his shafts and sinking pits and thereby preventing the charge of water engines, and also recovering a large vein of coal by that means, which was in vain attempted by other artists ; and his new sailing wagons, for the cheap carriage of his coal to the water-side, whereby one horse does the work of ten at all times, but when any wind is stirring, one man and a small sail does the work of twenty, do sufficiently show what his genius is capable of in matters of that nature.

"And I believe he is the first gentleman in this part of the world that hath set up sailing engines on land, driven by the wind, not for any curiosity, but for real profit."

Sir Humphry's schemes for enlisting the force of the wind in his service are also referred to by Yalden in his poem, where he says of him :

> "The winds thy slaves their useful succour join,
> Convey thy ore, and labour at thy mine."

After mentioning Sir Humphry's prudent methods for reducing all his undertakings to a certainty, "his copper-men working by the tun, and his colliers by the weigh at a certain price," Waller refers to the convenient situation of his copper works (where coal was evidently being used in smelting the ore), "which is such," he says, "that his men may run the coal with wheel-barrows into the very furnaces, and bring the ore by water to within a stone's cast of the work."

Sir Humphry's railway, or waggon-way, from his collieries to the waterside, crossed the highway from Neath to Cardiff. After it had been in use above eight years a difference arose between him and the burgesses of Neath, and the latter succeeded in obtaining a verdict from the Grand Jury at Cardiff declaring the waggon-way to be a "nusance," and a portion of it was torn up and the rails cut in pieces. In some evidence brought forward, probably about 1706 ("The Case of Sir Humphry Mackworth on the Report of his Complaints for Breach of Privelege"—undated), to rebut the verdict of the Cardiff jury, which is stated to have been obtained by surprise, the following interesting passage occurs relating to the early use of railways :

"These waggon-ways are very common, and frequently made use of about Newcastle, and also about Broseley, Bentall, and other places, in Shropshire, and are so far from being Nusances, that they have ever been esteemed very useful to preserve the roads, which would be otherwise made very bad and deep by the carriage of coal in common waggons and carts."

In connection with the above case there is mention of a colliery at Britton-ferry, where the Mansells, the owners of the lands, had long been shipping away coals.

CHAPTER XXII.

THE SEVENTEENTH CENTURY.—CONTINUED.

Coke-making. Blasting with gunpowder. Rise of great mining and smelting companies. Improvement of rivers; and erection of lighthouses on the coast.

IN connection with the efforts being made in various directions in this era to substitute coal for wood and charcoal, the process of coking, or cooking, the mineral, in order to free it from smoke and sulphur, received a considerable amount of attention, and was made the subject of a number of patents.

In 1620 a grant was made to a company consisting of Sir William St. John, Sir Giles Mompesson, Sir George Ayloffe, Knights, Lewis Powell, Walter Vaughan, John Pruthero and Henrie Vaughan, Esquires, and Henrie Stubbes, Gentleman, for charking sea coal, pit coal, stone coal, turf, peat, etc., and employing the same for smelting ores and manufacturing metals and other purposes; the process being the invention of one Hugh Grundy. The names indicate this company to have belonged to one of the coalfields of the south-western district.

In 1627 a patent was granted to Sir John Hacket and Octavius de Strada (the latter of whom, two years before, had been attempting to smelt with coal in Hainault), for a method of rendering sea coal and pit coal as useful as charcoal, for burning in houses, without offence by the smell or smoke (Macpherson's *Commerce*, vol. ii., p. 345). Hacket was the name of a family of coal owners in Fife, Scotland.

Again, in 1633, a patent was granted to a company consisting of Sir Abraham Williams, John Gaspar van Wolfen, Edward Hanchett, Amadis van Wolfen, Walter Williams, Henry Reynolds, John Brown, and Gaspar Frederick van Wolfen, for a new way of charking sea coal, and other earth coal, and for preparing, dressing, and qualifying them so as to make them fit for the melting and making of iron and other metals, and many other good uses. These patentees were probably introducing some Continental system of coking, judging by the foreign names of so many of them.

Among other cokemaking projects was one entertained by Sir John Winter, who purposed to employ the product as a superior fuel for household purposes. His method of coking is thus described by Evelyn in his diary under date 11th July, 1656 :

"Came home by Greenwich Ferry, where I saw Sir John Winter's new project of charring sea coale to burne out the sulphure and render it sweete. He did it by burning the coals in such earthen pots as the glassemen mealt their mettal, so firing them without consuming them, using a barr of yron in each crucible or pot, which barr has a hook at one end, and so the coales being mealted in a furnace wth other crude sea coales under them, may be drawn out of the potts sticking to the yron, whence they are beaten off in greate halfe-exhausted cinders, which, being rekindled, make a cleare pleasant chamber fire, deprived of their sulphur and arsenic malignity. What successe it may have, time will discover."

Sir John is said to have sent some of his cooked coal, together with a new-fashioned grate, to a number of great men for a trial, but his enterprise did not succeed ; though as appears from a petition presented by him in 1661 (*Cal. State Papers*, Dom., 1660-61, p. 507), he still had faith at that date in his process of charring, or calcining, coal in pots.

Up till the seventeenth century the chief, if not the only methods, by which miners were able to cut their subterranean passages, were such as had been known from remote antiquity. Where hand labour was insufficient, fire-setting continued to be the process made use of, just as it had been by Hannibal in forming a road for his army across the Alps. This consisted in expanding the rock by kindling fires against it, and then suddenly contracting it by throwing water, or vinegar, upon it. Such was the system practised by the metalliferous miners of England, and sometimes, though probably rarely, by the coal miners, down to the reign of Charles I.

This ancient and tedious process was, however, on the eve of being superseded by a new and more rapid method, consisting in the employment of gunpowder in blasting rock. This was first practised on the Continent, and is heard of in Germany and Hungary almost simultaneously. In the former country it is stated (Smyth's Lectures, *Min. Jour.*, No. xvii., 1876) to have been proposed at Freiberg in 1613, but not to have been employed till 1632 ; while in the latter, blasting is said (*Col. Guard.*, Dec. 18, 1896, p. 1,170) to have been invented at Schemnitz in 1627.[1]

Writing in 1686, Dr. Plot informs us (*Staffordshire*, p. 165) that blasting was first practised in England at the Ecton Hill copper mines in North Staffordshire by German miners, who had left before he came to the county. From another source (*Col. Guard., ut sup.*) we learn that this occurred in 1638. The earliest published reference to the subject is contained in a paper communicated to the Royal Society, by Sir R. Moray, in 1665 (*Phil. Trans.*, No. 5, p. 82), on " M. du Son's method of breaking rocks." But we have no mention of the adoption of the new process by English miners till 1683, at which period it had come into use at the lead mines of the Mendip Hills in Somersetshire (*ib.*, No. 167, p. 854); which was followed by its adoption at Cornish mines in 1689 (*Col. Guard., ut sup.*). For a long time the methods of stemming, or plugging up, the shot holes, appear to have been very imperfect, and the operation of firing the charge difficult and dangerous.

There is no mention of the use of gunpowder in coal mines till the beginning of the following century ; the earliest reference to the subject, known to the writer, occurring in 1719 (*Phil. Trans.*, No. 360, p. 968), when it is spoken of as sometimes used in dealing with a hard rock encountered in the sinking of pits in Somersetshire.

The last decade of the seventeenth century is remarkable for the rise of a number of large mining and smelting companies. The movement had its origin in some legislation affecting metalliferous mines. Hitherto the claims of the Crown, not only to mines of gold and silver, but likewise to those of tin, copper, and argentiferous lead, had operated to retard the prosecution of metalliferous mining in England. But in 1689, to a large extent due to the influence of Mr. Boyle (*Elements of the Art of Assaying*, p. 455), an Act of Parliament was passed repealing a statute enacted in the reign of Henry IV. against multiplying gold and silver ; which was followed, in 1693, by another act to prevent disputes and controversies about royal mines. By these Acts it was declared that mines of copper, tin, iron, and lead, were not royal (Anderson's *Hist. of Commerce*, vol. i., p. 466 ; Macpherson, vol. ii., p. 635). The immediate result was the formation of the companies above referred to. Of these :

The Company of the Mine Adventurers of England was formed

---

[1] Reference occurs (*Report on Condition of Mines*, 1864, Append. B, p. 264) to a much earlier use of gunpowder at Rammelsberg in the 12th century, but what foundation there is for the statement the writer is unable to say.

in 1690 (Anderson, *ut supra*, vol. ii., p. 197) to work mines of lead and copper found in the lands of Sir Carberry Price, in Cardiganshire, South Wales.

The Copper Miners Company in England was incorporated in 1691-92 (Jones's *Index to the Originalia*, 3 Will. and Marie), to work mines in England and Ireland.

The Governor and Company for melting down lead with sea coal and pit coal was incorporated in 1692-93 (*ib.*, 4 Will. and Marie).

The Governor and Company for making iron with pit coal was incorporated in 1693-94 (*ib.*, 5 Will. and Marie).

The Governor and Company of Copper Miners in the Principality of Wales was incorporated in 1694-95 (*ib.*, 6 Will. and Marie).

We have already seen that copper was being smelted with coal previous to the close of this century.[1] The smelting of lead also with coal, numerous efforts to effect which had been made from time to time, appears now to have been accomplished ; and in 1697 a patent was granted to a Mr. Robert Lydall for separating silver from lead with pit coal. Tin, in like manner, is stated to have been first successfully smelted with coal in 1703-4 (Phillips and Darlington, *Records of Mining and Metallurgy*, p. 25), when a Mr. Liddell —probably the individual above mentioned—with whom was associated a Mr. Moult, obtained a patent for the process.[2]

The period at which coal began to be systematically employed in smelting iron is involved in greater obscurity. The difficulty of obtaining a sufficiently powerful blast, by means of the appliances then in use, was probably the chief barrier in the way of its accomplishment; heat of much greater intensity being necessary for smelting ores of iron than of other metals, and coke fuel requiring a much stronger blast than sufficed for charcoal. Whatever amount of success may have attended the attempts which continued to be made to effect this, a considerable time elapsed before the manufacture of iron with coal began to assume any degree of practical importance.

In the seventeenth century some attention began to be directed to the improvement of the commerce of the country, both by providing greater facilities for internal communication by making

---

[1] An isolated instance of the use of coal (stone coles), or of its partial use in conjunction with peat, in smelting silver ore, is heard of in Scotland between 1607 and 1619 (*Trans. Fed. Inst.*, vi. 193, 196).

[2] It may be mentioned, however, that John Joachim Beecher, in his *Alphabetum Minerale*, written at Truro, in 1682, claims to have introduced the process into Cornwall (*Trans. Roy. Geolog. Soc. of Cornwall*, vol. iv.).

rivers navigable, and also by giving greater security to vessels by the erection of lighthouses at many points on the coast.

Lord Bacon (*Works*, vol. iii., p. 579, ed. 1730) had drawn attention to the profit likely to be obtained by making rivers navigable ; and even in 1618 patents began to be taken out for machines for dredging rivers.

One of the earliest projects of the kind was brought forward in 1635-36 (*Cal. State Papers*, Dom., 1635-36, vol. cccxv. 79) by Mr. Sandys, of Flatbury, Worcestershire, who proposed to make the River Avon passable for boats through counties Worcester, Gloucester, and Warwick, near to Coventry ; and also a good part of the River Teme lying towards Ludlow, " whereby the said counties may be better supplied with wood, iron, and pit coals, which they want." But though the scheme was regarded with a considerable amount of approval, it was nipped in the bud, along with some other similar projects, by the outbreak of the Civil War.

The subject was revived in 1670, and the construction of mediterranean canals was also proposed (Gough's *Topography*, ed. 1780, ii. 223), but little progress appears to have been made down till the end of the century. In 1698-99, however (10 and 11 Will. III.), Acts of Parliament were passed for making and keeping the River Tone navigable from Bridgewater to Taunton, in Somersetshire ; also the rivers Aire and Calder, in Yorkshire; and likewise the River Trent. Other Acts for making rivers navigable followed soon afterwards, but it was not till half-a-century later that the era of the construction of artificial canals, or navigations, began in England.

Though two lighthouses had been erected at the mouth of the Tyne as early as the reign of Henry VIII., little progress was made in the lighting up of the coasts at night previous to the Restoration. From whatever cause, lighthouses seem to have suddenly become very popular at the commencement of the reign of Charles II.

In the years 1664 and 1665 (*Cal. State Papers*, Dom., 1664-65, p. 457) patents were granted for their erection at Dungeness, Harwich, Milford Haven, Hampton or Hunstan Cliff, near Lynn Regis, in Norfolk, and Tynemouth (to be re-built); and petitions lodged (*ib.*, pp. 205, 447) for leave to erect others at the Isle of Wight, Portland Road, Rames Head, the Lizard Point, and Holyhead. In 1669, as already mentioned, a patent was granted for the erection of one at Sunderland ; and in 1675 two at a place on the Yorkshire coast, which is curiously described in a chronological index of patents as " at the monte of Lymber," but which is intended for Spurn Point, "at the mouth of Humber"—these being stated to be specially required to protect the traders of Newcastle.

The way was thus prepared for an extension of the shipping season, which followed in course of time. In 1626 (*Cal. State Papers*, 1625-26, vol. cviii. 59), in estimating the cost of a convoy to protect the coal fleet from the Dunkirkers, only eight months were allowed for—"the trade ceasing in winter."

CHAPTER XXIII.

THE EIGHTEENTH CENTURY.

First great colliery explosions in the Northumberland and Durham coalfield.

IT was in the opening years of the eighteenth century, when the maximum depth of the pits in the north of England (which were at the same time the deepest in the kingdom) was about 400 feet, that there took place the first of the long series of great colliery explosions which have ever since continued to occur from time to time.

So long as coal was only worked at shallow depths, the ventilation of the mines had been attended with little difficulty. Pits were sunk in large numbers and worked very small areas. Adits, where such existed and were not of excessive length, tended to promote a natural circulation of air; and if mines drained in this way were sometimes troubled with chokedamp, they were rarely infested with firedamp. Where the water was raised by machinery, likewise, the leakage and loss of water in the pit employed for the purpose, supplied a considerable ventilating power.

As the depth increased it became essential that fewer pits should be sunk, and larger areas worked from each centre, which conduced to enfeeble the natural ventilation. The pits were also now beginning to penetrate into the region under the watery strata; and the miners at times were able to dam the water out, and work dry beneath it, thereby losing the ventilating power associated with the drawing of water.

Though firedamp, as we have seen, has sometimes been encountered in very shallow pits, and even found escaping at the surface, these conditions are somewhat exceptional. As a rule, in the uppermost strata, the fissures in the coal seams and associated rocks are filled either with water or chokedamp, and it is only as the workings attain to lower levels that firedamp begins to be met with.

Into this drier and more fiery region the pits of the Tyne and Wear were now descending; and while the miners had to some extent learnt the art of evading their old enemy, water, they were coming into all the closer contact with their newer enemy, fire-damp: a subtle and perilous foe which they were ill prepared to combat.

As the collieries increased in size, the number of workpeople employed was likewise augmented, thus exposing more lives at a time to the risk of accident.

The pits in the old mining district of Gateshead were among the deepest in the coalfield. As the upper coal seams became exhausted, lower ones were sunk to; the Bensham seam taking its name from Bensham, near Gateshead, and this being also the point, according to Sykes (*Account of the Wallsend Explosion*, 1835, p. 31), where the Low Main seam was first worked in the neighbourhood of Newcastle.

Reference has been made to the fact of the first accident on record occasioned by firedamp having taken place in a pit at Gates-head in the early part of the seventeenth century. Here also it was that the first great colliery explosion, involving the loss of a considerable number of lives, occurred nearly a century later. This happened about the 3rd or 4th of October, 1705, over thirty indi-viduals perishing by the blast.

The following notice of the interments of the victims of this early explosion appeared in the *Newcastle Daily Chronicle*, 10th September, 1880, having been extracted from the burial register of St. Mary's Church, Gateshead, the melancholy list being headed by the remark:

"These were slain in a coal-pitt in the Stony Flatt, which did fire.

"October 4—Cuthbert Richinson, Michael Richinson, Ralph Richinson, brothers; William Robinson; John Liddel; John Broune, Clement Broune, William Broune, brothers; Robert Broune, son to Clement Broune.

"BLOWN UP THE PIT.

"John, son of John Broune; Adam Thompson; Joseph Jackson; Abigail Jackson, daughter to Joseph Jackson; John Hastings, overman; Michael Walker, his servant.

"October 5—Leonard Jordan; John Green; John Distans; Richard Fletcher; John Hall; William Maine; Thomas Riddel; Thomas Huggison.

"October 6—Bryon Thornton; Michael Thompson; Robert Cooke; Matthew Hastings, overman, son to John Hastings.

"October 7—John Sayers.

"October 10—Edward Jordan ; John Todd.

"October 13—Thomas Ridsdall."

The contributor of the article on "Old Gateshead and her Colliery Explosions" to the *Newcastle Chronicle* supposed the expression "blown up the pit" to apply to the six succeeding names, remarking that "in 1705 Abigail Jackson was among the sufferers blown up the pit"; but from the notice of the explosion contained in the pages of the *Compleat Collier*, it would appear only to apply to one of the victims. It is here stated that, "There was one thing very strange in it, as I was told, that a youth of fifteen or sixteen years of age was blown up out of the pit and shaft, and carried by the blast about forty yards from the shaft, the corps was found all intire, save the back part of his head, which was cut off, though the shaft is said to be odd of 60 fathom (over 360 feet) deep, which is an argument of the mighty force this blast is of."

The above explosion is obviously the same as that which is spoken of as having taken place in a field at the head of Jackson's Chare (*Trans. North of Eng. Inst.*, vol. xv., pp. 239 note, 271), when Jackson's daughter and sundry men lost their lives.[1] It is perhaps also the explosion said to have occurred at Bensham "about the year 1710," which usually heads the lists of great colliery explosions. There is no mention in the Gateshead burial register of any other explosion having taken place in that neighbourhood during the years 1705-10 (as the writer is informed by Mr. Turner, who has been so kind as to examine the register), the only other colliery cases referred to being :

"1705, November 24—William Robson, slain in a coal pit in the Quarry Close.

"1709, September 10—Robert Vardy, drowned in a pit."

Not long did the Tyneside remain the only district in which any great colliery explosion had occurred. Just three years later, the Wear district was the scene of a similar and even more terrible catastrophe. Regarding this explosion a greater amount of information has been preserved, an account of it having been communicated

[1] From a copy of the above record in Bell's *Collection* (vol. i., Library of the Royal School of Mines), it appears that Jackson was the owner of the pit, and that the explosion took place on October 3rd ; also that the expression "blown up the pit" only applies to the case of Robert Broune. An old plan in the same volume shows Jackson's house and pit, the depth of the pit being given as 67 fathoms. Previous to Jackson's time, the road had been called Colliers' Chare.

to the Royal Society at the time by the Rev. Dr. Arthur Charlett, Master of University College, Oxford, and published in the *Philosophical Transactions* (No. 318, p. 215).

It occurred on the 18th of August, 1708, at Fatfield, in the parish of Chester-le-Street, at three o'clock in the morning; the sudden eruption of violent fire discharging itself at the mouths of three pits, with as great a noise as the firing of cannon, or the loudest claps of thunder, and sixty-nine persons were instantly destroyed. Three of them, viz., two men and a woman, were blown quite up from the bottom of the shaft, 342 feet deep, into the air, and carried to a considerable distance from the mouth of the pit.

The engine used for drawing up the coals, which was of great weight, was removed and cast aside by the force of the blast; and singularly the fish in a rivulet flowing within about twenty yards from one of the pits were found dead in large numbers, floating on the surface of the water.

After explaining the effects of "stith," or chokedamp, and "sulphur," or firedamp, the narrator proceeds to say :

"To prevent both these inconveniences, as the only remedy known here, the viewer of the works takes the best care he can to preserve a free current of air through all the works, and as the air goes down one pit it should ascend another. But it happened in this colliery, there was a pit which stood in an eddy, where the air had not always a free passage, and which in hot and sultry weather was very much subject to sulphur; and it being then the middle of August, and some danger apprehended from the closeness and heat of the season, the men were with the greatest care and caution withdrawn from their work in that pit and turned into another; but an overman, some days after this change, and upon some notion of his own, being induced, as is supposed, by a fresh, cool, frosty breeze of wind, which blew that unlucky morning, and which always clears the works of all sulphur, had gone too near this pit, and had met the sulphur just as it was purging and dispersing itself, upon which the sulphur immediately took fire by his candle, which proved the destruction of himself and so many men, and caused the greatest fire ever known in these parts."

From the above account it is obvious that the Fatfield pits were at this date still dependent upon such circulation of air as could be obtained from natural ventilation.

Among the Sloane MSS. in the British Museum (4025,40) is an "Account of the firing of three pits at Fatfield in the parish of Chester-le-Street, 1708," by John Hedworth, which is probably the

original of the above narrative. Fatfield formed part of the estate
of Harraton, already referred to as having been the property of the
Hedworths. This place was the scene of several similar disasters at
a later date.

In connection with the above explosions, we learn incidentally
that women were still employed underground, at least to a small
extent, in the collieries of the Tyne and Wear.

CHAPTER XXIV.

THE EIGHTEENTH CENTURY.—Continued.

Invention of the steam engine.

THE invention of the steam engine may safely be said to have been the most important event that has ever happened in the annals of mining—as, indeed, it proved to be an event of vast importance in the annals of mankind. Previous to its invention innumerable mines had already become drowned, and to all appearance hopelessly lost; the task of draining them being beyond the power of any machine in existence.

The steam engine is one of the richest gifts made to the world by modern science. As an early writer puts it (*Universal Magazine*, Sep. 1747): "It is the most admirable, curious, and compounded machine, amongst all those inventions which have been owing to modern philosophy." The idea of the machine had not been conceived until the discovery of the atmospheric pressure had given the *coup de grâce* to the ancient dogma, that "Nature abhors a vaccuum"; until, indeed, the air-pump had been invented, in 1650, from which contrivance the steam engine is lineally descended.[1]

It was to utilize the pressure exerted by

The viewless columns of incumbent air

upon a piston sliding in a vacuous cylinder, that the machine first began to be thought of. It was by those engaged in making experiments with the newly invented air-pump that the possibility of devising such a machine was brought into notice, and the first rudimentary models constructed. The problem was how to produce, and repeat, the necessary vacuum under the piston.

[1] To carry it a step further back, the rudiments of the steam engine are to be found in the cylinder and piston of the common syringe.

In 1654, Otto von Guericke, the inventor of the air-pump, demonstrated to Ferdinand III. and his Court, at the Diet of Ratisbon, the great power that might be thus brought into play, by

FIG. 12.—GUERICKE'S CYLINDER AND PISTON MACHINE, 1654.

forming a vacuum under the piston by means of a small air-pump, or by attaching to the cylinder a vessel from which the air had been previously exhausted with an air-pump.

About twenty-four years later (1678-79), Huyghens constructed a similar but more highly developed machine at Paris, in which the vacuum under the piston was produced by the explosion of a small quantity of gun-powder within the cylinder.   But this method was found expensive and inefficient; the vacuum obtained being very imperfect, owing to the amount of uncondensed gas remaining in the cylinder.[1]

A great advance was made by Papin, in 1690, who suggested the condensation of steam as a means of producing a perfect vacuum under the piston at small cost; but this ingenious individual never

[1] In England, Dr. Robert Hooke is stated to have proposed "a steam engine on Newcomen's principle" in 1678. See Life of Hooke in Brewster's *Edinburgh Encyclopædia*.

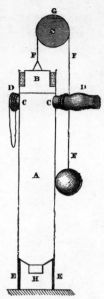

HUYGHENS'S GUNPOWDER AND AIR ENGINE, 1678-9.

HUYGHENS'S ENGINE, 1682 (Hautefeuille).

PAPIN'S GUNPOWDER AND AIR ENGINE, 1687.

PAPIN'S STEAM AND AIR ENGINE, 1690.

got beyond the stage of raising the steam in the cylinder itself, by the application of fire to it ; this single vessel being thus at the same time boiler, cylinder, and condenser.

To Newcomen, of Dartmouth, in Devon, belongs the honour of making a practical success of the projects of the scientists above mentioned, and triumphantly to " harness science to the industrial car." By adopting a separate boiler for supplying steam to the cylinder, and adding numerous highly ingenious contrivances, notably an arrangement whereby the machine was rendered automatic or self-acting—an idea which had previously been sug. gested by Papin—this distinguished inventor produced an engine of vast power and utility ; the most wonderful invention, and the nearest approach to animal life, to which human ingenuity had ever given birth.[1]

Though the engines of Newcomen and Savery were invented almost simultaneously, as machines they had nothing whatever in common; they had totally different origins. The Newcomen engine had no affinity with any of the contrivances for utilizing the elastic force of steam. In its original rudimentary form it was not a steam engine at all ; and even as a working engine none of its power was derived from steam, which was only used in a passive way for producing a vacuum in the cylinder, and of a pressure ranging usually from about $1\frac{1}{2}$ lb. above to $1\frac{1}{2}$ lb. below the pressure of the atmosphere.

The engines of Newcomen and Savery were, however, accidentally brought into very close relationship on account of Newcomen's invention having been anticipated by Savery's patent for raising water by fire ; and Newcomen, as Switzer informs us (*Hydrostaticks*, vol. ii., p. 342), was glad to be admitted into partnership with Savery, being otherwise debarred from introducing his invention, to which fire was indispensable. Thus the Newcomen engine was brought out under the same patent as Savery's, and like it was commonly spoken of as a " fire engine."

Regarding the first introduction of the Newcomen engine into practical use, Dr. Desaguliers (*Experimental Philosophy*, vol. ii., pp. 332-33) gives the following account :

"About the year 1710, Tho. Newcomen, ironmonger, and John Calley, glazier, of Dartmouth, in the county of Southampton

[1] Newcomen is known to have been in communication with Dr. Hooke on the subject of vacuum or atmospheric engines, previous to the death of the latter in March, 1702-3. He also appears to have been associated with Papin in some experiments.

(Anabaptists), made then several experiments in private, and having brought it to work with a piston, etc., in the latter end of the year, 1711, made proposals to draw the water at Griff, in Warwickshire ; but their invention meeting not with reception, in March following, through the acquaintance of Mr. Potter, of Bromsgrove, in Worcestershire, they bargained to draw water for Mr. Back, of Wolverhampton, where after a great many laborious attempts they did make the engine work. . . . They were at a loss about the pumps, but being so near Birmingham and having the assistance of so many admirable and ingenious workmen, they soon came to the method of making the pump valves, clacks, and buckets (1712), whereas they had but an imperfect notion of them before."

Unfortunately for the memory of Newcomen, Dr. Desaguliers consistently endeavours to belittle his great invention, which circumstance, combined with the fact of the invention being brought out under Savery's patent, and being consequently regarded by many as merely an improvement of Savery's engine, is probably the principal reason why the father of the steam engine has not been honoured with a loftier niche in the Temple of Fame.

Newcomen condensed the steam in the interior of the cylinder of his engine by injecting cold water into it :

" Bade with cold streams the quick expansion stop
And sunk the immense of vapour to a drop "

—the same vessel serving both as cylinder and condenser. Immediately upon the vacuum being produced, the piston was driven to the bottom of the cylinder by the atmospheric pressure, and the pumprods at the other end of the beam drawn up, together with the water.

An engraving of the first Newcomen engine above referred to, built at a Staffordshire coal pit in 1712, is still extant, and shows the wonderful achievements of Newcomen. It is entitled, "The Steam Engine near Dudley Castle, Invented by Capt. Savery and Mr. Newcomen, erected by ye later 1712, delin. and sculp. by T. Barney 1719." This engraving is referred to by Gough, in treating of Staffordshire, in his *British Topography*.

Shaw informs us (*Staffordshire*, vol. ii., part i., p. 120) that the engine was placed "on the left hand side of the road leading from Walsall to the town [of Wolverhampton] over against the half mile stone." Its brass cylinder was 21 in. in diameter ; and the water was raised, in two lifts, from a depth of 153 feet.

As the dates at which the steam engine, or fire engine as it was more usually called in the early period of its history, was introduced into various districts have hitherto been to some extent a matter of guess, or based upon uncertain tradition reduced to writing long subsequently, the following authentic information supplied by an official announcement, published in the *London Gazette* for August 11 to 14, 1716 [1] (see *The Engineer*, April 7, 1882, p. 253), is of special interest:

"Whereas the invention of raising water by the impellent force of fire, authorized by Parliament, is lately brought to the greatest perfection, and all sorts of mines, etc., may be thereby drained, and water raised to any height with more ease and less charge than by the other methods hitherto used, as is sufficiently demonstrated by diverse engines of this invention now at work in the several counties of Stafford, Warwick, Cornwall, and Flint. I have now therefore to give notice that if any person shall be desirous to treat with the proprietors for such engines, attendance will be given for that purpose every Wednesday, at the Sword Blade Coffee-House, in Birchin-lane, London, from three to five o'clock; and if any letters be directed thither to be left for Mr. Eliot, the parties shall receive all fitting satisfaction and dispatch."

The above announcement, made on behalf of the patentees, or proprietors, of the steam engine, in 1716, must be held to supersede Stuart's statement,[2] quoted by Mr. T. J. Taylor in his "Archæology of the Coal Trade" (*Proc. Arch. Inst.*, Newcastle, 1852, vol. i., p. 194), that of four steam engines in existence in 1714, two of them were on mines at Newcastle. Instead of this it is clear that up till 1716 no steam engine had yet been built in the Newcastle-on-Tyne district.

This official announcement likewise throws a new light upon one or two early steam engines, regarding which uncertainty existed as to whether they were on Savery's or Newcomen's construction.

It cannot be doubted that the Warwickshire engine was the early steam engine at Griff, near Coventry, which, according to one account (Farey's *Steam Engine*, p. 155 note), was the first of Newcomen's engines. Being placed second on the list it was most probably the second, and built about the year 1713. It is reported to have had no working gear; the cocks being opened and shut by hand. It may be mentioned, however, that early steam engines

---

[1] Perhaps in connection with arrangements made after the death of Savery, which took place in 1715 or 1716.

[2] *Anecdotes of Steam Engines*, ii. 618. This seems based upon the notes appended to p. 155 of Farey's *Treatise on the Steam Engine*.

were sometimes worked by hand, though possessing automatic gear, as they could be driven rather more quickly in this way.

Previous to the erection of the steam engine, more than fifty horses were employed in raising water at Griff Colliery, at an expense of not less than £900 a year (Desagulier's *Experimental Philosophy*, ii., 482); whereas the annual cost of the engine never exceeded £150, or one-sixth of the previous amount.

FIG. 13.—ENGINE AT GRIFF COLLIERY, WARWICKSHIRE.

Henry Beighton, who was a native of Warwickshire, and resided at Griff, interested himself greatly in the machine; and as early as 1717 constructed a table showing the power of engines of different sizes, up to cylinders of 40 inches diameter, and depths of 300 feet. So closely was he identified with Newcomen's engine—on which, indeed, he made some small improvements—that it has been even figured under the name of Beighton's fire engine.

The first steam engine in Cornwall, Mr. Carne informs us (*Transactions Royal Geological Society of Cornwall*, vol. iii.), was erected on Huel Vor, a tin mine in Breage, which was at work from 1710 to

1714. On account of the early date it was thought that this might have been one of Savery's engines; but there is no reason to doubt that it was the engine mentioned third on the official list. Regarding the engine at work in Flintshire in 1716, we have no further information.

It must have been immediately after the publication of the official announcement above mentioned, that a steam engine was built by the patentees at a mine at Austhorpe, near Leeds, in Yorkshire, inasmuch as Mr. Calley or Cawley, Newcomen's associate, is stated (Farey's *Steam Engine*, p. 155 note) to have superintended its erection, and to have died at Austhorpe in 1717. Mr. Smeaton, who resided at Austhorpe, made many inquiries regarding this early engine. He was informed that the patentees had £250 a year for working and keeping it in order, and that they burned out four boilers in the time it was worked, which was only about four years. The early boilers were made of copper.

The above engine was said by tradition to have been erected "about the year 1714," and the same period is assigned to the introduction of the steam engine into the north of England, regarding which the following account is furnished by Brand (vol. ii., p. 686):

"The first steam engine in the north is said to have been built upon a moor called Washington Fell, about nine miles south-east of Newcastle-on-Tyne, for a colliery upon the River Were.

"The next, as I was informed by a very old man concerned in coal mines, was at Norwood, near Ravensworth Castle, in the same neighbourhood.

"About the year 1713 or 1714, the first fire engine on the north side of the River Tyne is said to have been erected at Biker Colliery, the property of Richard Ridley, Esq. The engineer was the reputed son of a Swedish nobleman, who taught mathematics at Newcastle."

The dates of the erection of the above engines rest upon no documentary evidence, but on the mere *on dit* of popular tradition, collected by Brand about seventy years afterwards. It is clear from the announcement made in the *London Gazette* that no engine can have been built in the north so early as 1713 or 1714. The Swedish engineer, also, was doubtless Martin (afterwards Sir Martin) Triewald, who did not arrive in England, according to Stuart (*Anecdotes of Steam Engines*, vol. ii., p. 618), till 1716, when he came to learn the mode of mining followed at Newcastle. That the steam engine was not in use in the north in 1716 is likewise supported by the circumstance that in an estimate of the expense of winning Walker Colliery, made in that year (Brand, ii. 685 note), "the charge of water was therein calculated as if to be drawn by horses."

Indeed, we have no satisfactory record of the existence of any steam engine in the north previous to the year 1718, at which date, as Desaguliers informs us (*Experimental Philosophy*, vol. ii., p. 533), one was built at Newcastle-upon-Tyne, by Mr. Henry Beighton. Where this engine was applied we are not informed, but we have independent evidence that an engine must have been erected at Elswick Colliery about this date, from the statement of a witness examined at Newcastle in 1722 (Brand, ii. 686 note), who avers that this colliery "had a few years ago been won, and, by the help of fire engines, was then a working colliery." According to Edington (*Treatise on the Coal Trade*, 1813, p. 118), "about ninety years ago, Wortley Montague, Ledger, and some others, were then working Elswick and Benwell collieries ; they erected the first fire engine for collieries upon Elswick Quay for drawing water out of mines, it was there the Low Main was first wrought."

Triewald remained in the Newcastle-on-Tyne neighbourhood for some years, and was employed as an engineer at a coal mine. If his acquaintance with the Newcomen engine was obtained at Byker, an engine must have been erected there previous to 1722, inasmuch as in that year a patent for an atmospheric engine of some kind was granted to Martin Triewald, of Newcastle-on-Tyne (No. 449). He returned to Sweden in 1726, and erected an atmospheric engine, the parts of which he got fabricated in England.

Though we have no contemporary records relating to the erection of other engines in the Newcastle-on-Tyne neighbourhood, the machine was evidently well known there, and it seems probable that a few had been built, previous to 1722, from the familiar way in which the witnesses examined by Sir Robert Raymond in that year (Brand, ii., pp. 685-86 note) refer to fire engines, and to their superior efficiency and economy as compared with horse-power.

Shortly afterwards an agency for the erection of steam engines was established at Chester-le-Street, as appears from the following advert-isement (Brand, *ib.*) from the *Newcastle Courant* of January 27, 1724 :

"This is to give notice to all gentlemen, and others, who have occasion for the fire engine or engines for drawing of water from the collieries, etc., to apply to John Potter, in Chester-le-Street, who is empowered by the proprietors of the said fire engines to treat about the same."

The Potter family were very intimately connected with the New-comen engine in its early days. It was through a Mr. Potter that Newcomen obtained the order for his first engine. It is to a boy, Humphrey Potter, that Desaguliers assigns the merit of inventing the "scoggan," whereby the previously-existing automatic gear was so much improved that the speed of the engine was nearly doubled. It was a Mr. Potter who built the first engine on the Continent about 1723. Now we find John Potter established as agent at Chester-le-Street. And particulars are extant (Bald's *View of the Coal Trade*, p. 18) regarding an engine built in Scotland, in 1725, by this John Potter and Abraham Potter, his brother german; though two or three engines were in use there previous to this date.

In addition to all the localities already mentioned, the Newcomen engine had likewise been applied at Whitehaven collieries, Cumberland. So that previous to his death in London, in 1729 (*Arch. Journal*, vol. xxx., p. 437), Newcomen had seen his invention brought into use far and wide, and on all occasions with the greatest success. Dr. Allen, writing in 1730 (*Specimina Ichnographica*, p. 14), refers to him as "my good friend, the ever-memorable Mr. New-comen, whose death I very much regret." And Switzer, at nearly the same date (*Hydrostaticks*, 1729, vol. ii., pp. 341, 335), speaks of Newcomen's great modesty and judgment; and characterizes his invention as "the beautifullest and most useful engine that any age or country ever yet produced."

M. Belidor, the author of *Architecture Hydraulique*, in his second volume published at Paris in 1739 (p. 324), gives drawings and a detailed description of a Newcomen engine erected by English engineers at a coal mine at Fresnes, near Condé. The cylinder of the engine was 30 inches in diameter. Previous to its erection, fifty horses and twenty men, working night and day, had been required to raise water from the mine; whereas the engine, with a single attendant, in forty-eight hours' working, cleared the colliery of water for a whole week. As was to be expected, he ascribes the invention to Savery, but he remarks that in one of the letters on the subject which he had received from the Royal Society, Mr. New comen had been mentioned as having greatly contributed towards bringing it to its present state of perfection.

"We must avow," he says, "that this is the most marvellous of all machines, and that there is not a single other of which the mechanism has so much resemblance to that of animals. Heat is the cause of its motion, a circulation takes place in its different tubes like that of the blood in the veins; it has valves which open and close at the proper moment; it feeds itself, it rejects what it has used at regular intervals, it draws from its own work everything that it requires for its support."

FIG. 14.—ENGINE AT FRESNES, NEAR CONDÉ.

During a period of about seventy years from the date of its invention, the steam engine was almost solely employed in draining mines, and more particularly coal mines. It could only perform the simple see-saw motion of pumping, being at this stage of its history truly, as described by Coleridge, "a giant with one idea"—a coal-devouring giant.

CHAPTER XXV.

THE EIGHTEENTH CENTURY.—Continued.

Mining in the Northumberland and Durham coalfield during the first half of the eighteenth century. Early railways. Artificial ventilation by fire. Pillar working.

THE collieries of Elswick, Benwell, and Fenham, appear to have been in abeyance in the latter part of the seventeenth and the early part of the eighteenth century. In Benwell and Fenham, as we have seen, a severe underground fire raged for a prolonged period; while an attempt to win Elswick Colliery, made about 1680, proved a failure, the appliances at command being inadequate to the task.

The winning of the Low Main seam at Elswick was one of the first achievements effected by the aid of the steam engine on its introduction into the north. New life was thus infused into this old mining neighbourhood, and it again became a busy centre of colliery enterprise.

It is somewhat uncertain whether the Low Main seam was first worked at Elswick, or on the south side of the Tyne at Gateshead, Sykes averring it to have been at the latter, Edington (*Coal Trade*, p. 118) at the former place. It is certain, however, that this seam had been worked at Elswick previous to 1722, as appears from the affidavits of certain viewers made in this year (Brand, ii. 680), who state that, "In Benwell, Elswick, and Fenham collieries, there have been before the working thereof certain seams of coal called the upper main coal, the metal coal, the stone coal, and the lower main coal." From this it would appear that the Low Main coal had been partially worked in these collieries previous to their abandonment in the course of the seventeenth century.

"By the help of fire engines," the working of this seam was now resumed with great activity. It was likewise continued through the Montague estate (Edington, p. 118), and into Benwell and

Fenham.   Upwards of 600 or 700 carts and wains, as already mentioned, were required to lead the coals to Scotswood Quay, and 300
or 400 pitmen were employed, who resided at Benwell village.

The Benwell pitmen are described by Edington as a set of strong,
healthy, and resolute men, who set the law at defiance; no officer
dared to execute a warrant against them.   They make some figure
in the general literature of the district.

A curious, but not very praiseworthy production, entitled, " A
most Pleasant Description of Benwell Village, in the County of
Northumberland," by Q.Z., late Commoner of Oxon., was published
at Newcastle in 1726—said by Mr. Hodgson (*Northumberland*,
Stannington, p. 329), to have been written by Cuth. Ellison, A.M.,
curate of All Saints, Newcastle, 1708; vicar of Stannington, 1724-
44.   A few stanzas are devoted to the pitmen, who formed the
bulk of the congregation, on the occasion of his "Sunday's Trip
to Benwell," as the reverend gentleman informs us in the following
lines :

> " Th' assembly small,
> A man might call,
> An herd of Pitmen's race ;
> For earth's black air
> Like gloss did share
> And tincture to their face."

Benwell was also the scene of another poetical effusion belonging
to this period, viz., " The Collier's Wedding," by Edward Chicken.
Events of this kind would appear to have been at times celebrated
with a great amount of display about the middle of the eighteenth
century, if we may judge from the following description of such a
function (Sykes's *Loc. Rec.*) : "October 14, 1754.   William Weather-
burn, pitman, belonging to Heaton, was married at All Saints'
Church, in Newcastle, to Elizabeth Oswald, of Gallowgate.   At the
celebration of this marriage there was the greatest concourse of
people ever known on a like occasion.   There were five or six
thousand at church and in the churchyard.   The bride and bride-
groom having invited their friends in the country, a great number
attended them to church ; and being mostly mounted double, or a
man and woman upon a horse, made a very grotesque appearance in
their parade through the streets.   The women and the horses were
literally covered with ribbons." [1]

[1] The author of "The Pitman's Pay" laments the decadence which had
taken place in the style of the colliers' weddings when he wrote about seventy
years later.

REFERENCES

By Figures, to the several Members.

1   The Fire Mouth under the Boyler with a Lid or Door.
2   The Boyler 5 Feet, 6 Inches Diameter, 6 Feet 1 Inch high, the Cylindrical part 4 Feet 4 Inches, Content near 13 Hogsheads.
3   The Neck or Throat betwixt the Boyler and the Great Cylinder.
4   A Brass Cylinder 7 Feet 10 Inches high, 21 Inches Diameter, to Rarifie and Condense the Steam.
5   The Pipe which contains the Buoy, 4 Inches Diameter.
6   The Master Pipe that Supplies all the Offices, 4 Inches Diameter.
7   The Injecting Pipe fill'd by the Master Pipe 6, and stopp'd by ½ Valve.
8   The Sinking Pipe, 4 Inches Diameter, that carries off the hot Water or Steam.
9   A Replenishing Pipe to the Boyler as it wastes with a Cock.
10   A Large Pipe with a Valve to carry the Steam out of Door.
11   The Regulator moved by the 2 Y y and they by the Beam, 12.
12   The Sliding Beam mov'd by the little Arch of the great Beam.
13   Scoggen and his Mate who work Double to the Boy, Y is the Axis of him.
14   The great Y that moves the little y and Regulator, 15 and 11 by the Beam 12.
15   The little y, guided by a Rod of Iron from the Regulator.
16   The Injecting Hammer or F that moves upon it's Axis in the Barge 17.
17   Which Barge has a leaking Pipe, besides the Valve nam'd in N° 7.
18   The Leaking Pipe 1 Inch Diameter, the Water falls into the Well.
19   A Snifting Bason with a Cock, to fill or cover the Air Valve with Water.
20   The Waste Pipe that carries off the Water from the Piston.
21   A Pipe which covers the Piston with a Cock.
22   The Great Sommers that Support the House and Engine.
23   A Lead Cystern, 2 Feet square, fill'd by the Master Pipe 6.
24   The Waste Pipe to that Cystern.
25   The Great Ballanc'd Beam that Works the whole Engine.
26   The Two Arches of the Great Ballanced Beam.
27   Two Wooden Frames to stop the Force of the Great Ballanced Beam.
28   The Little Arch of the Great Ballanc'd Beam that moves the N° 12.
29   Two Chains fix'd to the Little Arch, one draws down, the other up.
30   Stays to the great Arches of the Ballanc'd Beam.
31   Strong Barrs of Iron which go through the Arches and secure the Chains.
32   Large Pins of Iron going through the Arch to stop the Force of the Beam.
33   Very strong Chains fixed to Piston and the Plugg and both Arches.
34   Great Springs to stop the Force of the Great Ballanc'd Beam.
35   The Stair Case from Bottom to the Top.
36   The Ash-hole under the Fire, even with the Surface of the Well.
37   The Door-Case to the Well that receives the Water from the Level.
38   A Stair-Case from the Fire to the Engine and to the Great Door-Case.
39   The Gable-End the Great Ballanc'd Beam goes through.
40   The Colepit-mrouth 12 Feet or more above the Level.
41   The dividing of the Pump work into halves in the Pit.
42   The Mouth of the Pumps to the Level of the Well.
43   The Pump-work within the Pit.
44   A Large Cystern of Wood 25 Yards or half way down the Pit.
45   The Pump within the House that Furnishes all the Offices with Water.
46   The Floor over the Well.
47   The Great Door-Case 6 Feet square, to bring in the Boyler.
48   Stays to the Great Frame over the Pit.
49   The Wind to put them down gently or safely.
50   A Turn-Barrel over the Pit, which the Line goes round, not to slip.
51   The Gage-Pipe to know the Depth of the Water within the Boyler.
52   Two Cocks within the Pit to keep the Pump work moist.
53   A little Bench with a Bass to rest when they are weary.
54   A Man going to Replenish the Fire.
55   The Peck-Ax and Proaker.
56   The Centre or Axis of the Great Ballanc'd Beam. *that Vibrates 12 times in a Minute & each stroke lifts 10 Gall: of water 55 yards ppendr*

THE FIRS

ERECTED BY NEWCOMEN AT

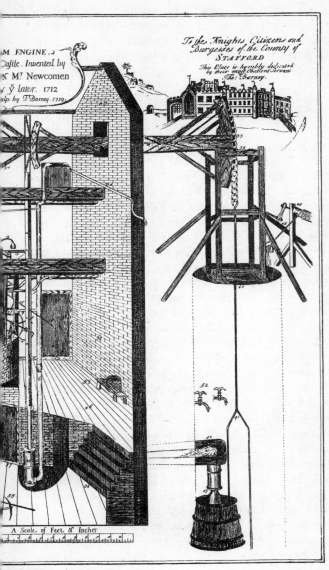

M ENGINE
Caſtle. Invented by
M.ʳ Newcomen
ɏ later. 1712
ulp: by T.Barney. 1719.

To the Knights, Citizens and
Burgeſſes of the County of
STAFFORD
This Plate is humbly dedicated
by their moſt Obedient Servant
The: Barney.

A Scale. of Feet, & Inches.

ENGINE.

STAFFORDSHIRE IN 1712.

On the south side of the Tyne, about 1725 (*Trans. N.E. Inst.*, xv. 202), the River Derwent, between where it flows into the Tyne and the village of Swalwell, was a great rendezvous of coal keels, indicating a large amount of activity in the working of coal in the surrounding district. Here—the locality being known as Derwenthaugh—were no fewer than fifty-five berths or "keel-rooms." Many of these belonged to Axwell Colliery. Among the lessors' and lessees' names were those of George Pitt, Esq., Sir James Clavering, Mr. Shaftoe, of Whickham, Mr. Blackiston, of Durham, and Mr. Montague.

At this time the village of Stella was chiefly inhabited by coal-workers (Bourne's *Newcastle*, p. 166), and had staiths in it. And regarding other villages on the Tyne above Newcastle—viz., Blaydon, Lemington, Swalwell, Delaval, Redheugh, etc.—it is stated that "several of them have staiths belonging to them; such are the staiths of Lady Clavering, Sir Henry Liddell, Bart., Richard Ridley, Esq., George Liddell, Esq., Edward Wortley Montague, Esq., George Bowes, Esq., Geo. Pitt, Esq, Geo. Malliber, Esq., Mr. John Simpson, and Mr. Joseph Ledger."

In this era coal lying beyond a depth of 360 feet was considered to be almost inaccessible. On this supposition (Dunn's *Coal Trade*, p. 43) a powerful co-partnery, consisting of the Ravensworth, Strathmore, and Wortley families, was formed to secure large tracts of coal within the known powers of winning, some of which had hitherto been kept out of the market by distance, but was now brought within range by the employment of railways.

The original partners in this great company—known as the Grand Allies (Surtees, ii. 209 note, 239)—were Colonel Liddell, the Hon. Chas. Montague, and George Bowes, Esq., of Gibside. The deed of co-partnership (*Trans. N.E. Inst.*, xv. 202) is dated June 27, 1726.

Though some of the large collieries on the Tyne, situated near the place of shipment, continued to adhere to the old method of conveying their produce by means of wains and carts, long lines of railway were now being constructed, with great care and cost, to collieries placed at greater distance from the river.

A very inadequate idea of the character of the railways of this period has been spread abroad, even by writers who might have been expected to have been authorities on the subject. It is clear from the first allusion we have to railways in the north, that at their very inception efforts were made to preserve the road at as uniform a gradient as possible; and that cuttings, embankments, and bridges, were formed to accomplish this desirable object. Yet

Mr. Matthias Dunn (*Coal Trade*, p. 39), speaking of the wagon-ways of the early part of the eighteenth century, states that they "were most rudely constructed, being laid nearly according to the undulations of the ground; for the idea of inclined planes had not at this period entered into the notions of mankind." Mr. Nicholas Wood, likewise, in his *Treatise on Railroads* (ed. 1831, p. 18), states that, "except levelling down abrupt undulations, little care was taken to make the road with an uniform descent. For many years after the introduction of the wooden railway, a wagon containing nineteen bolls, or about 42 cwt., was the universal load attached to a horse, and the road was levelled accordingly, the only desideratum being to enable a horse to convey that quantity."

That this was by no means the case is sufficiently demonstrated by the account furnished by an eye-witness, Dr. Stukeley, who visited the Tyneside in the course of his northern tour, made in the year 1725, and who is the first writer to describe the railways here, after the brief notice of them by Roger North.

"The manner of conveying the coals from the pits down to the river side," he says (*Itin. Cur.*, 2nd ed., Cent. II., pp. 68, 69), "is very ingenious: a cart-way is made by a frame of timber, on which the wheels of the carts run without horses, with great celerity; so that they are forced to moderate the descent by a piece of wood, like a lever, applied to one of the wheels.

"We saw Col. Lyddal's coal-works at Tanfield, where he carries the road over valleys filled up with earth, 100 foot high, 300 foot broad at the bottom; other valleys as large have a stone bridge built across, and in other places hills are cut through for half a mile together; and in this manner a road is made and frames of timber laid, for five miles to the river side, where coals were delivered at 5s. the chaldron."

The stone bridge referred to was the once famous Tanfield Arch, or Causey Arch, having a span of 103 feet and a height of 63 feet (Brand, ii. 306; Sykes's *Loc. Rec.*, i. 143), built for the above railway from Tanfield to the Tyne by Colonel Liddell and the Hon. Chas. Montague—the founders of the partnership called the Grand Allies —at a cost of £1,200. The arch fell down after being built, but was rebuilt forthwith. The mind of the architect (a country mason) became so unhinged by the fear lest it should fall a second time, that he committed suicide by leaping from the top. It has long been disused, and exists now as a picturesque ruin. It bore date 1727. A view of it is given by Mr. T. Sopwith in his treatise on *Isometrical Perspective*.

The testimony of Dr. Stukeley may suffice to establish the fact, that the early railway engineers in the north were not so destitute of skill and enterprise as they have been represented, even in the era of wooden lines.

The object aimed at in the construction of railways at this period was to form them into one long inclined plane, so that the loaded wagons might run from the pits to the river side by their own gravitation. In this early method of conveying loaded wagons by free gravitation, it was customary for the horse destined to bring back the empty wagon to travel down behind, or in other words, to put the cart before the horse. An improvement on this, which was subsequently adopted in some cases on long slopes (Wood's *Railroads*, 2nd ed., p. 303), consisted in employing a low carriage, attached to the rear of the train, in which the horse was conveyed down, thus making the cart carry the horse, an arrangement which horses are stated to have got accustomed to very soon, and to have been fond of. Such a method continued in use within recent years on a railway in the neighbourhood of Stella; and so well versed was the horse in the performance of this easy and agreeable part of its duties, that it is said to have almost understood to "take seats" when the down train was about to start.

Colonel Liddell's colliery at Tanfield took fire in 1739 (Sykes's *Loc. Rec.*, i. 159); an accident attributed to the carelessness of some boys. The pit is described as having been changed into a terrible volcano, thundering out eruptions of hot cinders of considerable weight into the open air, to an incredible height and distance. The flames were extinguished by closing up the pits.

By an indenture, dated April 26, 1731, between Dame Jane Clavering and George Pitt, a right of wayleave from collieries in this district to the rivers Tyne or Derwent was granted for 500 years, on payment of 2s. 6d. for every ten of coals carried along the wagon-ways. (Fordyce's *Coal and Iron*, p. 97.)

The Tanfield district was remarkable for the depth to which free drainage was carried. According to Edington (*Coal Trade*, p. 130) pits were thus drained to a depth of 360 feet. The length and narrowness of the water-courses is referred to by Mr. Greenwell (*Mine Engineering*, 2nd ed., p. 195). The great value attached to them is shown by the fact that in 1729 (*Trans. N.E. Inst.*, xv. 205) a water-course out of Sir Francis Clavering's mines at Beckley, through Mr. Dawson's Colliery at Tanfield, was charged at the rate of £2,000.

At a slightly later date, doubtless in consequence of the extension of the railway system, the Tanfield and Pontop district became a stirring arena of mining operations.

While the great bulk of the coal exported from the Tyne, in the early part of the eighteenth century, still came from the district lying to the west of Newcastle and Gateshead, or in other words above Newcastle bridge, and required to be brought down to Newcastle in keels, some progress was now being made in sinking to the deeper coal to the east of these places, both on the north and south sides of the river.

On the Newcastle side collieries were being worked in the Heaton and Byker estates, by the help of steam engines to raise the water. The engine at Byker has been already referred to as one of the earliest on the Tyneside.   Of the date of the erection of the Heaton engine we have no record, but it was some time previous to 1747, inasmuch as a writer in the *Universal Magazine* for September in that year alludes to the impossibility of working several collieries without the assistance of fire engines, "as the proprietors of Elsick, Heaton, Biker, etc., near Newcastle-on-Tyne, can bear me witness."

The subjoined brief report (*Trans. N.E. Inst.*, xxxviii. 189) relates to a landsale colliery on the estate of Gosforth, the property and residence of the Brandling family, the coal from which was carried in carts to Newcastle :

"14 Feby., 1740.   We whose names are here underwritten, having taken a water-level from the Dean Pit in Gosforth Colliery, and finds y^t it runs about 60 yards to the west of the borehole at Salter's Bridge, and so will run on to Killingworth Moore for about 800 yards before it gets into North Gosforth grounds, and we are of opinion that there may be about 40 acres of ground in Gosforth y^t may have coal in it which may be about 1 yd. or 4 feet thick, and about 40 fathoms depthness.

"An Estimate of the Expense of working Gosforth Colliery :

	£	s.	d.
Hewing, per score, ...	0	2	0
Putting, ...	0	1	0
Abstract of other expenses, ...	0	2	10
	£0	5	10

Which at 10xx to the ten, will cost per ten, £2 18s. 4d.   The above is our opinions, as witness our hands.

AMOS BARNES.
EDW. SMITH.
GEO. CLAUGHTON."

On the opposite side of the river reference has been made to the working of coal at Gateshead in the beginning of the century, in connection with the accidents which occurred there.

In the manor of Felling, a possession of the Brandling family, in the same neighbourhood, the uppermost coal seams are stated (Hodgson's *Account of the Felling Explosion*, p. 5) to have been extensively wrought at this time.

Friar's Goose, or Tyne Main Colliery, is mentioned in 1744 (Dunn's *Coal Trade*, p. 42), in connection with the price of coal there. Referring to the skill of the early miners in cutting deep and narrow water levels, Mr. Greenwell (*Mine Engineering*, 2nd ed., p. 195) speaks of having seen one of them in the old workings of this colliery, the depth of which was 16 feet, and the width at the top not more than 3 feet.

Coal was also being worked in this neighbourhood by Mr. Blackett, whose colliery was doubtless situated at Heworth.

An account of the points from which coal was being shipped below Newcastle Bridge, at the time when he wrote (about 1730), is furnished by Bourne (*Newcastle*, p. 172), who observes that "in going down the river we meet with several staiths; such are the staith of Richard Ridley, Esq., and Matthew White, Esq., at the Glass-House Bridge; the staiths of Richard Ridley, Esq., at St. Lawrence and St. Peter's Keys; of Walter Blacket, Esq., and Mr. John Wilkinson, of Francis Rudston, Esq., and of Edward Wortley Montague, Esq."

Few records seem to exist relating to collieries in other parts of the great northern coalfield during the first half of the eighteenth century. Dr. Stukeley in 1725 (*Itin. Cur.*, 2nd ed., Cent. II., p. 70) speaks of there being great coal works in the neighbourhood of Chester-le-Street. In the south of Durham we hear (*Trans. N.E. Inst.*, xv. 199) of a lawsuit in 1715 relating to a coal mine in the Barony of Evenwood.

The following passage occurs in a viewer's report on Butterknowle Colliery, dated 27th June, 1726 (*ib.*, p. 203 note), relating to the engine, which appears to have been a water-wheel: "It is necessary to have a house over ye engine to prevent idle persons from doing any damage to ye same, also it preserves ye engine from ye drought in summer, and by having a house there may be a fire made on in winter, to prevent frosts, which hath often hindered engines from performing their proper use."

Water-wheels continued long to be employed in some places for pumping water, where the circumstances were favourable. "Within recent years," says Mr. Green (*ib.*, p. 200 note), "a gigantic water-wheel might have been seen situate by the side of Beamish Burn, where it had been used to pump the Beamish Colliery water."

In Northumberland (*ib.*, p. 200), coal of good quality was still being shipped at Cullercoats in 1718. Reference occurs to the colliers of Tweedmouth (Raine's *North Durham*, p. 236 note), in the extreme north of this county, in 1726.

About 1745 the corves used for drawing coals out of the pits in the Northumberland and Durham coalfield, are stated (*Trans. N.E. Inst.*, xv. 206) to have commonly contained 12 pecks, or about 3¾ cwts., for the sake of convenience of winding with horse gins.

The following notice of a colliery explosion occurs in an account of travels in the counties of Northumberland and Durham in 1727, ascribed to Defoe (*ib.*, p. 278 note) : "Here (at Chester-le-Street) we had an account of a melancholy accident which happened in or near Lumley Park, not long before we passed through the town. A new coal pit being dug or digging, the workmen workt on in the vein of coals till they came to a cavity, which, as was supposed, had formerly been dug from some other pit ; but be it what it will, as soon as upon the breaking into the hollow part, the pent-up air got vent, it blew up like a mine of 1,000 barrels of powder, and getting vent at the shaft of the pit, burst out with such a terrible noise as made the very earth tremble for some miles round, and terrified the whole country. There were near three score poor people lost their lives in the pit, and one or two, as we were told, who were at the bottom of the shaft, were blown quite out though sixty fathom deep, and were found dead upon the ground." This explosion, however, requires verification, the exact date and place not being mentioned. There is a possibility that it may be a slightly inaccurate version of the explosion which occurred at Fatfield in 1708, to which in some respects it bears a striking resemblance.

At North Biddick Colliery, also in the River Wear district, an explosion occurred January 18, 1743 (Sykes's *Loc. Rec.* ; Sykes's *Account of the Wallsend Expl.*, p. 32), occasioning the death of seventeen persons. This accident, like the foregoing, is said to have resulted from cutting into a drift which communicated with an old waste.

We have seen that at the period when the *Compleat Collier* was written, the miners of the north dreaded the idea of introducing fire into their pits. Since then a change had taken place in this respect. Artificial ventilation had become a necessity, as the pits became deeper and more extended; and fire, being the best agent known for producing it, now began to be employed for the purpose.

Fire lamps, according to Mr. Dunn (*Coal Trade*, p. 42), were first known at Fatfield Colliery in 1732, and he elsewhere states (*ib.*, p. 48) that they were first introduced in that year at the Scrog Pitt, Chartershaugh Colliery, by Edward Smith.

Soon afterwards they are heard of on the Tyne. In a view of Byker Colliery, in 1740 (*Proc. Archæol. Inst.*, Newcastle, 1852, i. 201), the viewers observe that: "This colliery will be attended with difficulties occasioned by the great quantities of sulphur; but from experience we find, by using a fire lamp to rarefie and put the air in motion, hath removed almost all difficulties in that way."

Simultaneously with the introduction of fire lamps into the northern mines to produce artificial ventilation, we hear of the first beginnings of an important modification of the bord-and-pillar system of working—viz., the removal of the pillars of coal by a second working.

According to Mr. Dunn (*Coal Trade*, p. 49) the working away of pillars in fiery collieries was first practised at Chartershaugh, on the Wear, in 1738, Edward Smith being then viewer. It is a somewhat singular coincidence that the same individual should have been the first alike to introduce pillar working and fire ventilation; pointing to the probability of both ideas having been brought from some of the southern coalfields, where, as we have seen, fire lamps had been in use for a period of fifty years, and where, under the long-wall system of working, no pillars at all were left in the mine.

It is true that Mr. Nicholas Wood (*Trans. North of Eng.' Inst.*, vol. xv., pp. 205, 209) expresses the opinion that pillars had been worked previous to 1730; but as he furnishes no details in support of the statement, neither giving exact dates nor localities, it is somewhat difficult to know whether the system had really been commenced in the north so early as he supposed. That an unauthorized removal of part of the pillars intended to be left was sometimes practised, would seem to be indicated by the expression "robbing the pillars," which curiously is still applied to pillar working in the north of England.[1]

It is clear at all events that even sixteen years subsequent to

---

[1] A reference to this surreptitious practice being pursued in Yorkshire in 1713, occurs in an account of a colliery on the Shibden Hall estate, near Halifax (*Leeds Mercury Supplement*, May 16, 1885), where we are told that because of the length of the underground roads some of the colliers would "frequently get in the posts."

the above date, the viewers on the Tyne only contemplated removing such a portion of the pillars as was considered obtainable without occasioning a subsidence of the strata.   In a report on Byker Colliery, signed by five viewers, and dated 10th October, 1746 (*Proc. Archæol. Inst.*, Newcastle, 1852, i. 199 note), it is set forth that: "We whose names are underwritten, have viewed Byker Colliery, and find ye same to be fairly and regularly wrought, 9 yards to ye winning, ye pillars 5 yards thick, and to ye best of our opinion there may be three quarters of a yard taken off the walls in the Hogg and Bird Pits, and one yard taken off the walls in the Chance, Speedwell, and Virgin Pits."   They add, however, "When this is done, we cannot certify the colliery will be upstanding."

It is not till some years after the middle of this century, that we began to meet with distinct records relating to the entire removal of the pillars in the Tyneside collieries.

In addition to the progress being made in various directions at the collieries themselves, some extension of the shipping season had likewise now taken place.   In illustration of this it is recorded (Sykes's *Loc. Rec.*) that on February 11, 1739, the principal coal fitters under Sir Henry Liddell, Edward Wortley, and George Bowes, Esq.—the Grand Allies—with 200 men, cut away the ice and opened a channel from below Newcastle bridge to their staiths above bridge, being nearly one and a-half miles in length, by which keels passed to load ships.   The "colliers" evidently no longer lay up till the month of April, as had formerly been their wont; at least such of them as traded with the above powerful company : a fact which is confirmed by a letter of William Scott's—the father of Lords Stowell and Eldon, who was fitter to George Bowes, Esq., of Gibside—dated 18th February, 1745-46 (*Extracts from the Letter-book of William Scott*, Newcastle, 1848, p. 32), in which he informs his correspondent that "the ships are beginning to trade."

The export of coal from the Tyne in 1752 (*Proc. Archæol. Inst.*, Newcastle, 1852, i. 194 note) was 300,000 chaldrons, and from the Wear 170,000 chaldrons, which together with the quantities exported from Blyth and Hartley Pans, was supposed to amount to over 500,000 chaldrons.   The local consumption in salt-pans, glassworks, ironworks, and fire coal, was estimated at 100,000 chaldrons; making the total quantity raised from the mines 600,000 chaldrons, or 1,590,000 tons.

CHAPTER XXVI.

THE EIGHTEENTH CENTURY.—Continued.

Iron little used at collieries previous to the middle of the eighteenth century. Union effected between coal and iron. Cast iron cylinders begin to be used in steam engines, and cast iron pipes for pumps. Great building of engines in the north of England.

Down till the middle of the eighteenth century iron continued to be a very scarce and dear and sparingly-used commodity. The old charcoal iron manufacture was dying out for want of fuel. The number of furnaces had decreased from 300[1] to 59; and in 1740 only 17,350 tons of pig iron were made in England. The large proportion of the iron used in the kingdom was imported from Sweden and other countries on the Continent. Under these circumstances it is not surprising that the quantity of iron used for mining purposes was minimized to the lowest possible point.

Even in the early steam engines, and their associated pumping apparatus, almost no iron at all was used. The cylinder and piston, as well as the working barrel and buckets and valves of the pump, were made of brass. The top of the boiler was made of lead. The great beam of the engine, which constituted the *pump handle*, was of wood (as its name indeed implies), as were also the pump rods, and pump trees, or pipes, in the pit; the latter being of the form known as spigot and faucet, bored out of the solid wood, and usually only about 8 or 10 inches in diameter. Thus iron was only employed in the lower part of the boiler on which the fire acted (though in some of the earliest engines even this was made of copper); in the chain connections of the beam and other small fittings, and sometimes in hooping the pump trees to impart greater strength to them.

---

[1] So estimated by Dud Dudley in his *Metallum Martis* (reprint 1854, p. 36); but supposed by Mushet to be highly exaggerated (see *Report of the Royal Coal Commission*, iii. 30).

In the early railways, in like manner, iron was conspicuous by its absence—their name at the present day being, indeed, derived from the material originally used in their construction. Rails, sleepers, and even the pins by which they were fastened together (known as tree-nails) were all made of wood ; as were also the wheels of the wagons which ran upon the wooden road. It is probable that the axle-trees of the wagon were made of iron from the first, on account of the considerable weight conveyed ; though this word itself had obviously a wooden origin.

Some interesting details regarding the railway material of this period are preserved in a small pamphlet entitled "Extracts from the Letter-book of William Scott" (who has been already referred to as coal-fitter to George Bowes, Esq.), published at Newcastle-on-Tyne, by M. A. Richardson in 1848. From these extracts it is clear that railways must have come into extensive use in the north towards the middle of the eighteenth century, their construction and maintenance having given rise to a considerable importation into Newcastle and Sunderland, of rails, planks, and wagon wheels, from various parts of the south of England, particularly from Sussex and the New Forest.

These articles formed a frequent subject of correspondence between Mr. Scott and his business friends in the south, furnishing a variety of particulars regarding the kinds of wood used, the prices paid, etc. Thus we find him writing :

1745-46, 31st January.—"The wheels made up of the pieces you sent are yet unsold, the prices runs very low at present occasioned by too many wheels being imported last year, the dealers mostly having six or nine months' stock by them at this place, and you may judge by the following advertisement how full Sunderland is. January 25. To be sold at Sunderland a fresh parcel of birch wheels and beech rails and plank at the lowest prices, enquire of Thos. Smith, who will shew the same. Who these wheels, etc., belongs too, I know not, but the advertisement standing in our newspaper makes the dealers here expect wheels and rails for almost nothing."

28th February.—"You say you have bought a parcel of rails you formerly wrote about, if you mean ash rails theyl come too late, for the gentleman that wanted them is already served. . . . I find the best oake rails will scarcely give 6d. per yard this year, as there will be a great many cut in this country and led to the wagon ways at 6d. per yard. This parcel of rails proved very indifferent and were badly squard."

1746, 8th June.—"I expect to get sold this week at or about 7s. a wheel."

— 13th July.—"The best wagon wheels will now scarce give 5s."

1747, 27th March.—"No less than about 2,000 (wheels) com'd within these 14 days from Lyndhurst."

— 20th October.—"It may not be amiss to inform you some people begin to want wagon wheels . . . my friends Mr. Shafto and Mr. Bell begin to own they want, and there will be beach rails wanted."—"The sooner 10 or 15 load of more plank comes the sale would be made more certain, for in the spring there will be of it coming from other parts and better wood. About 100 wagon wheels of large sizes would not come amiss now."

1747-48, 8th January.—"Beach rails will not be wanted as formerly. I mean not so many, the long wagon ways being on the decrease."

From the last extract it would appear that some long railways were constructed on the Tyneside just before the middle of the century. It was probably at this period that Wylam railway was formed, along the north side of the Tyne, said to have been one of the oldest in the north of England; as also those from the Stella neighbourhood to Whitefield (or Chopwell) and Hedley Fell, the tracks of which are still marked by the cuttings and embankments which remain to the present day. The Wylam railway passed within a few yards of the door of the house where George Stephenson was born a generation later.

According to Mr. Dunn (*Coal Trade*, p. 39), "In 1745, the cost of a yard of wooden way was 4s. 2d., viz., two yards of oak rails, 1s. 2d.; three sleepers, 2s. 6d.; pins, 1d.; laying, 3d.; filling and ballasting, 2d." The railways were still and for some time afterwards of what is known as the "single way" description. At a subsequent period they were made stronger and more durable by employing two tiers of rails, one above the other, in the form known as the "double way."

In other colliery departments, in like manner, almost no iron was used. The gins, and frame-work over the pit, as also the sleds used for the conveyance of the corves on the underground roads, were of wood; the corves themselves, as already mentioned, were made of hazel twigs. The water-tight frames (or "tubbing"), sometimes applied for damming water out of the shafts, were also constructed with wood. The ropes were made of hemp. Iron may perhaps have been used in the wheels, or pulleys, over the pit, for carrying the ropes; and the sleds were at times shod with this material.

But a great revolution was approaching.   From having been in a special sense the metal of Mars for ages, iron was now destined to gradually become likewise the backbone of the arts of peace; the promoter of industry and commerce; the minister of progress and civilization—this new era in the history of the world being a result of the union of the coal and iron industries.   After nearly 150 years of fruitless efforts, this happy event was at last consummated at Coalbrookdale Foundry, in Shropshire; but in so quiet a fashion that even the date at which it was first successfully effected has not been recorded.   It appears to have been about 1740, however, that the results of this achievement first began to be felt.   From this time the coal and iron industries rendered mutual aid to each other —coal enabling more iron to be produced, iron again enabling more coal to be produced; the two together bringing in their train a host of benefits hitherto unknown.

Thus the second half of the eighteenth century was a period of transition.   At its commencement iron was only employed to an insignificant extent; before its close the metal had come into common and extensive use.

Nowhere were the effects of the union of coal and iron earlier felt than at the collieries themselves; the pumping apparatus, the most vital part of the plant, being the first department in which a transformation was brought about.   Here the cast iron cylinders, supplied by the Coalbrookdale Foundry, began to rapidly supplant the brass cylinders which had previously been in use.

It is curious to find Dr. Desaguliers, in 1744, condemning this innovation.   "Some people," he says (*Experimental Philosophy*, vol. ii., p. 536), "make use of cast iron cylinders for their fire engines, but I would advise nobody to have them; because, though there are workmen that can bore them very smooth, yet none of them can be cast less than an inch thick, and, therefore, they can neither be heated nor cooled so soon as the others, which will make a stroke or two a minute difference, whereby an eighth or a tenth less water will be raised.   A brass cylinder of the largest size has been cast under one-third of an inch in thickness, and at long run the advantage of heating and cooling quick will recompense the difference in the first expense, especially when we consider the intrinsic value of the brass."

The greater cheapness of iron cylinders, however, quickly carried the day, and the brass cylinders of the steam engines were among the first of colliery furnishings to be supplanted by substitutes made of iron.   Only after this change was made could it be said—as D. Erasmus Darwin has it—that:

"Press'd by the ponderous air, the piston falls
Resistless, sliding through its iron walls."

In the pipes in the pit, likewise, iron began to be substituted for wood equally early. This Dr. Desaguliers speaks of as an unnecessary expense.

Referring to a lift of 150 feet, he says (*ib.*, p. 478): "If we endeavour to do it in one lift we shall burst the lower pipes, unless they be of iron, which will be costly; but wood will serve very well if we divide the work into three lifts of fifty foot each." But if wooden pipes were cheap they were weak, and there was great difficulty in keeping the joints tight; and the rapidity with which cast iron pipes were adopted is shown by the fact that within twenty or thirty years from the time when Dr. Desaguliers wrote (1744) they had come into general use at collieries.

From this time mining enterprise advanced at an accelerated pace, the period immediately following the middle of the eighteenth century being marked by the building of great numbers of steam engines, due doubtless in no small degree to the facility with which large cast iron cylinders could now be obtained; while again, the building of these engines may be regarded as synonymous with the establishment of new, and for the most part deeper collieries, which were now being opened out by their aid.

Up till about 1750 the number of steam engines in the north of England must have been somewhat limited, if we may accept Mr. Dunn's statement (*Coal Trade*, p. 41), that when William Brown built an engine at Throckley, in 1756, the machine was "then a great rarity."

Fig. 15.—Pumps at Griff Colliery.

Immediately after this, however, numerous engines, some of very large size, began to be erected, William Brown above mentioned playing a conspicuous part in their introduction. Where Mr. Brown obtained his knowledge of steam engine building we are not informed. According to Edington (*Coal Trade*, p. 123) he was bred from his youth in colliery affairs at Throckley, a place situated on the north side of the Tyne between Walbottle and Wylam. Being in want of a friend to bring him forward, he was taken by the hand by Mr. Bell, who leased Throckley Colliery, and appointed him manager, with a handsome salary and one-fourth share of the colliery. Mr. Dunn states (*ib.*, p. 41) that this occurred in 1756, and that in this year he built the engine there above referred to.

No sooner had Mr. Brown shown his capacity for engine-building at Throckley, than his services came into great request for the erection of others elsewhere, as appears from the following list of these machines fitted up by him at different times, given by Mr. Dunn (*ib.*) :

"In 1757, one at Birtley North Side, one at Lambton, and one at Byker. In 1758, two at Walker, and one at Bell's Close. In 1759, one at Heworth. In 1760, two at Shire Moor, and one at Hartley. In 1762, one at Oxclose, one at Beamish, and one at Benwell (which had not only three boilers, but 24-in. wooden pumps, formed of staves). In 1763, one at West Auckland, with wooden pumps[1] 18 in. diameter. In 1764, one at North Biddick, one at Low Fell, and three in Scotland (viz., one at Borrowstoness, one at Pittenweem, in Fifeshire, and one near Musselburgh. In 1766, one at Lambton. In 1772, one at Fatfield. In 1775, two at Willington and one at Washington (with its house contrived to take in a second). In 1776, one at Felling." A record of engine building by one colliery viewer, which has probably been rarely if ever beaten.[2]

According to the same writer the Allerdean engine at Ravensworth was built about the year 1750; up to which period scarcely any pumps exceeded 8 or 9 inches in diameter, and scarcely any engine had more than a single haystack boiler.

Regarding the progress which had been made in the erection of Newcomen steam engines, some statistics have been preserved. They were almost all placed either at collieries in the north, or at metalliferous mines in Cornwall; comparatively few having been employed at first in the shallow collieries of the midland districts. Mr. Smeaton, we are told by Farey (*Steam Engine*, p. 233), collected information regarding the engines in use, and in 1769 obtained a list of one hundred which had been erected at collieries in the

[1] Wood probably being still employed in this and the preceding case, on account of the unusually large size of the pipes.

[2] Mr. Brown seems to have been the most eminent viewer in the north in his day. Many of his reports on collieries are preserved in the Museum of the Society of Antiquaries in the Castle of Newcastle (see address on *The Rise and Progress of Coal Mining*, by Mr. J. B. Simpson, published in the *Colliery Guardian*, 4th Dec., 1896).

Newcastle-on-Tyne district; but it appears that many engines in the list had been worn out and given up, and that the number actually at work was fifty-seven. The average pressure (*i.e.* effective atmospheric pressure) on the piston, was computed to be 6·72 lb. per square inch.

The list of engines subjoined, quoted by Mr. Dunn (*Coal Trade*, p. 24) from the books of Mr. Brown above mentioned, and dated 1769, is doubtless either the original or a copy of that supplied to Smeaton; liberty, however, has been taken to arrange the engines according to the districts in which they were built:

	No.	Diam. of cylinder.		No.	Diam. of cylinder.
Tyneside, North:			**River Wear:**		
Elswick,	2	28, 27	South Biddick,	2	
Jesmond,	4		Newbottle,	2	36, 48
Byker,	6	42, 42, 60	Pensher Tempest,	2	
Heaton,	4		Morton Hill,	2	
Benton,	5	60	Black Fell,	1	
Tynemouth Moor,	4	60, 42, 75, 70	Chester Burn,	1	28
Newbiggin,	4	42, 42, 44, 60	Fatfield,	2	62, 47
Chirton,	1	43	**South Durham:**		
Walker,	2	73, 72	Auckland,	1	48
West Denton,	2	36, 38	**Northumberland (Tyneside excepted):**		
East Denton,	1	60	Plessey,	1	32
Benwell,	1	75	Choppington,	1	16
Lemington,	1	42	Black Close,	1	13
Newburn,	1		Eshott,	1	
Throckley,	4	36, 13, 48, 60	Felkington,	1	20
Wylam,	2	47, 60	Hartley,	2	42, 62
Gosforth,	1		Unthank,	1	36
Tyneside, South:			Shilbottle,	1	42
Norwood,	1	13	Fallowfield lead mine,	1	42
Bushblades,	2	42, 52	**Nottinghamshire:**		
Rise Moor,	1	60	Nottingham,	1	60
South Moor,	1	47	**Cumberland:**		
Ravensworth,	3	48	Workington,	1	28
Gateshead Fell,	1		Grey Southen,	1	24
Salt Meadows,	1	32	Whitehaven,	4	28, 36, 42, 42
Heworth,	2	52, 72	Parton,	1	42
River Wear:			**Scotland:**		
Ouston,	1	48	Duddingston,	1	66
North Biddick,	2	62	Borrowstoness,	2	
Washington,	2	62			
Chartershaugh,	1	36	In all,	99	
Lambton,	2	42, 64			

The above list doubtless comprises the bulk of the Newcomen

engines erected at collieries up till this date, but it is not by any means complete, as independent records exist relating to others built previously at collieries in the Midland counties, Wales, and Scotland. Large numbers of engines had likewise been applied at Cornish mines. According to Price, who wrote in 1778 (*Mineralogia Cornubiensis*, introduction, p. 14), above sixty engines had been built since the remission of the coal duty by Government in 1741; and more than half of them rebuilt, or provided with larger cylinders.

CHAPTER XXVII.

THE EIGHTEENTH CENTURY.—Continued.

The collieries, explosions, etc., in the Northumberland and Durham coal-field, 1750-1775. Walker colliery. Large steam engine. Shiremoor colliery, etc. Working of pillars at Gosforth, and Long Benton. Collieries at Byker, Brunton, Prestwick, Benwell, etc. Kitty's drift. Throckley, Wylam, Prudhoe, etc. The Tanfield district. The yearly bond. Collieries near Gateshead. List of collieries on the Tyne. The Wear collieries, explosions, etc. Hartley and other collieries in Northumberland.

WHAT with the extended use of the steam engine, the more liberal employment of iron, and the assistance of gunpowder, which was now beginning to be utilized in the north for blasting rock, the hands of the miners had been greatly strengthened, enabling them to win coal seams at depths hitherto deemed unattainable.

The centre of activity consequently began to move towards the eastern and deeper part of the coalfield, where the greater depth was more than compensated by the superior quality of the coal for household purposes, and by the greater facilities obtained for shipping away the produce of the collieries. This rendered abortive the schemes for monopolizing the more shallow coal, which had been entertained in the early part of the century.

The most notable colliery of this period was situated at Walker, on the north bank of the Tyne, a few miles below Newcastle. Walker estate—the coal in which formed part of the deep tract already referred to as the "Tyne Basin"—was forfeited to the Corporation of Newcastle in 1721 (Sykes's *Loc. Rec.*, i. 140), and in the following year (Brand, ii. 685-86) an inquiry was held regarding the probable cost of winning the coal in it. No attempt to effect this appears to have been undertaken till the coal was leased by a company about 1758, in which year, as we have seen, two steam engines were erected here by Mr. W. Brown. These seem to have proved insufficient, a third engine of monster size being added a few years later. This great engine is thus referred to in the local records of the district, 1763 (Richardson's *Table Book*, H.D., ii. 109):

"A fire engine cylinder was landed at Wincomblee coal staith, on the River Tyne, for the use of Walker Colliery, which surpassed everything of the kind which had been seen in the north. The diameter of the bore measured upwards of seventy-four inches, and it was ten and a-half feet in length. Its weight, exclusive of the bottom and the piston, was six and a-half tons, containing altogether between ten and eleven tons of metal. The bore was perfectly round and well polished. It was considered a complete piece of work, and did honour to Coalbrookdale foundry, in Shropshire,[1] where it was manufactured. When this engine, to which the cylinder was attached, was completed, it would have a force to raise 307 cwt. of water."

When this engine had been erected it is said to have been pronounced "the most complete and noble piece of ironwork that had up to this time been produced." Dr. Smiles (*Early Engineers*, ed. 1874, p. 152) states that this engine was built by Brindley, but the reference which he gives seems insufficient to support the assertion.

Regarding this "fire-pump," and its connections, M. Jars, a French engineer, who visited the north of England and other districts in 1765, and published an account of his travels, under the title of *Voyages Métallurgiques*, in 1774, informs us (vol. i., pp. 195-96), that it was the largest in the north, and perhaps the largest yet made in Europe. To supply it with steam four very large boilers were employed, three of which were always in use, each boiler having its own chimney as well as furnace. The tops of the boilers were made of lead, with the exception of the one immediately under the cylinder, the top of which was made of copper. He remarks, however, that it was no longer customary to employ two different materials in the construction of boilers, but to make them entirely of wrought iron; and that in some cases the boiler was not placed underneath the cylinder but alongside of it. The piston, which was made of iron, was packed with hemp rope; and the usual stratum of

---

[1] A relic of the ancient connection between this distant foundry and the northern collieries was discovered in breaking up some old iron at Hebburn colliery in 1872; a fragment being preserved and brought to the office as a curiosity, having the word COALBROOKDALE cast upon it.

water was kept on the top of it, to preserve the packing soft and air-tight. On account of the large size of the cylinder, three water-jets were required to effect the condensation of the steam. The pumps, which were in three lifts (the two upper sets having each two columns of pipes), raised the water 534 feet, to an adit which conveyed it away to the Tyne : the total depth of the pit being 600 feet. All the pumps were made of cast iron : with reference to which point M. Jars remarks, that in all the north, and perhaps in all England and Scotland, the pumps were entirely made of this material. The stroke of the piston and pumps was 6 feet, and from eight to ten strokes were made per minute. The cost of the pumping apparatus was from £4,000 to £5,000, and of the whole undertaking £20,000.

An explosion occurred at Walker Colliery (Sykes's *Loc. Rec.*) April 2nd, 1765, causing the loss of eight lives ; and another (*ib.*), March 18th, 1766, with the loss of ten lives.

M. Jars speaks (*Voyages*, i. 198-99) of another new mine, six miles from Newcastle, having a steam engine with a 60-inch cylinder, with three injection jets, and making twelve strokes per minute. Here two boilers were used, made wholly of wrought iron, and placed apart from the cylinder. This was probably Shiremoor Colliery, which Edington tells us (*Coal Trade*, p. 123) was leased by Mr. Bell; and where, as we have seen, two engines were built by Mr. W. Brown, in 1760.

In the same neighbourhood there is mention (Richardson's *Table Book*, H.D., ii. 124) of Mr. Kent's pit, near North Shields, in 1764 ; probably situated at Chirton, where a steam engine was built previous to 1769. Another incidental reference to the collieries in this locality occurs in 1771 (*ib.*, p. 198), when we hear of General Paole being attended by W. Charlton, Esq., one of the Duke of Northumberland's auditors, to Tynemouth, and the coal works in that neighbourhood.

Improved shipping facilities were now being provided on the lower part of the Tyne. A dock at Howdon Pans (*ib.*, ii. 79) was completed in 1759; while in 1771 (Sykes's *Loc. Rec.*, i. 280) new staiths at Shields occasioned a strike of the keelman, who recognized the danger which this portended to their craft.[1] These improvements doubtless gradually led to the discontinuance of the shipment of coal at Cullercoats.

---

[1] As early as 1633 (Charleton's *Newcastle Town*, p. 234) the keelmen had petitioned Charles I. against the erection of " keyes and staithes " between Newcastle Bridge and the sea.

If pillar working, as it would appear, had not been commenced on the Tyneside at the date of the Byker report in 1746, it must have begun to be practised within a few years afterwards. Thus in a view of Gosforth Colliery by J. Watson, dated 21st March, 1753 (*Trans. N.E. Inst.*, xxxviii. 190), the first pit is spoken of as "wrought out both whole and walls."

A little later an alarming surface subsidence at Long Benton, caused by the removal of pillars, furnishes a more forcible illustration of the fact :

"November 27, 1765.—At this date Long Benton street opened up and closed again from end to end, and some fields sunk about 2 feet, occasioned by the colliery of Long Benton having been wrought entirely out. The coal pillars had been worked away, and slight wooden ones fixed in their stead, which not being sufficient to support the rock, the whole sunk together" (Sykes's *Loc. Rec.*). The colliery was 450 feet deep, but even this was insufficient to admit of the pillars being removed with impunity.

Pillars are also stated to have been removed under Newcastle town moor as early as 1765 (*Min. Jour.*, xix. 102).

The working of the pillars may not improbably have had some connection with the various "blasts," or explosions, which occurred at Long Benton Colliery in this era. One of these happened (Richardson's *Table Book*, H.D., ii. 73) November 18th, 1757, with the loss of three lives ; another (*ib.*, p. 89) June 15th, 1760, with the loss of one life ; another (*ib.*, p. 102) December 8th, 1761, but happily unattended with any loss of life. The celebrated Dr. Hutton is said (*Fossil Fuel*, 1835, p. 289) to have been originally a hewer at Old Long Benton Colliery.

Though the High Main seam was exhausted at Long Benton in 1765, the colliery was soon re-established, either by sinking to a deeper seam, or by means of a new winning. In 1772 Smeaton built the first of his improved Newcomen engines here (Farey's *Steam Engine*, pp. 134, 172, 235 n.), having a cylinder 52 inches in diameter.

Among other notices of collieries on the north side of the Tyne at this period, there is mention (Wallis's *Northumberland*, i. 130) of an explosion at Byker Colliery, June 4th, 1761, by which two over-men, father and son, were killed.

Mr. T. J. Taylor (*Proc. Arch. Inst.*, Newcastle, 1852, i. 170) refers to an estimate to work Brunton Colliery, in the Whorlton seam, made by John Watson in 1755, in which the ten is stated to consist of "twenty-two wagons of twenty bolls each," being 440 bolls.

Mention occurs (Richardson's *Table Book*, H.D., ii. 141) of a colliery near Newcastle in 1766. In 1771 a new colliery for landsale was won at Prestwick, belonging to Mr. Jonathan Thompson (*ib.*, p. 193), on which occasion the country people assembled at Ponteland, and great rejoicings were made.

Reference has been already made to the erection of steam engines at Benwell in 1762, and Bell's Close in 1758, by Mr. W. Brown. Engines had also been applied at Gosforth, Newbiggin, Lemington, West Denton, East Denton, Throckley, and Wylam, previous to 1769. We also hear (*Trans. N.E. Inst.*, viii. 39) of an engine at Killingworth Colliery, the cylinder of which was cast at Coalbrookdale in 1767.

About 1770 a drift, or tunnel, was driven from the Tyne, near Scotswood Bridge, to Old Kenton Colliery, a distance of nearly two miles, by Christopher Bedlington, an eminent viewer of the period, after whom it came to be known as "Kitty's Drift." It was intended to serve both for the drainage of the colliery, and the conveyance of the coal to the river. It is said to have been found to be ineffectual in great measure, as it only cut the rise part of the colliery (*Trans. N.E. Inst.*, xv. 210); but according to Edington (*Coal Trade*, p. 120), a large tract of coal some thousands of acres in extent, including East and West Brunton, Fawdon, and Coxlodge, could never have been wrought without it. There is an account of a visit paid to East Kenton Colliery, through this subterraneous wagon-way, in Rees' *Cyclopedia*, where it is spoken of as three miles in length.

At West Denton a winning was made by Edward Montague, Esq., in 1766 (Sykes's *Loc. Rec.*, i. 258). The coal was said to be equal in quality to Long Benton, then wrought out.

Throckley Colliery, as already mentioned, was being worked at this period by Messrs. Bell and Brown; while we hear of Wylam Colliery being inundated to the extent of 300 acres by the great flood in November, 1771, which swept away all the bridges on the Tyne except that at Corbridge (*Trans. N.E. Inst.*, xv. 211), which was built on a Roman foundation. It was to this flood, as flowing past Paradise, near Benwell, that a Tynesider of the name of Adam referred, when he astonished the judge at Newcastle, according to the local story, by the successive statements, that his name was Adam, and he came from Paradise, and had lived there since before the flood.

At Prudhoe, on the south side of the Tyne, nearly opposite to Wylam, and situated on the western edge of the coalfield where the

lowest seams cropped out on the hill sides, coal was still being
worked as in the early days of coal mining, by the primitive method
of drifts, or day-holes.   There is mention (Richardson's *Table Book*,
H.D., ii. 142) of a fox followed by a pack of hounds running into a
drift here in 1766.[1]   It was no doubt in such a drift that Thomas
Bewick, the famous wood engraver, was employed in digging coal at
an early age (*Fossil Fuel*, 1835, p. 290).   The Bewick family has for
some generations worked a coal drift in the vicinity of their residence
at Cherryburn, near Prudhoe, where Thomas was born, as intimated
by a brass plate on the door of a building now used as an outhouse
—a small tribute to his memory placed there by the thoughtfulness
of the late R. Simpson, Esq., of Moorhouse, Ryton.

Regarding the collieries of the Ryton, Stella, and Blaydon, neighbourhood, as also those of Winlaton and Whickham, little is heard
at this period.   The case is otherwise with the more distant but
newer district of Tanfield and Pontop, where mining was being
carried on with considerable activity.

There is mention in 1760 (*Trans. N.E. Inst.*, xv. 206) of a colliery
at Pontop Pike being leased under rather stringent conditions,
recommended by a Mr. Wm. Newton.   The term of the lease was
for twenty-one years, with a certain or fixed rent of £900 per
annum, and a tentale rent of 16s.   The wagon load to consist of
twenty bolls, or 44½ cwt.   No coals to be allowed for the use of the
lessees, or for workmen's firing.   As we learn at a later period (*ib.*,
215) it was customary for the tenants of the coal owners to find
horses for leading the coals from Pontop Pike Colliery to Derwent-
haugh.

Other collieries here, as well as some matters of interest connected
with the working of them, are heard of (*ib.*, p. 108) in connection
with the signing of a Yearly Bond in 1763.   The bond referred to
was made between Lady Windsor and John Simpson, alderman of
Newcastle, owners of Harelaw, Pontop Pike, Harperley, and Collierley
collieries, and their work-people.   It was stipulated that "The
parties hired shall continue at work, without striking, combining, or
absenting themselves; shall deliver one corf of coal gratis every pay,
or fourteen days; shall be fined one shilling for every corf sent to
bank less than wood full, and shall be immediately drawn to bank if
the banksman call him, and shall deliver one corf of coal gratis for
every corf of coals set out (*i.e.* condemned on account of containing
stones among the coals); and for the true performance of all and

[1] We also hear (Sykes's *Loc. Rec.*, i. 222) of a fox and hounds entering a
coal drift in 1758.

singular these conditions, the hewers, drivers of sledge horses, drivers of gin horses, onsetters, and banksmen, bind themselves severally and respectively, their and each of their several and respective heirs and assigns, in the penal sum of £18."

To this bond, which is stamped, are attached the names of 110 hewers and 55 drivers, all opposite seals. Very few of the parties appear to have signed their own names. The period of binding commenced on the 3rd of December. Sixpence each appears to have been the hiring money. Mr. Green remarks that some of the conditions and restrictions contained in this bond, were much more severe than many complained of by the pitmen "in the present bonds" (1866).

Though little or nothing is heard of the Yearly Bond previous to this period, it can scarcely be doubted that it had existed ever since serfdom was abolished. From this time forward the pitmen appear to have become increasingly sensitive on the subject, any alteration of the date or term of binding usually resulting in a strike. Such a strike occurred in 1765 (*ib.*, p. 209), and was attended with considerable violence, riots being said to have taken place at all the coal works, with the exception of Mr. Delaval's (Macpherson's *Commerce*, iii. 420).

In the bond above referred to, we meet with one of the earliest notices relating to the use of horses underground in the north of England mines.

In 1768 a new colliery was opened out on Tanfield Moor, the property of the Earl of Kerry, the coals from which were led to Derwenthaugh (Sykes's *Loc. Rec.*, i. 265; Dunn's *Coal Trade*, p. 23).

At Ravensworth Colliery an explosion occurred in 1757, causing the loss of sixteen lives (Sykes's *Loc. Rec.*, i. 217). In the same neighbourhood a steam engine was erected, in the above year, at Birtley North Side; followed by another at Low Fell in 1764; one had also been built at Salt Meadows previous to 1769. A pit at Norwood, 420 feet deep, is mentioned in 1766 (Richardson's *Table Book*, ii. 144).

We hear of the sinking of a new pit on Gateshead Fell in 1757 (*ib.*, p. 73). On the east of Gateshead, Mr. Blackett's colliery, at Heworth, is mentioned in 1758 (*ib.*, p. 78). A steam engine, as we have seen, was erected here in 1759. Notice occurs of a girl falling into a pit at Heworth in 1764 (*ib.*, p. 126). We also hear of a girl falling, the same year, into an old pit on Blackburn Fell, near Gibside (*ib.*, p. 125).

According to one account (*Report of the Royal Coal Commission*, iii.

41 ; Dunn's *Coal Trade*, p. 232), there were only thirteen collieries on the Tyne in 1770 ; another account (*Trans. North of Eng. Inst.*, xv. 211) puts the number working at the same date at twenty-one. The latter estimate is obviously the more correct, as appears from the following list of collieries, together with the quantity of coals vended, in the year 1767 (*Report of the Royal Coal Commission*, iii., Appendix, p. 3) :

Collieries.	Chaldrons.	Collieries.	Chaldrons.
1. Wylam Moor, . . .	14,000	15. South Moor, . . .	34,000
2. Greenwich Moor[Throck-		16. Andrew's House, . .	6,000
ley], ...	18,000	17. Hutton Main,. . .	8,000
3. Holywell Main, . .	18,000	18. J. M. Edge, . . .	12,000
4. Montague Main, . .	5,000	19. Silver Top, . . .	20,000
5. Byker, ...	11,000	20. Pontops,. . . .	50,000
6. Benton, ...	27,000	21. Lunds, ...	5,000
7. Walker,. . . .	12,000	22. Barleyfield [Barlowfield],	5,000
8. Tynemouth Main, .	13,000	23. Whitfield [Whitefield], .	12,000
9. Chirton, . . .	14,000	24. Rise Moor, . . .	6,000
10. Chapter Main, . .	8,000		
11. Fellon [Felling], . .	13,000	Total chaldrons,	359,000
12. Huntley's . . .	5,000		or
13. Team, ...	26,000	Total tons, .	951,350
14. Tanfield Moor, . .	17,000		

In 1772 Walker Colliery is spoken of as being the only best coal colliery below Newcastle Bridge (Dunn's *Coal Trade*, p. 25).

The greater part of the notices relating to the collieries on the Wear, at this period, have reference either to the building of steam engines or to accidents from explosion.

Chartershaugh, or Chatershaugh, Colliery was the scene of an explosion, August 11, 1756, by which four lives were lost. The following account of it is given by Sykes (*Loc. Rec.*) : "About two o'clock in the morning a dreadful accident happened at Chatershaugh Colliery, on the River Wear. The foul air in one of the pits ignited, by which four men were instantly killed and torn to pieces. The explosion was so violent that a corf full of coals was blown up the shaft from a depth of 80 fathoms (480 feet) into the open air, and a vast quantity of coaldust and rubbish was thrown to a great distance, discolouring the surface of the ground round about."

At Lambton Colliery a steam engine was erected in 1757, and another in 1766. An explosion occurred at this colliery, September 4, 1757 (Richardson's *Table Book*, ii. 72), with the loss of two lives ; and again, August 22, 1766, with the loss of six lives. The latter explosion was caused by the fire lamp used for ventilating the mine, under circumstances recorded as follows in the Newcastle newspapers at the time (Brand, ii., Appendix, p. 683 note):

"A most melancholy accident happened at Lampton Colliery, near Chester-le-street, in the county of Durham. The workmen, to the number of a hundred, had but just left off work, and three masons, with as many labourers, had been let down in order to build a partition to secure the coals from taking fire by the lamp; when the said lamp, being let down at the request of the masons to rarefy the air, the latter in an instant took fire with a terrible explosion, and made its way up the pits, destroying men, horses, and all in its passage. The noise of the explosion was heard above three miles round, and the flash was as visible as a flash of lightning. The men below were drove by the force up through the shaft or great tube, like balls out of a cannon, and everything that resisted shared the same fate.

"The neighbourhood being alarmed, collected itself in order to give assistance; but found only heads, arms, legs, thrown out to a great distance from the mouths of the pits. The ground for acres was covered with timber, coals, etc. All the partitions, trap doors, corves, wood props, and linings, were swept away, together with the engine for drawing up the coals, and all its apparatus."

At South Biddick Colliery two steam engines were erected previous to 1769. An explosion occurred at this colliery, April 16th, 1766, with the loss of twenty-seven lives (Sykes's *Loc. Rec.*, i. 258; Richardson's *Table Book*, ii. 149).

At Fatfield Colliery a steam engine was built in 1772. This colliery exploded in 1763, with the loss of fifteen lives (Dunn's *Coal Trade*, p. 23); and again, March 27, 1767, with the loss of thirty-nine lives (Sykes's *Loc. Rec.*, i. 261). The depth of the mine was 480 feet.

Commenting on the frequency of explosions about this period, the *Newcastle Journal* of March 21, 1767, makes the following observations:

"As so many deplorable accidents have lately happened in collieries, it certainly claims the attention of coal owners to make a provision for the distressed widows and fatherless children occasioned by these mines, as the catastrophe from foul air becomes more common than ever; yet, as we have been requested to take no particular notice of these things, which, in fact, could have very little good tendency, we drop the farther mentioning of it; but before we dismiss the subject, as a laudable example for their imitation, we recommend the provision made in the Trinity House for distressed seamen, seamen's widows, etc., which in every respect is praise-

worthy, and confers honour on that brotherhood" (Sykes's *Account
of the Wallsend Explosion*, p. 31).

At North Biddick Colliery a steam engine was erected in 1764.
An explosion occurred here December 6, 1773, with the loss of
twelve lives (Sykes's *Loc. Rec.*, i. 296; Richardson's *Table Book*, ii.
223). The depth of the pit was 480 feet.

Among other matters connected with the Wear collieries at this
period, notice occurs of the erection of steam engines at Beamish and
Oxclose collieries in 1762; and in the list of engines dated 1769,
others are mentioned at Washington, Ouston, Newbottle, Pensher,
Morton Hill, Black Fell, and Chester Burn.

Beamish Colliery is stated to have commenced working in 1763
(*Trans. North of Eng. Inst.*, xv. 208); and a colliery on Pelton
Common is mentioned as having been wilfully set on fire by the pitmen during the binding strike in 1765 (Richardson's *Table Book*, ii.
137).

During the great flood of 1771, the collieries of North Biddick,
Chatershaugh, and Low Lambton, were inundated (Sykes's *Loc. Rec.*,
i. 288).

A report on South Birtley Colliery, dated August 17, 18, 31, 1773
(*Trans. N.E. Inst.*, xv. 211), was made by the following ten viewers:
Christopher Bedlington, Peter Donnison, Thomas Bedlington,
Anthony Waters, John Bedlington, Edward Smith, John Daglish,
John Donnison, John Allison, and William Gibson. They state
that they have examined seventeen pits, which, however, seem only
to have worked about 30 acres each. Some districts they speak of
as having been wrought in both the whole mine and pillars.

In regulating the coal trade in 1771 (*ib.*) three-fifths of the vend
was apportioned to the Tyne, and two-fifths to the Wear; or
386,000 chaldrons to the former and 254,000 to the latter river.
The issues for the year were 890 per 1,000.

Regarding the inland or landsale collieries of Durham at this
period, little or nothing is heard, though their number must have
been considerable. The building of a steam engine at West Auckland by Mr. W. Brown, in 1763, is almost the only item of information
we have.

At Hartley, in Northumberland, great industrial activity appears
to have prevailed, fostered by the Delaval family. The coal of
Hartley and Blyth, if less suitable for household use, is said to have
been in great favour among the bakers of the metropolis. In 1752
a considerable export was already going on from Hartley Pans—also
known as Hartley Haven and Seaton Sluice (*Proc. Archæol. Inst.*,

Newcastle, 1852, i. 194 note). Here also greatly improved shipping accommodation was provided about this time (Edington's *Coal Trade*, p. 151; Sykes's *Loc. Rec.*, i. 244); a new cut or harbour being excavated out of the solid rock to a depth of upwards of 50 feet.

A new winning, or sinking, appears to have been executed here about the same time. There is mention (*Proc. Archæol. Inst.*, Newcastle, 1852, i. 170) of an estimate to work Hartley Colliery, dated 1756, in which the ten is made to consist of "ten score of eighteen peck corves," or 450 bolls. In 1760, as we have seen, a steam engine was erected here by Mr. W. Brown—the chain pumps so much approved by Sir Ralph Delaval, a hundred years earlier, having now become obsolete.

An explosion occurred at Hartley Colliery, December 1st, 1761 (Sykes's *Loc. Rec.*), causing the loss of five lives. It was at this colliery the first attempts were made, in 1763, to apply the steam engine to draw coals out of pits, as will be adverted to hereafter. In 1776 (Brand, ii. 310 note), Hartley Haven exported 18,000 chaldrons, or 47,700 tons of coal. At the same date Blyth exported 14,000 chaldrons, or 37,100 tons.

Among other notices relating to collieries in Northumberland, mention occurs in 1758 (Richardson's *Table Book*, H.D., ii. 74) of a colliery at Mitford, near Morpeth; and of another in 1773 (*ib.*, p. 213) at Newton West Bank, in the same vicinity. There is also a notice (*ib.*, p. 177) of a horse and cart falling into a pit at Wooler in 1769. While from the list of steam engines bearing the same date we have evidence of the existence of collieries, about the middle of the century, at Plessey, Choppington, Black Close, Eshott, Felkington, Unthank, and Shilbottle.

CHAPTER XXVIII.

THE EIGHTEENTH CENTURY.—Continued.

Colliery engineering in the Northumberland and Durham coalfield, 1750-1775 : Attempts to improve the winding apparatus, and to employ the steam engine to draw coals. Wooden railways introduced underground, with trams drawn by horses. Coursing the air adopted in lieu of face-airing. Fire lamps and air tubes. M. Jars's account of the collieries, railways, etc., in 1765. Screens. Coke ovens. Gunpowder used in sinking pits. M. Jars's memoir on natural ventilation. Watt's improved steam engine invented.

THE deepening of the mines, now successfully effected by the aid of the steam engine, attended as it was by a heavier expenditure of capital, created a necessity for improvements being made in almost every department of colliery engineering. The outputs of coal required, being both larger and at the same time brought from greater depths, called for the introduction of more powerful and rapid hoisting or winding machinery. The conveyance of the coal from greater distances underground, demanded improvements being made in the haulage arrangements. The mines being now alike more extensive and more fiery, the system of ventilation which had formerly sufficed was becoming inadequate.

With a view to the more efficient raising of the coals in the pits, attempts were made both to improve upon the previously existing machinery, and to invent new appliances altogether; but the solution of the problem was found to be attended with considerable difficulty.

At Walker Colliery, alike the deepest and most important in the north of England at this period, a horse engine of a new construction was employed during the first few years after the opening up of the colliery. In order to gain greater speed a large horizontal cast-iron wheel was used, the teeth of which drove the drum or rope roll, this being of smaller diameter. The large wheel was actuated by four levers, to each of which two horses were yoked. But though the eight horses went at a rapid trot, the performance of the machine was limited to raising a basket, containing 6 cwt. of coals, from the depth of 600 feet in two minutes.

M. Jars, who describes this machine in 1765 (*Voyages*, i. 194), states that it was attended with a great amount of friction. He was informed that the reason why larger baskets were not made use of was on account of the difficulty of conveying them underground. But he was of opinion that it would have been better to have had a drum of greater diameter, and to have employed larger baskets in the pit, though this involved the double operation of emptying the smaller ones into them at the bottom of the pit. This machine was not a success, and its use was discontinued within a few years.

Among the various schemes brought forward at this period, we hear of a patent being granted, in 1749, to William Newton, of Burnopfield, and Thomas Stokoe, of Bryan's Leap, in the county of Durham, both gentlemen of great experience in the coal works, for a newly-invented method of drawing coals, stones, etc., out of deep pits or mines (*Patent List; Trans. N.E. Inst.*, xv. 206), but there appears to be no further reference to it.

A few years later one Michael Meinzies, or Menzies, Esq., brought forward a method of raising coals out of pits, a monopoly of which he is said to have secured to himself by Act of Parliament. We have a notice of one of Menzies's machines for drawing coals by the descent of a bucket of water, being employed at Chatershaugh Colliery, on the Wear, in 1753, where it is described as raising a corf of coals of about 600 lb. weight, out of a pit 300 feet deep, in two minutes (Brand, ii. 308; *Proc. Arch. Inst.*, Newcastle, 1852, i. 194).

Where no adit existed the water let down in this way required to be pumped back to the surface by means of a steam engine. Though this arrangement was not sufficiently effective to lead to its adoption at the northern collieries, it subsequently came into considerable use in other districts, particularly in situations where free drainage existed and the water did not require to be re-pumped. In the form known as the "balance-tub" system it continued to be used, with excellent results, at a number of collieries, and also at slate quarries in Wales, far down into the present century (Smyth's *Coal and Coalmining*, ed. 1867, p. 161).

Other inventors applied themselves to the task of adapting the steam engine to the work of drawing coals as well as pumping water. The idea of employing the force of the steam engine to produce a rotary motion may be said to have been as old as the machine itself, having even been entertained by Papin. But while the engine, at this period of its history, was well suited for performing the see-saw motion required in pumping water—the piston pulling up the pump rods with the water, and the pump rods again, by their preponderance of weight, pulling up the piston on the admission of steam under it—it was badly suited for producing rotary motion directly, on account of being only a single-acting machine. It could pull, but could not push. To make up for the deficiency on the part of the engine, complicated mechanism required to be employed.

The use of the steam engine to raise minerals from mines was proposed by Mr. Keane Fitzgerald in 1758. This gentleman's attention had been drawn to the subject in consequence of being requested by Dr. Hales to adapt the engine to work his revolving ventilators, which he accomplished by devising a mechanism in which the power was obtained direct from the arch-head of the beam of the engine. In his communication made to the Royal Society in the above year (*Phil. Trans.*, vol. l., part ii., p. 727), entitled "An attempt to improve the manner of working the ventilators by the help of the fire engines," Mr. Fitzgerald remarks that the machine may also be applied to turn a wheel to raise coals, or whatever else is wanted to be raised from the mine.

A machine of this description, driven partly by a steam engine and partly by horses, appears to have been applied at Walker Colliery shortly after the date of M. Jars's visit. Wallis, speaking of this colliery in 1769 (*Northumberland*, i. 128, 129), remarks that, "There are two ventilators worked with a machine by the help of the fire engine. This machine is also applied to turn a wheel for raising coals, bringing up a corf of 20 pecks (6 cwt.), 100 fathoms (600 feet), in the space of a minute, the horses moving in a walk." This complex apparatus, which might be described as a steam-and-horse-ventilating-and-winding-machine, was probably unique of its kind.

Another attempt to apply the steam engine to raise coal—spoken of as drawing coals by fire—was made at Hartley Colliery, under a patent obtained by a Mr. Joseph Oxley in 1763. The first machine was built in this year, and was looked upon as the greatest improvement in the coal trade since the invention of the fire engine. A second and improved machine was built by Mr. Thomas Delaval in 1765, which is said to have drawn up the coal at the rate of a corf a minute, and to have been of so simple a construction that the whole

worked upon two axletrees of about 5 feet long (Sykes's *Loc. Rec.*,
i. 242, 251 ; *Trans. N.E. Inst.*, xv. 209).

Oxley's machine continued to be used at Hartley for a number of
years, and attracted a considerable amount of attention.   M. Jars
went to see it in 1765, but did not succeed, as it was out of order at
the time, and the house which contained the wheelwork was closed.
He was informed that it was very complicated, and subject to frequent breakages.   It is curious to find him suggesting (*Voyages*,
i. 208) that it would be better to employ the steam engine to raise
water on to a wheel wherewith to draw the coal, a system which
came to be extensively adopted in the north of England not long
afterwards.   James Watt likewise visited Hartley to see this
machine about 1768; doubtless when on his way to London to
obtain the patent for his own first great improvement of the steam
engine.   He remarks that it went sluggishly and irregularly, having
no flywheel (Muirhead's *Life of Watt*, 2nd ed., p. 274).[1]   Oxley's
machine, like the others already mentioned, was not attended with
a sufficient amount of success to lead to its coming into extended
use.   A more efficient winding apparatus had still to be invented.

In the underground conveyance of the coal—perhaps the most
slavish and toilsome of all kinds of colliery work—some improvement was effected in this era.   In 1750 a patent was granted to
Michael Meinzies, Esq., for improved methods of carrying coals from
the "face," or hewer's working-place, to the pit, and from the pit to
the "heap," or place where they were emptied at the surface.[2]
This consisted in the employment of self-acting inclined planes,
whereon the loaded wagons in descending were made to haul up
the empty ones.   The credit of the invention of this most ingenious
contrivance would thus appear to be due to Meinzies.   Its similarity
to his method of winding by a water balance is sufficiently obvious.

We have already seen that horses had begun to be applied on the
underground roads in 1763.   Referring to this point at the time of
his visit to the north of England in 1765, M. Jars states (*Voyages*,
i. 192) that horses were taken down into the mines, and wooden
railways, resembling those on the surface, were constructed, on

[1] A notice regarding this and some other attempts to derive a continued
rotative motion from the Newcomen engine, made in 1767 and 1769 by Mr.
John Stewart, and Mr. Dugald Clarke, occurs in Robison's *Mechanical Philosophy*, ed. 1822, ii. 107 note ; see also Farey's *Steam Engine*, p. 408.

[2] Menzies also took out a patent in 1761 for a pick machine to dig coals,
intended to be actuated by means of rod and chain connections from the steam
engine on the surface ; but nothing further is heard of it.

which four-wheeled rolleys (*charriots*) were made use of for carrying the panniers, or corves, full of coals. Where there were no railways made, young boys used little sleds (*traineaux*) for drawing to the pit or horse road.

The frequency with which colliery explosions continued to take place, led to the introduction into the north of England of improvements in the methods of ventilating the workings, and lighting dangerous parts of the mines, brought from the Cumberland coalfield, where they had been invented shortly before.

Hitherto it had been deemed sufficient to cause the ventilating current merely to sweep round the points where the miners were actually at work getting coal—an arrangement known as "face-airing"—to the neglect of the portions of the mine standing in pillars, and known as the waste. So long as the extent of the workings so left unventilated had been very limited, this method of ventilation had probably not been attended with much danger. But as the mines became deeper and more fiery, while at the same time the unventilated areas increased in extent, this arrangement became more and more inadequate, inasmuch as these spaces were liable to become magazines of firedamp, ready to be driven suddenly out into the workings by heavy falls taking place, or to steal out owing to changes of the atmospheric pressure, or in other ways to be brought accidentally into contact with the lights of the miners, and so at any moment carry death and destruction through the mine.

The improved method of ventilation known as "coursing the air" consisted in forming the whole of the excavated passages into one vast labyrinth, by placing stoppings usually in every second row of pillars, accompanied by the necessary doors, thus compelling the air-current to sweep through every part of the mine between its entrance at the downcast and its exit at the upcast pit, and so leaving no part of the workings stagnant.

This system of coursing the air is said by Mr. Dunn (*Coal Trade*, p. 44) to have been first put in practice in the north of England, at Walker Colliery, by two viewers from the Wear district, who had been sent for after an explosion. This was doubtless either in 1765 or 1766. The system, however, came from Cumberland, as above mentioned.

The steel mill was introduced at the same period. According to the same writer (*ib.*, p. 23) steel mills were first used at Fatfield Colliery, on the Wear, after an explosion which occurred in 1763 ; having been brought from Whitehaven, where they had been invented shortly before by the ingenious Mr. Spedding.

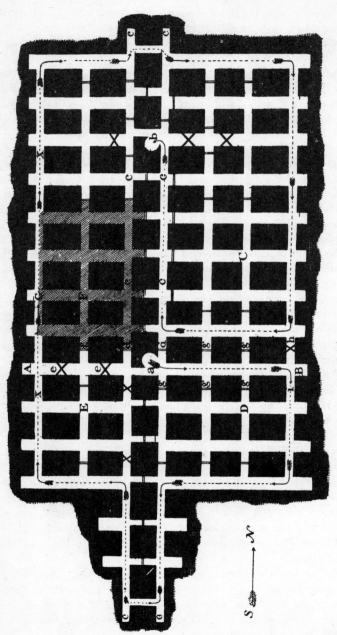

FIG. 16.—FACE-AIRING.

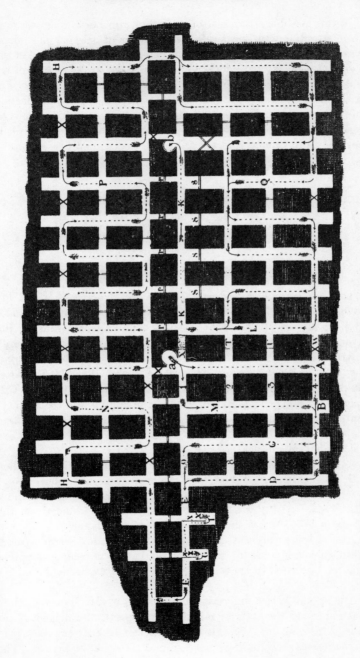

Fig. 17.—Coursing the Air.

In this machine a thin disc of steel, 5 or 6 inches in diameter, was made to rotate with great velocity by means of a wheel and pinion arrangement; and on a piece of flint being applied to the edge of the revolving disc, a continuous flow of brilliant sparks was emitted, which afforded a glimmering light sufficient to enable a group of five or six miners to carry on their work. At the date of its introduction into the north of England this instrument appears to have been regarded as absolutely safe, though almost immediately afterwards it was known in Cumberland not to be so.

FIG. 18.—THE STEEL MILL.

This appliance had evidently become well known on the Tyne previous to 1769. Wallis, writing in this year (*Northumberland*, i. 131), speaks of Mr. Carlisle Spedding, of Whitehaven, as having invented the system of piping off the gas, and the steel and flint mill.

Artificial ventilation, usually by means of fire placed in the mine, had also become common. The same writer (*ib.*, 130-31), after referring to noxious gases and particularly firedamp, remarks that "against this vapour, or damp, a large iron lamp full of coals is kept continually burning in the mine; and to guard against both kinds, a free currency of air is circulated through all the works, entering one and coming up another."

At times the ventilating fire was placed at the surface, in connection with a tall chimney, or tube, after the manner already referred to as practised at Liége a century earlier. The first air tube (Dunn's *Coal Trade*, p. 42) was built at North Biddick Colliery, on the Wear, in 1756, Mr. William Allison being then viewer.

At the same period a commencement was made to employ more substantial stoppings, to guide the ventilating current; stoppings built of brick (*ib.*, p. 48) being first introduced at Fatfield Colliery in 1754.

Among the varied information furnished by M. Jars, regarding the mines and the state of mining in the north of England at the date of his visit in 1765, this writer informs us that the rents paid by the lessees of collieries ranged from £100 to £800 a year. The greatest depth attained by bores was 600 feet. Seams of coal less than 2½ feet thick were considered to be not worth working.

The common depth of the pits was from 180 to 240 feet, the deepest pit (Walker) was 600 feet. The pits were sometimes of an oval form, but were usually round, and from 10 to 12 feet in diameter.[1]

From the surface to the rock the pits were sometimes secured by a wood framework of a polygonal form, but more commonly by means of circular curbs, placed 2 or 3 feet apart, with planking behind. Turfs, or clods of earth, were sometimes made use of, with rings of timber placed at intervals; or masonry consisting of bricks or stone.

There being no ladders in the pits, the men attached themselves to the rope in entering and leaving the mine. Underground the pillars of coal were made from 13 to 15 yards square; and the working-places were from 5 to 15 feet wide. The pillars were left till all the whole coal was exhausted. The miners were paid a fixed price, and dug the coal by means of two-pointed picks and iron wedges.

At Walker Colliery he informs us that the thickness of good coal was 6 feet, part of the seam (altogether 8 feet 5½ inches thick) not being worked except for the engines. The men worked six or seven hours out of the twenty-four, and dug from fifteen to twenty-five and even thirty baskets of coal—commonly twenty to twenty-five. For each basket, weighing 6 cwt., they were paid five farthings, making their earnings average from about 2s. to 2s. 6d. per day.

The boys remained in the mine from 2 a.m. till a little after 4 p.m. They filled the baskets, and took them to the pit, with the aid of twenty horses, earning about 1s. 2d. Walker mine was very dangerous for bad air.

All the coal owners constructed railways (*nouvelles routes*) from the pits to the depôts at the river side, which were laid off as much as possible with a uniform descent, great expense being incurred to accomplish this desirable arrangement, and even small elevations being cut out. Oak sleepers, from 4 to 8 inches square, were placed at distances of 2 or 3 feet apart, and to these the rails, 6 or 7 inches broad by 4 or 5 inches thick, and sawn truly square, were secured with wooden pins. Bands of iron were sometimes used at the joints of the rails. The ordinary gauge of the rails was about 4 feet.

As early as 1753 a commencement had been made to substitute cast-iron wagon wheels for the older wooden ones (Nicholas Wood, *Railroads*, ed. 1831, p. 21). At the date of M. Jars's visit both kinds

[1] Unless intended for the maximum size, this seems somewhat overstated.

were in use.   One pair of wheels were always higher than the other, according to the gradient of the road.   A horse was employed for each wagon, which in descending followed behind the wagon.   A representation and description of a coal wagon is given in the *London Magazine* for March, 1764, by an artist hailing from Chester-le-Street. The wagons were hopper-shaped, and furnished with a hinged bottom. This greatly facilitated the discharge of its contents at the staith, but was open to the objection that it occasionally got shaken loose, with the result that the coals were prematurely deposited on the wagonway—an incident of a troublesome kind known among the workmen as "a caud (cold) pie."

At some collieries double lines of railway were constructed; and some of the railways were nine or ten miles in length; serving to convey the coals from several mines.   The longest line belonged to a rich company, of which Lord Bute was the principal partner; this road was almost always covered with wagons.

Arthur Young, who visited the Newcastle-on-Tyne district a year or two later than M. Jars (1768), informs us (*A Six Months' Tour through the North of England*, 2nd ed., ii. 8, 9) that "The people employed in the coal mines are prodigiously numerous, amounting to many thousands, the earnings of the men are from 1s. to 4s. a day and their firing.   The coal wagon roads, from the pits to the water, are great works carried over all sorts of inequalities of ground, so far as the distance of nine or ten miles.   The track of the wheels are marked with pieces of timber, let into the road, for the wheels of the wagons to run on, by which means one horse is enabled to draw, and that with ease, fifty or sixty bushels of coals."

Iron was not yet sufficiently abundant to admit of its being used for rails; though this wholesale application of it was drawing near. As early as 1767, at the suggestion of Mr. Richard Reynolds, plates of cast iron, placed on the top of wooden rails, began to be used at the great iron-producing centre of Coalbrookdale, in Shropshire— the first step in the development of our iron roads.

Whether the practice of screening coals at the pits had yet been commenced is somewhat difficult to determine, though the probability seems to be that it had not.   Mr. Dunn (*Coal Trade*, p. 25) states that wooden screens were introduced about 1770; and in the same volume (pp. 41, 42) he states that the first screen is said to have been introduced by Mr. W. Brown, at Willington Colliery, about the year 1740.   These statements are sufficiently conflicting, and are rendered all the more so by the circumstance that Willington Colliery was not sunk till 1775.   From this it follows that if the screen was an invention of Mr. Brown, and was first used at Willington, its introduction must have taken place subsequent to this date.

Coke ovens are stated to be first mentioned in 1763 (*Trans. N.E. Inst.*, xv. 208), though references to coke-making in the north occur at least ten years earlier (*ib.*, xxxviii. 190). M. Jars speaks of the existence of nine furnaces on the bank of the river at Newcastle, in 1765, for destroying the sulphur contained in the coal, of one of which he gives a drawing. This date coincides with the commencement of the regular importation of cinders into London (Atcheson's *Letter to Rowland Burdon, Esq.*, Table No. iv.), 393 London chaldrons, or 501 tons, having been received there in 1766.

Reference has been made to the use of gunpowder for blasting rock. The earliest notice of the use of this agent in the north of England which has come under the observation of the writer, occurs in connection with an explosion which happened October 7, 1776, in sinking Ovington's pit, East Rainton, under circumstances described as follows (Sykes's *Account of Wallsend Explosion*, p. 32) :

"Michael Smurthwaite having made preparations for a blast in the stone, working downwards or sinking, fastened a rope, called the centre line, in the hole, for the purpose of running a hot iron ring from the top of the pit to a train of gunpowder, and being drawn up from the bottom so as to be considered safe, the ring was run down the line by the other man William Wilson, which caused the explosion, and they were both lost. Wilson had gone to work that day for another man whose turn it was."

It may be here mentioned that in this era a considerable amount of light was shed on the fundamental principles of mine ventilation by M. Jars, who appears to have been one of the first [1] to make a scientific inquiry into the phenomena connected therewith, and who gave an account of the results of his investigations in a memoir written in 1764, and subsequently published in his *Voyages Métallurgiques* (i. 139), entitled "Observations on the Circulation of the Air in Mines; means to be employed to maintain it."

He had frequently inquired why it was customary to build tall chimneys on the surface to promote a circulation of air in mines, but failing to obtain a satisfactory explanation, set about examining into the matter himself. He soon discovered that the difference of temperature, and consequently of weight, between the atmosphere at the surface and the air in the mine, was the cause of natural ventilation taking place. Thus, in winter, when the external air was heavier,

[1] M. Triewald is stated to have investigated the subject in Sweden in 1740 (*Report of South Shields Committee*).

the current entered the mine by the adit, or lower opening, and escaped by the shaft, or higher exit. In summer, on the other hand, when the relative densities were reversed and the external air the lighter of the two, the air entered by the higher and escaped by the lower opening; the difference of weight of two columns of air of equal altitude being the power whereby the current was produced.

This explained why the air-current changed its direction in summer and winter, and why it was more or less stagnant in spring and autumn. It also showed how the building of a chimney, by accentuating the difference of altitude, served to promote a cir- culation of air. And it further demonstrated how the employment of fire, to rarefy, or lighten, the column of air in one of the shafts, rendered the mine independent of natural changes of temperature, and produced a steady current of air always flowing in the same direction.

So highly was this memoir of M. Jars valued by the South Shields Committee (to be hereafter referred to) that they appended a translation of it to their report published in 1843, indicating that even at that date it was still regarded as the most able exposition of the subject.

It is a curious coincidence that the year in which we obtain what might be termed the earliest (indeed the only) census of steam engines, was the very year in which James Watt secured a patent for the first of his series of splendid improvements of the machine. It is entitled, "A new method of lessening the consumption of steam and fuel in fire engines," and is dated 5th January, 1769. This had reference to his great invention of the separate condenser.

The circumstances under which Watt's attention was drawn to the improvement of the steam engine are well known. After he had become established as a mathematical instrument maker within the precincts of Glasgow University, a model of a Newcomen engine, belonging to the laboratory of the Natural Philosophy class, was put into his hands to be repaired. Watt proceeded to repair it, as a mere mechanician, and when this had been accom- plished he tried to get it to work, but found a difficulty owing to the large supply of steam which it required, which he ascertained by experiment to be four times as much as was necessary to fill the cylinder. This he saw was chiefly due to the condensation of steam resulting from the cooling down of the cylinder, caused by the injection of cold water into it—the method employed for producing the vacuum in the Newcomen engine. How to obviate this, and

keep the cylinder as hot as possible, was the problem which he set
himself to solve.

The idea then occurred to him that the injection of the cold
water might be made in another vessel in communication with the

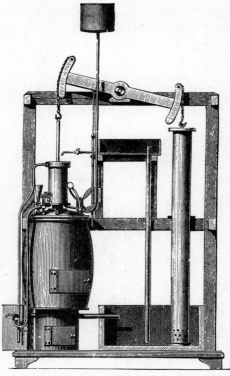

Fig. 19.—MODEL OF NEWCOMEN'S ENGINE (belonging to Glasgow University).
The boiler is directly under the cylinder, and enclosed in the outer casing or
firebox. The chimney is now wanting in the model.

cylinder, without cooling down the cylinder at all. By experiments
he found this arrangement of a separate condenser to completely
answer his expectations.

With the same object of keeping the cylinder as hot as possible,
he arranged to exclude the air from it altogether and envelope it in
an atmosphere of steam. This he effected, in the first instance, by
placing it in a casing in free communication with the boiler, the
piston-rod sliding through a stuffing-box in the cover of the steam
case. Soon afterwards, however, a less expensive method of applying the envelope of steam was employed, the top of the cylinder

itself being closed in, and its sides surrounded by an outer cylinder or steam-jacket arrangement.

To add further to the efficiency of the machine, he placed the vessel in which the steam was condensed in a cistern kept constantly filled with cold water.

The single vessel employed by Papin in his embryo vacuum engine, had now been differentiated into three—boiler, cylinder, condenser.

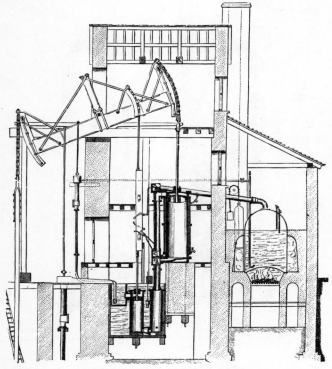

FIG. 20.—WATT'S SINGLE-ACTING ENGINE.

By the improvements above mentioned, and other alterations which they necessitated, such as the employment of an air-pump for clearing out air and water from the condenser, Watt brought the steam engine to the highest degree of perfection of which it was capable as a single-acting vacuum engine. Little or none of the power of Watt's engine was derived from steam. Though well aware of the superior economy of working expansively, with a view to safety he continued throughout to employ steam in the same passive way as was done in Newcomen's engine, and of not more than one or two pounds above the pressure of the atmosphere.

The foregoing improvements effected by Watt at the outset of his connection with the steam engine, prepared the way for other and even more important improvements which he subsequently made. Having reaped no benefit from his inventions for several years after the date of his first patent, in 1775 he succeeded in obtaining an Act of Parliament (similar to that granted to Savery) securing to him a monopoly of his engine for a term of twenty-five years from that date, or, in other words, down till the year 1800. From this time, in conjunction with Mr. Boulton, of Soho Works, Birmingham, he proceeded actively with the building of his engines, which soon came into extended use.

Without wishing to detract in the smallest degree from Watt's merits as an inventor, which, as all the world knows, were sufficiently brilliant, it is necessary to correct an erroneous impression conveyed by some writers, who speak as if Newcomen's engine became extinct forthwith on the appearance of Watt's improved engine. Such was by no means the case; on the contrary, Newcomen engines continued to be built at collieries in larger numbers than ever during the continuance of Watt's patent; and even for a considerable time after its expiration, this engine was still in general use for draining coal mines (*Edinburgh Encyclopædia*, vol. xiv., p. 335).

Superior as Watt's engine was to Newcomen's in efficiency and economy, the latter had the advantages of simplicity and cheapness. And while Watt's engines (after their introduction about 1778) rapidly supplanted Newcomen's at the mines of Cornwall, where economy of fuel was of the first importance, the case was quite otherwise in the colliery districts, where they were only employed to a very small extent for many years subsequent to their invention, and indeed till further improvements had been made upon them by Watt himself and his successors.

CHAPTER XXIX.

THE EIGHTEENTH CENTURY.—Continued.

The collieries of the Tyne and Wear, 1775-1790. Opening out of Wallsend Colliery; difficulties with firedamp. Lists of collieries on the Tyne and Wear. Employment of water gins for drawing coals. Watt invents the double-acting steam engine. Great increase in the production of iron; its use on railways extending. Underground sledges and trams. The manufacture of coal tar in the north.

WE have seen that Walker Colliery was the only colliery on the Tyne below Newcastle producing the best quality of coal in 1772. It did not long remain so, various important sinkings to the High Main coal, in the Tyne basin, being effected soon after this date.

Foremost among these was the sinking of a colliery at Willington, near Howdon Pans, by Messrs. Bell & Brown, where the High Main seam was won in 1775 (Sykes's *Loc. Rec.*, i. 304), at a depth of 606 feet.

Almost immediately afterwards a commencement was made to open out the famous Wallsend Colliery; the coal in this manor—which belonged to the Dean and Chapter of Durham, and was situated between Walker and Willington—having been leased by Messrs. Chapman & Co. in 1778, when the winning of the High Main seam was begun.

The first pit was lost in a quicksand, and a second narrowly escaped the same fate; but by means of piling it was carried through the sand, though its diameter was reduced in the process to 5 feet 11 inches. Two pits (placed on the site of the ancient Roman fort of Segedunum, at the eastern extremity of the Great Wall) each provided with pumping engines, and known as the A and B pits, the latter being 9 feet in diameter, were at length carried down to the seam in 1781 at a depth of about 600 feet, when Messrs. Chapman & Co., after having spent "a fortune" on the venture (*Tyne,*

Wear, and Tees, 2nd ed., p. 254), sold the colliery to Messrs. Russell & Wade.

Though Wallsend Colliery eventually became exceedingly prosperous and profitable, so much so that its fame extended over both hemispheres and even to the antipodes, during the first period of its history it was the scene of a succession of most discouraging disasters, as related by Mr. Buddle in his memoir on *Mining Records* (*Trans. Nat. Hist. Soc. of Northumberland,* etc., vol. ii., p. 309 *et seq.*).

Thus, on October 21, 1783, a "blower" of firedamp ignited at the candle of a hewer, who ran away without attempting to extinguish it. The overman made a courageous effort to reach it, but was overcome by the smoke and noxious gases and suffocated; and the coal and brattice, or ventilating partition in the working-place, having evidently been set on fire, the district was flooded with water in order to extinguish it.

This entailed no great delay, and though two small fatal explosions occurred in 1784, which were supposed to have been caused by the steel mill (Sykes's *Account of the Wallsend Explosion,* p. 32), nothing serious took place till the 9th of October, 1785, when the ventilating current, being overloaded with firedamp, ignited at the ventilating furnace, and produced a severe blast in the upcast, or B pit. No lives were lost, but the woodwork supporting the pumps in this pit was blown out, and the coal at the pit bottom set on fire, rendering it necessary to seal up the mouths of both pits and flood the workings with water a second time.

When the pits were opened up again, on November 2, three men descended the B pit to examine its condition by the light of a steel mill; but when they had reached a depth of 420 feet from the surface an explosion took place, by which they were all killed. Up to this time, according to Mr. Buddle, implicit reliance had been placed in the steel mill, so that this explosion caused great consternation. The use of the instrument was, however, continued, and the repairs in the shaft proceeded with by its light.

On November 11, while two men were working in the A pit by the light of a steel mill, an explosion took place which killed both. This caused a great panic. It was imagined that it had arisen from some fire in the workings under water, or other mysterious cause, as the steel mills were still not suspected.

Again, on December 21st, when two men were working in the B pit by the light of a steel mill, an explosion took place which killed them, and caused the utmost consternation.

This accident shook the confidence of the miners in the steel mill to such a degree that for some time they preferred working by such other feeble light as they could obtain. The daylight received from above being dim and imperfect, fish in a phosphorescent state, and various preparations of phosphorus, were tried, but with little benefit. Another method, accidentally discovered, afforded material service. It happened that a carpenter, engaged upon some work at the top of the pit, in which he made use of a bright new hand-saw, turned the blade to such an angle as to throw a flash of light down the pit. The sudden gleam so alarmed the men below, who thought the pit had fired, that they demanded to be drawn up with all speed. The discovery of the cause of their alarm led to the employment of a mirror at the top of the pit, which proved of great service during periods of sunshine.

The progress of restoring the colliery being slow and tedious, the season being the depth of winter, the steel mill began again to be partially used. But on February 4, 1786, another explosion took place in the B pit, by which three men were severely burnt. The mill was, in consequence, thrown once more into discredit, and the work carried on very much in the dark. None but the most intrepid miners would venture down the pit. Two men descended at a time in a sinking corve, with a rope round their bodies to attach them to the chain. They grubbed about and filled the corve with their hands as best they could, and then returned to the top with it. This constituted their "shift," or day's work, for which they were paid 5s. each, with a small allowance into the bargain.

By continuous struggling in this manner the pits were at length cleared, and the water lowered sufficiently to allow a current of air to pass between them, after which the operations for restoring the colliery went forward more briskly. The steel mill was again introduced, as the only light available underground, and all went well till June 9, 1786, when an explosion took place in the workings near the bottom of the A pit. This explosion did not kill any of the workmen, and was distinctly ascertained to have been occasioned by a spark from the steel mill. The overman, who was "playing," or turning, the mill at the time, saw the gas igniting at the sparks which it produced. The explosion did little damage beyond paralyzing the exertions of the workmen for a time. Work, however, was soon resumed, and on July 10, 1786, the drawing of coal was again commenced at the A pit, after a cessation of nine months.

The repairs of the B pit were still proceeding when an explosion took place here by which six lives were lost. This happened at the steel mill on the 3rd of November. The men were engaged in making a communication between the two pits, a distance of 95 yards, and were under the necessity of working among firedamp. Having no alternative but to use the steel mill, or to work in absolute darkness, they preferred the former course, and the result was fatal to them. The communication was subsequently effected without light of any kind, and bore the name of the "Dark Wall" ever after.[1]

The B pit was got to work on January 7, 1787, the ventilation having been improved by placing a powerful furnace at the pit bottom, and other measures. But, notwithstanding this, another explosion happened on August 21 following. Fortunately it took place in the afternoon, when most of the men and boys had left the pit. As it was, the back overman, one hewer, and four trappers, or little boys who attended to doors, were killed, and another boy died of the injuries which he had received soon afterwards. This explosion was occasioned by the overman drawing props out; a fall of roof ensuing which brought down a blower, the gas from which overpowered the ventilating current, and ignited at a light. No more props were in consequence allowed to be drawn while the pits were working.

The interruptions and accidents which had happened at Wallsend[2] pointed out the necessity of having more shafts; and about 1786 the sinking of the C and D pits was commenced. These pits were both 8 feet in diameter, but at a depth of 180 feet a heavy feeder of water was encountered in the C pit, and below this point the shaft was enlarged to 10 feet diameter. The feeder of water, which was estimated to be equal to 1,700 gallons per minute, was effectually stopped back by tubbing, consisting of oak cribs 9 inches in the bed, built one above the other, with ½ inch fir sheeting between the joints for wedging. These pits came into operation in 1790, and greatly assisted to promote the success of the colliery.

With the exception of an explosion which occurred at Wallsend, October 4, 1790, causing the loss of seven lives (Sykes's *Account of Wallsend Explosion*, p. 32), no other accident of the kind occurred here for a long time subsequently.

Mr. Buddle states that at the opening out of Wallsend Colliery, the working of pillars in a fiery colliery was not deemed practicable.

[1] At a subsequent period we hear (*Trans. N.E. Inst.*, xxxiii. 11) of a wall at Felling Colliery being holed with wooden picks.

[2] The dates of these various accidents are those given by Mr. Buddle. They do not quite accord with those given by Sykes in the list appended to his *Account of the Wallsend Explosion*, p. 32. See also Hodgson's *Northumberland*, vol. ii., p. 275 *et seq.*

As much of the coal was therefore taken in the first working as was thought safe, and no more left in the pillars than was considered barely sufficient to support the roof. The pillars were in consequence made 8 yards broad and the bords 4 yards; and holings 2 yards wide were made through the pillars, or walls, at intervals of 22 yards. Thus 39 per cent. of the coal was obtained, and 61 per cent. left in the pillars, almost two-thirds of the coal being intended to be permanently sacrificed at a depth of 600 feet, under the bord-and-pillar system of working, as practised in the best collieries at this period.

Another colliery, known as Bigge's Main, 570 feet in depth, and contiguous to Walker and Wallsend, must have been sunk about the same time as Wallsend, but little is heard regarding it.

At Long Benton Colliery an explosion is mentioned as having occurred on November 18, 1787, by which three lives were lost, including Mr. George Rawling, borer, and Mr. Ralph Unthank, viewer (*Trans. N.E. Inst.*, xv. 272).

On the south side of the Tyne a steam engine was erected, as already mentioned, at Felling in 1776. This colliery was won by Charles Brandling, Esq., in 1779 (Sykes's *Loc. Rec.*, i. 315).

Regarding other collieries in the same neighbourhood, notice occurs of the erection of an engine by Smeaton at Gateshead Park, in 1778 (Farey's *Steam Engine*, p. 242 note); while we hear of an explosion taking place at the Fauld pit, Gateshead, May 17, 1782, by which four persons perished (Sykes, *Acc. of Wallsend Expl.*, p. 32).

Brand (ii. 688-89) furnishes the following complete list of collieries shipping coal on the Tyne in 1787, with their depth, and distance from the river, viz.:

On the North Side.

Names.				Depth of seam.		Distance from the river.
				Fathoms.	Feet.	Miles.
Below Newcastle:						
High Flatworth,	.	. .	.	40	(240)	. . 3
Long Benton,	.	. .	.	90	(540)	. . 2½
Willington,	.	. .	.	102	(612)	. . 1½
Walls End,	.	. .	.	105	(630)	. . ¼
Bigge's Main,	.	. .	.	95	(570)	. . 1¼
Walker,	.	. .	.	95	(570)	. . ¾
Walker Hill,	.	. .	.	75	(450)	. . 1
Byker,	.	. .	.	75	(450)	. . ¾
Above Newcastle:						
Montague's Main,	.	. .	.	60	(360)	. . 1½
Baker's Main,	.	. .	.	24	(144)	. . ¼
Greenwich Moor,	.	. .	.	35	(210)	. . 3

Names.	Depth of seam.		Distance from the river.
	Fathoms.	Feet.	Miles.
Holywell Main, ...	36	(216)	. . 3¾
Wallbottle Moor, ...	50	(300)	. . 2½
Heddon, ...	30	(180)	. . 2½
Wylam, ...	30	(180)	. . 5

On the South Side of the Tyne.

Below Newcastle :

Usworth or Russell's Main, . .	76	(456)	. . 4
Brandling's Main, ...	70	(420)	. . ½
Gateshead Park, ...	45	(270)	. . ¼

Above Newcastle :

Sheriff Hill, ...	80	(480)	. . 2
Low Moor, ...	60	(360)	. . 2¼
Team, ...	55	(330)	. . 4
South Moor, ...	45	(270)	. . 8½
Pitt's Tanfield Moor, . . .	50	(300)	. . 7
Marley Hill, ...	36	(216)	. . 5
Windsor and Simpson's Tanfield Moor, ...	50	(300)	. . 7½
Silvertop's Pontop, ...	50	(300)	. . 8½
Windsor and Simpson's Pontop, .	80	(480)	. . 9
Bladon Main, ...	24	(144)	. . 1
Whitefield, ...	45	(270)	. . 5½

The vend of coal from the Tyne in 1787 (*Royal Coal Com.*, iii. 23 note) was 480,000 chaldrons, or 1,272,000 tons. The number of persons employed at the Tyne collieries, including those dependent upon them, was estimated by Dr. M'Nab, in 1792, as 38,475, but of these only about one-fourth were directly engaged in colliery work.

In the River Wear district we hear of several new sinkings being made, and of various colliery explosions occurring at this period.

At Washington, where a steam engine was built in 1775, a new winning was effected in the following year (Richardson's *Table Book*, ii. 250). An explosion occurred here in May, 1783, with the loss of two lives; followed by two others shortly afterwards, the exact dates of which are not recorded, but each attended with the loss of two lives (Sykes, *Acc. of Wallsend Expl.*, p. 32).

In a report of Smeaton's, dated May 15, 1777 (vol. ii., p. 346), we find him advising as to the dimensions suitable for a steam engine to be erected at Lumley Colliery, for a new winning about to be made there.

Waldridge Fell Colliery, near Chester-le-Street, the property of

William Jolliffe, Esq., was won in 1779, the coals being shipped at Fatfield staith (Sykes, *Loc. Rec.*, i. 317); and reference occurs to Flatts Colliery, in the same neighbourhood, in 1789 (*ib.*, p. 350).

A severe explosion occurred at Chatershaugh Colliery, December 8, 1778, twenty-four lives being lost (Sykes, *Acc. of Wallsend Expl.*, p. 32); one at Birtley North Side, August 21, 1780, with the loss of three lives; and various others happened about this period (1783-94)—viz., at Lambton's A pit, Bourn Moor, with the loss of one life; at Lambton's B pit, Bourn Moor, with the loss of several lives; and at Lambton's Lady Ann pit, Morton, with the loss of two lives (*ib.*).

Lists of the collieries on the Wear in 1778 and 1779 are published in the *Report of the Royal Coal Commission* (vol. iii., Appendix, p. 3).

The collieries shipping coal and the quantities exported from them in the year 1784, were as follow (Dunn's *Coal Trade*, p. 26):

			Newcastle chaldrons.
Black Fell,	. .	Lord Ravensworth and Co., .	19,238
Beamish, .	. .	Sir J. Eden, ...	16,120
Lambton Collieries,	.	——	41,247
Tempest, .	. .	——	31,001
Chatershaugh, etc.,	.	W. Peareth, Esq., . . .	21,746
North Biddick, .	.	— Hudson, ...	17,028
Oxclose, .	. .	——	13,579
Fatfield, .	. .	Sir R. Milbank, Bart., . .	17,533
Newbottle,	. .	J. Nesham, Esq., . . .	13,997
Washington,	. .	W. Russell, Esq., . . .	14,608
[Waldridge Fell],	.	H. Jolliffe, Esq., ...	12,167
Leefield, .	. .	Humble and Co., . . .	10,097
North Biddick, .	.	Biss and Allan, ...	894
South Biddick, .	.	——	15,230
		Total, . . .	244,485

or 647,885 tons. The number of persons employed at the Wear collieries, including those dependent on them, was estimated by Dr. M'Nab, in 1792, as 26,250, of whom, however, only about 7,000 were actually engaged directly in connection with colliery work.

The attempts made to adapt the steam engine to raise coals in the pits having been attended with no satisfactory results, this work continued to be performed almost universally by means of horse gins up till 1777.

Brand, writing in 1789 (ii. 684), mentions three sorts of gins:— The common coal gin, of which he says there is an engraving in Emerson's *Mechanics*—this is a cog-and-rung gin; the other two are the "whim gin" and the "Macaroni gin." What the latter consisted of we are not informed. It does not appear to be mentioned by any other writer, from which it would seem either to have been employed to a very limited extent, or to have been short-lived. One of the Shiremoor pits was known by the name of the Macaroni pit, as appears from an old plan of this colliery.

In a note which he appends, the same writer adds that "there are other kinds of gins for drawing coals, some wrought by water, others by the vibrating lever of the fire engine."

The projects for utilizing the steam engine directly in the work of drawing coal not having proved a success, an indirect method of applying it, through the medium of water-wheels, was now hit upon, which, being found superior to anything yet tried, was rapidly adopted as a substitute for horse gins at the deeper collieries.

Though the idea of employing his fire engines to raise water for driving water-wheels, and thereby giving motion to mill work, had been one of Savery's projects, and had occurred to M. Jars on his visit to the Hartley engine as a better method than that of attempting to apply the steam engine itself directly to the work of raising coal, no one seems to have thought of following out the idea at collieries previous to 1774, when, curiously, the subject of employing water-wheels to draw coals is heard of at three different points simultaneously.

Water-wheels with double buckets arranged in reverse order, for reversing the motion, had been employed for raising ore at the mines in Germany in the time of Agricola (*i.e.* about 1550), who gives a figure of the machine in his treatise, *De Re Metallica*; and one of these had been erected early in the eighteenth century for drawing coal at the Alloa collieries in Scotland, the supply of water being obtained from large ponds constructed for the purpose. We are told (Sinclair's *Stat. Acc. of Scotland*, viii. 614 note) that Mr. Brown, the famous engineer and operative coalmaster at Newcastle, when at Alloa, in 1774, was so much struck with this machine that he took a drawing of it, and on his return to Newcastle contrived one on the same principle to answer for the deep pits there. It was likewise in this year that M. Jars's suggestion above referred to was published in his *Voyages Métallurgiques*; while at the very same date Smeaton is found (Farey's *Steam Engine*, p. 297) erecting a water-wheel for drawing both coals and water at Griff Colliery in Warwickshire.

At Griff, as well as at Alloa, a natural supply of water seems to have been available; but so smooth and easily managed was the water-wheel, compared to the spasmodic and intermittent action of the steam engine—Watt's engine at this period being no better than Newcomen's in this respect, inasmuch as it also was still only a single-acting engine—that the idea of applying it to draw coals, even in situations where it might be necessary to provide a supply of water by means of a steam engine erected for the purpose, began to take a practical form.

FIG. 21.—DOUBLE-BUCKET WATER-WHEEL (for winding).

Among Smeaton's *Reports* (ii. 375) there is a "comparative estimate of drawing coals by horses, or by a coal engine worked by water supplied by a fire engine." It is dated 14th August, 1776, and shows a considerable saving by the latter method.

In the following year (1777) Smeaton designed a "water coal gin" of the above description, for the Prosperous Pit, at Long Benton Colliery (*Reports*, ii. 435; Farey's *Steam Engine*, p. 297). It was found to be a great improvement on the horse gin previously in use, doing the work of sixteen horses and four men, and drawing a basket containing $6\frac{1}{2}$ cwt. of coal, from a depth of 492 feet, in two minutes.

Another of these water gins was built by Mr. W. Brown, at Willington Colliery, and set a-going in November, 1778 (Sykes, *Loc. Rec.*, i. 314). Its performance is stated to have "exceeded the most sanguine expectations," uniformly drawing thirty corves, of 6 cwt. each, in an hour, from a depth of 101 fathoms (606 feet).

Smeaton employed a single-bucket wheel in his water gins, in order to economize water; the reversing of the drum, or rope-roll, being accomplished by means of gearing. But the greater simplicity of the double-bucket wheel led to its being generally adopted (Dunn's *Coal Trade*, p. 45).

Similar machines, designed by a Mr. Thomas Hunt, of London, are figured and described in the *Universal Magazine* for February, 1782; and two of these are there stated to have been then recently erected at Killingworth Moor Colliery, belonging to John Pitt, Esq., and on the colliery near Walker, belonging to John Chapman, Esq., of Newcastle, by which a considerable number of horses before employed at these collieries were rendered unnecessary. While about the same time we hear (Fordyce's *Durham*, ii. 682) of Mr. James Hall, of Greenside, near Ryton, erecting steam engines at Chopwell Colliery, near Coalburns, and at Stella Grand Lease, or Towneley A Pit, to raise water from ponds constructed for the purpose to a cistern 52 feet in height, to drive water-wheels for drawing men and coals up the shafts.

These useful but clumsy machines were rapidly adopted at the deeper collieries in the north of England, and to a small extent in other districts as well, being found to be the most efficient means for drawing coals out of pits which had up till this time been invented.

But their career was short-lived;[1] though Smeaton was of opinion that this application of the steam engine was the best means of procuring rotative motion from it, and that "to confer directly the movements of rotation on the axis would never practically become either useful or economical" (Arago's *Life of Watt*, 2nd ed., p. 60 note)—relegating the steam engine to the humble position of hand-maiden to the water-wheel.

Others, however, were more sanguine than Smeaton regarding the possibilities of the steam engine, and attempts continued to be made to derive a rotary motion from it. In 1779 Mr. Matthew Wasbrough, of Bristol, took out a patent for a steam engine intended to produce continuous circular motion by ratchet wheels, in a manner similar to what had been attempted by others before, but with the addition of a *fly-wheel*, which was then employed for the first time in steam engines.

Several of these engines were erected by Wasbrough, one in his own workshops at Bristol, for turning lathes; another was set up at

[1] The two double-bucket water-wheels above mentioned, at Chopwell and Towneley A Pit, were among the last seen in the Tyne district, one of them being abandoned in 1800 and the other in 1808. In the Wear district one continued in use at Leafield Colliery, near Chester-le-Street, till 1812.

Mr. Taylor's sawmill and block manufactory at Southampton; some others were made for grinding corn. One of these engines was erected by Wasbrough at Birmingham (Farey's *Steam Engine*, p. 409), where Watt now resided. We are told that the frequent breakages and irregularities of this engine recalled to Watt's mind a method formerly conceived by him for converting the reciprocating motion of an engine into a circular motion, and that he proceeded to make a model which answered his expectations, in which he made use of a

FIG. 22.—NEWCOMEN ENGINE WITH CRANK AND FLY-WHEEL, 1780.

crank. The application of the crank is stated to have been communicated by a workman employed to make the model, to some of the people connected with Wasbrough's engine, who in 1780 removed the ratchet wheels and substituted a crank in lieu of them, the fly-wheel being still retained. Thus simplified, the engine answered much better than anything that had been tried before. The application of the crank to the steam engine was patented by Mr. James Pickard, of Birmingham, August 23, 1780 (No. 1263), which is stated to have occasioned Watt considerable mortification (Farey's *Steam Engine*, p. 423; Muirhead's *Life of Watt*, 2nd ed., p. 276).

Whether the above story of the crank having been pirated from
Watt is reliable or not we are unable to say. Others would have it
that Pickard was a *bona-fide* inventor, and that the use of the crank
(a very old appliance) in connection with the steam engine, had not
only been suggested but even patented before (see *The Engineer*,
April 7, 1882, p. 253). Be this as it may, on finding himself shut
out from using the crank Watt set himself to devise other means of
effecting the same end, and on October 25, 1781, patented five
different methods of producing a continued rotative motion from a
reciprocating one without it, among which was the well-known
expedient of the "sun and planet wheels."

Not yet, however, was the steam engine ripe for producing a
smooth and regular rotative motion. Its force was still only exerted
in one direction. By another great stroke of genius Watt at length
mastered this difficulty. He arranged to produce a vacuum alternately above as well as below the piston, the steam being at the
same time applied on the opposite side, thus making the engine work
equally in both directions, or, in other words, double-acting. This
form of engine he patented March 12, 1782. This was the crowning
improvement of the steam engine, and at once solved the difficulty
of applying it directly to produce a continuous rotative motion.

Thus the Newcomen engine was rendered available for producing
rotative motion fairly well in 1780, and Watt's engine much better
so in 1782. During the first seventy years of its history, the sole
accomplishment of the steam-giant had been to draw a straight
line. It had now been taught a new idea, viz., how to describe a
circle—an addition to its *répertoire* which was of infinite value to
the world.

At first Watt employed a toothed rack and sector in lieu of the
chain previously used, to enable the double-acting engine to push
and pull equally; but this arrangement was superseded soon after
by the invention of the parallel motion, which he patented April 28,
1784.

There is a notice of one of Watt's rotative engines erected by
Boulton and Watt at Walker Colliery, Newcastle, in 1784 (*Industrial
Resources of the Tyne*, 2nd ed., p. 291). This engine, it is stated, was
purchased by Mr. Losh, in 1806, for the Walker Alkali Company,
and in 1863 was still to be seen "working daily at Walker, with its
wooden beam and bedplate, and sun-and-planet crank motion."[1]

[1] It is recorded (*Trans. N.E. Inst.*, xxxvi. 134) that the iron work of an
engine erected by Boulton and Watt at Walker was charged 2s. 6d. per lb.,
or £285 per ton.

Another of Watt's engines was erected at Wallsend C pit in 1786 (*Trans. N.E. Inst.*, ii. 125).

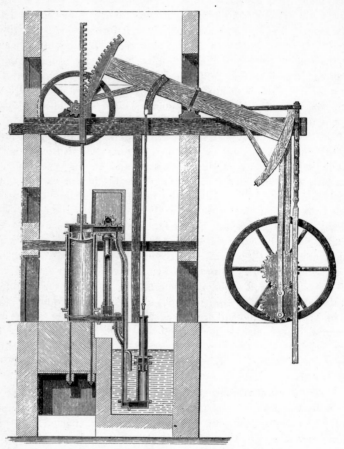

FIG. 23.—WATT'S DOUBLE-ACTING ENGINE, 1782.

From this period the machine begins to cease to be almost exclusively a mining appliance used for raising water, and enters upon a vastly wider field.   The first steam engine grinding wheel at Sheffield (*Beauties of England and Wales*, 1807, p. 825) was set a-going in 1786.   The engine for Albion Mills, London, was built by Boulton and Watt also in 1786—an engine which Mr. Muirhead (*Life of Watt*, 2nd ed., p. 282), speaks of as one of the first completed for sale which combined all Watt's improvements.   While at nearly the same date we hear (Gough's *Camden*, 1789, iii. 134) of Mr. Ark-wright's cotton factory at Manchester being worked by a steam engine. And so its use continued to extend as a source of power for all purposes; and it affords a curious illustration of the force of use and wont that, notwithstanding Watt's splendid improvements on the Newcomen engine, even in applying his engine to duties so different from pumping as driving the machinery of a mill, or blowing the blast of an iron furnace, he continued to make use of the beam, or pump-handle.

Fig. 24.—Albion Mills Engine, 1786.

The success achieved in smelting iron with coal at Coalbrookdale, in Shropshire, was at first imagined to be due to some peculiarity of the coal of that county (*Fossil Fuel*, p. 325); but it was gradually discovered that the coals of other districts could be equally adapted to the process, with the result that blast furnaces became established in one coalfield after another, leading to a continual increase in the quantity of iron produced. The growing abundance of iron was now beginning to tell on the production of other metals. Thus the state of the metal manufacture in 1783 is described (Macpherson's *Commerce*, iv. 16) as: Lead stationary; tin declining; iron rapidly increasing. The quantity of iron produced in 1788 is set down (*Rep. Royal Coal Com.*, iii. 29 ; *British Assoc. Rep.* 1846, p. 114) as :

Charcoal Pig Iron.

	Furnaces.	Tons.
Gloucestershire, .	4	2,600
Monmouthshire, .	3	2,100
Glamorganshire, .	3	1,800
Carmarthenshire, .	1	400
Merionethshire, .	1	400
Shropshire, . .	3	1,800
Derbyshire, . .	1	300
Yorkshire, . .	1	600
Westmoreland, .	1	400
Cumberland, . .	1	300
Lancashire, . .	3	2,100
Sussex, . . .	2	300
	24	13,100
Scotland, . .	2	1,400
	26	14,500

Coke Pig Iron.

	Furnaces.	Tons.
Shropshire, . .	21	23,100
Staffordshire, . .	9	6,900
Derbyshire, . .	7	4,200
Yorkshire, . .	6	4,500
Cumberland, . .	1	700
Cheshire, . .	1	600
Glamorganshire, .	6	6,600
Brecknockshire, .	2	1,600
	53	48,200
Scotland, . .	6	5,600
	59	53,800
Charcoal pig iron, .		14,500
Coke pig iron, . .		53,800
Total make of iron in 1788,		68,300

and so rapidly did the iron industry develop that from this time (1788) the quantity of iron made began to double itself every eight or ten years (*ib.*, p. 30).

Though the railways in the north of England still continued to be all formed of wood, the employment of iron in their construction was making some progress in other parts of the kingdom.

Thus, at Ketley, in Shropshire, Mr. William Reynolds employed a double iron railway in forming an inclined plane as a substitute for locks in connection with his canal there, which was completed in 1778 (Plymley's *Shropshire*, p. 291)—an invention the merit of which is ascribed to him by Tredgold, though according to Rees's *Cyclopædia* (art. Canal) the mode of lowering and raising boats by inclined planes was first adopted by one Davis Drekart, near the Tyrone collieries, in Ireland, about the year 1776.

Light bars of malleable iron $1\frac{3}{4}$ inches broad, and $\frac{3}{4}$ inch in thickness, laid on the top of a substantially-constructed wooden railway of the "double way" type, were used at the Alloa collieries, on the Firth of Forth, in 1785 (Sinclair's *Stat. Acc. of Scotland*, viii. 614). Wagons with cast-iron wheels $27\frac{1}{2}$ inches diameter were employed, carrying 30 cwts. of coal, and three wagons were linked together. At the date of its construction this railway was acknowledged to be " the most complete in Britain."

In Leicestershire cast iron rails of the usual edge pattern, were employed by Mr. Jessop in constructing the public railway at Loughborough in 1789 (Wood's *Railroads*, ed. 1831, p. 24); and at the same period the employment of light cast iron rails of the "plate rail" pattern was commenced by Mr. Curr, who applied them both above and underground at the Duke of Norfolk's collieries at Sheffield. Mr. Curr has indeed been said to have introduced these rails as early as 1776 (*ib.*, pp. 21, 22), but this statement, though frequently repeated, appears to rest upon a misquotation of his words, which will be referred to hereafter.

Iron was also now beginning to be used as a substitute for wood in forming the "bows" of the corves employed in drawing coals out of the pits (Brand, ii. 681 note); and a singular application of this material was made by the much-contriving Mr. William Brown, who, we are told (*Fossil Fuel*, p. 246), invented a contrivance intended for digging coal, which was popularly known as Willy Brown's *Iron Man*.[1]

Speaking of the conveyance of coals underground at this period, Brand (ii. 681) states that "in high seams, or strata, the coals are drawn by horses from the hewers to the shaft in sledges; in low seams, on trams, pulled by two small cords called soams by a boy before, and pushed on at the same time by another boy behind." Trams, he explains in a note, are a kind of sledge on which the coals are brought, from the places where they are hewn, to the shaft. A tram has four wheels, but a sledge, properly so called, is drawn by a horse without wheels. From this it would appear that in 1789, when Brand wrote, the vehicles employed in the underground conveyance of coals in the north of England, were in some cases provided with wheels, and in others were still without them.

The employment of women and girls underground in this district is stated (*Newcastle Weekly Chronicle*, 9th May, 1874, p. 2) to have been wholly discontinued about the year 1780. In the *Report of the Children's Employment Commission* (Append. i., p. 613), however, a case is mentioned of a woman being employed at Denton Burn Colliery, near Newcastle, a number of years subsequent to this date, the last instance known of a female working in the northern mines.

The manufacture of tar from coal appears to have received considerable attention at this period. The earliest reference to the

[1] Mr. Wilkinson, the Shropshire iron master, is also said to have essayed to construct iron men (*The Wilkinsons*, by J. Randall, p. 31).

subject in the north of England occurs in a notice of the death of
one Baron von Haake, at Gateshead, in 1780 (Brand, ii. 311),
described as a native of Silesia, who had come to this country
for the purpose of extracting tar from coal.

The matter was taken up by a Mr. Dixon, whose works at
Cookfield were supposed by Bailey (who was evidently ignorant
of the existence of the industry long previously in Shropshire) to
be "the first of the kind established in the kingdom for extracting
tar from coals." Mr. Dixon began his operations in 1779 (*Proc.
Arch. Inst.*, Newcastle, 1852, i. 204), and continued making tar until
1783, "when he dropped the business, on account of the heavy
expense of land-carriage to Sunderland, where the tar and pitch
were principally used for shipbuilding."

In the meantime, however, Lord Dundonald took out a patent
for extracting coal tar and other products from coal in 1781. This
nobleman erected works in Shropshire and Staffordshire, and about
1781-82 entered into agreements with Mr. William Chapman and
Mr. Liddell, of Newcastle, with a view to the carrying on of the
process on the Tyne (*Description of the Estate and Abbey of Culross*,
p. 34); but misfortune seems to have dogged the unfortunate nobleman's footsteps, and his ventures in the coal tar line only served to
plunge him more deeply into debt. Chapman failed immediately
afterwards. Under date September 22, 1782, Brand quotes (ii. 311
note) an announcement of the sale by auction, by order of the
assignees of William and John Chapman, bankrupts (among other
things), of "the two-fifths share of the benefit of certain letters
patent, granted to the Earl of Dundonald, for the exclusive exercise
in the kingdom of Great Britain and Ireland, of his invention for
extracting pitch, tar, essential oils, mineral acids, volatile alkalies,
and cinders, from pit coal; with the two-fifth shares of certain tar
kilns now erected."

While Lord Dundonald entertained such sanguine views of the
value and importance of the coal tar industry, his contemporary
Williams, writing in 1789 (*Mineral Kingdom*, i. 253), deprecates it
as a "pernicious manufacture" save when carried on in connection
with ironworks, where the coke produced could be utilized for
smelting purposes.

Curiously, even at this period in the history of coal distillation,
the tar, etc., were the valuable products, the gas evolved in the
process a mere waste product.

CHAPTER XXX.

THE EIGHTEENTH CENTURY.—Continued.

Colliery engineering, etc., in the Northumberland and Durham coalfield, 1790-1800: John Buddle, sen., and John Buddle, jun. Deep sinkings in the Tyne basin. Introduction of Watt's steam engine into the north. Tubbing. Numerous explosions in the Wear collieries. Drawbacks of the bord-and-pillar system of working. Creeps. Mr. Barnes's method for recovering a portion of the pillars. Iron rails. Self-acting planes. Preservation of mining records.

THE movement of the principal sphere of mining operations towards the coast, already adverted to, made further progress at this period; a number of important sinkings being made to the deeper and superior coal in the Tyne basin, accompanied by a corresponding decrease in the productiveness of the shallower and more distant collieries.

Speaking of this era, Mr. Dunn remarks (*Coal Trade*, p. 27), under date 1790, that the principal scene of the operations of the coal trade had greatly changed. The collieries delivering at Derwent-haugh had mainly declined, as well as those at Throckley, Team, Dunston, etc. The distant collieries of the Wear too had given place to those nearer to the place of shipment.

The collieries of the Shiremoor district were on the eve of becoming shut up by their younger and more vigorous rivals in the proximity of the Tyne. If tradition is to be relied upon, the viewers employed to give counsel in the matter recommended that the coal should be left; adding the consolatory reflection that it would serve to warm the shins of future generations.

Among those who now played a prominent part in conducting collieries, and carrying out new and deep sinkings on the Tyne, were John Buddle, sen., and his more distinguished son of the same name; the latter of whom subsequently attained to a position of such pre-eminence as a mining engineer, and authority on all associated subjects, as to be popularly designated "the King of the Coal Trade."

John Buddle, sen., resided in early life at Chester-le-Street, the centre of the mining district of the River Wear, where he is stated (*Gent.'s Maga.*, xxi., new series, p. 100) to have conducted a school. He was a frequent contributor to the *Ladies' and Gentleman's Diaries*; and from a mathematical question propounded by him in the latter periodical for 1763 (p. 43), and answered in the issue for the following year (1764, pp. 24-26), we learn that he was born on July 13, 1743. Between 1758 and 1766 he removed to Bushblades (Kyo), near Tanfield; a district where, as has been seen, coal mining was at this time being prosecuted with great activity.

Mr. Buddle is stated to have been a person of considerable literary and scientific attainments, and to have corresponded with Emerson, Hutton, and other eminent individuals, on subjects in which they took a common interest (Fordyce's *Durham*, i. 181 n.). He was very fond, we are told, of solving mathematical and scientific problems. He seems also at times to have addressed himself to solving others of more immediate human interest than those relating to unknown quantities. Thus, in reply to the query propounded in the *Gentleman's Diary* for 1767 (p. 31), "Which would you chuse?

> " A wit without beauty, or a beauty without wit,
> When each is endorsed with a deal of conceit,"

Mr. Buddle replies (1768, p. 43) :

> " Were I from these to chuse a mate,
> The wit, I'd love, the beauty hate ;
> For in the witty head is sense
> Which ever will drive folly thence :
> But beauty, with conceited brain,
> In folly ever will remain."

In the above reply the name is given as "Mr. John Buddles," being frequently spelt in this way in these diaries.

At Bushblades, Mr. Buddle must still have kept on a school for a considerable time, if not, indeed, during the whole of his residence there, inasmuch as it appears that the only schooling young Buddle got—who was born there in 1773—consisted in a year's attendance at his father's school at an early age (*Newcastle Weekly Chronicle*, July 24, 1875, p. 3; Fordyce's *Durham*, i. 181-82 note).

From an edition of the Marquis of Worcester's *Century of Inventions*, with historical notes relative to the invention of the steam engine, issued by Mr. Buddle (afterwards re-published by his son), the preface of which is dated Kyo, near Lanchester, 1788, it would appear that up till this period he continued to reside at Bush-blades.

It was probably immediately afterwards that Mr. Buddle abandoned the "delightful task" for the more arduous but more remunerative profession of colliery viewer. How he obtained his knowledge of the art of coal mining we are not informed, though it has been suggested that he, like Dr. Hutton, may have originally been a pitman. His name would seem to point to an ancestry connected with metalliferous mining; a machine employed for washing lead ore being known as a *buddle*. Be this as it may, from Kyo he removed to Greenside, near Ryton, to superintend the colliery operations there; and subsequently he was selected by Mr. Russell to fill the position of viewer at Wallsend Colliery, where he entered upon his duties in 1792, and where his son, now a lad of nineteen, acted as his assistant (*Report on Accidents in Mines*, 1835, p. 178).

Among the numerous deep shafts sunk in the Tyne basin during the last ten years of the eighteenth century was the Wallsend E pit, 8 feet in diameter, commenced in 1791 and completed in 1793. This pit required no pumping engine, the water being drawn in tubs by a double bucket water-wheel machine (*Trans. Nat. His. Soc. of Northumberland*, ii. 321).

The sinking of the first pit—the A pit—at Hebburn, on the south side of the Tyne, was commenced in 1792 and completed in 1794, by Mr. King, sen. (Richardson's *Table Book*, H.D., ii. 351; Dunn's *Coal Trade*, p. 46). This shaft was about 12 feet in diameter and 774 feet in depth. It was considered the most difficult sinking up till this time attempted, on account of the large quantity of water met with, said to have amounted to 3,000 gallons per minute.

Among other shafts sunk in the same neighbourhood at this period, the sinking of the King pit, at Walker Colliery, was effected by Mr. Barnes in 1795-6 (Dunn's *Coal Trade*, p. 47). The winning of Percy Main Colliery was commenced by Mr. Buddle in 1796 (*ib.*), and the High Main seam was reached in 1799, at a depth of 708 feet. The Hebburn B pit was sunk by Mr. King, jun., about 1797 (*ib.* p. 46), being 792 feet to the High Main.

In connection with the above sinkings we begin to hear of the systematic introduction of Watt's improved double-powered or double-acting engine, at the northern mines. According to Mr. Dunn (*ib.*), the first engine upon this construction for pumping water was erected at St. Anthony's about 1790,[1] and is said to have been a failure—in what respect he does not explain. The sinking of the first pit at Hebburn (1792-94) was accomplished before Watt's double-acting engine had come into use. To Mr. Barnes is accorded "the praise of first introducing the machines of Messrs. Bolton and Watts, of Soho, Birmingham, into this country" (*Agricultural Maga.*, 1800, vol. iii., p. 367), from which it would appear that after the erection of the engine at Walker in 1784, as already referred to, little further progress was made for a number of years. Another of these engines was successfully applied at Walker Colliery in 1796 (Dunn's *Coal Trade*, p. 46), and was followed by the adoption of a similar engine in the sinking of the Hebburn B pit, in 1797, and so at other deep sinkings subsequently.[2]

The advantage obtained by the use of the double-acting engine, according to Mr. Dunn (*ib.*), consisted in doing part of the work of pumping from the cylinder end of the beam, by means of a diagonal spear connected with the pump rods a certain distance down the shaft. Water was thus raised at the up stroke, as well as the down stroke of the piston, and the engine more evenly balanced: an arrangement found to be beneficial under the state of matters existing at this period, though afterwards discontinued (Dunn's *Winning and Working*, sec. ed., p. 62).

Though the steam used in the Boulton and Watt engines was of similar low pressure to that made use of in the Newcomen engines—steam of one or two pounds per square inch above the pressure of the atmosphere being then all that was demanded from the hay stack boilers, which were sometimes 15 or 16 feet in diameter—a better result was obtained in the improved engines. To realize an effective atmospheric pressure of 7 or 8 pounds per square inch on the piston, was considered good in a Newcomen engine (Curr's *Coal Viewer*, 1797, pp. 39, 40); but in the new engines, with their atmosphere of steam, and superior condensing arrangements, a pressure of 10 or 12 pounds could be commanded (Dunn's *Coal Trade*, 46), not to speak of their economy of fuel.

Notwithstanding the aid afforded by the steam engine, and the circumstance that cast iron pumps of 12, 14, 16 inches diameter

---

[1] This may perhaps be the rotative engine already referred to as having been erected at Walker in 1784.

[2] Messrs. Boulton and Watt are also stated to have erected an engine for unwatering Wylam Colliery, the workings of which, as we have seen, were inundated by the Tyne during the great flood in 1771 (*Trans. N.E. Inst.*, ii. 161).

could now be obtained, the sinking of some of the collieries above mentioned would have been still impracticable but for the resources of mining art in damming, or tubbing, the water out of the shafts, which was effected in various ways.

The simplest, and probably the original method from which the process derived its name, was known as plank tubbing. This was constructed of tiers of cribs or curbs, 6 or 8 inches square, placed at intervals of 2 or 3 feet, to which were spiked planks $2\frac{1}{2}$ or 3 inches thick, and 8 or 10 feet in length, dressed to the sweep of the pit and made water-tight; the whole tub resting on two oak wedging curbs 8 or 9 inches square. This kind of tub sufficed for the top of the pit, but where considerable pressure had to be resisted, the planking was further supported by placing other tiers of curbs inside of it at intervals of from 6 to 20 inches apart, and faced with deals to present a smooth surface to the corves used in drawing coal. A tub of this description was capable of withstanding a pressure of 100 lb. per square inch. But in addition to the amount of room which it required, the chief drawback to its use lay in the fact that the iron spikes were liable to become corroded and give rise to leakage (*Trans. Nat. Hist. Soc. of Northum. and Durham*, vol. ii., 1838, p. 229; Dunn's *Coal Trade*, p. 46; *Winning and Working*, 2nd ed., p. 47).

A stronger and more durable form of tubbing, already referred to as having been resorted to in the sinking of the C pit at Wallsend, and known as crib or curb tubbing, consisted of segments of solid wood built one above the other; the joints being filled with slit deal, and the whole wedged up watertight. A tub of this description could sustain a pressure of 300 ft. of water, or 130 lbs. per square inch (Greenwell's *Mine Engineering*, 1st ed., p. 135). It was open to the objection that a very large amount of wedging was required, causing its construction to be attended with considerable cost.

In addition to the employment of regular tubs, crevices from which water issued were carefully wedged up—a process known as riming and wedging (*Trans. Nat. Hist. Soc. North. and Dur.*, ii. 321).

To obviate the drawbacks attending the use of wood tubbing, cast iron now began to be adopted in the process. This material was employed by Mr. Buddle, sen., in 1792 (the year in which the Act of Parliament was obtained for building the cast iron bridge over the River Wear at Sunderland), for damming back a quicksand at the Wallsend A pit (*Trans. Nat. Hist. Soc. of Northumberland*, ii. 320 n.); one of the first acts of his administration there.

A few years later (1795) a cast iron tub, consisting of cylinders the whole diameter of the pit, placed one above the other, and the joints wedged in wood, was employed by Mr. Barnes at the King pit, Walker Colliery (Dunn's *Coal Trade*, p. 47); the tubbing being said to have been cast at Messrs. Boulton and Watt's Soho Works, Birmingham.

The use of cylinders of cast iron was, however, inconvenient, except at the top of the pit, but this difficulty was overcome by the employment of segments of suitable size and building them together in the shaft. This arrangement was adopted by Mr. Buddle in the sinking of the Percy Main pit (1796-99). In this case the segments were 4 feet long and 2 feet high, and were provided with flanges projecting into the pit for bolting them together (*ib.*). But shortly afterwards a superior method of turning the flanges outwards, and dispensing with bolts altogether, was introduced.

Regarding other collieries on the Tyneside little is heard at this period. There is notice of an explosion at Benwell, in the Paradise, or West pit, April 24, 1795, with the loss of eleven lives; and of two others at the Hope pit, Sheriff Hill—viz., on December 27, 1793, with the loss of fourteen lives, and on December 21, 1794, with the loss of several lives (Sykes's *Wallsend Expl.*, p. 32).

The number of collieries on the Tyne in 1800 is stated to have been upwards of thirty (Dunn's *Coal Trade*, p. 232). The vend of coals in the same year (*ib.*, p. 72) was: Coastwise, 537,793 chaldrons; foreign, 47,487 chaldrons; total, 585,280 chaldrons, or 1,550,992 tons.

The annals relating to the collieries of the River Wear district at this time consist in large measure of notices of explosions, these disasters having been of very frequent occurrence here towards the close of the eighteenth century. The following are recorded to have taken place:

Washington Colliery, 1793, with the loss of four lives, including the viewer and two overmen (*Trans. N.E. Inst.*, xv. 272). The B pit, Washington, April, 1796, with the loss of two lives (Sykes's *Wallsend Expl.*, p. 32); the same pit, February 27, 1798, with the loss of seven lives.

New Washington Colliery, February 12, 1796, with the loss of seven lives.

Picktree Colliery, Rickleton pit, June 9, 1794, with the loss of thirty lives.

Harraton Colliery, June 11, 1794, with the loss of twenty-eight lives.

Oxclose Colliery, Glebe pit, November 1794, with the loss of two lives; same pit, May 22, 1798, with the loss of four lives; the A pit, August 13, 1799, with the loss of one life.

Newbottle Colliery, Jane pit, 1799, with the loss of one life. Coal set on fire. Remains of lost man recovered in 1865 (*Trans. N.E. Inst.*, xv. 99).

Lumley Colliery, October 11, 1799, with the loss of thirty-nine lives.

There were about eleven collieries on the Wear[1] in 1800, the vend of coal at this date being: Coastwise, 298,837 chaldrons; foreign, 4,622 chaldrons (Dunn's *Coal Trade*, p. 72); total, 303,459 chaldrons, or 804,166 tons.

In 1799, Hartley and Blyth exported together (*Royal Coal Com.*, iii., Appendix, pp. 4, 5): Foreign, 127 chaldrons, or 336 tons; London and coastwise, 41,689 chaldrons, or 110,476 tons; total, 41,816 chaldrons, or 110,812 tons.

The aggregate vend of coal from the northern ports in 1800, as appears from returns furnished by the Customs (*ib.*, p. 13), was coastwise, 2,381,986 tons; foreign, 138,089 tons; total, 2,520,075 tons.

Some manufacture of coke, or as it was more commonly termed in the north at this period, "cinders," was now going on in the northern coalfield, both for local consumption and for exportation. At the end of the century this trade had attained to considerable proportions, the quantity imported into London, in 1800, amounting to 7,939 chaldrons, or 10,122 tons. Though the districts from which the supply was brought are not specified, the bulk of it probably came from the Tyne.

The export of cinders from the Wear was a decreasing quantity at the end of the century, being in 1791 (Surtees, i. 265) 844 Newcastle chaldrons, or 2,236 tons, and in 1800, 616¾ chaldrons, or 1,635 tons.

Coke ovens are spoken of (*Trans. N.E. Inst.*, xv. 215) as being in existence at the outcrop of the Brockwell seam at Cockfield, Woodland, and Old Woodifield collieries, in South Durham; but the ordinary way of burning coke is stated to have been in the open air, in what was called "cinder rows."

The last decade of the eighteenth century witnessed the commencement of a number of important new departures in mining practice. Among these were the systematic employment of steam engines to raise the coal in the pits; the counterbalancing of the load by means of various expedients, to assist the winding engine; a modification of the bord-and-pillar system of working, consisting

[1] The number on the Tyne and Wear together being stated as forty-one in 1799 (*Trans. N.E. Inst.*, xv. 215).

in leaving larger pillars with a view to their more effectual sub-sequent removal; a general commencement to substitute iron for wood in the construction of railways; and the employment of self-acting inclined planes in the conveyance of coal.

Very little information seems available regarding the early use of steam engines for drawing coals out of the pits in the north of England. This may perhaps be accounted for, to some extent, by the circumstance that all the important collieries had been newly supplied with water-wheel winding engines, immediately before the steam engine became practically available for this work. Writing in 1797, Mr. Curr, in his *Coal Viewer and Engine Builder's Practical Companion* (p. 34), estimated that there were at that date thirty or forty of these water coal gins with their concomitant fire-engines in use in the north; a number which must have comprised nearly the whole of the deeper pits in the coalfield. Immediately after this date, however, these machines rapidly disappeared; their removal being doubtless synonymous with the substitution of steam winding engines in lieu of them.

In the north of England coal may be said to have continued to be universally drawn up the pits in corves, or circular baskets, for nearly half-a-century longer. To reduce the risk of damage from collision between the ascending and descending corf, after the more rapid winding by machines was introduced, the motion was temporarily slowered at the point known as "meetings," where the corves passed each other. This was accomplished by an automatic arrangement in the machines erected by Smeaton.

With the deepening of the pits the weight of the winding rope became itself a load upon the winding engine at starting. To remedy this, various expedients were resorted to. Smeaton had employed conical drums. Counterbalances of various kinds were now made use of, which rendered great assistance (*Trans. Soc. of Arts*, xvii. 338; Dunn's *Winning and Working*, 2nd ed., p. 17). A form which came into considerable use consisted of a chain weighted with heavy links at its lower end, and suspended in a small pit, or staple, sunk for the purpose. This wound on a small drum on the same shaft as the main drum, winding off during the first half of the run, winding on again in the opposite direction during the second half, being thus always ready to counterpoise the weight of the rope (see *Fossil Fuel*, p. 203; Hair's *Sketches*, p. 23).

The difficulties connected with the efficient raising of the coals in the deeper pits, which had for a long time in a manner blocked the way of improvements being made in other directions, having now been to a large extent overcome, and the more powerful and rapid winding machinery employed enabling larger quantities of coal to be dealt with, a necessity for corresponding improvements in the underground conveyance of the coal began to be felt. Though railways, as we have seen, had been introduced underground at the date of M. Jars's visit in 1765, it would appear that their employment was by no means general, and that in the majority of cases a sledge carrying a single corf was drawn by a horse from the working-places to the shaft. Towards the end of the century, however, the use of wooden railways underground on the main roads became general, and on these a horse drew a rolley carrying two or three corves at a time. On this point Mr. Curr (*Coal Viewer*, p. 8) remarks as follows :

"The prevailing practice, till of late, in the working of collieries in the neighbourhood of Newcastle-upon-Tyne and Sunderland, was to draw a single corf on a sled from the workings to the shaft of the pit, which, as these workings were extended and the prices and maintenance of horses enormously increased, became an intolerable burden to the proprietors of such works ; therefore the viewers or superintendents of collieries have with a great deal of propriety introduced wooden rails, or wagon ways underground, for that purpose (or what is generally distinguished by the name of New-castle roads), and fixed a frame upon wheels capable of receiving two or three of these basket corves, which upon these carriages and roads are drawn by one horse."

Single corves were still conveyed over the floor of the mine on trams or sledges, either by putters or horses. Mr. Buddle (*Trans. Nat. Hist. Soc. of Northumberland*, ii. 315) speaks of the floor of the Main coal seam at Wallsend Colliery being, when dry, as it generally was, an excellent road for the broad-wheeled rolleys, which carried a 24-peck corf, and were drawn from the face of the workings to the railways leading to the pit by horses. At the railway siding a crane was provided by means of which the corves were transferred to the larger rolleys which ran on the railway.

About this period the drawbacks attending the original method of working coal by the bord-and-pillar system, began to reach a climax in the deep collieries of the Tyne basin. As at the earliest period of coal mining in this district, so in these deep mines only such a proportion of the seam was excavated as was deemed practicable without inducing a subsidence of the superincumbent strata. But while in the early shallow collieries a small proportion only of the seam required to be sacrificed for this purpose, the greater part of the coal was now consumed in the process.

The pillars having been left as nearly as possible only of such size as was necessary to carry the weight above, the removal of even a small part of the remaining coal brought on a movement termed a "creep," which begins to be heard of for the first time at this period, and which became a fruitful source of difficulty and danger, as well as expense, in the Tyne collieries for a considerable time subsequently.

Though both the creep and the crush (already mentioned) led to the same result of closing up the workings, they were quite different. The progress of the latter movement was more rapid, and it crushed and ground down the pillars before it. The creep, on the other hand, was usually slow and insidious in its advance, and the pillars themselves were not greatly damaged by it; but they sank by imperceptible degrees into the floor of the mine, the soft and yielding materials of which rose into and filled up the excavated passages, till the whole became a solid mass. Creeps are stated to have sometimes been arrested by the bold expedient of removing a tract of pillars, and relieving the weight by inducing a fracture of the upper strata (*Proc. Arch. Inst.*, Newcastle, 1852, i. 199; *Encyclo. Britan.*, 3rd ed.. art. Coalery); but where a large area was affected almost nothing could be done to prevent the movement from running its course. In a MS. left by an old Hartley pitman it is recorded that the viewer there consumed a ship's cargo of strong wooden baulks, cut into lengths, in an endeavour to arrest a creep, but, says the narrator, "they didn't stop the creep" (Fordyce's *Coal and Iron*, p. 75).

Up till this time $45\frac{1}{2}$ per cent. was considered to be the maximum produce obtainable in the deep Tyne collieries under any mode of working (*Trans. Nat. Hist. Soc. of Northumberland*, ii. 323). The first to conceive a partial remedy for this unsatisfactory state of matters was Mr. Thomas Barnes, viewer of Walker Colliery. On this colliery being wrought out in the High Main seam in 1795, and nothing but pillars left in the mine, Mr. Barnes projected a scheme for recovering a portion of the pillars without endangering the total closing of the mine. This consisted in dividing the workings into small sections of from ten to twenty acres, around which artificial barriers were formed by refilling the excavated passages with stones and refuse for a breadth of 40 or 50 yards.

By this means he succeeded in removing the half of each alternate pillar, or one-fourth of the remaining coal, and raising the produce of the seam from about 39 to 54 per cent. The result was invariably to bring on a creep, by which the remainder of the tract was buried up ; but this was prevented from spreading into the adjoining tracts by the barriers before mentioned. Having proved successful at Walker, this method was adopted soon afterwards at Bigge's Main, and likewise at a number of other deep collieries in the same neighbourhood when the working of the pillars commenced.

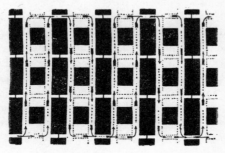

FIG. 25.—BARNES'S PLAN OF ROBBING PILLARS.

Already, however, the idea of introducing a radical change into the bord-and-pillar system of working had begun to be entertained with a view to the more effectual subsequent removal of the pillars. This consisted in forming the pillars, in the course of the first working, of larger size than was deemed necessary for barely supporting the weight which they had to carry.

The advantage of leaving strong pillars of coal, for the purpose of ultimately obtaining a larger proportion of the seam, begins to be heard of in 1797. A writer in the *Encyclopædia Britannica* of this date (3rd ed., art. Coalery), after referring to the hard nature of Scotch coal as being better suited for its removal as much as possible by a first working, and the softer nature of English coal rendering it necessary to leave large pillars, which, however, was of little consequence, as the coal was of so rich a quality, and worked small in any case, the writer proceeds to say :

"The ancient method of working was to work away as much of the coal as could be got with safety at one working only ; by which means the pillars were left so small as to be crushed by the weight of the superior strata, and entirely lost. As great quantities of coal were lost by this method it is now generally exploded, and the former adopted in its place, by which a much larger quantity of coal is obtained from the same extent of ground, and at much less expense in the end."

It was probably about this period, or not long afterwards, that the size of the winnings at Wallsend Colliery was enlarged, as a

preparatory step towards a second working. Without specifying
the exact date, Mr. Buddle informs us (*Trans. Nat. Hist. Soc. of
Northumberland*, ii. 323), that after about a third of the colliery had
been worked by means of twelve-yard winnings (four yards to the
board, eight yards to the wall, or pillar), in which no more coal was
left in pillars than was deemed barely sufficient to support the roof,
the size of the winnings was increased to fifteen yards (five yards to
the board, and ten yards to the pillar). "This change of size," he
states, "was not made for the purpose of obtaining a greater produce
in the first working of the seam. But the notion of a future working
of the pillars then began to be entertained, and the increased size of
the winnings was considered a more favourable apportionment of
the excavation and pillar for the attainment of this object." This
was the first small step we hear of being made beforehand, with a
view to the institution of the second working in the deep Tyne
collieries.

Iron was now beginning to be commonly employed in the construction of railways in all parts of the kingdom, and among others
in the North of England. As early as 1794 it was partially used at
Walbottle Colliery by Mr. Charles Nixon (*Proc. Arch. Inst.*, Newcastle, 1852, i. 98), who employed light bars of malleable iron of an
oblong section, the narrow edge of not more than three-quarters of
an inch wide being presented for the wheels to run upon.

But the systematic employment of rails of cast iron commenced
here in 1797, when Mr. Barnes constructed a railway, with stone
supports, from Lawson Main Colliery to the Tyne, which Mr. N.
Wood (*Treatise on Railroads*, ed. 1831, p. 22) characterizes as the
first iron railroad laid down in the neighbourhood of Newcastle-upon-
Tyne. Immediately afterwards a general commencement was made
to substitute cast iron railways for the wooden ones previously
employed in the conveyance of coal to the river.

The introduction of self-acting inclined planes in the north was
contemporaneous with that of iron railways: these appliances having
already been adopted in a number of instances in connection with
canals in various parts, *e.g.*, the Shropshire and Shrewsbury Canal,
completed 1792 (Plymley's *Shropshire*, p. 292); the Duke of Bridgewater's Canal, 1795-97 (*Trans. Soc. of Arts*, xviii. 265). These also
were introduced by Mr. Barnes, who constructed the first in the
north at Benwell Colliery in 1797: the full wagon descending by
its own gravity, and the empty one being drawn up by means of a
balance weight. The incline was 864 yards in length, and the time
occupied in running two and a-half minutes (*Agricultural Magazine*,

vol. iii., p. 367 ; Dunn's *Coal Trade*, p. 52).   The method of employing a counterbalance was soon superseded by the superior arrangement of making the full wagons themselves pull up the empty ones.

Immediately afterwards self-acting inclines began to be introduced
underground, the first in this district being applied by Mr. James
Hall, at Townley Colliery, in 1800 (*Trans. N.E. Inst.*, xv. 216).

Mr. Thomas Barnes, who played such a leading part in the
advancement of mining in the north in the last few years of this
century, and whose career was so full of promise, died at Walker,
in 1801, at the early age of thirty-six years.

Already at this period the desirability of a systematic preservation
of mining records was beginning to receive attention, both with a
view to the prevention of accidents—such as happened at Slatyford,
Northumberland, in 1796 (Sykes's *Loc. Rec.*), when six persons were
drowned by a sudden inundation from an old waste—as also to
indicate the extent of coal left unwrought and which might be
available in the future.   In 1797 Mr. Thomas, of Denton, read a
paper on the subject to the Literary and Philosophical Society of
Newcastle-on-Tyne, proposing a voluntary registration of such records,
but his scheme failed to elicit a sufficient amount of interest to lead
to its being carried out.

CHAPTER XXXI.

THE EIGHTEENTH CENTURY.—Continued.

The Yorkshire, Derbyshire, and Nottinghamshire coalfield. Mines near Halifax. Explosion at Middleton Colliery near Leeds, in connection with use of gunpowder in sinking. Mr. Curr's improvements. Small wheeled carriages; conductors, or guides; cast iron rails; flat ropes. Use of steam engine in drawing coal. The hard and soft coals of Derbyshire. Ventilation by fire. Outram's cast iron railway. The Leicestershire coalfield. Firing the gas. Cast iron railway at Loughborough.

The great extent to which coal digging was being carried on in Yorkshire in the early part of the eighteenth century is indicated by the statement made by Thoresby in his *History of Leeds*, published in 1714 (Preface, p. vi.), to the effect that the coal mines in this county were "now without number."

A considerable amount of interesting information regarding the state of mining in the pits on the Shibden Hall Estate, near Halifax, in the early part of the eighteenth century, was communicated by Mr. Lister, to the *Leeds Mercury Supplement*, and published in that paper in May, 1885. The pits were of small depth, and worked a very limited area, as already referred to, sixty yards all round being regarded as sufficient. The number of "getters" in a pit did not often exceed half-a-dozen, and a like number of boy "hurriers." The wages of getters, when working by the day, were 10d. and 1s. The viewer was paid 1s. for each weekly inspection. The wright charged 1s. apiece for shoeing scoops.

The shafts were rectangular in shape, and in the lower half the length was reduced. Thus in a shaft sunk in 1749, to a depth of 210 feet, the dimensions were three and a-half yards by one and a-half yards to the middle, and thence two yards by one and a-half yards to the bottom. In the sinking of this shaft mention is made of the use of gunpowder.

THE EIGHTEENTH CENTURY.   321

In connection with an explosion of firedamp at Middleton Colliery, near Leeds, we learn that gunpowder was now used in sinking pits here also. In 1758, operations were commenced to deepen a shaft which had been previously sunk to a depth of 180 feet. The explosion was caused by the miners throwing down fire from the top to ignite a charge of gunpowder (*Phil. Trans.*, vol. lxiii., p. 217)—a rude method of discharging shots said to have been commonly practised in this era (*Fossil Fuel*, p. 185).

What was probably the first railway in Yorkshire, was constructed between this colliery and the town of Leeds, under a private Act of Parliament obtained in 1757-58 (31 Geo. II., No. 22), entitled, "An Act for establishing agreements made between Charles Brandling, esquire, and other persons, proprietors of lands, for laying down a wagon way, in order for the better supplying the town and neighbourhood of Leeds, in the county of York, with coals"; being doubtless the first railway Act passed by the legislature.

Smeaton designed a large Newcomen steam engine for Middleton Colliery in 1780 (Farey's *Steam Engine*, p. 242 note). The cylinder was 72 inches in diameter, the dimensions being the same as those of the famous engine built by him at Chacewater, in Cornwall, five years previously.

In the latter part of the eighteenth century a series of notable improvements in the mechanical engineering of collieries were introduced by Mr. John Curr, of Sheffield, who may not inaptly be designated the "William Brown" of the Yorkshire coalfield. Like Brown, Curr devoted a great amount of attention to the (Newcomen) steam engine; and though we have no account of the number of engines erected by him, it is evident from his book entitled *The Coal Viewer and Engine Builder's Practical Companion*, published in 1797, that he was a thorough master of the subject.

Mr. Curr was a native of the north of England, having been brought up in the West Durham colliery district; according to Mr. Dunn (*Coal Trade*, p. 50), at Greenside, but according to another account he was born at Kyo, near Lanchester, and brought up at Pontop Pike, in the Tanfield neighbourhood. He went to the Duke of Norfolk's collieries at Sheffield—a place in the vicinity of which M. Jars tells us a great many coal mines existed at the date of his visit in 1765—in a subordinate capacity, but was subsequently entrusted with their entire management, when he effected various novel and successful alterations in the methods of conveying the coals under ground, and raising them in the shafts to the surface.

The first of his improvements consisted in the substitution of railways and small four-wheeled carriages under ground for the sledges previously in use, introduced by him twenty-one years previous to the publication of his book (Preface), or about the year 1776. Mr. Curr is usually credited with having employed

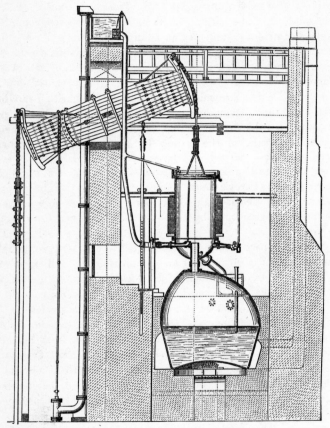

FIG. 26.—SMEATON'S CHACEWATER ENGINE.

light cast iron rails instead of wooden ones thus early, but this statement appears to be based on a misquotation of his words. He makes no claim to having introduced "cast iron railroads" at that date, as represented by some writers, but merely "rail-roads and corves," and it seems evident from his own account (p. 9) that he first began to use cast iron railways some seven years previous to the publication of his book, or about 1790. It is to be remarked that Mr. Curr, throughout his book, applies the name of "corves" to the four-wheeled carriages of which he made use, distinguishing the original corves, to which this term properly belonged, by the name of "basket or wicker corves."

Though small four-wheeled carriages, running on wooden railways, had been in use at coal mines in Shropshire, as we have seen, long before their introduction by Mr. Curr into the Sheffield district, we only hear of them being employed there in cases where the mines were entered by horizontal drifts. To Mr. Curr appears to belong the credit of being the first to use these carriages in connection with vertical pits. Being rectangular in shape, it is obvious that the process of raising them in the shaft must have been attended with much greater risk of damage from collision between the ascending and descending ones, than in the case of circular baskets —a risk which must have been much enhanced when the drawing of coal with increased rapidity by machines was commenced : these having been introduced by Mr. Curr at two of the Duke of Norfolk's collieries previous to 1790.

The mastering of this difficulty constituted Mr. Curr's brightest achievement. This he effected by the invention of guides, or conductors, forming as it were vertical railways in the shaft. This arrangement he secured by letters patent (No. 1,660), dated 12th August, 1788, for methods of "raising coals, lead, and other minerals, out of mines, so as to prevent the corves running foul of each other ; platform for landing and delivering."

The conductors, as described by their inventor (p. 36), were "nothing more than two or three upright rods of deal 4 inches by 3, braged upon opposite sides of the pit, forming mortices or channels, by which the corves are conducted, being suspended upon cross-bars with rollers at their ends, which run within the mortices."

On arriving at the surface the carriage was raised a little distance above the mouth of the pit, when a wooden platform was introduced beneath upon which it was lowered. It was then detached from the rope and run off; and an empty carriage having been substituted, and raised so as to admit of the platform being withdrawn, the winding recommenced ; the speed attainable with this improved arrangement being stated by Mr. Curr (p. 12) to be as much as 420 feet in half-a-minute.

Mr. Curr's next great engineering achievement consisted in the invention of his light cast iron railways. Having, he says (p. 9), "introduced machines for drawing coals at two of his Grace the

Duke of Norfolk's collieries, near Sheffield, I had still a difficult point to accomplish, which was to contrive an easy and expeditious mode of conveying the coals to the bottom of the pit, in which I have been successful far beyond my expectations, and perhaps have hit upon a mode far superior to anything heretofore practised, as the result of seven years' experience informs me; I have, therefore, herein offered to the public the plans and directions for executing both the roads and the corves, and everything relating to the invention, by which means a horse takes, at a moderate draught, nine or ten corves of equal size to those at Newcastle-upon-Tyne and Sunderland, of which even by their improved mode of conveyance, a horse takes only two or three."

The iron rails hitherto employed had usually consisted of plates of iron laid upon the top of wooden rails—whence doubtless the name of "platelayer," still applied to the workmen employed in placing rails on a railway. Though flat they were really of the edge-rail type, the flange being on the wheels of the wagons. Mr. Curr adopted a different pattern, now known as the plate rail, or tram plate form; the flange being transferred from the wagon wheels to the rails. His rails were commonly 6 feet long, 3 inches broad in the trod, and $\frac{1}{2}$ inch thick; the margin, or flange, being 2 inches higher than the plate. They were laid upon oak sleepers about 3 feet 4 inches long, 5 inches broad, and $2\frac{1}{2}$ inches thick.

The corves, or carriages, held $5\frac{1}{2}$ or 6 cwt. of coal, and were provided with wheels from 10 to 13 inches in diameter. The wheels were made plain, with a narrow periphery to lessen friction. Coupling chains were provided for attaching the carriages together, thereby enabling a horse to haul a train of about ten at a time. On account of the carriages being drawn up the shaft suspended below the cross-bar, and the method employed of landing or striking them at the surface, there was a difficulty of raising more than one at a time, though this would appear to have been at times attempted, inasmuch as there is a drawing of the arrangement extant, showing two carriages hanging side by side.

Mr. Curr introduced his cast iron rails both under ground and on the surface. By their use self-acting inclined planes, whereby a train of full carriages in descending was made to pull up an empty train at the same time, could be employed whenever the fall of the road amounted to 3 inches per yard.

The invention of the flat rope was another notable achievement of Mr. Curr. For this he obtained a patent (No. 2272), 17th

November, 1798.[1] It consisted of several small round ropes stitched together, and was made to lap upon itself in winding, serving the purpose of a counterbalance. Thus at the commencement of a run the loaded rope began to coil upon a small diameter gradually increasing, while the empty rope began to coil off a large diameter gradually decreasing—an arrangement which rendered great assistance to the winding engine.

Mr. Curr's improvements were a great step in the direction of modern appliances. His cast iron rails and flat ropes came into general use throughout the kingdom; but his shaft fittings were not sufficiently matured to admit of their introduction into the deeper mines of the north of England, though they were adopted, and answered remarkably well, in the shallower collieries about Sheffield, Barnsley, Leeds, and other parts in the south.

The introduction of cast iron rails (or plates) underground, relieved enormously the slavish labour of the barrow men or coal putters, who conveyed the coal between the working places and the horse roads. It would appear from the following stanzas (The *Pitman's Pay*, by Thomas Wilson) that the improvement was received with much gratitude :

> " But heavy puttin' 's now forgotten,
>   Sic as we had i' former days ;
>   Ower holey thill[2] an' dyels[3] a-splittin',
>   Trams now a-run on metal ways.

> " God bless the man wi' peace and plenty
>   That first invented metal plates,
>   Draw out his years te five times twenty,
>   Then slide him through the heevenly gates.

> " For if the human frame te spare
>   Frae toil an' pain ayont conceevin',
>   Hae aught te de wi' gettin' there,
>   Aw think he mun gan' strite te heeven."

The machines Mr. Curr speaks of having introduced for drawing coals at the Duke of Norfolk's collieries, were the water gins so much in vogue at that time in the Newcastle-on-Tyne district. With regard to the application of the steam engine directly to the drawing of coal, without the intervention of a water-wheel, he refers (p. 35) to three methods of effecting this as in use in 1797. "One," he says, "is the invention of Messrs. Bolton and Watts, another of Mr.

---

[1] Ten years later (1808) Mr. Curr obtained a patent for "applying flat, or round ropes, lines, bands, or belts, for catching and detaining whales."

[2] The *sill* or floor of the mine.   [3] Deal boards.

Cameron, which does not differ much in principle, and the third is the common fire engine, which was first reduced to practice by the engineers of Colebrook Dale collectively." And he proceeds to remark that as the machines with a water-wheel and fire engine had been chiefly built before the direct application of the fire engine was made manageable, and as the latter did not require more than half the power, and one-third of the expense, the further introduction of the water-wheel, under ordinary circumstances, stood condemned. It is obvious that the adoption of steam winding engines had already made some progress in the Yorkshire coalfield previous to 1797.

The systematic improvement of internal communication was commenced in Yorkshire, as elsewhere, about the middle of this century. In 1751 the Don was made navigable to near Sheffield (*Beauties of England and Wales*, art. Yorkshire). In 1752 a petition was prepared for Parliament for rendering the Calder navigable (*Report of Royal Coal Com.*, iii. 15), the chief object being the conveyance of coal. A reference to the coal trade on this river occurs in 1768, when we hear of a coal boat being sunk in the Calder, two miles below Wakefield.

The old unfenced coal pits and lead mines on the Derbyshire moors are spoken of (Stukeley's *Itin. Cur.*, 2nd ed., Cent. I., p. 54) as a source of considerable danger to travellers in the early part of the eighteenth century.

Some information regarding the Derbyshire coal is furnished by Pilkington in his *View of the Present State of Derbyshire*, published in 1789. He divides it into two general classes of soft and hard. The soft coal he speaks of as being much used for burning limestone, and the manufacture of iron goods, and being largely converted into "coak." The hard coal he characterizes as more useful and valuable; and he describes its appearance and qualities as found at Smalley, West Hallam, and Ilkeston; at Heanor and Shipley; at Denby, Ripley, Swanwick, and Alfreton; at Normanton and Blackwell; at Chesterfield and Eckington; at Newhall and Measham; and near Burton.

At this period artificial ventilation by means of fire, though on a somewhat primitive scale, had been introduced into the Derbyshire mines. "In working mines of coal," says the above writer, "water and foul air are often found to be very troublesome. To relieve them from the latter they have recourse to the same means which are employed in lead mines. But to free the pits from inflammable and mephitic air, with one or both of which they are often troubled, a method somewhat different is used. At most works there is, besides the large shaft, by which the coals are drawn up, a smaller one at a distance of a few yards.   This is about 4 feet wide, and 15 or 16 feet deep, and from the bottom of it a pipe is carried into and down the larger shaft to that part of the mine where the men are at work.   A vessel of burning coal, holding about four pecks, is then suspended in the smaller shaft.   By this contrivance the air is immediately rarefied, and a fresh column rushing upwards to supply its place, a circulation is produced and maintained in every part of the mine."

Gough, who wrote at the same date (*Britannia*, ed. 1789, ii. 315) speaks of carts bringing a load of slack—the small part of the coal— from about Sheffield and Chesterfield to Stoney Middleton, where they received for it a load of lime.   Among the MSS. relating to mines in Derbyshire in the British Museum (6,680, f. 52), are articles concerning a coal mine at Wheatcroft, dated 1760.

In 1800 Mr. Benjamin Outram constructed a public railway at Litton Eton in this county (Wood's *Railroads*, 2nd ed., p. 22), in which he made use of cast iron plate rails (Mr. Curr's pattern) and stone supports, as had been done by Mr. Barnes in the Newcastle-on-Tyne neighbourhood three years previously.   While the use of iron in railway construction had been going on for a considerable time, and was gradually extending as this material became more abundant and cheaper, it cannot be doubted that a considerable impulse was given to the movement by the publication of Mr. Curr's book in 1797.

Very little is heard of the Leicestershire coalfield in this era. That firedamp was not unknown in the mines here is indicated by the circumstance recorded by Mammatt (*Geological Facts*, p. 26) that firing the gas was at one time practised in this district.   This, he tells us, was accomplished by means of a lighted candle fixed in clay on a board, and drawn forward by means of a string passing through a hook fastened in the roof at the extremity of the working-place.

It was at Loughborough in this county, as already adverted to, where the first public railway was constructed by Mr. W. Jessop in 1789.   The rails were of the edge rail pattern (Wood's *Railroads*, 2nd ed., p. 24).   Their upper surface was level, and the under elliptical, or fish-bellied ; the flanges were on the wagon wheels, as in the case of the wooden railways.

Farey in his *Agriculture and Minerals of Derbyshire*, etc. (i. 358), informs us that the first coal-winding steam engine in the district over which his survey extends was erected at Oakthorpe Colliery, in Measham, in 1790.   Whether this was a Newcomen or a Watt engine is not specified.

CHAPTER XXXII.

THE EIGHTEENTH CENTURY.—Continued.

The Lancashire coalfield. Artificial canals. The Staffordshire coalfield. Damps. Canals. Collieries near Stourbridge. Watt's steam engine. Square work. Firing the gas. Coal tar manufacture. Cast iron railways. The Warwickshire coalfield. Griff colliery. Water gin. Watt's steam engine.

THAT Lancashire was well to the front in point of engineering skill in the early part of the eighteenth century, is shown by the circumstance that when a plan was projected in Scotland, in 1708, for draining coal mines by means of windmills and pumps, no person being known competent to put the scheme into execution except one millwright of Montrose, it was suggested (Bald's *View of the Coal Trade*) that if the services of this individual could not be obtained, advice on the subject should be sought from the Mechanical Priest of Lancashire.

In the latter half of the century also, Lancashire appears to have supplied engineering experts to other districts. Thus we hear (*Leeds Mercury Supplement*, May 23, 1885) of water-wheels for working the pumps of a colliery established by Mr. Jeremy Lister, at Mytholm, in Yorkshire, being erected in 1775, at a cost of about £1000, by "Horrocks, the Lancashire workman."

Mention occurs of coal pits near Knowsley, in 1725 (Stukeley's *Itin. Cur.*, 2nd ed., Cent. II., p. 19).

Some interesting information regarding the Wigan cannel coal, and noxious gases in the mines, is furnished by Pennant in the account of his *Tour in Scotland in* 1772 :

"This neighbourhood (Haigh and Wigan) abounds with that fine species of coal called canal, perhaps *candle* coal, from its serving as chief light for the poor to spin by, during the long winter evenings : it is found in beds of about 3 feet in thickness; the veins dip one yard in twenty; are found at great depths, with a black bass above and below, and are subject to the same damps fiery and suffocating as the common coal. It makes the sweetest of fires, and the most chearful: is very inflammable; and so clean that at Haigh Hall a summer-house is built with it, which may be entered without dread of soiling the lightest cloaths."

An ingenious fellow at Wigan, he also states, "turns canal coal into vases, obelisks, and snuff-boxes, and forms excellent blackmoors' heads out of the same material."

In the Manchester neighbourhood steam engines were in use in 1795 "for winding up coals from a great depth in the coal pitts" (Aikin's *Description, etc.*, p. 177); a process which is described as being performed with a quickness and ease not to be conceived. Steam winding engines were likewise in use at Bolton at the same date (*ib.*, p. 264). Regarding the engines employed at both places it is remarked that a few of them were Boulton and Watt's.

At Dukinfield, in Cheshire, at this time, the pits were from 200 to 300 feet deep (*ib.*, p. 455).

It was in this district the foundation was laid of the system of artificial canals (or navigations), with which the whole country was intersected in the latter half of the eighteenth century. In 1720 an Act passed for making navigable the rivers Mersey and Irwell, as far as Manchester (Housman's *Cumberland*, 1800, p. 491); and in 1727 the little river Douglas, which passes near Wigan, was widened, deepened, and made navigable by locks, almost to the mouth of the Ribble (Pennant's *Tour in Scotland*, 1772); and used to convey coal to supply the north of the county and part of Westmoreland, limestone being brought back in return.

But the making and keeping of rivers navigable was attended with many inconveniences; and when, in 1755, an Act of Parliament was obtained for improving the navigation of the Sankey Brook, to provide an outlet to the Mersey for the coal of the St. Helens district, the natural channel was abandoned, and a lateral channel or canal, about eleven miles in length, constructed, on which the water could always be kept at the proper level by means of locks.

The superior advantages of this arrangement were quickly appreciated, and before the completion of the canal the Duke of Bridgewater had commenced (about 1759) his famous water-way; the first part of which was designed to connect his coal works at Worsley with the town of Manchester, seven miles distant.

Immediately afterwards innumerable schemes were brought forward, and the construction of navigable canals commenced to unite the ports of London, Bristol, Liverpool, and Hull, with the adjacent towns and rivers (Gough's *Topography*, 2nd ed., i. 501-2). Between 1770 and 1800 no fewer than 113 bills for the construction of canals, and the improvement of river navigations, were brought before Parliament (*Report of the Royal Coal Com.*, iii. 17 ; see list in same volume, Appendix 22).

In some cases cast iron railways were employed as accessories to the canals, as already referred to in connection with the use of self-acting inclined planes for lowering and raising boats. An account of such an (underground) incline at the Duke of Bridgewater's collieries at Worsley—where probably subterranean canals were first used for conveying coal out of mines[1]—begun in 1795, and completed in 1797, is contained in the *Transactions of the Society of Arts* for the year 1800 (vol. xviii., p. 265).

The consumption of coals in the manufactories at Ravenhead in 1795, is stated (*Report of Royal Coal Com.*, iii. 14) to have amounted to 700 tons per week. Here existed works for the manufacture of iron and copper, plate glass, white lead, lamp black, vitriol, alkali, and also sugar refineries.

We have seen that it was at a coal pit near Wolverhampton, in Staffordshire, where the first steam engine was erected by Newcomen himself, in 1712. The depth of the pit is stated to have been 153 feet.

In the same year a description of the several strata of earth, stone, coal, etc., found in a coal pit at the west end of Dudley, was communicated to the Royal Society by Mr. Fettiplace Bellers, and published in the *Philosophical Transactions* (No. 336, p. 541).

Speaking of the coal mines about Dudley and Wolverhampton at the time of his visit in 1725, and of the faults, or breaches, in the coal seams, Dr. Stukeley observes (*Itin. Cur.*, 2nd ed., Cent. II., p. 20), that "sometimes the ends of the coal at these breaches bend the contrary way; this shows the breaches were made before the coal was perfectly hardened."

Regarding the treatment of men suffering from the effects of noxious gases, the same writer informs us that "when the damps exanimate a man at these coal pits they draw him up instantly and make a round hole in the earth, put his head in, and cover it with fresh mold, which infallibly restores him." This curious practice is

---

[1] Underground canals appear to have been used to a considerable extent in South Wales (*Fossil Fuel*, p. 189). One or two of the collieries in Farey's list (*Agriculture and Minerals of Derbyshire*, i. 188) either were being or had been worked by tunnels for boats.

heard of in many districts, and continued to be pursued down till
recent times.   The object aimed at in so doing is stated (*Trans. N.E.
Inst.*, vol. ii., p. 11) to have been to lessen the quantity of air
inhaled ; though another idea was that the benefit was derived from
the smell of the soil (*1835 Report*, p. 177 ; see also *Child Employ.
Com.*, Appendix i., p. 92).

An Act of Parliament was obtained in 1767 (Hutton's *Birmingham*)
for making a canal between Birmingham and the coal mines about
Wednesbury.   On its completion, coal which had been previously
brought by land at a cost of 13s. per ton, was brought by water at
6s. 8d.   It had been common to see a train of carriages for miles, to
the great destruction of the road and annoyance of travellers.   The
boats carried about 25 tons, and were drawn by one horse.

Nash, in his *History of Worcestershire*, published in 1782 (ii. 212)
thus refers to the collieries in the neighbourhood of Stourbridge, and
the benefits accruing from the construction of canals : " Within
three miles of this town, but in the county of Stafford, the mines
of coal are very extensive, and the strata ten yards thick, affording
sufficient to last more than a thousand years, supposing 120,000
tons to be raised each year from 20 pits, one half of which belong
to Lord Dudley ; on this account the new canal from these parts to
Staffordshire cut, which empties itself into the Severn, will be of
great use to all places supplied with coal from that river."

This writer speaks of the clay as lying 150 feet below the surface,
and about 45 feet below the coal, making the depth of the coal 105
feet.   Much deeper sinkings must, however, have existed at this
time in South Staffordshire, as we learn in connection with the
introduction of Watt's improved steam engine, a few of Watt's
engines having been built at collieries in the midland district even
before they began to be adopted in Cornwall, and long before they
came into regular employment at the northern mines.   Singularly,
Watt's engine, as well as Newcomen's, may almost be said to have made
its *début* in the South Staffordshire coalfield.   In a letter to Smeaton,
dated April, 1776 (Farey's *Steam Engine*, p. 320 note), Watt informs
him that they "have now two large engines going, one about ten
miles from Birmingham, the cylinder 50 inches diameter, intended
to work a $14\frac{1}{4}$ inch working barrel, to lift water from 100 yards
deep ; but the pit is only sunk to 40 yards at present."   The other
engine was at an iron foundry in Shropshire ; and mention is made,
in the same letter, of another engine, with a fifty-eight inch cylinder,
in course of construction for Warwickshire, to which there will be
occasion to advert hereafter.

Among other notices relating to this coalfield we hear of a vein of good pit coal having been discovered at Over Arley, in the extreme west of the county (Gough's *Britannia*, 1789, ii. 381)—a place which appears to be identical with the Ernley of the twelfth century previously referred to—but lying so deep and near the Severn, that it could not be worked without too great expense.

Bradley Moor is spoken of by Shaw in 1801 (*Staffordshire*, vol. ii., part i., p. 172) as "very remarkable for a curious phenomenon commonly known here by the name of the Wild-fire, which is supposed to be owing to a vein of coals having taken fire a great number of years ago, and still continues to burn."

The extraordinary liability of the Staffordshire Thick Coal to ignite spontaneously, and the circumstance of this having given rise to the adoption of a system of working peculiar to this coal seam, has been already referred to. It is known by the name of Square Work, and was designed with a special view to afford facilities for the prevention, or ready extinction, of underground fires in the workings. It consists in dividing the area to be worked into a number of large chambers, or compartments, termed "sides of work," surrounded on all sides by barriers of solid coal,

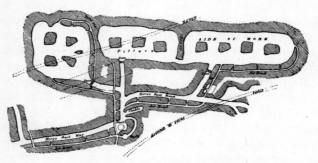

FIG. 27.—SQUARE WORK (South Staffordshire).

known as *fire ribs*, through which no openings are made save such only as are essentially necessary for the extraction of the coal and the ventilation of the working-places. In these chambers the working of the coal is prosecuted on the post-and-stall system, pillars being left to support the roof; and as soon as all the coal that can be got has been obtained, the whole excavation is dammed off by the insertion of air-tight stoppings in the few openings made through the barrier.

The method of ventilating each side of work at this period, while it continued in operation, was by means of a small passage brought from the downcast pit, known as the *air-head* ; and as the current introduced was often insufficient to dilute and sweep away the firedamp which accumulated in the upper part of the chamber— the working of the coal being, indeed, purposely carried on with a minimum of ventilation, this being thought to conduce to the prevention of spontaneous combustion—the process of firing the gas at periodical intervals was systematically practised in the latter part of the eighteenth century.

During this operation all the workmen were withdrawn from the mine save only those actually engaged, known as the "fire men." The underground stables were usually adopted as the base of operations, and were strongly barricaded for the purpose. From this point a copper wire, termed the "firing line," was led to the part of the mine where gas was supposed to have accumulated. Approaching as near to the place of danger as was consistent with their own safety, the fireman raised the wire aloft by means of a long pole (or series of poles fitting into each other like a fishing-rod) provided with a small wheel, or sheave, at the extremity, for carrying the line. Having fixed the pole in the required position, and secured to the end of the line on the floor of the mine a lighted candle weighted with a piece of lead to keep it steady, the firemen retired to the stable, where, pulling in the wire through a crevice, they elevated the lighted candle at the other end and so exploded the gas. If the collection of gas was considerable, as was frequently the case, a violent explosion ensued, which passed the firemen in their retreat with a thundering noise and with great velocity (*Edinburgh Encyclopædia*, 1820, art. Mine). If by any accidental circumstance the candle became extinguished and the explosion did not take place, the firemen were sometimes left in a state of the greatest suspense, and being afraid to sally out, remained pent up for a length of time imprisoned in their own stronghold.

In some instances this dangerous operation had to be repeated several times a day. Thus at the Netherton pits, belonging to Lord Dudley, in 1798 and subsequent years, the firing of the gas was regularly practised three times a day, viz., at four o'clock in the morning, at noon, and at seven in the evening. How this unsatisfactory state of matters was remedied will be seen hereafter.

The manufacture of tar from coal was introduced into this district by Lord Dundonald. In his *View of the Estate and Abbey of Culross*, published in 1793 (p. 39), he states that the only productive, properly placed and constructed tarworks, are those in Shropshire and Staffordshire, planned and superintended in their erection by

himself. Whether these are the works at Bradley referred to by
Shaw in 1801, the writer is unable to say, but if so their success
was of short duration.   " At this place," he observes (*Staffordshire*,
vol. ii., part i., p. 172), "are still a large range of ovens of a peculiar
construction erected by Lord Monboddo a few years ago for the
purpose of extracting tar from coal by a chemical process, which not
succeeding, they are now pulled down."   It would appear probable
that "Lord Monboddo" is an error for Lord Dundonald.

In North Staffordshire the working of coal was being actively
prosecuted in the neighbourhood of Newcastle-under-Lyne at the
time of M. Jars's visit in 1765, who states (*Voyages*, i. 253) that there
were a large number of mines here.   They were, however, of shallow
depth, the deepest being 120 feet, but more commonly only 50 or 60
feet.   They were drained by adits.   The royalty of a large tract
belonged to the king as lord of the manor.

The employment of iron in railway construction had commenced
in Staffordshire previous to the close of the eighteenth century.   Mr.
Curr in 1797 (*Coal Viewer*, p. 13), speaks of a lime-work at Froghill,
where they had a land conveyance for their limestone, three or four
miles in length.   The roads were upon the plan of what he calls
Newcastle wagon roads, being laid in a firm manner upon wood,
after stoning 10 or 12 inches thick for a foundation.   "Upon this
wood," he states, "is laid cast iron an inch and a-half thick, a part
of which weighs in every single yard forward one hundred and
fifty-one pounds, and other models weigh only eighty-one pounds :
when the waggons come upon these roads, which together with the
limestone weighs in the sundry kinds of carriages they do and have
made use of, not less than four, five, and six tons, and I believe as
much as seven tons even, which besides being all laid upon four feet
in length, the above roads, although enormous in the first expense,
are nothing too strong."   Mr. Curr thought the employment of his
light rails and small carriages would have been preferable.

An account written in 1798 (*So. Staff. Inst., Mr. Scott's Address*,
1886), states that "Modes have been lately introduced of winding up
the coals from the bottom of pits by small fire engines instead of
horses, and of conveying the coals to the wharves along iron railroads."

Speaking of Warwickshire at the time of his visit there in 1725,
Dr. Stukeley observes (*Itin. Cur.*, 2nd ed., Cent. II., p. 19) : "Griff
coal works here, forty ells deep, of vast compass.   No sort of fossils
found in them.   Griff, from grave, groof, digging.   The soil sandy
from Coventry hither, then black earth.   The coal mine runs from

Coventry to Tamworth in a line: here are such breaches that intercept the strata, and such trapping and dipping as in Somersetshire: the fissures upon breaking the track and parallelism of the strata make them diverge generally. Great old toads are often found in solid coal, leaving a cavity of their own shape. They draw away the water from the mines by an invention originally of the Earl of Worcester, improved by Captain Savery and others: it works with a vast power from the atmosphere pressing into a receiver exhausted of air by vapor and then condensed."

Dr. Stukeley called upon Beighton, and found him engaged on his map of Warwickshire, which was published in the same year. From this map it is evident that the collieries were now very numerous; upwards of fifty being shown ranging along the eastern edge of the coalfield, and a detached group of seven in the neighbourhood of Wilnecote. Fire-engines are indicated at Griff, and at other two collieries between this place and Coventry.

Reference has been made to a water-gin erected by Smeaton at Griff in 1774. Bray thus refers to it in his *Tour into Derbyshire and Yorkshire*, the first edition of which was published in 1777 : "Near Bedworth is a coal mine of Sir Roger Newdigate (whose seat is not far off) from which he has made a cut to communicate with the navigation. He has here a wheel 36 feet diameter, which throws out the water, and draws up the coals at the same time." The pit was 300 feet deep. The wheel was of the over-shot description, as usual in this kind of machine, and 1 foot wide, the buckets being 10 inches deep. It drew up a corf containing 5 cwt. of coal, from 300 feet in $1\frac{1}{2}$ minutes (Farey's *Steam Engine*, p. 297).

The engine with a 58 inch cylinder, mentioned by Watt in his letter to Smeaton in 1776, as intended for Warwickshire, was doubtless one erected by his firm at Hawkesbury Colliery. Price, writing in 1778 (*Mineralogia Cornubiensis*), speaks of it as "justly supposed to be the most powerful engine in England."

Considerable coal mines are mentioned (*Agriculture of Warwickshire*) as existing in 1794, about Bedworth, Griff, Chilvers Coton, Oldbury, and extending in the same line to Atherston, Polesworth, and Wilncot. The coal is described as sulphureous in quality, but making durable hot fires.

Jago, in his poem of Edgehill, published in 1767 (Book iii.), devotes a few lines to a notice of a coal mine—a subterraneous city with covert streets—and to the difficulties which beset the miners arising from damps, water, and underground fires.

CHAPTER XXXIII.

THE EIGHTEENTH CENTURY.—Continued.

The Shropshire coalfield. Burning well at Broseley. Smelting iron with coal at Coalbrookdale. Cast iron rails. Self-acting inclines. Coal tar manufacture. The Forest of Dean coalfield. Extension of distance between levels. Water-wheel pumping engine. Fire engine. The Somersetshire coalfield. Use of gunpowder in sinking pits. Probable adoption of long wall system of working. Account of northern and southern districts. The steam engine being applied to draw coal. Water gin near Midsummer Norton.

In this era the small Shropshire coalfield still maintained a leading position, and was the scene of various important new departures.

Among matters of note connected with it was a once famous burning or boiling well, resembling the burning well at Wigan already mentioned, and, like it, occasioned by firedamp discharging itself at the surface of the earth. It attracted considerable attention, and accounts of it have been left by several writers. It was situated at Broseley, near Wenlock, and in the vicinity of the Severn, and was discovered about June, 1711 (*Phil. Trans.*, No. 334, p. 475). What led to its discovery was a great noise in the night, which waked some people living near, who proceeded to ascertain the cause of the disturbance, when a lighted candle which they carried ignited the escaping gas. To prevent the spring from being destroyed, an iron cistern was placed about it with a cover to be locked, and a hole in the middle through which it could be viewed. So it continued for a number of years, and a poor man who exhibited it derived considerable profit from the company resorting to see it. But the supply of inflammable gas becoming gradually exhausted, the flame grew weaker, and at last would burn no more.

In 1747, however, the same old man, having his attention attracted as before, succeeded in finding a similar well at a point about thirty yards distant from the former one (*Phil. Trans.*, No. 482, p. 370). "The well," we are told, "on the application of a candle, immediately took fire, and flamed like spirits of wine to the height of 18 or 20 inches; the heat was so intense as to boil a common tea kettle in about nine minutes; mutton stakes, and slices of bacon, were broiled very soon and with an excellent flavour. The old man sometimes boiled his family pot over it" (*Gent.'s Maga.*, vol. xxv., p. 302).

The place where it was situated was surrounded by coal pits, though none were very near it. But about 1752, a pit was sunk close to the spot, to a depth of 264 feet, the workmen being greatly annoyed by firedamp (wild-fire) during the operation. This pit having on one occasion become filled with inflammable gas, it was judged expedient to fire it, which caused a terrible explosion, alarming the whole neighbourhood—the people imagining it to have been an earthquake. It shook the windows, pewter, and even the casks in the cellars. This "seem'd like the dying groan of the burning well, which since that time has entirely ceased to burn."

Though it is generally agreed that the first notable revival of the iron trade, resulting from the substitution of coal for charcoal in the smelting operations, took place at Coalbrookdale Ironworks, in Shropshire, there is some difficulty in determining the exact period when the new fuel began to be employed. According to Scrivenor (*Iron Trade*, 1854, p. 56) the manufacture of iron with pit coal was commenced here by the first Abraham Darby in 1713. Later writers, however, declare this statement to be erroneous, and maintain that coal fuel did not begin to be used till about twenty years subsequently.

That attempts were being made in some parts of England to substitute coal, burnt or calcined into cinders, for charcoal in iron smelting shortly after 1730, we have evidence from a work, published on the Continent in 1734 (Swedenborg's *Regnum Subterraneum, Dresdæ et Leipsiæ*, 1734, p. 156). According to the statement of Mrs. Abraham Darby (Dr. Percy's *Metallurgy: Iron and Steel*, 1864, p. 888), it was at this period, or between 1730 and 1735, that Abraham Darby, the second, began to employ coked coal at Coalbrookdale. To increase the power of his water-wheels of 24 feet diameter, and obtain a stronger blast, he set up a "fire engine" to return the water to the top.

The earliest contemporary notice we have relating to this revolution in iron smelting at Coalbrookdale, is contained in the account given by the Rev. Mr. Mason in the *Philosophical Transactions* for the year 1747 (No. 482, p. 370), who speaks of several attempts having been made to run iron ore with pit coal, and thinks it has not succeeded anywhere, as no accounts existed of its having been practised; "but Mr. Ford, from iron ore and coal, both got in the same dale, makes iron brittle or tough as he pleases; there being cannon thus cast so soft as to bear turning like wrought iron."[1]

Reference has been made to the employment of iron in railway construction having been first practised at Coalbrookdale Ironworks. It appears from the books of this company (Wood's *Railroads*, 1831, p. 21) that between five and six tons of rails were cast on the 13th November, 1767, as an experiment, at the suggestion of Mr. Reynolds, one of the partners. The rails were 4 feet in length, 4 inches in breadth, and $1\frac{1}{4}$ inches in thickness, and were laid upon and secured to the previously-existing wooden rails. They were found to improve the railway so much that the same course was pursued with all the railways at the works (*Letters of Richard Reynolds*, by H. M. Rathbone, 1852, p. 27).

Here also it was that the first iron bridge was constructed in 1777 (Plymley's *Shropshire*, p. 316); while in the same neighbourhood (at this period the most important iron-producing district in England) one of the most curious of all the modern applications of iron, the construction of *iron boats*, was commenced in 1787-88, by Mr. Wilkinson,[2] of Willey, who had some years before, however, built a small boat of this material for conveying peat on a private canal from a turbary to ironworks in Furness (*The Wilkinsons*, by John Randall, F.G.S., pp. 19, 55).[3]

Another branch of the iron industry appears to have been specially developed at Broseley, which is spoken of in 1789 (Gough's *Britannia*) as famous for its pipes.

The following notice of a strike of colliers in Shropshire appeared in the *Leeds Intelligencer* for November 23, 1756: "On Monday last the bargemen and colliers from Brosely, Madelywood, and Bontale, rose and did much mischief at Winlock. On Tuesday were joined by the colliers about Dawley and Oaken Gates, and came to Shiffnall about 700 in number." There were corn riots, and much

[1] It is on record, however (Randall's *Wilkinsons*, p. 38), that even as late as 1803 a portion of the fuel used at Coalbrookdale consisted of charcoal.

[2] Mr. Wilkinson constructed the first railway in France for the use of the foundries at Creusot in 1783 (*Popular Encyclopædia*, art. Railways).

[3] The first iron boat in Scotland is stated (*Glasgow Herald*, 28th Sept., 1897, p. 3) to have been built at Faskine, on the Monkland Canal, by Mr. Thomas Wilson in 1818, for use on the Forth and Clyde Canal, and to have been named the "Vulcan."

terror prevailed till the rioters were dispersed (*Report of Royal Coal Commission*, iii. 19).

That a self-acting inclined plane was constructed by Mr. Wm. Reynolds, of Ketley, for lowering and raising boats in connection with his canal, and was completed in 1788, has been already adverted to. The canal ran from Oaken Gates to the ironworks at Ketley, a distance of one and a-half miles. The incline consisted of a double iron railway. Writing in 1803, Plymley remarks (*Shropshire*, p. 313) that since 1797, roads with iron rails had been adopted to a considerable extent. In the case of the self-acting incline in connection with the Shropshire and Shrewsbury canal, of which this author gives a drawing, cast iron rails of a channel section were adopted, having flanges on both sides.

The above Mr. Wm. Reynolds, about 1793 (*ib.*, p. 52 note), revived the open-cast or quarry method of digging his coal and ironstone in the parish of Wombridge; a system soon afterwards followed in other works in the district, where the minerals lay sufficiently near the surface. The maximum depth attained in Shropshire at the end of this century was 462 feet (*ib.*, p. 55).

We have seen that in the second half of this century Shropshire had been a noted centre for the manufacture of (Newcomen) steam engines, sending them as far even as the north of England. In the last decade of the century some new forms of the steam engine originated here, designed by J. Sadler, Adam Heslop, J. Hornblower, Glazebrook, and others, for pumping, blowing blast furnaces, winding coal, etc. One of these was an engine "without a beam," erected at Wombridge in 1794, for raising coal (Randall's *Wilkinsons*, p. 37). Adam Heslop's peculiar engine, for the same purpose, will be heard of hereafter.

It is stated (Plymley's *Shropshire*, p. 340) that in 1802 there were on the south side of the Severn 25 fire engines and on the north side 155 fire engines, at the different coal and iron works. Thirty years previously there were not twenty in the same district. The works of Madely Wood, Coalbrookdale, and others, employed 6,000 hands. About 260,000 tons of coal were annually raised in the district.

The coal tar manufacture seems to have been a more prosperous industry in Shropshire than in Staffordshire. "Near Jackfield," says Plymley (*ib.*, p. 71), "on the north side of the River Severn, is carried on the manufacture of coal tar, for which Lord Dundonald formerly obtained a patent. In coaking the coal, which is here done in close vessels, they obtain the volatile products which are raised in vapour by the heat of the operation of coaking, and condensed in a chamber covered with lead plates, over which water is constantly running. These products are a water and an oil; the former of which contains a portion of volatile alkali, and the latter is boiled down to a consistence of tar or pitch. The oil which is caught during the boiling down is used as a solvent for resin, and forms an excellent varnish for ships, or any woodwork exposed to weather."

It was probably this industry to which the translator of Beckman's *History of Inventions* refers (vol. i., p. 339), when, writing in 1798, he remarks that "at present the burning of coals, in order to procure from them rock oil, used particularly by the leather manufacturers, and which on that account must not be exported, is much practised in England" (*Fossil Fuel*, 1835, p. 405 note).

The coal mines in the Forest of Dean were still in a primitive condition in the eighteenth century.   According to Mr. Nicholls (*Forest of Dean*, p. 239), they consisted generally of levels driven from the lower grounds, which served alike for the extraction of the coal and the drainage of the workings.   The levels, he states, were divided horizontally by a flooring consisting of broad slabs of timber, thus forming the passage into an intake and return airway, while the flooring served at the same time as a road for the coal trams to run upon.   It would appear probable, however, that the coal was more commonly raised out of pits connected with the levels.

The pits are stated to have rarely exceeded 75 feet in depth. They were made of a square form to admit of being more readily secured with timber.   The skips used in raising the coal appear to have been also rectangular in shape.

By an order of the Mine Law Court in 1728 (*ib.*, p. 234), the distance between adjoining works was augmented from 300 yards to 500 yards in all levels.   In 1741 it was directed that "the vearns belonging to the levels which are between Drybrooke and Cannop's Bridge, and between Seridge and Ruardean Town, shall get coal out of no more than two pitts at one time, belonging to one level, till the said two pitts are worked quite out, and those who keep two pitts in work on one level shall not sinke any other new pitt till the old ones are quite worked out."

In 1754 a further great augmentation was made of the distance between adjoining works, the Court ordering that "none shall sink any water pit and get coal out of it within the limits or bounds of 1,000 yards of any level, and that the water-wheel ingine at the Oiling Green, near Broadmore, be taken to be a level to all intents and purposes as all other levels brought up from the Grassmore."

The water-wheel engine for working the pumps at Oiling Green

Colliery is supposed to have been the first of its kind in the Forest. Up till about 1779 (Rudder's *Gloucestershire*) no steam engine had yet been introduced, but one is understood to have been erected about this time (Nicholls's *Forest of Dean*, p. 236). The Fire Engine Colliery is mentioned as one of the principal works in 1788.

In the above year there were in the Forest 121 coal pits (thirty-one of which were not actually in work), producing 1,816 tons of coal weekly (*ib.*, p. 237), or an aggregate production of about 94,000 tons per annum.

Some information regarding the Somersetshire coalfield in the early part of the eighteenth century, is obtainable from two papers communicated to the Royal Society by John Strachey, Esq., and published in the *Philosophical Transactions*. From the first of these (*Phil. Trans.*, No. 360, p. 968), dated 1719, we learn, as previously adverted to, that gunpowder had then already begun to be sometimes employed here in perforating an unusually hard bed of rock met with in the sinking of pits.

It also appears that seams of coal only 10 inches in thickness were at times worked. What the system of working pursued consisted of we are not informed, but with seams of such extreme thinness it could scarcely have been other than some species of longwall; and this receives support from the circumstance that in the second paper (*Phil. Trans.*, No. 391, p. 395, anno 1725), in speaking of certain pits in Northumberland and Scotland, the author remarks that "all these agree in this that the pits generally need no timber, and have a good roof, which is supported with pillars of coal which they leave in working"—leading to the inference than in Somersetshire a different state of matters existed, and such pillars of coal were not left.

Speaking of the district in the neighbourhood of Bath, Stukeley, who travelled there in 1723, remarks (*Itin. Cur.*, 1776, Cent. I., p. 149) that the country abounded with coal pits. He refers to the impressions of plants, particularly ferns, on the slates accompanying the coals, observing that they "gave their forms to the soft matter at the Deluge."

At Radstock, in this county, Jonathan Hornblower erected the first of his compound steam engines in 1782 (Muirhead's *Life of Watt*, 2nd ed., p. 388). It does not appear to have been a success. Watt, however, proceeded to Bristol and cautioned Hornblower's employers and the public against using this form of engine, as being a direct infringement of his patent (Smiles's *Boulton and Watt*, 1874, pp. 255-57).

From an account of the Somersetshire collieries in 1795 (Billings-ley's *Agriculture of Somerset*) it appears that at the northern collieries the coal seams dipped 9 inches per yard, and were nineteen in number, ranging from 10 inches to 3 feet in thickness, but were

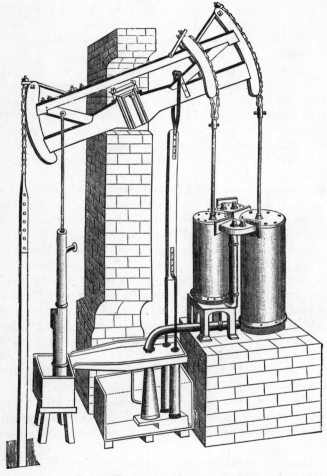

FIG. 28.—HORNBLOWER'S COMPOUND ENGINE.

seldom worked under 15 inches. Coal was being generally worked from 400 to 500 feet in depth; in a few places deeper; "and by the late introduction of machinery to raise it by the steam engine" it is remarked "a much greater depth of working will be obtained."

The production of coal here was from 1,500 to 2,000 tons weekly. The permanence of the works is spoken of as amply secured by various contrivances in preventing the admission of the springs into the deep workings. The freeholders received one-eighth of the gross receipts of sale, sometimes less, to encourage deep working.

In the southern district the working of coal was on a more limited scale. Here the seams dipped from 18 to 30 inches per yard, and were sometimes even perpendicular. They were twenty-five in number, ranging from 6 inches to 7 feet (?); but were seldom worked under 18 inches. The depth of working was from 200 to 350 feet, but it is stated that "by the steam engines which are now erecting in this district a much greater depth will be obtained."

The production of coal was from 800 to 1,000 tons weekly. Reference is made in this case also to an improved method of working lately adopted, by which the springs were prevented from inundating the deep workings. In both the northern and the southern districts canals were under construction in 1797 (*ib.*, 2nd ed.).

The collieries of the southern district had formerly been known as the "Mendip Collieries," but the term had become obsolete. They are supposed to have been once within the verge of this forest, though now surrounded with old enclosures.

Mention is made of a water gin being in use at one colliery, where evidently a natural supply of water was available. "At Welton, a work in the northern part of Midsummer Norton, the coal has lately been drawn up by a water wheel on a new construction, the use of horses being entirely superseded and the consumption of fuel as in the new way by the steam engine altogether saved."

According to the weekly production of the collieries above stated, the average annual production of the coalfield at this period would amount to 138,000 tons.

Reference occurs (Macpherson's *Commerce*, vol. iii., p. 648) to tar being manufactured at Bristol in 1779. Owing to the failure of the supply of tar from America, occasioned by the war, the proprietors of a lamp-black manufactory here experimented on the oil produced from coal at their works, and found that by different degrees of boiling it could be reduced to the consistency of tar or pitch. The Earl of Dundonald, it is stated, improved this process, so as to make coal produce oil, volatile spirits, and varnish, as well as tar, pitch, and coak.

CHAPTER XXXIV.

THE EIGHTEENTH CENTURY.—Continued.

The Cumberland coalfield. Carlisle and James Spedding. Gins fire engine. Stukeley's account of Whitehaven mines. Saltom pit. Piping the gas. Steel mill. Gunpowder used in blasting rock. Wooden railways. Sir John Clerk. Coursing the air. M. Jars. Thomas Pennant. Water gin. Steam engines applied to draw coal. Workington. Boulton and Watt's engines. Long-way system of working near Sebergham, and in Scotland. The North Wales coalfield. Mostyn. Brymbo. Ruabon. The South Wales coalfield. Export of coal. Collieries and copper works near Swansea. Kidwelly. Merthyr-Tydvil. Manufacture of iron with coal. Canal and cast iron railway from Blaenavon to Newport.

The coal mines at Whitehaven, in Cumberland, occupied a position of great prominence, and received a large measure of attention in the eighteenth century. Picturesquely situated on the sea coast, they were carried on with great spirit and prosperity, and called into existence a considerable town and harbour. They were unique at this period in working coal under the sea. The workings were also carried down to greater depths than had been reached in any of the other coalfields. The mines were accessible by means of sloping roads from the surface, and were visited by various distinguished tourists who have left accounts of them. From this neighbourhood, also, emanated some of the most notable mining improvements of the century.

For the importance to which they attained, the Whitehaven mines were indebted not only to the liberality and enterprise of the Lowther family, but also in great measure to the energy and skill of the two eminent mining engineers, Carlisle Spedding and his son James Spedding, who succeeded him in their management.

Carlisle Spedding was born about 1696, and was the fourth son of he principal steward of the Lowther estates. Being a promising youth, he was selected by Sir James Lowther as engineer of his collieries. It is stated (Hutchinson's *Cumberland,* ii. 69, 70) that previous to entering on his duties at Whitehaven, he was sent *incognito* to Newcastle-on-Tyne by Sir James, to acquire a knowledge of the methods of mining pursued in that district. Here under a fictitious name he obtained employment as a hewer or hagger of coal, making in the meantime all the inquiries and discoveries he could relative to the colliery operations.

After continuing in this capacity for a considerable time Spedding, who was there known by the name of "Dan," had the misfortune to be burnt by firedamp, whereupon a message was sent to Newcastle to procure the best medical assistance possible in order to recover him. The extraordinary attention paid to a person in the apparent situation of Spedding by such eminent practitioners, led to the discovery of his true character and motives; accordingly after his recovery, having already accomplished to a large extent the object of his mission, he returned to Whitehaven and set about the improvement of the collieries.

Carlisle Spedding must have been a contemporary of Triewald's at the great northern *alma mater* of coal mining. Like him, he appears to have become enamoured of the steam engine, just introduced there; the building of a "fire engine" at a pit in the Gins, in 1718, being supposed to have been one of the first acts of his administration upon entering upon the management of the Whitehaven mines (*Archæology of the West Cumberland Coal Trade,* by Isaac Fletcher, M.P., F.R.S.; *Trans. of the Cumberland and Westmoreland Antiq. and Arch. Society,* iii. 279). This engine was purchased at London by Sir James Lowther (Hutchinson, ii. 60), and sent by sea to Whitehaven. A tradition existed that it had been used at some waterworks in London, and was the second fire engine in England. It is referred to by Bradley in his *New Improvements of Planting and Gardening,* part iii., 2nd ed. (p. 180), published in 1718, where he speaks of the engine belonging to —— Louder, Esq., of Whitehaven, as "above all others that I have yet heard of for ingenious contrivance."

This early steam engine had a brass cylinder, 28 inches in diameter (*Trans. Fed. Inst.,* vii. 622); a copper boiler, 10 feet in diameter, with a lead top; wooden pumps, 8 inches in diameter; and a brass working-barrel. It was erected at a pit 121 feet deep, afterwards known as the Gins Fire Engine Pit. It is stated to have been a great success, the expensive and inefficient horse gins, previously employed in raising the water, being got rid of at once and for good.

Regarding Whitehaven and its mines in 1725, Dr. Stukely informs us (*Itin. Cur.*, 2nd ed., Cent. II., p. 52) that "it is a new sea-port town standing in a little bay, sprung up from its conveniency for the coal mines hard by. There are many salt works on the coast. . . . They transport great quantities of coals to Ireland and other places. We walked two miles in these coal works, the stratum of pure coal being all the way about 10 foot thick, declining gradually, about one foot in five, till we got 300 foot below the surface : a rock of stone overhead all along. Their method of digging is generally to run the grooves in a strait line, others going out on both sides at right angles ; so that square pillars of coal are left to support the incumbent rock ; hence some roads are made along the descent and others parallel to the declivity. There are trappings now and then, but not very frequent nor great, and these are both along the declivity and sideways. Their methods of conveying the coal to the shafts where they are drawn up, and of conveying air from one passage to the other to prevent damps and stagnations, and of drawing up the water from one height to another are very dextrous, and worth seeing. At last the famous fire engine discharges the water, which is a notable piece of machinery, working itself entirely : it creates a vacuum by first rarefying the air with hot steam, then condenses it suddenly by cold water ; whence a piston is drawn up and down alternately, at one end of the beam : this actuates a pump at the other end, which, let into the works, draws the water out : it makes about 14 strokes a minute ; so that it empties 140 hogsheads in an hour with moderate working."

He proceeds to state that with this quantity of declivity the coal "goes towards the sea and below it at present," from which it would appear that thus early a commencement had been made to work under the sea at Whitehaven. It was not, however, the first instance in which this had been done. As early as 1618 (Taylor's *Pennyles Pilgrimage*) the coal workings at Culross, in Scotland, had been carried the distance of a mile underneath the Firth of Forth.

Shortly after this period a sinking of much greater depth and importance than any hitherto attempted at Whitehaven—perhaps, indeed, in any other part of the kingdom—was undertaken by Mr. Spedding. Having made a boring at a place called Saltom on the sea shore, about half a mile distant from the Gins, and ascertained the Main band, or seam, to exist there in perfection at a depth of about 480 feet, he proposed to sink a pit, and erect a steam engine, which would drain many hundreds of acres under the land, and an unknown extent under the sea.

The sinking at Saltom, which has been characterized as the most remarkable colliery enterprise of its day, was commenced in 1729, within twenty yards of high water mark. The shaft was made oval in form, 10 feet by 8 feet, in order to admit of drawing coal and pumping water being both carried on to it.

An eruption of firedamp encountered in the course of sinking this pit, formed the subject of a paper communicated to the Royal Society by Sir James Lowther, in 1733 (*Phil. Trans.*, No. 429, p. 109). At a depth of 252 feet the sinkers pricked a small bed of black stone, 6 inches in thickness, and full of fissures, overlying a seam of coal 2 feet thick. Contrary to expectation, very little water was met with at this point; but instead of this a "blower," or strong discharge of firedamp, came off, "which bubbled through a small quantity of water then spread over that part of the pit, and made a great hissing noise." On a candle being held towards the spot the gas ignited and burned fiercely on the top of the water. The blower having been lighted and extinguished several times, and being found to give off a continuous flow of gas, all lights were excluded from the pit till it was sunk quite through the bed of stone and coal; when a tight framing of timber was constructed to dam back the gas out of the pit; and a small pipe, 2 inches square, was led to the surface from behind the framing, which carried it off to the open air.

At the date of the writing of the paper the discharge had continued, without any sensible diminution, for two years and nine months. Some bladders filled with gas from the blower had been sent to the Royal Society by Sir James Lowther, and experimented upon a few months previous to the reading of the paper.

Though this was doubtless the most notable eruption of firedamp which had as yet occurred in the Whitehaven mines, this gas appears to have been known there long before. In the pay-bills from the earliest times (*Trans. Fed. Inst.*, vii. 624), there are said to be frequent entries, such as "fireing damp," "oyle and brandy for a burnt man," paying money to "burnt men," and an annual payment of £20 to a medical man "for cureing burnt men." The entry first quoted has no doubt reference to the process of firing the gas, regarding which Dr. Dixon remarks, in his account of the White-haven mines (*Life of Brownrigg*, p. 104), that: "To prevent its accumulation, it was formerly a practice with the workmen to set fire to it by the flame of a candle, using the precaution of lying prostrate on the ground during its explosion."

The first great accident recorded to have been occasioned at

Whitehaven by an explosion of firedamp, occurred at the Corpsill, or Corporal, pit, in 1737.   In the pay-bill of this pit for August 10 of this year (Fletcher's *Archæology*, etc., *ut sup.*, p. 286), the following entry is made : "5th, Friday.   Firedamp killed 22 at 4 o'clock in ye M."   And also an item of £8 3s. 10d. "for searching for and taking up 22 dead (persons) and three horses, mending thirls, etc., after the Great Fire Damp."   Sir James Lowther immediately ordered £100 to be distributed among the families of the sufferers.

 To combat this danger Carlisle Spedding made his celebrated invention of the steel mill.   Reference is made in Sir James Lowther's paper, in 1733, to the use of flint and steel to give light to the miners in places where candles were inadmissible, but whether the steel mill had then been invented is not stated.   The first account of it is contained in Dr. Dalton's "Descriptive Poem addressed to two Ladies on their return from viewing the mines near Whitehaven," written in 1753, and in which Spedding is spoken of by the name of Prospero, where this ingenious instrument is referred to (p. 5) in the following lines :

> " For at your presence toil is o'er,
> The restless miner works no more,[1]
> Nor strikes the flint, nor whirls the steel
> Of that strange spark-emitting wheel,
> Which, form'd by Prospero's magic care,
> Plays harmless in the sulphurous air,
> Without a flame diffuses light,
> And makes the grisly cavern bright."

 As a further precaution Spedding carried out the system of piping off the gas where possible, in the same way as was done with the blower in the Saltom pit.   Careful search was made for crevices yielding gas (*ib.*, p. 3 note), and such places were dammed off, and pipes led from them to carry away the discharge to the surface, where it was usually consumed at the top of the pit.

 Such a pipe was led into the laboratory of Dr. Brownrigg (Dixon's *Life of Brownrigg*, p. 7), who made many experiments upon it, and employed it as a substitute for fire in chemical operations.   In prosecuting his inquiries, he experienced occasional interruptions from certain irregularities in the quantity and motion of the firedamp ; which were the effect of a sudden transition of the atmosphere.   By observing the rapidity with which the mercury descended in the barometer, he is stated (*ib.*, p. 10) to have been able to

---

[1] Having been granted a holiday.

foretell the exact period of an explosion ; his prediction being said to be too frequently verified by such an event.

Spedding even conceived the idea of utilizing the firedamp by conveying it in pipes to different parts of the town, for the purpose of lighting up the streets at night. We hear of his having made such a proposal to the town authorities (Jars's *Voyages Métallurgiques*, i. 248); but there is no reference to any attempt having been made to carry out the project.

The use of gunpowder for blasting purposes was introduced at Whitehaven by Spedding. This is supposed to have taken place as early as 1730 (*Trans. Fed. Inst.*, vii. 624). If so it would probably be first used in the sinking of the Saltom pit. For a long period it was only used in breaking rock. Dr. Dalton, in his poem already mentioned, written in 1753 (p. 9), alludes to its employment in cutting through interruptions occasioned by dislocations of the strata :

> "Dissever'd by the nitrous blast,
> The stubborn barrier yields at last."

Wooden railways were also first constructed by Spedding at Whitehaven, though the exact date of their introduction, as well as the name of the pit first provided with this method of conveyance, are somewhat uncertain. According to Hutchinson (*Cumberland*, ii. 66) the earliest was constructed between the Parker pit and the staith, a distance of half-a-mile. This railway is shown in a print entitled, *A Bird's-eye View of Whitehaven* (*Trans. Fed. Inst.*, vii. 625), engraved from a painting made in 1738.

An account of the pit at Saltom at this period is given in a letter from Sir John Clerk to Mr. Gale (*Reliquœ Galeanœ*, pp. 326-28; Gough's *Britannia*, 1789, iii. 180), dated 1739 : "Amongst the extraordinary works of this place," he says, "I could not but admire those on the sea coast to the westward. The sink goes down perpendicularly 80 fathoms (480 feet) below the sea, and many underneath it. Sir James's riches in part swim over his head, for ships pass daily above the very ground where his colliers work. The coals are drawn up by an engine, worked by two horses, which go a full trot every eight hours, and three changes are employed in a day and a night. The quantity drawn up is about twenty *corfs* in an hour, each corf consisting of an oblong square 32 inches long, 18 broad, and 22 deep, which costs 7½d. Thus I found the quantity of coal brought up in a year (Sunday excepted) amounted to about 4,200£, but out of this the colliers and other expenses being paid, he cannot clear above 500 or 600£ a year out of his largest coal work. He draws the water from his coal seams by a fire engine with four pumps and four lifts; one of the pumps goes down 80 fathoms, which brings up the water to a cistern at 60 fathoms deep; from thence another pump raises it to a cistern of 40 fathoms deep from the surface on the top of the sink; a 3rd brings it up to 20, and a 4th to the level of the sea at high water.   The cylinder which gives life to this motion is of brass 42 inches diameter, fixed in a boiler of about 11 feet diameter.   The coal, when brought up to the level of the sea, is put in slips and conveyed to the cavity of a hill, whence it is drawn up by a second engine.   There it is put on great carts with low wheels, which gently roll down to the harbour on oak boards."   A wooden railway evidently existed here also at this time.

During Carlisle Spedding's term of office, numerous other pits were sunk at Whitehaven. From the notes appended to Dr. Dalton's poem (published in 1755) we learn that a vertical depth of 780 feet had been attained. From the greater depths the coals were raised in several stages, by means of underground horse gins and blind pits, or staples, from one seam to another:

> ".   .   .   in a triple story end
> Mines that o'er mines by flights ascend."

In the deep parts of the mine, the pillars of coal left are stated to have been about 12 yards square.   There were now four fire, or steam engines, at Whitehaven, employed in raising water.

The mines are described as "greatly infested with fulminating damps; large quantities of them being frequently collected in those deserted works, which are not ventilated with perpetual currents of fresh air."   The coal had several times been set on fire by the fulminating damp.   There would appear to have been numerous doors employed in connection with the ventilation of the mines:

> "Tho' he with hundred gates and chains
> The Demons of the mine restrains."

After conducting the Whitehaven collieries with wonderful ability during the long period of about thirty-seven years, Carlisle Spedding himself had the misfortune to fall a victim to the "demons of the mine."   He was killed by an explosion on 8th August, 1755, while underground performing his duties in the mine, being then fifty-nine years of age.

Reference has been made to an improved system of ventilating mines known as "coursing the air."   While it is agreed that this improvement came from Cumberland, writers are at variance as to whether the system was the invention of Carlisle Spedding, or his son James Spedding, who succeeded to the management of the collieries belonging to the Lowther family at Whitehaven and Workington, and who, in 1763, became a partner in extensive ironworks established at the latter place.

The earliest allusion to the inventor of the new system, known to the writer, is contained in Mr. Buddle's letter to Sir Ralph Milbanke in 1813 ("First Report of a Society for Preventing Accidents in Coal Mines," Newcastle, 1814), where it is stated (p. 17) that "the late ingenious Mr. Spedding, of Whitehaven, to whose memory our tribute of gratitude is due, suggested the idea of *coursing the air.*" Mr. Buddle's statement could only properly refer to Mr. James Spedding who died in 1788; and that it was meant to do so is amply corroborated by his evidence before the Committee of the House of Commons in 1835 (*Report on Accidents in Mines*, 1835, p. 134), where he specifically ascribes the invention to Mr. James Spedding, of Workington. But previous to this the indefiniteness of his first statement had already begun to cause writers, evidently quoting from it, to ascribe the invention to Mr. Carlisle Spedding. Thus, Mr. Bald, in 1820 (*Edinburgh Encyclopædia*, vol. xiv., p. 368), ascribes it to "the ingenious Mr. Charles Spedding, a native of Cumberland"; adding almost in the words of Mr. Buddle, "To the memory of Mr. Spedding every tribute of respect is due." Then Mr. Matthias Dunn (*Winning and Working of Collieries*, sec. ed., 151), whose words indicate his information to have been derived from the same original source, states that "the ingenious Mr. Spedding, who is recorded as the inventor of the steel mill, suggested the *coursing of the waste.*" Mr. Dunn omits the clause about the tribute of gratitude, and substitutes the reference to the steel mill for it, but in doing so he obviously vitiates Mr. Buddle's statement. Unless further evidence relating to the subject can be produced, we are bound to accept the coursing system as the invention of Mr. James Spedding, notwithstanding the circumstance that so many writers ascribe it to his father; that is assuming Mr. Buddle to be correct in the first instance.

Artificial ventilation had not yet been introduced at the Whitehaven mines at the time of M. Jars's visit in 1765, but there being numerous openings to the surface at different altitudes, the mines were favourably situated for obtaining the best results from natural ventilation. This writer speaks (*Voyages*, i. 249) of there being several conduits made of planks (probably air-crossings for passing one current over another), and many doors in the mines which produced a very good effect.

M. Jars further informs us that the Whitehaven mines were worth £15,000 per annum.   He refers to the workings extending to the distance of a quarter of a mile under the sea, and describes the method of drawing up the water from the dip workings by means of a horse gin, with water chests running on a double railway; the empty chest descending while the full one was being drawn up. The signalling between the top and bottom of the incline was performed by means of a bugle.

The working-places underground were all made 15 feet wide, and the pillars left 15 yards square.   The coal was got with picks and wedges.   The colliers worked eight or ten hours, and earned from eighteen to twenty pence.   They were mostly at a fixed price.   The minimum wage was 1s. per day.

There were more than thirty horses in the mines, which entered and returned each day by a slope road.   Wooden railways and four-wheeled trams were in use on the underground roads; though in some parts sledges were still employed.

From the same authority we learn that at the neighbouring collieries at Workington a depth of 360 feet had been attained. Like the mines at Whitehaven they were much infested with "bad air," which at the two places had cost the lives of a very large number of workmen.   The steel mill was already known not to be absolutely safe; an explosion having recently occurred where no other light was being used.

During the time of M. Jars's visit an explosion occurred at Workington, by which two men were killed, and several burnt. The men who were killed were not burnt, causing M. Jars to comment on the circumstance that more lives were lost by the "return of the air" than by the actual explosion.   One of the overmen who had been in several explosions, ascribed his escape to his having thrown himself on his face.

The openings to the surface at Workington being upon the same level, the ventilation of the mines appears to have been very defective.   The workmen kept continually calling to each other to make sure that none of their number had succumbed to the noxious gases, and scarcely ever a week passed without some one requiring to be carried to the surface.   M. Jars proposed to remedy this by constructing a conduit from the extremity of the workings and connecting its outer end with the furnace of the fire engine.   At this time gas was piped to the surface and burning there at Workington.   M. Jars thought it extraordinary that the flame did not communicate with the workings of the mine.

This writer was informed that the mines of Whitehaven, Workington, Harrington, and Maryport, produced daily a thousand tons of 14 cwt. each, which was mostly sent to Ireland.

A traveller of a different type visited Whitehaven shortly afterwards in the person of Thomas Pennant, one of the most prolific and popular writers of "Tours" at this period, in the course of his tour to Scotland in 1772. In his account we hear of a further improvement in the ventilation having been made, consisting of the airing of individual working-places seemingly. The steel mill, however, still continued in use:

"Reach the first bed of coal," says this writer, "which had been worked about a century ago; pillars 15 yards square, not above a third of the coal having been worked. . . . At about 80 fathoms (480 feet) began to see the working of the rods of the fire engine, and the present operations of the colliers, who work now in security, for the firedamps formerly so dangerous are almost overcome; at present they are prevented by boarded partitions placed a foot distant from the sides, which causes a free circulation of the air throughout; but as still there are some places not capable of such convenience, the colliers, who dare not venture with a candle in spots where firedamp is supposed to lurk, have invented a curious machine to serve the purpose of light; it is what they call a steel mill." The men who worked among the firedamp, it is stated, "inhaled the inflammable air, and if they breathed against a candle, puffed out a fiery stream."

Pennant tells us that he "enquired for

'The swart fairy of the mine,'

and was seriously answered by a black fellow at my elbow that he really had never met with any; but that his grandfather had found the little implements and tools belonging to the diminutive race of subterranean spirits."

This writer gives the quantity of coal annually exported to Ireland as 218,000 tons.

In 1776 a steam engine was introduced underground at Whitehaven, for the purpose of raising the water from the dip workings (Farey's *Steam Engine*, p. 238); being the earliest instance recorded of an engine having been erected in the workings of a mine.

In 1781 the Whingill or north-east side of Whitehaven Colliery, was capable of raising 1,732 tons weekly, and the Howgill or south-west side 2,124 tons (*Trans. Fed. Inst.*, vii. 629) or an aggregate of about 200,000 tons per annum. The quantity actually produced, however, appears to have been about three-fourths of this. The number of horses employed at this period was very large. At Howgill Colliery there were 69 tram horses underground; and on the surface 80 gin horses, and 24 bank horses; or altogether 173 horses, about one-third of which were provided by the neighbouring farmers. Estimating the Whingill Colliery to have required a like number of horses in proportion to its output of coal, the number there would have been about 140, or a total for both collieries of 313 horses.

At this period (1781) Mr. Bateman succeeded to the management, and the underground haulage arrangements appear to have been considerably improved immediately afterwards. Writing in 1801, Dr. Dixon informs us (*Life of Brownrigg*, p. 102) that "about 18 or 20 years ago the daywork [*i.e.* dark or darg] of a horse consisted in carrying only 8 baskets; which circumstance very much increased the expense of obtaining the coal. To remedy this inconvenience, and to expedite the operations of the workmen, several of the pits were sunk below the coal, and levels driven until they intersected the beds of coal to the dip of the shaft. Wagon roads were then laid along these levels, and the coal was conveyed in baskets placed upon flat sledges. By this ingenious contrivance one horse carries four baskets, instead of one according to the former practice, and travels one-third greater distance." Being found to be attended with a great reduction of expense, this plan was generally adopted at Whitehaven.

An inundation took place at the Whitehaven mines in 1791 (Fletcher's *Archæology of the West Cumberland Coal Trade*), caused by tapping the water in some old workings, by which two men and a woman, with five horses, were drowned. The old workings collapsed in consequence, occasioning a subsidence of the surface, attended with considerable damage to buildings.

Accidents from firedamp doubtless also continued to occur, though we are without any record of them. In describing the anxious care exercised in opening out new works infested with this gas, Dr. Dixon (*Life of Brownrigg*, p. 99) tells us that "as few people as possible are allowed to be in the pit, lest any of them should forget to shut the doors, which they have occasion to open; such a neglect, if undiscovered for a few minutes, has often proved fatal to every person employed."

The substitution of machines for the horse gins previously employed in raising the coals in the shafts, began at Whitehaven, as elsewhere, in the latter part of this century. The first application of a machine to draw coals at Whitehaven was made in 1787 (Hutchinson's *Cumberland*, ii. 399), when a water gin, consisting of a double-bucket water-wheel and auxiliary Newcomen engine, was erected at the George pit, Whingill Colliery. This machine continued working till 1803.

Within a few years after the erection of the above machine, however, a general commencement was made to apply steam engines directly in raising coal, Whitehaven in this respect being early in the field. The form of engine employed was a peculiar one, and appears to be heard of nowhere save in the Cumberland coalfield, where it came into extensive use. It is known as the Heslop engine, and was patented by Adam Heslop, of Ketley, in Shropshire, in 1790. It was provided with two cylinders, one at each end of the beam, named respectively the hot and cold cylinders, the former resembling the cylinder of an ordinary Newcomen engine, while the latter was used as a separate condenser for the condensation of the steam. The engine was undoubtedly an infringement of Watt's patent rights, but he does not appear to have interfered with it.

The first of these singular steam engines, which seem to have been well adapted for producing rotary motion, is stated (*Trans. Fed. Inst.*, vii. 630) to have been erected at the Davy pit, Whingill Colliery, by Messrs. Heslop and Millward, of Seaton Ironworks, near Workington, as early as 1791.[1] Other engines of the same type are stated to have been applied at Kells pit, Howgill Colliery, in 1793, and at Lady pit, Whingill Colliery, in 1795. The Kells pit engine is now in the South Kensington Museum.

The deepest pit working at Whitehaven, and supposed to be the deepest coal pit in England, in 1801 (Dixon's *Life of Brownrigg*, p. 128), was the Thwaite pit, Howgill Colliery, which was drawing coals from a depth of 149 fathoms, or 894 feet. The King pit, at the same colliery, had been sunk (in 1793) to a depth of $165\frac{1}{2}$ fathoms (993 feet), but appears to have been drawing coal only from a depth of 121 fathoms, or 726 feet (*ib.*, pp. 125, 128).

In the deeper pits at this period the pillars were made from 18 to

[1] It may be mentioned, however, that Dr. Dixon (*Life of Brownrigg*, 1801, p. 98) speaks as if the Davy pit engine was erected in 1794, and also as if it was the first steam engine applied to raise coal directly at Whitehaven.

The earliest notice of the employment of the steam engine to draw coals in Scotland occurs in the account of Old Monkland parish in Sinclair's *Statistical Account of Scotland*, vol. vii., p. 389, where it is recorded that : Here last spring (1792) Mr. Hamilton erected a machine for drawing up the coal to go entirely by steam. It is on an improved plan, the first of the kind in Scotland.

20 yards square (*ib.*, p. 102), only one-third part of the coal, or 4 yards in breadth, being taken out. The workings now extended to a distance of about half-a-mile under the sea (*ib.*, p. 95). The production of coal at Whitehaven between 1780 and 1800, according to Mr. Fletcher's account, averaged about 160,000 tons per annum.

At Workington, in 1794 (Hutchinson's *Cumberland*), there were fourteen coal pits, nine of which belonged to Mr. Curwen. In this year Mr. Curwen completed an important sinking to the depth of 516 feet. The shaft is spoken of as upwards of 12 feet diameter. Here Watt's improved engine appears to have been first introduced into Cumberland, almost simultaneously with its introduction into the Northumberland and Durham coalfield. According to a contemporary writer, quoted by Mr. Fletcher, Mr. Curwen had, within these few years, "erected six fire engines, which are employed both in winding up coals and pumping water. Infinite are the advantages resulting from Messrs. Boulton and Watt's improvements in the fire engine, which can nowhere be better seen than by these erected here."

At this period Mr. Curwen exported 100,000 tons of coal yearly, and other colliery owners about 50,000 tons, making the quantity exported from Workington 150,000 tons per annum.

Numerous pits were likewise being worked at Harrington and Maryport; the latter place, according to Mr. Fletcher's account, shipping away upwards of 100,000 tons annually before the close of the eighteenth century. It would thus appear that the total quantity shipped at the Cumberland ports in 1800 amounted to about 400,000 tons.[1]

While the bord-and-pillar system of working was being pursued in the thick seams of West Cumberland, and from one-half to two-thirds of the coal left in the mine, pillar working not having yet commenced here, we hear of the long-wall system of working, or something approaching to it, having been already introduced in another part of this county, viz., at Warnell Fell, Sebergham, where a seam of coal 16 inches in thickness was being worked, and all the coal obtained.

[1] Mr. Fletcher's quantities are perhaps slightly over-estimated. On the basis of the actual exports during the years 1781-1792, as given by Hutchinson (see also *Report of Royal Coal Commission*, vol. iii., Appendix No. 19), the quantity exported in 1800 should have been about 330,000 tons. Reference to the coking of coal in open heaps, at Clifton furnace, in this coalfield, occurs in the pages of M. Jars (1765); and we hear (*Trans. N.E. Inst.*, xxxiv. 105) of an old plan of a colliery at Boonwood, Distington, showing the existence of a cinder oven there in 1768.

Hutchinson, writing in 1794 (*Cumberland*, ii. 390), speaks of a pit having been lately sunk to this seam, at a depth of 333 feet. About 12 inches of the roof stone, consisting of a black slate metal, was taken down by the miners for height. "They form it," he says, "in a sort of wall behind them, which prevents the roof from tumbling in, as else it might do, inasmuch as they seldom leave any pillars to support it."

A similar method of working appears to have obtained a footing at an early period in the Scremerston coalfield, in the extreme north of Northumberland (*Trans. N.E. Inst.*, ix. 206). The system of working without leaving pillars of coal had also found its way further north into Scotland, being first heard of at Carron and Kinneil, where it had been introduced by Dr. Roebuck, of Birmingham, one of the founders of the famous iron works established at Carron about 1760, who is stated (*Trans. Fed. Inst.*, vi. 384) to have imported colliers from Shropshire for the purpose. In an account of the underground workings at Carron in 1765 (Jars's *Voyages*, i. 268), it is stated that "they leave no pillars at all in the mine, but they work at first only on one side, and the workmen support the rock with pieces of straight timber, 6 or 7 inches in diameter, which they withdraw as they advance, leaving behind them the rubbish, on which the rock settles without inconvenience, being always supported by props in the parts where they are working." [1] A plan of Dr. Roebuck's colliery at Kinneil is also still extant, dated 1770, on which a part of the working is marked as worked by "the long way." [2]

At Kinnaird, near Falkirk, long wall is stated (*Iron and Coal Trades Review*, liv. 165) to have been in use in 1775.

A little later, the Shropshire method of working is heard of at Cleland, in Lanarkshire, in a report on the collieries on the line of the Forth and Clyde Canal, dated 1793, special mention being made in this case of the *buildings* employed under this system; and in his *View of the Estate and Abbey of Culross*, published in the same

[1] This description would seem to apply to the bank-work system of working.

[2] The writer has been favoured by Mr. James Barrowman with the following excerpt from Mr. Burrel's Journal, under date August 18, 1761, relating to the introduction of the new method of working at Kinneil Colliery : "Yesterday Mr. Gibbons was here and bargained with the Shropshire men to drive 45 yards headway for opening the bit for long work at 8s. per fathom. 25 yds. is already made, and when the other is done Mr. Gibbons purposes to take the whole 70 yards abreast at a time. He seems fully satisfied that there is no danger in doing so, nor that it can be attended with any bad consequences to the works."

year, we find Lord Dundonald advocating (p. 55) an alteration of the method of working coal in Scotland, "viz., board ways fashion as at Newcastle, or the long way as in Shropshire, instead of post and staal."

Again, in an account of Clackmannan Colliery, dated 1795 (Sinclair's *Statistical Account*, xiv. 621), it is stated that "in this coal work the long way is now introduced: that is, no part of the coal is left for pillars, but the whole is taken out, which saves a great part of the coal." It is thus evident that a knowledge of the long way, or long-wall system of working, was spreading in the latter half of the eighteenth century.

Few records appear to have been brought to light relating to the collieries and coal trade of Wales at this period. We have seen that a steam engine was built in Flintshire as early as the year 1716, but as to the place where it was applied we are not informed.

The collieries of Mostyn and Bychton are described by Pennant (*Tours in Wales*, ed. 1810, i. 23) as in a low state in this era, owing partly to the rise of the works at Whitehaven, but more to the loss of the channel of the Dee, which had changed to the opposite shore. We hear (Gough's *Britannia*, 1789, ii. 592) of a coal mine on the shore at Mostyn having taken fire, and burnt out. The heat had given a slaked appearance to the rocks in the neighbourhood. This estate is spoken of as abounding with coal works.

Brymbo is referred to (Pennant, *ut sup.*, p. 404) as a township on the heights, where coal was produced; and Ruabon (Gough's *Britannia*, 1789, ii. 585) as a village on the top of a hill among coal pits. In Anglesea, in 1794, one coal work existed (*Report of Royal Coal Commission*, iii. 23) producing ten tons per day.

The great coalfield of South Wales was still little developed in proportion to its vast resources. Much of its finest coal was less suitable for domestic use than that produced by the other coalfields. Its inland coal was shut up from the market for want of outlets to the sea.

In its western portion, however, the working of the mineral was going on with some degree of activity, and a steady rate of progress, as evidenced by the following quantities exported to London (*Report of Royal Coal Com.*, iii. 22) in the middle of the century:

Years.	Milford.	Tenby and Haverford-west.	Caermarthen.	Swansea and Neath.	Total.
	Tons.	Tons.	Tons.	Tons.	Tons.
1745	1,516	298	43	—	1,857
1755	2,517	—	124	186	2,827
1765	3,122	807	119	45	4,003

Improved facilities for the conveyance of coal to the sea-board began to be introduced into this coalfield in the latter half of the eighteenth century, more particularly towards its close, by the construction of canals at various points. The Kidwelly Canal is stated (*Report of the Royal Coal Com.*, iii., Appendix No. 22) to have been sanctioned in 1766. The Glamorganshire Canal, from Cardiff to Merthyr, was commenced in 1790 and completed in 1794; and two years later an Act was obtained for its extension to the sea, which was accomplished in 1798. The Neath Canal was commenced in 1791; the Monmouthshire Canal, in 1792; the Brecknock and Abergavenny Canal, in 1793; the Swansea Canal, in 1794. The construction of cast iron railways also followed closely upon that of canals.

The exports from Swansea had attained to considerable proportions at the end of the century. In 1799 upwards of 3,000 vessels were loaded; the quantity of coal exported (*ib.*, Appendix No. 14, p. 6) being: foreign, 33,228 tons; coastwise, 211,748 tons; total, 244,976 tons. In addition to this, the copper trade on the spot is stated to have consumed from 1,500 to 2,000 tons weekly; while up the river much culm was required for the lime trade. The production of coal in this neighbourhood consequently cannot have been less than from 300,000 to 350,000 tons per annum.

The deleterious effects of the smoke and fumes here at this period are referred to by Skrine in the account of his tour made in 1798 (p. 66), where he states: "After visiting the imperfect remains of Neath Abbey, crossed a hill to reach those numerous collieries and copper-works, which, occupying an immense tract of country towards the north of Swansea, blast the soil all round with their sulphureous influence, destroying the appearance of verdure, and preventing cultivation."

The same writer likewise speaks (p. 73) of becoming environed with collieries on his way from Pembray to Kidwelly; the traffic from which appears to have caused the state of the roads to be the reverse of agreeable to tourists.

The coal in the Merthyr Tydvil neighbourhood, we are told (Wilkins's *Merthyr Tydvil: Report of Royal Coal Com.*, iii. 21), was first developed in a very small way by Mr. John Guest, more for the use of the farmers and villagers than for his furnaces. The farmers were in the habit of taking a sack of lime to Mr. Guest, and for one halfpenny they received a sack of coal in exchange. The load, generally borne on a horse, consisted of three sacks. The farmer would travel to Brecon, and sometimes to Kington, in Herefordshire, and sell his "black diamonds" for 10d. the sack.

The manufacture of iron with coal was introduced into South
Wales shortly after the middle of the eighteenth century (Coxe's
Tour in Monmouthshire, 1801, p. 229), giving a new impulse to the
iron trade.   This is doubtless what is referred to by a local poet,
who, writing probably about 1770 (*Report of Royal Coal Com.*, iii.
21), sings of

> "Taff's remoter vale,
> Late by the magic of Vulcanian ore
> Grown populous."

About 1755 Mr. Bacon obtained a lease for ninety years of a
tract of minerals in the neighbourhood of Merthyr Tydvil, which
was unique alike with respect to the extent of the area and the
smallness of the rental.   It measured eight miles in length and four
miles in breadth, and the rent was only £200 per annum.   It was
colloquially known as "Bacon's Mineral Kingdom."

About 1783 he leased portions of it for the remainder of the
term—Cyfartha works, the largest portion to Mr. Crawshay, for
five thousand pounds per annum; Penderyn to Mr. Homfray, at
two thousand pounds per annum; Dowlais Ironworks to Messrs.
Lewis & Tait, and a fourth part to Mr. Hill (*ib.*, p. 22; *Trans. So.
Wales Inst.*, vii. 217; Malkin's *South Wales*, 1804, p. 174).   Altogether his sub-leases were computed to yield him a rental of ten
thousand pounds per annum.

Up till the end of this century the coal mines of Monmouthshire
were in great measure shut up from general use.   At this period,
however, new life was infused into the district by the construction
of a canal from Blaenavon to Newport (Coxe's *Historical Tour*, 1801,
p. 47), begun in 1792 and finished in 1798; together with the
formation of a cast iron railway, almost simultaneously, between
the same points.   Previous to this period little or no coal had been
shipped at Newport (*Fossil Fuel*, 1835, pp. 394-95), but from this
time it made rapid progress.

Cast iron railways were coming rapidly into use in Monmouthshire at this time.   Coxe was much interested in the new method
of conveyance.   He observed the process of making a railroad near
Blaenavon.   The rail used was a bar of cast iron 4 feet long, 3
inches thick, and $1\frac{1}{2}$ inches broad.   Its ends were concave and
convex; and the rails were mortised and tenoned into each other,
and fastened at the ends to the sleeper by two wooden pegs.
Regarding a railway in operation, he observes (*Tour*, p. 231), "the
road, sometimes conveyed in a strait line, sometimes winding round
the sides of precipices, and the cars filled with coals or iron, and

gliding along occasionally without horses, impress the traveller who is unaccustomed to such spectacles with pleasing astonishment."

The iron railroads were pushed as far as the shafts (drifts ?) were worked. The longest subterraneous passage at the time of Coxe's visit (*ib.*, p. 228) was three-quarters of a mile. At this period the veins of coal and iron ore in the vicinity of most of the ironworks in Monmouthshire and Glamorganshire (*Phil. Trans.* for year 1806, p. 342) were drained and worked by levels, or horizontal drifts, advantage being taken of the deep valleys for the purpose. The greatest depth attained by pits in South Wales was about 480 feet.

As early as 1776 application was made to Messrs. Boulton and Watt for a steam engine for a coal mine in Wales (Muirhead's *Mechanical Inventions*, etc., ii. 101). But little is heard of the employment of steam engines in South Wales till a later period, doubtless on account of the shallowness of the great bulk of the mines.

To the same reason may be ascribed the great degree of immunity from firedamp which appears to have prevailed here. That this gas was not unknown in the mines is shown by the circumstance that the process of firing it had sometimes to be resorted to. In one case that we hear of (*Trans. Fed. Inst.*, vi. 242) the fireman was paid 5s. a day to examine the workings. "In the different workings to be examined, holes were sunk in the bottom just large enough to allow a man getting in and stooping down. It was his duty to examine every place, and if there was firedamp, he lighted his candle outside the danger, placed it in clay, sticking the clay on a small board to which was attached a piece of string. He then got into the hole, having on a thick flannel jacket and his head and hands covered also; and having placed a couple of small boards over his head, got as low in the hole as he could, and then drew the board with the lighted candle in to him and exploded the gas."

Among the notable improvements in coal mining introduced in the course of the eighteenth century, may be mentioned the general substitution of steam engines for horses in raising water from the mines; the adoption of gunpowder for blasting rock; the artificial ventilation of the workings by means of fire; and the coursing of the air-current through the whole of the mine to prevent accumulations of gas from taking place. Horses had also come into use in the haulage of the coal underground; and railways and four-wheeled vehicles had been to some extent substituted for the sledges previously employed.

The end of the century was marked by a general commencement

to substitute iron for wood in the construction of railways; and to apply steam engines to raise the coal out of the pits.

Regarding the depth at which coal was now being worked, we hear of pits (which, however, in some cases may not have been quite the maximum depth attained) in Staffordshire and Warwickshire, 300 feet deep; in Yorkshire, 420 feet;[1] in Shropshire, 462 feet; in South Wales, 480 feet; in Somersetshire, 500 feet; in Northumberland and Durham, 822 feet; and in Cumberland (Thwaite Pit, Whitehaven), 894 feet; while in the same coalfield a sinking (King Pit) had reached the depth of 993 feet. In the two latter coalfields the pits had attained to a maximum diameter of 12 feet. At Wallsend the pillars of coal were made 8 or 10 yards broad by 20 yards long (from 160 to 203 superficial square yards); at Whitehaven they were made from 18 to 20 yards square (from 324 to 400 superficial square yards), the latter being exactly double the area of the former. The creep was a thing almost if not altogether unknown at Whitehaven; it became a fruitful source of annoyance in the collieries of the Tyne.

The extraction of a portion of the pillars in fiery mines, by a second working, may be said to have only commenced to become a regular part of the bord-and-pillar system of working at this period; though it could only be effected after a very partial and incomplete manner so long as the miners had to depend upon the insecure light afforded by candles and steel mills. The long-wall system of working appears also to have been beginning to be more extensively adopted.

Though coal was now being employed for a variety of purposes, it was chiefly as a fuel for domestic requirements that it had for a long time been used. In the absence of exact statistics to enable a computation to be made of the total quantity of the mineral raised at this period, it has been estimated (Smyth's *Coal and Coalmining,* 1867, p. 11; *Report of the Royal Coal Commission,* 1871, iii. 32), that in 1800 the total annual production of the United Kingdom amounted to about 10,000,000 tons.

[1] The maximum depth in Farey's list (*Agriculture and Minerals of Derbyshire*, i. 213) of above 500 collieries in Derbyshire and surrounding district, made out in 1811, is at Warren Hill Furnace, on Ashby Wolds, Leicestershire, where 606 feet had then been reached.

CHAPTER XXXV.

THE NINETEENTH CENTURY. 1801-1816.

Greatly increased use of coal. Invention of gas-lighting. Formation of numerous cast iron railways. Extended use of the steam engine.

THE nineteenth century has been the great age of coal. But for coal, in enormous quantities, the civilization of the present day would be an impossibility. The coal trade might almost be said to have only commenced at the beginning of this century, the development to which it had previously attained being as nothing compared to the amazing rate with which it proceeded from this time forward.

Though there has been a large natural increase in the demand for coal for domestic purposes as well as for exportation, the vast extension of the use of the mineral which has taken place has been chiefly due to the absorbing requirements of the arts and manufactures.

Among the causes which have specially contributed to bring about this extraordinary drain upon our coal resources, a prominent place must be assigned to the general adoption of steam power. The steam engine—which might almost be called the coal engine— only became generally available in 1800, when Watt's patent privileges came to an end. From this time it entered upon a career of boundless and infinitely varied utility. Windmills, water-wheels, and horse engines—the best powers known to former days—all sank into insignificance before it. Soon every trade and industry felt the quickening influence of the new power obtained by means of coal.

While the manufacture of iron with coal was being carried on in many districts at the commencement of the century, this industry was then still only in its infancy. But such was the rapid expansion of the coal-iron manufacture in South Wales, Staffordshire, Scotland, etc., as to cause it of itself to require immense supplies of coal.

The early years of the century also witnessed the birth of an altogether fresh branch of the coal trade in the distillation of the mineral for the manufacture of gas. With this new departure it now for the first time became available as a source of light. That coal could be made to yield inflammable gas on being subjected to heat in a close vessel, had been known seemingly even in the time of Becher, or towards the close of the seventeenth century. But Dr. Clayton appears to have been the first to collect the gas so obtained, though merely as a curiosity. In the account of his investigations, which he designates "An experiment concerning the spirit of coal," communicated to the Royal Society in 1739 (*Phil. Trans.*, No. 452, p. 59; see also Sloane MSS., Brit. Mus., 4,437, 384, anno 1740), he states that his attention was drawn to the subject in connection with the natural discharge of firedamp from a ditch two miles from Wigan (the burning wells already referred to), and that he distilled coal in a retort on an open fire, filling bladders with the gas, and amusing his friends by pricking and compressing a bladder till all the spirit was compressed out. Lord Dundonald also, in 1786 (Gesner's *Coal, Petroleum*, etc., p. 15), had the gas from his coke ovens burned at the end of iron pipes for the amusement of his friends.

To William Murdock, however, a native of Old Cumnock, in Ayrshire, Scotland, who acted as superintendent of Messrs. Boulton and Watt's pumping engines in Cornwall, belongs the credit of first applying gas distilled from coal to purposes of practical utility. He is represented as having employed bladders filled with this new illuminant to light his way on dark nights over the Cornish downs, and to have occasionally scared the poor miners by giving an extra squeeze to the bladder and projecting a long flame as he passed them in the dark. From his paper, communicated by Sir Joseph Banks to the Royal Society, entitled "An Account of the Application of Gas from Coal to Economical Purposes" (read 25th February, 1808), it appears that Murdock lighted up his house at Redruth with gas in 1792; also that he fitted up gas-making apparatus at Messrs. Boulton and Watt's works, at Soho, in 1798, wherewith he illuminated the manufactory in 1802, in honour of the peace of Amiens—a sight which many spectators from Birmingham are said to have been attracted to witness; and that he likewise commenced to light up Messrs. Phillips and Lee's establishment with gas in 1805.

Meanwhile, in 1803 and 1804 (*Fossil Fuel*, p. 408), Mr. Winsor exhibited gas light in the Lyceum Theatre, London, and lectured there on the subject, and shortly afterwards (Clegg on *Coal Gas*) established the first public gas lamps in Pall Mall.

So novel was the project of lighting by means of coal gas conveyed from a central station through pipes, that the embryo industry had to run the gauntlet of considerable ridicule and opposition. Even the great Davy would appear to have doubted the feasibility of lighting towns in the manner proposed; and one member of a Parliamentary Committee is stated to have experienced considerable difficulty in grasping the idea of a light "without a wick."

The believers in gas lighting persevered, nevertheless, and in 1809 application was made to Parliament for an Act to incorporate a company, to be called the London and Westminster Chartered Gas Light and Coke Company, to carry on the operations commenced in Pall Mall. The Bill was thrown out at the time, but was granted in 1810.[1] Many difficulties were experienced during the first few years, but about 1813-14 better progress began to be made, and it was demonstrated that the lighting of towns with gas was neither impossible nor impracticable; and from this time town after town became rapidly supplied with its establishment of gasworks, gas pipes, and gas lamps, placing the means of obtaining a cheap, brilliant, and easily-managed light, at the command of every householder, and giving another onward impulse to the coal trade.

Thus the process of distilling coal was revolutionized; the gas which had formerly been a waste and useless product now becoming the chief desideratum, while the tar and other liquids evolved in the manufacture, sank into the position of residual products, some of which (*Fossil Fuel*, p. 409) were somewhat difficult to get rid of. As early as 1813, however (Hodgson's *Account of Felling Explosion*, p. 25), we hear of turpentine being distilled from coal tar; and in 1820 (Surtees's *Durham*, ii. 85), of red and black varnishes being procured from coal at Heworth manufactories, near Gateshead. There is also mention in 1816 (Holmes's *Treatise on the Coal Mines*, p. 18) of a manufactory near Sunderland, belonging to Messrs. Featherstone, similar to the one erected at Coalbrookdale by Lord Dundonald, for extracting tar, petroleum, etc., and ammonia from coal. A lamp black was also obtained in the same way as at the manufactory at Saarbruck, in Germany,—first beginnings of processes through which the utilization of the by-products of gasworks,

[1] That the introduction of gas-lighting was viewed with some degree of apprehension by the populace is curiously evidenced by the fact that one of the London theatres, in 1810, exhibited a placard bearing the words, "No gas used here" (*Col. Guard.*, 17th July, 1796, p. 130).

etc., grew in the course of time to become of itself an important industry.

The rapid expansion of the coal trade which now commenced was greatly facilitated by the general extension of the use of railways in the coal districts, enabling the produce of the collieries to be distributed more easily and economically. Overshadowed by and used as subsidiary to the canals during the great era of the construction of these "navigations" in the latter half of the eighteenth century, railways were now entering into successful rivalry with them. The canal mania had passed away; the railway was now coming into favour. The occupation of the canal constructors, or navigators, was gone; but an ample field of congenial occupation was opening up for them in the formation of railways, to which they transferred their services, preserving their original name notwithstanding their change of occupation, and continuing to be known as "navvies" to the present day.

It can scarcely be doubted that the revolution in favour of railways, was chiefly due to their improved efficiency in consequence of the transition from wood to iron which was taking place in their construction. Cast iron rails, both of the original or edge form, and also (perhaps at this period even more so) of the tram-plate form invented by Mr. Curr, were being adopted in all the newer lines— light tram rails coming especially into use in the formation of the underground railways in the mines.

The long-established wooden railway was at this period, and long afterwards, still extensively used in the Newcastle-on-Tyne district. The cost of constructing such a line, including timber, levelling, gravelling, and workmanship, is stated by Bailey, in his *Agricultural Survey of Durham*, to have been 5s. per yard, or £440 per mile. The same writer (ed. 1813, p. 34) remarks upon the change which was taking place in the substitution of iron railways for wooden ones in this district. As instances of this we hear (*Trans. N.E. Inst.*, xv. 217) of the wooden rails on the Wylam railway being taken up and replaced by plate rails of cast iron in 1808; of a metal railroad at Shilbottle (Sykes's *Loc. Rec.*, ii. 43) in 1809; of an iron railway at Benwell (*ib.*, i. 114) in 1810: cases which may be regarded merely as illustrations of the movement in substituting iron for wood which was going on in the railways of the north.

From all parts of the kingdom in like manner we hear of the construction of cast iron railways proceeding.

The Surrey Iron Railway Company was incorporated, in 1801, for making a railway from Wandsworth to Croydon. A continuation of this line, known as the Croydon, Merstham, and Godstone Railway, was constructed in 1803 (*Popular Encyclopedia*, art. Railways). It ran by the side of the Brighton road to Merstham, and thence to Reigate. Tram rails were used (Wood's *Railroads*, 2nd ed., p. x.).

In Yorkshire an iron railway was constructed from Middleton collieries to the town of Leeds (*Fossil Fuel*, 426) under an Act of Parliament obtained in 1803. In South Wales a railway was constructed from Merthyr to Cardiff, almost as early as the line from Blaenavon to Newport, having been in operation previous to 1804. In the Forest of Dean the construction of an extensive system of tramways was authorized by Act of Parliament in 1809 and 1810 (Nicholls's *Forest of Dean*, p. 198). While an agricultural report on Lancashire (p. 67) speaks of the existence of extensive cast iron railways at the collieries in 1815.

Scotland likewise was beginning to adopt the iron railway. In 1812 (Bremner's *Industries of Scotland*, p. 81) a railway was opened from the Duke of Portland's collieries at Kilmarnock to his harbour at Troon. And in an account of Dunfermline, published in 1815 (by John Fernie, p. 116), we are informed that "within these five years coals have been sent to the Forth, for exportation, on cast iron railways; and this mode of conveyance now saves the labour of not fewer than one hundred horses."

The above records serve to exhibit how widespread was the adoption of the iron railway during the early years of the century. The movement was not confined to the surface, but was proceeding underground in the mines as well. Thus, at Whitehaven, at the time of Daniell's visit in 1813 (*Voyage Round Great Britain*, ii. 151), there were twenty miles of iron railway underground.

This was peculiarly the era of cast iron railways; wrought iron not having yet become sufficiently cheap and abundant to be used. In one instance only do we hear of light rails of the latter material being applied. In 1808 (*Proc. Arch. Inst.*, Newcastle, 1852, i. 198; Wood's *Railways*, 2nd ed., p. 43) wrought iron bars $1\frac{1}{2}$ inches square were laid down at the Earl of Carlisle's Colliery at Tindale Fell. It has been said that in 1815 (*Trans. N.E. Inst.*, xv. 223) rails of the same material were introduced underground by Benjamin Thompson, at Ouston Colliery, on the Wear. This, however, is erroneous as, according to his own account (*Inventions, Improvements*, etc., pp. 28-31), the rails which he introduced there in 1816 were cast iron edge rails for the underground rolleys to run upon, in lieu of the tram plates previously used. It was not till a later period that the employment of wrought iron in railway construction began to make some headway. During the first twenty or twenty-five years of the century, rails of cast iron were universally employed. Whether of the plate or edge form, they were usually made in lengths of about 4 ft., and were dove-tailed together at the joints in a variety of ways.

Cast iron rails still continued in use on some of the older private railways in the North of England in 1863 (*Industrial Resources of the Tyne*, etc., 2nd ed., p. 324) ; and a few of them, resembling modern furnace bars, may perchance be seen in the less-used sidings of such a railway even at the present day. In this district also, where the wooden railway attained by far its largest development, this old-time appliance died a lingering death, being still in operation as late as 1860 (*ib.*, p. 27) ; having been used in the conveyance of coal during a period extending over two centuries.

Simultaneously with the spread of the iron railway, the steam engine was being brought into more and more extended use. The Newcomen engine was still the machine most generally employed. So long as the pressure of steam used in condensing engines continued to be very low (at this period it was from 2 to 4 pounds per square inch above the pressure of the atmosphere), and nearly all the power obtained from the vacuum, this machine held its ground in situations where a cheap and abundant supply of coal could be obtained, which was of course particularly the case at the collieries themselves, where the small coal in this era was of such little account as to be largely burnt in order to be got rid of. At the newer and deeper sinkings, however, where the best and most efficient engine that could be obtained was desiderated, Boulton and Watt's improved engine was gradually coming to be adopted. The high-pressure engine (or "puffer") also, was brought forward by Trevithick immediately on the expiration of Watt's patent rights,. in 1800 ; and on account of its great simplicity and cheapness soon came into some degree of favour.

The application of steam engines to the drawing of the coals out of the pits, which was commenced, as we have seen, towards the close of the last century, continued to proceed apace in all the coalfields in the early part of the present one.

Winding steam engines, which Bailey speaks of as lately introduced (*Agriculture of Durham*, p. 33 ; Mackenzie's *Northumberland*, p. 193), were superseding the horse-gins in which, in the deeper Durham pits, eight horses were frequently employed, many horses being dispensed with in consequence. The clumsy water-coal-gins, which for a short period had been so much in vogue, likewise speedily gave way to the simple rotary steam engine.

Among the steam engines employed drawing coal in the Newcastle-on-Tyne neighbourhood, several of Trevithick's high-pressure engines were at work at an early date. Writing on 23rd September, 1804 (*Life of Trevithick*, by F. Trevithick, ii. 3), he observes : " At Newcastle I found four engines at work, and four more nearly ready ; six of these were for winding coal, one for lifting water, and one for grinding corn." A high-pressure whim engine for winding coal was also set to work at one of Lord Dudley's pits (doubtless in the South Staffordshire coalfield) in the same year (*ib.*, i. 170).

Writing in 1811, Farey, in his *Agriculture and Minerals of Derbyshire* (i. 188, 338), speaks of coal-winding steam engines as being now extremely common. What kind of engines they were he does not specify ; but he remarks (*ib.*, p. 339) that he " met with no pumping engine on Bolton and Watt's principle at a coal pit ; the old atmospheric engine, well contrived and executed, being thought to answer better in such situations."

Steam engines were also in use in Leicestershire, in 1807 (*Beauties of England and Wales*), for drawing up the coals, as well as for draining the mines. While in the Forest of Dean, we hear of a number of steam engines being erected at the collieries in 1811 and subsequent years (Nicholls, p. 93).

The foregoing evidence may sufficiently indicate how widely extended the use of the steam engine in drawing coal was now becoming, in addition to its former work of raising water. It was likewise beginning to be put to other duties.[1] Among these was the employment of fixed engines for hauling coal wagons on railways by means of ropes.

Mr. Curr, of Sheffield, was the first to employ fixed steam engines in hauling wagons, though the application was made in the north of England. About 1805 (Dunn's *Coal Trade*, p. 52), this gentleman applied one to raise the coals from the valley at Birtley, near Gateshead, to the high grounds at Black Fell.

This was followed, in 1808 (*ib.* ; Wood's *Railroads*, 2nd ed., p. 102), by a great scheme on the part of Mr. S. Cook, of the firm of Harrison, Cook & Co., of conveying the coals from Urpeth or Bewick Main Colliery to the River Tyne, over the heights of Ayton Banks,

[1] Mr. Buddle states (*1830 Report*, p. 316) that the first engine underground was introduced in 1804, for what purpose he does not say. But we have seen that an engine for pumping had been placed in a Whitehaven mine considerably earlier than this.

by a succession of inclined planes, partly wrought by fixed steam engines. It appears to have excited a considerable amount of public interest, a concourse of 10,000 people (Sykes's *Loc. Rec.*) assembling on 17th May, 1809, to witness the inauguration of the haulage; when four wagons of small coals were brought up the first plane by the steam engine, amid discharges of artillery, to the great admiration of the spectators.

In the following year (*ib.*, ii. 54), Mr. Cook started a self-acting inclined plane between Bewicke Main Colliery and the Tyne, with a rope 1,600 yards long, on which fifty wagons of coal were run in an hour at a speed of ten miles an hour. The practicability of the scheme was fully established, but the cost so far exceeded expectation as to prove the ruin of the company, and cause the concern to change hands.

The employment of fixed engines in the haulage of coal wagons subsequently came into extensive use at the northern collieries, and continues to be practised on some of the private railways at the present day.

Meanwhile, attempts were being made to apply the steam engine to still more novel and important uses, an account of which will form the subject of the following chapter.

CHAPTER XXXVI.

THE NINETEENTH CENTURY. 1801-1816.

Invention of the locomotive engine. Steam navigation.

THE idea of employing the steam engine to propel carriages and boats was entertained as early as the time of Papin, and various attempts to carry it out were made during the course of the eighteenth century. Watt himself, who was no believer in steam locomotion, built a steam carriage (Muirhead's *Life of Watt*, 2nd ed., p. 445), "to try if God will work a miracle in favour of these carriages."

Notwithstanding that these early attempts led to no satisfactory result, individuals were not wanting who took a hopeful view of the situation, and were confident that this desirable consummation would eventually be attained; as witnessed by the well-known prophetic lines of Dr. Erasmus Darwin, in 1789 :

> "Soon shall thy arm, Unconquer'd Steam ! afar
> Drag the slow barge, or drive the rapid car."

But the era of steam locomotion and steam navigation properly commences from the expiration of Watt's patent privileges in 1800.

In the former field Trevithick occupies a foremost position; though it is indisputable that he was greatly indebted to his predecessor Murdock. The vacuum engines of Newcomen and Watt, with their beams and condensing apparatus, were alike only adapted for working in a fixed position. But when Trevithick stripped Watt's double-acting engine of these cumbersome appendages, and brought the high-pressure engine or "puffer" into use, a vast stride in the direction of applying the machine to locomotive purposes was at once effected. Thus simplified, the steam engine was almost prepared to run a race ; the iron horse was already half created.

Having previously built and experimented with several steam carriages on common roads, on the 24th of March, 1802, Trevithick, in conjunction with his friend Vivian, obtained a patent for improvements in steam engines, and their application to propelling carriages, etc., for a term of fourteen years. Mr. Davies Gilbert (or Giddy),

FIG. 29.—MURDOCK'S MODEL OF A STEAM CARRIAGE, 1784.

at one time president of the Royal Society, who took much interest in the infant locomotive, in a letter to the Rev. R. Polewhele, dated 1802 (Polewhele's *Cornwall*, iv. 137 note), refers to it in the following terms :

"Mr. Richard Trevithick has obtained a patent for moving carriages by steam. His machine consists of a fireplace, boiler, and cylinder, suspended near the centre of a wagon, from whence the power is transferred to the wheels by means of toothwork and cranks. If this contrivance answer the expectation of many persons well-informed on mechanical subjects, it will become of great national importance ; and assisted by iron-railed roads may prove eminently useful to the mining district of Cornwall, where a sum little short of a thousand pounds a week is now paid for transporting copper-ore and coals to the sea-coast and the mines."

This is the earliest allusion known to the writer to the application of a steam locomotive on a railway ; and clearly evidences that already far-seeing persons had begun to appreciate the possibilities which lay before the iron horse on the iron road.

The project was not suffered to remain long in abeyance, and it is somewhat singular that it should have been at Coalbrookdale, where the first iron rails were laid, that the first essay to apply a steam locomotive on them should also have been made. But this pioneer railway locomotive only appears as a shadow flitting across the page of history. It is merely mentioned in a letter from Trevithick to Mr. Gilbert, dated 22nd August, 1802 (*Life of Trevithick*, i. 155), wherein he informs him that the Dale Company had begun a carriage at their own cost for the railroads, and were forcing it with all expedition. We have no further information regarding it.

Of the career of the next railway locomotive a sufficiently substantial and detailed account is extant. This was built by Trevithick himself at Pen-y-darran, in South Wales, in 1803-4, and there was a bet of 500 guineas upon it; Mr. Hill, a gentleman living in the neighbourhood, having staked that amount against the possibility of conveying a load of iron on the railway from Merthyr to the canal basin by means of a steam locomotive. The engine was completed and a few preliminary trips made with it over part of the line, in the middle of February, 1804, when it was found to work well and to be more manageable than horses, and to have plenty of steam and power. But it was discovered to be much too strong for the work; and it was resolved after the first few days not to employ it permanently on the railway, but to utilize it to work a hammer: Trevithick intending to build a smaller engine for the railway work.

The journey which was to decide the wager on this patent iron cart-horse, was made on February 21, 1804, when the locomotive drew a train of five wagons, carrying 10 tons of iron, and seventy men, the whole distance of nine miles. The time occupied was four hours and five minutes, but several trees had to be cut down, and large rocks removed; the engine, when actually working, going nearly five miles an hour. The gentleman who made the bet rode the whole of the journey with Trevithick (*ib.*, i. 162), and was satisfied that he had lost.

The down run was quite a triumph for Trevithick, but the up run did not prove quite so successful. After about four miles of the homeward journey had been traversed, one of the small bolts that fastened the axle to the boiler broke, and all the water ran out of the boiler, causing the return of the engine to be delayed till the following evening. Whether Mr. Hill paid the bill, the writer cannot certify.

This locomotive, or travelling engine, as Trevithick begins to call it, made two more journeys to the shipping place, conveying a load of 10 tons of iron each time. During the third journey it went off the road, and broke both axles. This brought its

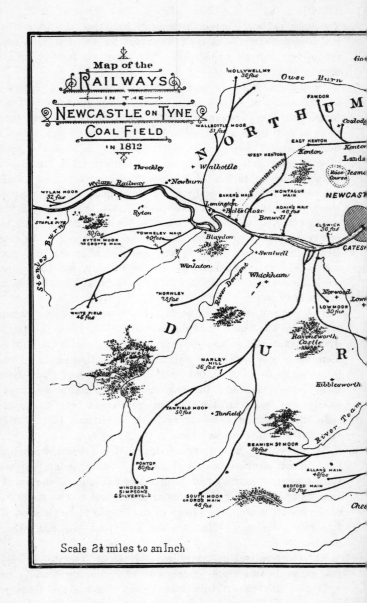

Map of the
RAILWAYS
IN THE
NEWCASTLE ON TYNE
COAL FIELD
IN 1812

Scale 2½ miles to an Inch

MURTON MAIN
45 fms

SHIREMOOR

LONG BENTON
105 fms

WILLINGTON
127 fms

LAND

ingworth Railway

North

Tynemouth

Sea

N° Shields

COLLINGWOOD
Main

S° Shields

PERCY MAIN
119 fms

GE MAIN
90 fms

WALLSEND
105 fms

FLATWORTH

TEMPLE
MANOR WALLSEND

RIVER TYNE

TEMPLE MAIN
126 fms

ALKER
00 fms

HEBBURN MAIN
132 fms

Jarrow

Monkton

River Don

Hurton

Whitburn

West
Boldon

M

Deep Part
of the
Coal Field

Monkwearmouth

ING
sir
+ Hepworth

NC MP

A

Great
Usworth

SWORTH
USSELS MAIN

RECTORY MAIN
77 fms

Washington

River Wear

SUNDERLAND

CLOBE
70 fms

WENTWORTH
70 fms
MILBANK &
BOUNDARY MAIN
75 fms

68 fms

WHARTON

PEARTH MAIN
60 fms

ARRATON
70 fms

60 fms
BIDDICK MAIN

EDEN MAIN
60 fms
HUTTON SEAM

Silksworth

Ryhope

LAMBTON MAIN
60 fms

BOURN MOOR
63 fms

PRIMROSE M°
60 fms

NEWBOTTLE
BOURN MOOR
60 fms

Magnesian Limestone
(overlying Coal Measures)

LUMLEY
80 fms

RAINTON
OR OLD DUCKS

Houghton le Spring

Seaham

short and chequered career as a locomotive to an end. It was brought back to Pen-y-darran by horses, and converted into a stationary engine.

Imperfect as this early locomotive was, with its cast iron boiler, single cylinder, and flywheel, the difficulties with which its working was attended were more due to extraneous causes than to the machine itself. There were heavy gradients and sharp curves on the railway. The weight of the engine broke many of the cast iron rails; and the hooks between the wagons likewise frequently gave way. We do not hear of Trevithick proceeding with the construction of the smaller engine he had in contemplation, nor of any further attempts being made to apply steam locomotion on the Merthyr railway; the experiments which had been made having doubtless sufficiently demonstrated that the road was not well adapted for this method of haulage.

Trevithick appears now to have turned his attention to the Newcastle-on-Tyne district. During his visit there, already referred to, in the autumn of 1804, he must have made arrangements relative to the building of locomotives, inasmuch as he speaks in one of his letters (*ib.*, i. 173) of going to Newcastle, in February, 1805, with the expectation of finding "some of the travelling engines at work." We know that a locomotive was actually built there about this time. There is also a record relating to plans of the first Newcastle locomotive engine, comprising—(1) well-executed perspective views of the engine from various points; (2) drawings of wagon engine, October 3, 1804; (3) regulating and throttle cocks for engine No. 1, September 17, 1804. The engine was constructed at Mr. Whinfield's (or Whitfield's) foundry, Gateshead; the engineer being one John Steel, who is stated to have worked at the making of the locomotive engine at Pen-y-darran. Whinfield was a sort of agent of Trevithick (see *Life of Trevithick*, vol. i., pp. 183, 186, 187; *Mining Journal*, October 2, 1858; Jeaffreson and Pole's *Life of Robert Stephenson*, i. 24).

This locomotive was intended for Mr. Blackett, the owner of Wylam Colliery, who had a railway, already referred to, five miles in length, for the conveyance of his coals to the navigable part of the Tyne. Mr. Robert Wilson—a Newcastle engineer, who himself subsequently effected a highly important improvement in the loco-motive—inspected the engine, and has left the following curious notice relating to it, which may be seen in the Patent Museum at South Kensington, where it is specified to be a "Copy from R. W.'s memorandums on steam engines":

"Memorandum May 1, 1885.—I saw an engine this day upon a new plan it is to draw three waggons of coals upon the wylam waggon-way the road is nearly leavle the Engine is to travile with the waggons each waggon with the coals weighs about three-and-a-half tons and the Engine weighs four-and-a-half tons the Engine is to work without a vacume. The cylinder is seven inches diameter three feet stroke and is placed inside the Boilar and the fire is inside also the spead they Expect to travle at is four miles Per houre.

ROBT. WILSON."

A temporary railway was laid down in the foundry yard for the trial of the engine, which ran backwards and forwards quite well in the presence of several gentlemen. But it never left the works. For some cause (probably on account of his railway being a weak wooden one at this time), Mr. Blackett did not take it, and it was converted into a stationary engine, and set to blow a cupola in the foundry. Mr. Wood refers to this engine (*Railroads*, 1831, pp. 128, 129), but supposes it to have been sent to the north by Trevithick.

FIG. 30.—TREVITHICK'S LOCOMOTIVE, "CATCH-ME-WHO-CAN," 1808.

Thus Trevithick failed in his attempts to introduce the steam locomotive on the railways of South Wales and Newcastle alike, and for some years nothing more is heard of it, Trevithick being engaged upon other work. But in 1808 he made another effort to turn his patent to account. He constructed a circular railway at London within an enclosure, on which he exhibited a locomotive; the public being admitted to the enclosure at a charge of a shilling each, which included a ride in the carriage attached to the engine for those who

were not too timid.   The engine was named "Catch-me-who-can,"
at the suggestion of a sister of Mr. Davies Gilbert (*Life of Trevithick*,
i. 192).   But after continuing in operation for some weeks the
enterprise was brought to an abrupt conclusion.   A rail broke, the
engine went off at a tangent and was overturned.   The affair had
not proved a pecuniary success, and the engine was not again set on
the rails.   Thus ended Trevithick's attempts to introduce steam
locomotion

Fig. 31.—Trevithick's Circular Railway at London, 1808.

Only six years of Trevithick's patent had yet expired, and had he
held on a little longer his fate might have been very different.
Just a year after he had abandoned his pet scheme of steam locomotion, an opportunity was offered him of introducing his locomotive
at Newcastle.   Though Mr. Blackett, of Wylam, had for some
reason declined to take the locomotive made for him in 1805, he
appears never to have given up the idea of ultimately adopting this
means of haulage in lieu of horses on his wagonway, which indeed
was particularly well suited for it.   Having reconstructed his railway by taking up the wooden rails and substituting cast iron plate

rails, he wrote to Trevithick (*Who Invented the Locomotive?* by O. D. Hedley; *Life of Trevithick,* i. 196) on the subject of an engine in 1809. In his reply Trevithick stated that he was engaged in other pursuits, and having declined the business could render no assistance. Thus Mr. Blackett's desire to adopt steam locomotion on his railway received another check.

Notwithstanding the seemingly unpromising position of the iron horse at this period, the patentee himself having turned it adrift, a brighter prospect for it soon began to open out. It now found a patron in the neighbourhood of Leeds, in Mr. John Blenkinsop, coal viewer at Middleton Colliery. From a correspondence which appeared in the *Newcastle Weekly Chronicle,* July 10th to October 2nd, 1880, and was afterwards printed in pamphlet form by Mr. George Lovejoy, Reading (who was so good as to favour the writer with a copy), we learn that Blenkinsop was a native of Walker, near Newcastle. He was a cousin and pupil of Mr. Thomas Barnes, the able viewer of Walker Colliery and the pits belonging to the Brandling family. On the death of Barnes in 1801, or shortly afterwards, Blenkinsop was appointed viewer of the collieries of Charles Brandling, Esq., at Middleton, near Leeds.

It was doubtless under Blenkinsop's administration that the iron railway connecting the collieries with the town of Leeds was constructed, under the Act of Parliament obtained in 1803, to supersede the previously existing wooden railway in accordance with the times. For some years after this, the haulage of the coal wagons continued to be performed by horses. Conceiving, however, that this work might be effected more economically by means of a steam locomotive, Blenkinsop—aided, according to Mr. Dunn (*Coal Trade,* p. 52), by the advice and suggestions of Mr. John Straker—succeeded in devising an admirable scheme for the purpose; and on 10th April, 1811, obtained a patent for "certain mechanical means by which the conveyance of coals, minerals and other articles is facilitated, and the expense is rendered less than heretofore." No form of locomotive engine is included in Blenkinsop's patent, Trevithick and Vivian's patent for the application of the high-pressure engine to propelling carriages extending forward till the year 1816, but the steam engine is mentioned as the motive power most suitable for the purpose.

The part of Blenkinsop's scheme which he patented consisted in the use of a rack-rail fixed in the centre of the railway, or forming part of the rails on one side; and the locomotive was designed to drive a pinion wheel working in the rack-rail, thus propelling itself

and the train attached to it.   The application of the rack enabled a
comparatively light engine to haul a heavy train of wagons, and to
ascend gradients which Trevithick's engine could not have sur-
mounted.

Blenkinsop employed Messrs. Fenton, Murray, & Wood, engineers,
Leeds, to build his locomotives, and this firm wrote to Trevithick
(*Life of Trevithick,* i. 237, 238) regarding his engine, and obtained a
drawing from him, and also paid for licence to erect engines under
the patent.   But in the Blenkinsop locomotive, not to mention its
wrought iron boiler, an immense improvement was made upon Trevithick's.   This consisted in the employment of *two steam engines*
working together and assisting each other, a regular and steady
action being thus obtainable without the use of a flywheel, and at
the same time power to start at any point.   This was the first
great improvement made in the mechanism of the locomotive.

Fig. 32.—Blenkinsop's Locomotive, 1812.

Blenkinsop's first engine (as appears from his own statement
quoted hereafter) commenced working on the railway from Middleton Colliery to Leeds in June, 1812.   Thousands of people assembled
to witness the trial of the new machine (*Mining Almanack for 1849,*
p. 370), which was "crowned with complete success."   From this
time Leeds was regularly supplied with coal by the steam locomotive.

In one of the plates of the *Costumes of Yorkshire*, published by Robinson at Leeds in 1813, in which a Yorkshire collier is portrayed, a Blenkinsop locomotive is shown hauling a train of coal wagons, and is thus referred to :

"In the background of the annexed plate is a delineation of the steam engine lately invented by Mr. Blenkinsopp, agent at the colliery of Charles Brandling, Esq., near Leeds, which conveys above twenty waggons loaded with coals from the pits to Leeds. By two of these machines constantly employed, the labour of at least fourteen horses is saved."

Blenkinsop's locomotive engines continued to work at Leeds (Wood's *Railroads*, 2nd ed., p. 359 ; *Fossil Fuel*, p. 426) for a period of twenty years. By the substitution of steam locomotion for horses, the cost of haulage was reduced to one-sixth of its previous amount.

Regarding his engines and their performances, Blenkinsop stated (Partington's *Steam Engine*, 2nd ed., p. 43) that an engine with two 8-inch cylinders weighed 5 tons, and drew twenty-seven wagons, weighing 94 tons, on a dead level, at three and a-half miles per hour, or 15 tons up an ascent of 2 inches in the yard ; when lightly loaded it travelled at ten miles an hour ; did the work of sixteen horses in twelve hours ; and cost £400.

Blenkinsop having made steam locomotion a practical success, was soon followed by numerous imitators, who took out patents forthwith for various methods of employing this mode of haulage without the use of his rack-rail. Indeed the different schemes which were on foot to effect locomotion by steam, causes the year 1813 to be a memorable one in the history of the invention. In the Newcastle-on-Tyne district Messrs. Chapman constructed an engine (patented December 30, 1812) designed to pull itself forward by means of a chain stretched along the road, which was tried (Wood's *Railroads*, 2nd ed., p. 130 ; Dunn's *Coal Trade*, p. 52) on Heaton Colliery railway;[1] and Mr. William Hedley, viewer of Mr. Blackett's colliery at Wylam, brought out an engine to work after the same manner as Trevithick's (patented March 13, 1813), which was applied on the Wylam Colliery railway; while in Derbyshire, Mr. William Brunton, of Butterley Ironworks, constructed an engine (patented May 22, 1813), designed to push itself forward by means of legs, or levers, projecting behind, which was tried at Crich limeworks (*Repertory of*

[1] Messrs. Chapman's apparatus was subsequently extensively adopted for haulage purposes on canals, working cross-river ferries, etc. (See *Min. Jour.*, xviii. 222).

Arts, vol. xxiv.), and two years later (Sykes's *Loc. Rec.,* ii. 92), at Newbottle Colliery, Durham.

The only one of the above schemes that came to anything was Hedley's. It appears that Hedley first turned his attention to steam locomotion in October, 1812 (*Who Invented the Locomotive?* by O. D. Hedley, p. 35; *Life of Trevithick,* i. 202), at the request of Mr. Blackett. Hedley's first engine is stated to have been built by one Thomas Waters, an ironfounder in Gateshead. In was almost an exact copy of Trevithick's engine, having a cast iron boiler, and a single cylinder, with a flywheel. Like it, also, it had smooth wheels, Hedley having satisfied himself, by some experiments which he made, that the Wylam Railway was strong enough to carry a locomotive of sufficient weight to drag the coal wagons simply by the adhesion of its wheels to the rails. In one respect, however, this engine differed from Trevithick's, in having a straight fire-tube, with the result that it went badly, being short of steam ("William Hedley," Newcastle, 1882, p. 13). Another engine was then constructed, having a boiler of wrought iron provided with Trevithick's return fire-tube, which was found to be an improvement. A short time after it commenced it regularly drew eight loaded coal wagons at the speed of four or five miles an hour. For some time the whole of the coals were taken down the Wylam Railway by a locomotive with a single cylinder (Wood's *Railroads,* 2nd ed., p. 134), though not without much trouble and inconvenience being experienced. An early Wylam locomotive, known as "Puffing Billy," is preserved in the Patent Museum at South Kensington.[1]

An event calculated to promote a more favourable impression of steam locomotion in the north of England than the performance of Hedley's engine at Wylam, was the arrival from Leeds, in 1813, of one of Blenkinsop's locomotives with two steam engines, to work on the Kenton and Coxlodge collieries railway. The great interest taken in the trial of this locomotive, on September 2, 1813, is evidenced by the following notice of it (Sykes's *Loc. Rec.,* ii. 74), which appeared in the local papers at the time :

"An ingenious and highly interesting experiment was performed in the presence of a vast concourse of spectators, on the railway

[1] To lessen the breakage of the cast-iron rails, the Wylam locomotive was at one time upon eight wheels. (See a drawing of it, given by Mr. Hedley to Partington, published as a frontispiece in the second edition of his *Account of the Steam Engine,* and a description of the same at page 177). There is another version of the name of the Wylam locomotive which the writer has heard in the neighbourhood, viz., that it was there known as the "puffing dilly," or devil.

leading from the collieries of Kenton and Coxlodge, near Newcastle, by the application of a steam engine constructed by Messrs. Fenton, Murray, & Wood, of Leeds, under the direction of Mr. John Blenkinsop, the patentee, for the purpose of drawing the coal wagons. About one o'clock the new invention was set agoing, having attached to it sixteen chaldron wagons loaded with coals, each wagon with its contents weighing 4 tons or thereabouts, making altogether an aggregate weight little short of 70 tons. Upon perfectly level road, the machine so charged, it was computed would travel at the rate of three and a-half miles per hour, but in the present instance its speed was short of that, owing, no doubt, to some partial ascents in the railway. Under all the circumstances, it was very highly approved of and its complete success anticipated. After the experiment was finished a large party of gentlemen connected with coal mining partook of an excellent dinner provided at the grand stand for the occasion, when the afternoon was spent in the most agreeable and convivial manner."

That the owners of Killingworth Colliery were represented among the large party of gentlemen who partook of the excellent dinner at the grand stand on the above occasion, may well be imagined. This colliery was situated in the near neighbourhood of Kenton and Coxlodge, and was one of the collieries belonging to the great company consisting of Sir Thomas Henry Liddell (Lord Ravensworth) and partners, already mentioned as known by the name of the Grand Allies. At Killingworth George Stephenson at this time held the position of colliery engineer, or chief enginewright; a post to which he was appointed in 1812.

There is a story that the boiler of Blenkinsop's engine shortly after blew up (*Trans. N.E. Inst.*, xv. 221 ; Smiles's *Life of George Stephenson*), and there was an end of it. The writer has not been able to discover any foundation for the tale. On the contrary, notices are extant relative to its continuing at work for some time afterwards. Thus it is referred to in the following letter, sent by Blenkinsop, along with a drawing of his engine, to the editor of the *Monthly Magazine* (vol. xxxvii., p. 394), which furnishes some interesting information regarding the locomotives on his construction which were at work in the early part of the year 1814 :

"Sir,—Permit me to lay before the public, through the medium of your very valuable publication, a sketch, with a description, of the patent steam carriage, which gives great facility to the conveyance of coals, minerals, and other articles, and is attended with a very material saving in the expense. (Here follows sketch and description.)

"The engine used on the railroad at Leeds is 4-horses power, being the most powerful one used at present, and is so constructed that by the operating aid of cranks (fixed at right angles) it puts in motion a cogged wheel, acting in teeth cast on one side of the railroad itself, or a separate rack, by which a considerable propelling power is given to the machine; a power so considerable that when the carriage is lightly loaded it travels at the rate of ten miles an hour, but when loaded with thirty coal wagons, which is frequently the case, each weighing 3½ tons, it is propelled on a dead level at the rate of three and a-half miles an hour.

"The use of these steam carriages has given the greatest satisfaction, and they promise to be attended with the most beneficial effects, particularly as it is clearly ascertained that at least five-sixths of the expenses of conveying goods by horses will be saved by the invention.

"The steam carriage has been fully employed at Leeds since June 1812, and, to the satisfaction of the patentee, was not impeded even during the great falls of snow in January last; and more waggons of coals were conveyed to Leeds in that severe month, by the locomotive engine, than in any preceding one by horses.

"Any gentleman wishing to see the performance of the steam carriage will be much gratified by visiting Middleton Colliery, Leeds, Yorkshire; Orrell Colliery, Wigan, Lancashire; or Kenton and Coxlodge Collieries, near Newcastle-on-Tyne, where they are daily at work.   JOHN BLENKINSOP.

"Middleton Hall, near Leeds.
        March 26, 1814."

From a statement of Farey, belonging to the following month (*Agriculture and Minerals of Derbyshire*, iii. 339; see also *Practical Mechanic's Journal*, iii. 226), it would appear that more engines on Blenkinsop's construction were then under order for the Newcastle-on-Tyne district. This writer speaks of "Mr. John Blenkinsop's patent 'Iron Horses,' which are made by Messrs. Murray and Wood, of Leeds, that have been more than 2 years at work at Middleton Colliery 2 m. S. of Leeds; to which place one of them daily brings 400 tons of coal or more; at Willington Colliery, near Newcastle, one of them has been some time in work, and two others are now making (April 1814) for the same Coal-master."

A few months later, in Thompson's *Annals of Philosophy* for

September, 1814 (vol. iv., p. 232), there is a note relating to two kinds of steam locomotives working at Newcastle, one with a rack and the other without it; the one with the rack being considered best.

The foregoing notices sufficiently establish the fact that Blenkinsop's locomotive did not vanish again soon after its arrival at Newcastle, but certainly continued at work from September 1813 to September 1814, and was considered the best locomotive there at the latter date: a state of matters very different from the impression conveyed by the baseless assertion that it blew up shortly after its arrival, and there was an end of it.

That Blenkinsop's locomotive was widely known is indicated by the reference made to it by Sir Richard Phillips, in his *Morning's Walk from London to Kew*, published in 1817, where (pp. 72-76), in alluding to the Surrey iron railway from Croydon to Wandsworth, he remarks that "a heavy sigh escaped me as I thought of the inconceivable millions which have been spent about Malta, four or five of which might have been the means of extending *double lines of iron railways* from London to Edinburgh, Glasgow, Holyhead, Milford, Falmouth, Yarmouth, Dover, and Portsmouth. A reward of a single thousand would have supplied coaches, and other vehicles of various degrees of speed, with the best tackle for readily turning out; and we might, ere this, have witnessed our mail coaches running at the rate of ten miles an hour, drawn by a single horse, or impelled fifteen miles by Blenkinsop's steam-engine!"

It must have been within a few months after Blenkinsop's locomotive commenced to work on the Kenton and Coxlodge Railway, that Lord Ravensworth & Co. determined to adopt steam locomotion on the Killingworth Railway.

It was in the early part of the year 1814, according to Mr. Wood (*Railroads*, 2nd ed., p. 134), that Mr. George Stephenson constructed his first locomotive. In doing so he closely followed the design of Blenkinsop's one, employing a cylindrical boiler of wrought iron, with an internal wrought-iron fire-tube passing through it; two steam engines, with their cylinders placed one in front of the other on the top of the boiler, and partly let into it; together with crossheads and connecting rods to work the propelling gear—the engines being on the second motion. At this point, however, he took the opportunity to deviate from Blenkinsop's plan; and avoiding the patent pinion and rack-rail arrangement, made use of smooth wheels as Trevithick and Hedley had done.

Stephenson's locomotive, which he called "My Lord" (Fordyce's *Coal and Iron*, p. 84), was tried on the Killingworth Railway on the

25th July, 1814 [1] (Wood's *Railroads*, 2nd ed., p. 134). Two days later (*ib.*, p. 136) it was tried upon a piece of road with edge rails ascending about one in 450; and was found to drag after it, exclusive of its own weight, eight loaded carriages, weighing altogether about thirty tons, at the rate of four miles an hour; and after that time continued regularly at work.

On account of the great noise and considerable jerks with which the working of the spur-gearing was attended, Stephenson shortly afterwards abandoned it, and attached the connecting rods of the engines to pins on the driving wheels, making use either of rods or

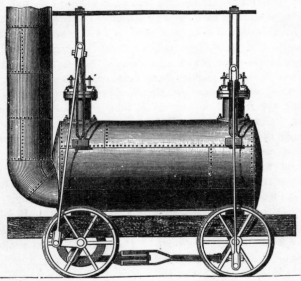

FIG. 33.—DODDS & STEPHENSON'S LOCOMOTIVE, 1815.

an endless chain to communicate between the two axletrees (Wood's *Railroads*, pp. 137, 138). This arrangement was patented by Messrs. Dodds & Stephenson, Feb. 20, 1815. A patent was also obtained by Messrs. Losh & Stephenson, in 1816, for a system of steam piston

[1] In after life Mr. Stephenson appears to have imagined that this locomotive was built two years earlier. "The first locomotive that I made," he is reported to have said at the meeting in Newcastle on the opening of Newcastle and Darlington Railway, in 1844, "was at Killingworth Colliery, and with Lord Ravensworth's money. Yes! Lord Ravensworth and partners were the first to entrust me with money to make a locomotive engine. That engine was made thirty-two years ago, and we call it 'My Lord'" (Fordyce's *Coal and Iron*, p. 84).

springs; but this being found open to numerous objections, steel springs were adopted at the suggestion of Mr. Nicholas Wood.

Stephenson's locomotives, however, failed to give much satisfaction, and in a number of instances were rejected after trial. By the abandonment of the spur-gearing, the two engines became more dissociated from each other than in the Blenkinsop locomotive, with the result that more or less slipping of the wheels took place at every stroke of the pistons (Wood's *Railroads*, 2nd ed., pp. 144, 314). Mr. Wood estimated the loss from this source at about one-third of the power of the locomotive (*ib.*, p. 317).

In 1816 a locomotive was purchased at Newcastle by Mr. Buddle to work on the railways at Whitehaven collieries (*Trans. Cumberland and Westmoreland Ant. and Arch. Soc.*, iii. 308), but its weight was found to be too much for the cast-iron rails, and after being tried for some time its use was discontinued.[1] Another was procured from Mr. Stephenson, in 1819, to work on the Duke of Portland's railway from Kilmarnock to Troon, but it also is stated (Bremner's *Industries of Scotland*, p. 81) to have proved a failure. The abandonment of three of the locomotives, supplied a few years later by Mr. Stephenson to work on the Hetton Colliery Railway, will be adverted to hereafter. Hedley's engine was only employed on the Wylam Railway.

Though, viewed from the standpoint of the present day, Blenkinsop's rack-rail arrangement may seem amusingly primitive, it cannot be doubted that his was the most compact and efficient of the early locomotives, and best adapted to suit the cast-iron railway period. It was Blenkinsop's locomotive and rack-rail which Thomas Gray—an earnest advocate for the general use of railways—proposed to employ, in his pamphlet issued in 1820, entitled *Observations on a General Iron Railway, or Land Steam Conveyance, to Supersede the Necessity of Horses in all Public Vehicles*; and in which he also suggested the construction of "the first link" between the towns of Manchester and Liverpool; a project which appears to have originated with Mr. James in 1803.

The rack-rail principle is still adhered to in the exceptional case of steep mountain railways.

The early history of steam locomotion has been distorted in an extraordinary manner by the biographers and partizans of different engineers. Notwithstanding the extravagant claims which have

---

[1] A Mr. Taylor Swainson is stated (*Trans. Fed. Inst.*, vii. 632) to have built a locomotive engine at Whitehaven in 1812, but regarding it the writer has. no further information.

been put forward on behalf of Hedley and George Stephenson, as inventors of the locomotive, it may truly be stated that neither of them contributed anything of note to the invention in addition to what Trevithick and Blenkinsop had done. They were ingenious imitators rather than inventors. From the time when Blenkinsop supplied the locomotive with its two steam engines, instead of the one used by Trevithick, no improvement of any consequence was made in the invention for a period of fourteen years ; and with the second great improvement—the fusion of the two steam engines into one *coupled engine*, which was effected in 1826, and laid the foundation of the modern locomotive—neither Hedley nor Stephenson had anything whatever to do. The idea of attaching two cylinders to one pair of wheels, appears to have originated with Robert Wilson, of Newcastle (Colburn's *Locomotive Engineering*, p. 21). As originally constructed, Wilson's engine seems not to have worked satisfactorily, but it was altered and carried to a successful issue by Timothy Hackworth, in his engine the Royal George ; in which also a more powerful form of steam blast was introduced. By these improvements, with the addition of the multitubular boiler —adopted by Mr. Robert Stephenson in the Rocket, at the suggestion of Mr. Booth, treasurer to the Liverpool and Manchester Railway Company (Wood's *Railroads*, 2nd ed., pp. 363, 387), and enabling an ample supply of steam to be obtained—the invention of the locomotive engine may be said to have been completed. The miracle which the illustrious Watt deemed humanly impossible, had been performed after all.

The progress made in the application of the steam engine to navigation was almost exactly synchronous with that of its application to locomotion. Here, however, less difficulty was encountered, the condensing engine being available with little alteration.

In the year 1801 experiments were made both on the Thames (*Monthly Visitor*, July 2, 1801; *Glasgow Herald*, June 17, 1891, p. 10) and on the Forth and Clyde Canal (Cleland's *Historical Account of the Steam Engine*, p. 49) without leading to any practical result. Robert Fulton, an American, who is stated to have examined and tried the boat on the Forth and Clyde Canal (*ib.*, 53, 55) in 1802, established steam navigation in America in 1807, the engine which he used having been obtained from Messrs. Boulton & Watts, Soho Works, Birmingham (Muirhead's *Life of Watt*, 2nd ed., pp. 426-27). But it is a singular coincidence that the first steamboat in Europe— the "Comet" of Henry Bell—was launched on the Clyde on

January 18, 1812, the very year that Blenkinsop established steam locomotion.

A few years later the application of steamboats to the towing of vessels in and out of harbours, put an end to the practice of both

FIG. 34.—THE "COMET," 1812.

ships and collieries lying up for two months in winter (Dunn's *Coal Trade*, p. 51)—the last remnant of the ancient custom of navigation ceasing entirely during the winter season—giving another considerable impulse to the coal trade.

CHAPTER XXXVII.

THE NINETEENTH CENTURY. 1801-1816.

Great activity in working the High Main coal in the Tyne basin. The terms "Main" and "Wallsend" as applied to coals and collieries. New sinkings to the High Main seam. Early attempts to work the Low Main seam. Boulton and Watt engines. Improvement in cast-iron tubbing. Difficulties and dangers attending the working of the deep collieries in the north.

THE collieries situated on the lower reaches of the Tyne, between Newcastle and the sea, in the tract already spoken of as the Tyne basin, were at the flood tide of their prosperity in the early part of the present century. The movement of the coal trade towards this district, which had been going on ever since the aid afforded by the steam engine enabled the miners to penetrate to greater depths, reached its climax at this period, leaving the collieries in the western part of the Tyne Valley at their lowest ebb, the tender and consequently small coal which they produced being at this time of comparatively little value.

The working of the Main coal, or High Main seam, so famed in the London market as the best coal for household purposes, was at the height of its activity. The coalowners who were so fortunate as to possess it, endeavoured to distinguish their collieries by affixing to them the name of "Main." But so powerful was the charm of the term, that it gradually came into such extended use as to become almost synonymous with the word mine—which, indeed, was sometimes substituted for it in Parliamentary reports (*e.g.*, *1835 Report*, 2,119, 2,200)—being adopted at collieries where the High Main coal had never existed, or had been worked out ; likewise applied to other seams of coal altogether, such as the Low Main, and the Low Low Main (*Fossil Fuel*, p. 135) ; and even the rubbish heap at the collieries, where poor people grubbed among the stones, and picked up the fragments of coal accidentally mixed with them, was dubbed with the name of Charity Main.

The Main coal being in great perfection, and long and extensively worked at Wallsend, led to this name becoming, in the course of time, a synonym for coal of the best quality, and to its being extensively adopted as an "open sesame" for coal in the market. Not only was the name of "Wallsend" applied to the produce of their collieries by the coalowners in the surrounding district on the Tyne, but by others on the Wear and Tees, and even in more distant parts of the kingdom.

From the desire to employ auspicious names, it so happened that most of the collieries confessed to two or more, while their produce had sometimes three or four—a state of matters somewhat perplexing to an investigator. An early writer on the coal trade (Edington, p. 72), in giving a list of prices of coal on the Tyne and Wear in 1813, omits a considerable cluster of collieries on the latter river altogether, appending a P.S. to the effect that their names had been so often changed, and prices altered of late, that to ascertain the present selling prices was beyond his power.

In the Tyne basin—the great theatre of mining operations in the north in this era—a number of new and important sinkings were now effected.

At Wallsend the sinking of the F pit, 8 feet in diameter, was completed in 1802 (*Trans. Nat. Hist. Soc. of Northumberland*, etc., ii. 321). Up till this time all the Wallsend pits (with the exception of a portion of the C pit, which, as we have seen, was 10 feet) had been made only 8 or 9 feet in diameter, and had been sunk in connection with each other. But in the case of the G pit, sunk two or three years subsequently as a separate winning, a larger diameter was adopted, variously stated by Mr. Buddle as 12 feet (*ib.*, p. 322),

FIG. 35.—BRATTICED SHAFTS.

13 feet (*ib.*, 351), and 14 feet (*1835 Report*, 1,988); the shaft being divided into three compartments by means of a three-tailed partition or brattice.

At this period it was the usual custom to divide the larger shafts into two, three, or four compartments—known respectively as double,

triple, and quadrant pits—so as to provide separate sections for
winding, pumping, and ventilating.   The brattices were usually constructed of wood.   An exceptional instance of a stone brattice being
used to divide a shaft into four compartments, occurred in the case
of the Countess pit, Whitehaven, a view of which is given in Mr. T.
Sopwith's treatise on *Isometrical Perspective*. The brattice system,
however, was fraught with danger, if no other outlet existed ; inasmuch as in the event of the partition becoming accidentally wrecked
or set on fire, all communication with the surface was cut off.

Percy Main, or Howdon Pans Colliery—the winning of which had
been attended with considerable difficulty and cost (Edington's *Coal
Trade*, p. 113), owing to quicksands and water—commenced shipping
coal on September 3, 1802 (Sykes's *Loc. Rec.*), when a procession,
attended by a band discoursing the inspiring strains of the "Keel
Row," accompanied the first wagon of coals to the shipping place.
A new winning known as the Howdon pit, 810 feet deep, was opened
in 1806-7 (Hair's *Sketches of the Coal Mines*, p. 17).

The above colliery having been set on fire, it became necessary to
drown up the workings ; and when the water was being drawn out
a few weeks afterwards, a succession of water-blasts, accompanied by
immense discharges of firedamp, occurred at intervals of half-an-hour
during a period of twenty-six hours, produced by the compressed
gas escaping from the workings to the rise of the shaft.

Jarrow Colliery, also called Temple's Main, and Temple's Wallsend, 840 feet deep (Surtees, *Durham*, ii. 73) was won by Mr. Temple
in 1803.   The shaft was 14 feet in diameter, and separated by
bratticing into three divisions (*Reports on the Gases and Explosions in
Collieries*, 1847, p. 15).   This colliery was situated in the deepest
part of the Tyne basin.   Its opening on September 26, 1803, was
made the occasion of what was probably the greatest celebration that
ever took place at an event of this kind :

Early in the morning the South Shields bells announced the
intended feast, and all the ships in Shields harbour immediately
hoisted their colours. A concourse of people, supposed not less than
10,000, assembled to witness the passage of the coals to the ship
"Fox," which lay, highly decorated with colours, to receive them.
Several of the clergy of the Cathedral of Durham, the corporation
barge of Newcastle with several members of that body, and a great
number of gentlemen from all parts of the county, having arrived,
Mr. Temple proceeded with the ceremony ; and the wagons being
loaded with coals were taken to the ship under the banners of the
South Shields Loyal Volunteers, which were then unfurled, amid a

general discharge of artillery; the music playing "Weel may the Keel Row," and other appropriate tunes. About three hundred gentlemen sat down to dinner in a tent prepared for their entertainment; the workmen, five hundred in number, dining at a long table without (Sykes's *Loc. Rec.*; Hair's *Sketches of the Coal Mines*, p. 30 note).

Mention occurs in 1805 (Bailey & Culley's *View of Northumberland*, 3rd ed., p. 13 note), of a pit lately sunk at Willington 840 feet deep. Willington Colliery on the Tyne is stated (*Trans. N.E. Inst.*, xv. 217) to have commenced about 1806.

At Killingworth Colliery, on the north side of the Ninety-fathom or Great Dyke, a pit 720 feet deep is heard of in 1806. It was 14 feet in diameter and was divided by bratticing into four compartments (*1835 Report*, 1,514).

South Shields Colliery, also called Chapter Main and Temple's Manor Wallsend, 750 feet deep (*London and Edinburgh Phil. Maga.*, iii. 94), was won by Mr. Temple, and opened amidst great rejoicings on April 23, 1810 (Sykes's *Loc. Rec.*).

At North Shields, an old colliery variously known as Chirton Colliery, Burdon Moor, Burdon Main, and Collingwood Main—the latter name being given to it in honour of Admiral Lord Collingwood, who lived at Chirton—was reopened in 1811, to work the unwrought part of the High Main coal (Edington's *Coal Trade*, p. 113; *Trans. N.E. Inst.*, xv. 220); and in the same year the High Main seam was sunk to at Fawdon Colliery on the nort' side of the Ninety-fathom Dyke (*Trans. N.E. Inst.*, xv. 220).

In addition to the above new collieries in the High Main seam, borings and sinkings had been made to the Low Main seam at some of the older collieries, the proprietors of which were now finding themselves under the necessity of seeking for "other fields and pastures new." The Low Main had been bored to at Long Benton and Walker collieries (Edington, p. 115), while further west it had been sunk to at Lawson Main Colliery, Byker, which is spoken of (Sykes's *Loc. Rec.*) as 822 feet deep in 1800; at St. Anthony's Colliery, in the same neighbourhood, which is mentioned in 1805 (Bailey & Culley's *Northumberland*, 3rd ed., p. 13), as 810 feet to this seam; and at Felling Colliery, or Brandling Main, near Gateshead, in 1810, the depth of the working pit being 612 feet (Hodgson's *Account of the Explosion in Brandling Main Colliery*, pp. 5, 6). But the early sinkings to this seam, on the north side of the Tyne, were not attended with success, owing to the tender quality of the coal and the white ashes which it yielded (Edington, p. 116).

These incipient efforts to utilize the Low Main seam were a sign of the times, and significant of the fact that in some of the older collieries the High Main seam was already beginning to fail. This is clearly set forth in the following little summary published in 1815 (W. Chapman's *Pamphlet*, p. 18), pointing out the changes in this respect which had taken place since the year 1797 :

Name of colliery.	What seam.	Remarks.
Walker, . . .	High Main, . .	Wrought out.
St. Anthony's, . . {	High Main, . .	Wrought out.
	Low Main, . .	Relinquished.[1]
Lawson's Main, . .	Low Main, . .	Relinquished.[1]
Felling Colliery, . .	High Main, . .	Wrought out.
Gateshead Park, . .	High Main, . .	Wrought out.
Flatworth, . . .	High Main, . .	Wrought out.
Bigge's Main, . .	High Main, . .	Wrought out.
Long Benton, . .	High Main, . .	Wrought out.
Kenton, . . .	High Main, . .	Relinquished.

From the like source we learn that during the same interval, in the district west of Newcastle, the collieries of Baker's Main, Throckley, and Heddon Hill, had ceased work; some of the seams having been wrought out and others only relinquished.

The deep sinkings made in the Tyne basin in this era were facilitated by the improved machinery now available. In some instances Boulton and Watt engines were employed, being specially mentioned (Dunn's *Coal Trade*, p. 46) in the case of the sinkings at Jarrow and South Shields.

In sinking pits at this period, wood tubbing was still extensively employed. Solid cribbing, of oak or elm, was much in favour about 1806 (*Trans. Nat. Hist. Soc. Northumberland*, ii. 230), and was used by Mr. King in sinking the two collieries above mentioned (Dunn's *Coal Trade*, p. 46). At Percy Main Colliery, where, as we have seen, tubbing consisting of segments of cast iron bolted together had been used by Mr. Buddle in sinking the first pit, an improved form of segment, with flanges projecting outwards, and put together without bolts, was introduced by the same gentleman in the sinking of the Howdon pit, in 1804-5 (*Trans. Nat. Hist. Soc., Northumberland*, ii. 230); a form of segment which has ever since continued to be used where cast-iron tubbing is employed under ordinary circumstances.

The working of the deep and extensive collieries on the Tyne and

[1] These two collieries appear to have been relinquished in consequence of the stoppage of the pumping engine at Felling Colliery when the High Main seam was abandoned and tubbed off there in 1811 (*Iron and Coal Trades' Review*, lvi. 297).

Wear was attended with much difficulty and great risk at the beginning of the present century.   Probably at no time was coal mining
carried on under more dangerous conditions.

The ventilating power consisted of a furnace,[1] which was occasionally placed at the surface in connection with a tall chimney or
air-tube, but more usually at the bottom of the upcast shaft, where
better results were obtained from it.   The furnace was well known
to be an element of danger,[2] but no other means existed so effectual
in producing a ventilating current.

Whether under the system of coursing the air, as on the Tyne, or
shething it, as on the Wear (*Trans. N.E. Inst.*, xv. 220), the whole
volume of air was carried in a single stream through or round the
workings of the mine.   While the coursing system served more
effectually to prevent noxious gases from accumulating in the old
workings, or waste, it was now being carried beyond the limits
within which it could be safely applied.   To guide the air-current in
its long labyrinthine passage through the mine, innumerable doors
and stoppings were required, the neglect or failure of any one of
which might lead to disastrous results ; and apart from this, the
enormous length of passage which the air had to traverse between its
entrance at the downcast and its exit at the upcast shaft constituted
a radical defect in the system.   At Walker Colliery, for example, in
1806 (*Address in reply to Dr. Trotter*, p. 43), in one system of ventilation, and though the pits were only half a mile apart, the air-current
traversed a line exceeding thirty miles in passing between them.
At Hebburn Colliery at the same period (Dunn's *Coal Trade*, p. 48),
the air-course was likewise calculated to be not less than thirty miles
in length.   The keeping open of this great length of passage was not
only attended with much expense, but the friction to which it gave
rise heavily taxed the ventilating power, which, doubtless, partly
accounts for the extremely small volume of air employed to ventilate
collieries at this period ; a column of air 36 feet square moving at
the rate of 3 feet per second, or from 5,000 to 6,000 cubic feet per
minute (*ib.*, p. 57), being all that was thought necessary even to
ventilate the fiery collieries around Hebburn.

[1] At the Duke pit, Whitehaven, in 1806, the firedamp was collected and
conveyed to the bottom of the shaft, and burned there to produce a ventilating
current.   It is stated that a velocity of four miles an hour was obtained,
whereas common furnaces seldom produced more than three miles an hour
(*Monthly Magazine*, xxiii. 499).

[2] Mr. Buddle mentions having known explosions to take place at the furnace
whether situated at the bottom or top of the upcast shaft (*Trans. Nat. Hist.
Soc. Northumberland*, i. 185).

The smallness of the air-current, combined with the length of its run, caused the air near the end of its course—the "last of the air," as it was termed—to be loaded with impurities, which, in the case of fiery collieries, was a source of much danger, the current becoming frequently so charged with firedamp that it flashed into large sheets of fire as it passed over the ventilating furnace (*1835 Report*, 1,555 ; Hair's *Sketches of the Coal Mines*, p. 33 ; Dunn's *Win. and Work.*, 2nd ed., p. 153) ; a phenomenon which was of such common occurrence at Hebburn Colliery as to be viewed by the workmen without alarm. At Walker Colliery, also, the same thing frequently happened (*Trans. N.E. Inst.*, xxv. 5).

When explosion was threatened from this cause, the only resource was to throw open the main doors (*1835 Report*, 2,995),[1] thus suspending the ventilation of the workings, and allowing the fresh air to pass directly from the downcast to the upcast pit, until the furnace could be extinguished ; when the doors were again closed, and some temporary expedient applied, such as a waterfall in the downcast pit, by means of which the vitiated air was driven safely over the cold furnace. Under the system of coursing the air, the furnace had frequently to be put out on very short notice (*ib.*, 1,999).

To relight the furnace in such a case was a task of much anxiety and danger. This was sometimes accomplished by charging it with tar and other highly inflammable materials, which were ignited by means of a red-hot iron ring run down a line from the surface (*Trans. Nat. Hist. Soc. Northumberland*, ii. 372 ; *1835 Report*, 2,002). On one occasion at Wallsend, when it was necessary that two furnaces should be lighted simultaneously, and the red-hot ring method was inapplicable on account of their distance from the bottom of the pit, Mr. Buddle, at the suggestion of a military friend, adopted a device practised in the artillery service, consisting in the employment of a quick and slow match, the latter affording sufficient time for the workmen to make good their escape to the surface before the ignition of the furnace took place. The same gentleman relates (*1835 Report*, 2,001) how on another occasion he required to watch the furnace at Hebburn almost daily for a period of six weeks before he got it lighted, and only accomplished it at last by taking advantage of a favourable state of the atmosphere.

The difficulties in the way of carrying on the deep collieries in the north were greatly aggravated by the creeps which took place in

[1] Mr. Buddle relates an instance when the gas fired at the furnace at Jarrow Colliery, but an explosion was averted by the presence of mind of the under-viewer in throwing open the main ventilating doors.

the workings, and which were extremely common in the early part
of the century.   In some instances they arose from the pillars of
coal having been left too small in the course of the first working; in
others they supervened after a partial working of the pillars had
been effected.   Thus at Walker, Bigge's Main, Wallsend, Heaton,
etc., the pillars had been partly worked before the creeps began
(Dunn's *Coal Trade*, pp. 49, 57); while in the case of the newer and
deeper collieries of Hebburn, Jarrow, Percy Main, etc., they took
place while the pillars were still intact.

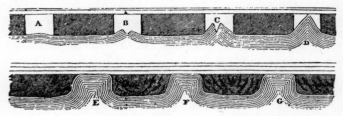

FIG. 36.—PROGRESSIVE STAGES OF CREEP.

The creeps were productive of much expense, inconvenience, and
danger, contracting the roads and airways, and shattering the
stoppings built to guide the ventilating current.   They were also
accompanied by immense discharges of firedamp (*ib.*, p. 50).   At
times the movement extended to the surface.   It is related that on
one occasion during divine service in the church at Long Benton,
near Newcastle, a portion of the building suddenly shrunk, to the
consternation of the worshippers.   "It's only a creep," said the
pastor, or church clerk.   The congregation, however, lost no time in
escaping to the open air, notwithstanding the reiterated assurance
that it was "only a creep, only a creep" (Latimer's *Loc. Rec.*, p. 117;
Our Coal and Our Coal Pits, p. 140).

A mode of working described as common in the north at this
period (Holmes's *Coal Mines*, p. 77), consisted in having the bords
four yards wide and eight yards apart, and connected by headways
twenty yards apart, leaving pillars of coal twenty yards by eight yards.
At Team Colliery, in 1811 (*Trans. N.E. Inst.*, vol. i.), the pillars are
stated by Mr. Barkus to have been made twenty-four yards by ten
yards; the bords being four yards and the walls two yards wide.   In
the Low Main seam at Felling, in 1812, the dimensions of the pillars
were twenty-six yards by eight yards (Mr. Hodgson's *Pamphlet*, p. 7).

In situations where the use of ordinary lights was inadmissible,
owing to the presence or fear of firedamp, the steel mill continued

to be resorted to as the only safeguard against explosion (Dunn's
Coal Trade, p. 57 ; *1835 Report*, 669) ; and notwithstanding its
known insecurity,[1] and the poor flickering light which it afforded,
and the cost with which its use was attended, it was still extensively
employed (*Trans. Nat. His. Soc. Northumberland*, ii. 331, 332). At
Hebburn Colliery sometimes as many as one hundred of these
machines were in daily use (Hair's *Sketches of the Coal Mines*, p. 33) ;
the cost incurred being stated (Holmes's *Coal Mines*, p. 95) to have
amounted to about £60 per month.

[1] While admitting that the inflammable gas had frequently fired at the
sparks of the steel mill, Mr. Buddle states that from all the facts he had been
able to collect, this only happened when the mills were played near the place
where the gas was discharged (*First Report of Sunderland Society*, p. 20).

CHAPTER XXXVIII.

THE NINETEENTH CENTURY. 1801-1816.

Colliery explosions. Heaton inundation. Sheriff Hill brattice fire.

THE following long list of colliery explosions exhibits the dangerous conditions under which coal mining was being carried on in the deep, extensive, and fiery mines of the north:

1801.—Stella, or Towneley Main, Greenside A pit.—Explosion by which several men were killed (Fordyce's *Durham*, ii. 682). The bodies were recovered by Mr. James Hall, father of Mr. T. Y. Hall, after the underviewer had declined to undertake the task.

1802.—Lawson Main.—A creep having stopped the air-course, some men were opening it up by the light of steel mills; no other light but steel mills being in the pit. A mill ignited the firedamp, which set the coal on fire. The workmen who were further in, feeling the concussion, made their way out in the dark, and had to pass under the flaming gas. One man took the wrong road; the pit was closed up and he lost his life (*1835 Report*, 662-673).

1803.—Lambton, Morton pit.—Explosion with loss of two lives (Sykes's *List*).

1803 (September 25).—Wallsend C pit.—Explosion (termed "a heavy fire") by which thirteen men and boys were killed, and nearly twenty burnt and injured.

A burst of gas (or "bag of foulness"), which came from the roof in the pillars behind the workmen, fired at a lamp in the leading excavation (the going headways). The bords were just turned away out of this place, "and the fire from the explosion sweeping along it," to quote Mr. Buddle's words, "struck all the people who were working in its range. The workings were very dry and dusty, and the survivors, who were the most distant from the point of explosion, were burnt by the shower of red-hot sparks of the ignited dust, which were driven along by the force of the explosion. The greater number of the sufferers perished by suffocation" (*Trans. Nat. Hist. Soc. Northumberland*, ii. 331).

1805 (April).—Oxclose A pit.—Explosion with the loss of two lives (Sykes's *List*).

1805 (October 21).—Hebburn.—Explosion with the loss of thirty-five lives (Sykes's *Loc. Rec.*).

1805 (November 29).—Oxclose.—Explosion with the loss of thirty-eight lives (*ib.*).

1806 (March 28).—Killingworth.—Explosion with the loss of ten lives. Mr. George Stephenson, who was employed as brakesman, or engineman, at the pit at the time, and witnessed this explosion (which he ascribes to the want of a ventilating furnace, *1835 Report*, 1,565), has furnished the following particulars :

"The pit had just ceased drawing coals, and nearly all the men had got out. It was some time in the afternoon, a little after mid-day ; there were five men that went down the pit, four of them for the purpose of preparing a place for the furnace, the fifth was a person that went down to set them to work ; this man had just got down to the bottom of the shaft, about two or three minutes, when the explosion took place ; I sent the man down myself. I had left the mouth of the pit, and gone about 50 or 60 yards away, when I heard a tremendous noise, looked round, and saw the discharge come out of the pit mouth like the discharge of a cannon ; it continued to blow, I think, for a quarter of an hour, discharging everything that had come into the current ; there was wood came up, stones came up, and trusses of hay, that went up into the air like balloons; those trusses had been sent down during the day, and I think the trusses had in some measure injured the ventilation. The ground all round the top of the pit was in a trembling state ; I went as near as I durst go, and everything appeared cracking and rending about me ; part of the brattice, which was very strong, was blown away at the bottom of the pits ; very large pumps were lifted from their places, so that the engine could not work. The pit was divided into four by partitions ; it was a large pit, 14 feet diameter, and partitions put down at right angles, which formed four. The explosion took place in one of these four quarters, but it broke through into all the others at the bottom, and the brattice or partition was set on fire at the first explosion. After it had continued to blow for a quarter of an hour, as I have stated, the discharge ceased, and the atmosphere all round poured into the pit to fill up the vacant place that must have been formerly occupied by the flame. In one of the other pits, that was connected with this one in which the explosion took place by some doors in a drift leading from one pit to the other, several men, who were in the adjoining pit, were not reached by the explosion, and several of them got up safe. The ropes in the first shaft were shattered to pieces by the force of the blasts, but the ropes in the other pits were still left uninjured, at least they were very little injured. Nobody durst go near the shafts, for fear of another explosion taking place, for some time ; at last we considered it necessary to run the rope backwards and forwards, and give the miners, if there were any at the bottom of the shaft, an opportunity of catching the rope as it came to the bottom ; whenever the rope went to the bottom it was allowed to remain a short time till we considered they had time to cling to it ; several men were got up in this way, and another man had got hold of the rope and was drawn away, when an explosion took place at the time he was in the shaft, but it was merely like the discharge of a gun, and it did not continue like the former blast. This man, it appeared, had been helped up so far with the increased current that came about him, and the rope running up at a great velocity, the man came up without being injured."

Four of the five men who went down, were afterwards found buried among the corves and little carriages at the pit bottom. The fifth, the overlooker, threw himself behind some pillars so that the current went past him. The flame came about him, and nearly all his clothes were burnt off his back, but he was one of those who escaped by the rope after the blast ceased.

The pit continued to blast every two or three hours for two days, the coal being on fire, but none of the explosions were equal to the first. The other shafts became wrecked very soon. The workings were drowned up in order to extinguish the fire, and the bodies of the unfortunate victims were not recovered for twenty-three or twenty-four weeks (*1835 Report*, 1,513-1,520).[1]

[1] "Of the two last accidents, which happened near Newcastle," says the writer of a pamphlet dated May 5, 1806, "the one, I understand, ensued in consequence of the pillars in the waste giving way to the superincumbent mass, and the pressure of the air, contained in that cavity, into the part of the mine then worked. In this instance, as much mischief was believed to have been effected by the azotic gas, called styth by the workmen, formed in consequence of the deterioration of atmospheric air by contact with the coal or with pyrites, as by the inflammation of the firedamp itself. The last unfortunate event occurred in an almost new workings, very much intersected by troubles, and was caused by the workmen suddenly penetrating into a large cavern filled with firedamp. The former might perhaps have been avoided by the indispensable provision of ventilating the waste ; but I do not see that any precaution would have obviated the latter."—*An Address in reply to Dr. Trotter*, London, 1806, pp. 28, 29.

1806.—Lambton, Morton West pit.—In sinking, at the depth of 315 feet, a blower of firedamp was encountered, which fired at the furnace, blasted, and blew out the whole of the brattice, and kept burning and blasting for five hours. It was afterwards piped to the surface by the aid of a large mirror, employed to reflect the sun's rays down the shaft (Dunn's *Winning and Working*, 2nd ed., pp. 51, 155). It was still blowing strongly ten years subsequently, as will be seen hereafter.

1808.—Shiney Row, New pit.—Explosion with loss of two lives (Sykes's *List*).

1808 (August 31).—Fatfield, Hall pit.—Explosion with loss of three lives (*ib.*).

1808 (November 29).—Harraton.—Explosion with loss of more than four lives :

An accident having happened to the machinery of the 6th pit, sixteen men and boys set out to travel through the old workings to the Row pit, carrying a torch (low-rope) to light their way. They wandered into the vicinity of a pair of dams, which shut off a considerable tract of workings charged with firedamp. An accumulation of gas having taken place in consequence of leakage through the dams, which were not provided with any relieving pipe, an explosion ensued. Such of the party as were slightly injured succeeded in finding their way to the Row pit, but the greater number, being more seriously burnt or injured, were left to their fate. The leakage of gas continued to supply fuel for several successive explosions, at lengthened intervals, which were felt at the top of the pit, though half a mile distant.

As soon as they seemed to have subsided, the overman and others went down in search of the unfortunate people, some of whom were dead, others grievously burnt; but scarcely had they reached the vicinity of the dams when another unexpected explosion took place, which killed the overman and two of his companions—fire having existed all along at the dams.

Next day a considerable party penetrated to the spot, and recovered all the bodies but one (that of a boy), which, however, was found the day after. Some of the bodies were very little burnt.

The coal being thought to be on fire, the pits were closed up for about seven weeks; and on the workings being examined subsequently by the light of steel mills, to the surprise of the explorers, a pony was found alive (*Trans. Nat. Hist. Soc. Northumberland*, i. 241-243; Dunn's *Win. and Work.*, 2nd ed., p. 188).

1808 (November 30).—Fatfield, Hall pit.—Explosion with loss of three lives (Sykes's *List*).

Rainton, Collings's pit.—Explosion with loss of two lives (*ib.*).

Oxclose, B pit.—Explosion with loss of one life (*ib.*).

Lambton, Houghton Gate pit.—Explosion with loss of two lives (*ib.* ; dates of the three last explosions not known to Sykes).

1809 (September 14).—Killingworth.—Explosion with loss of twelve lives (*ib.*). This explosion did not reach the shaft, and the men were killed principally by the afterdamp (*1835 Report*, 1,527, 1,528).

1812 (May 25).—Felling, or Brandling Main.—Explosion with loss of ninety-two lives.

This was the most appalling explosion that had ever happened. The disaster occurred on a Monday forenoon, at half-past eleven o'clock. The unusually great loss of life was occasioned by the circumstance that the fore-shift was being relieved by the back-shift, and both sets of men were in the mine at the time (Sykes's *Loc. Rec.*).

The High Main seam had been wholly wrought out in 1811, when it had been tubbed off by solid cribbing. The Low Main seam, which had been sunk to, as we have seen, in 1810, was now being worked, and twenty-five acres only had been excavated. The colliery was equipped after the most approved fashion of the day.

It was worked by means of two shafts. The John pit—the working and downcast pit—was 602 feet deep ; the other shaft was situated on an eminence 550 yards distant, and was known as the William pit.

The ventilation of the mine was arranged on the coursing system, the current being carried up two bords and down two bords through the whole of the workings. The ventilating power employed consisted of a furnace, placed on the surface at the William pit, in connection with a lofty chimney stalk.

No accident had occurred except a trifling explosion, which slightly burned two or three workmen. Candles were employed by the miners, and smoking was permitted in the mine ; the blasting of stone from the roof of the rolley-way bord was also in operation. "The mine was considered by the workmen a model of perfection in the purity of its air and orderly arrangement," and the concern wore the features of the greatest possible prosperity till the moment when the explosion took place.

The explosion was characterized by very great violence. "The subterranean fire broke forth with two heavy discharges from the John pit (the downcast), which were almost instantaneously followed by one from the William pit. A slight trembling, as from an earthquake, was felt for about half-a-mile around the workings; and the noise of the explosion, though dull, was heard to three or four miles' distance, and much resembled an unsteady fire of infantry. Immense quantities of dust and small coal accompanied these blasts, and rose high into the air in the form of an inverted cone. The heaviest part of the ejected matter, such as corves, pieces of wood, and small coal, fell near the pits; but the dust, borne away by a strong west wind, fell in a continued shower from the pit to the distance of a mile and a-half. In the village of Heworth it caused a darkness like that of early twilight, and covered the roads so thickly that the footsteps of passengers were strongly imprinted in it. The heads of both of the shaft-frames were blown off, their sides set on fire, and their pulleys shattered in pieces; but the pulleys of the John pit gin, being on a crane not within the influence of the blast, were fortunately preserved. The coal dust ejected from the William pit into the drift or horizontal part of the tube (*i.e.*, the passage between the pit and the chimney stalk), was about 3 inches thick, and soon burnt to a light cinder.[1] Pieces of burning coal, driven off the solid stratum of the mine, were also blown up this shaft."

By twelve o'clock, by means of the gin at the John pit, which was worked by men in the absence of horses, thirty-two persons, all that survived, were brought to daylight. At a quarter-past twelve, nine individuals descended the John pit, lighting their way by steel mills, as the firedamp would have instantly ignited at candles; but finding themselves unable to penetrate into the workings any distance on account of meeting with chokedamp, they determined to return to the surface. At two o'clock, after five had ascended, and when two were in the shaft, and the remainder still underground, a second explosion occurred, though much less severe than the first, and fortunately not attended with any serious consequences. The men in the shaft felt an unusual heat, but the uniformity of their ascent was not affected. The men underground threw themselves on their faces and kept firm hold of a strong prop, and experienced no other inconvenience from the blast than its lifting up their legs and poising their bodies in various directions, "in the manner that the waves heave and toss a buoy at sea."

After one or two more ineffectual attempts to enter the workings,

---

[1] When the workings were opened out, the barrow-way dust in some parts is described as burnt to a cinder, and to have felt under the feet "like frozen snow" (Mr. Hodgson's account, p. 44).

the coal having evidently been set on fire, it was determined to close up both shafts in order to extinguish it, which was accordingly done on May 27th; the recovery of the bodies of the unfortunate victims not being begun till July 8th, the operation being effected by the light of steel mills. On September 19th the pit was visited by candle-light, which had not been used in it for the space of 117 days. The furnace was relighted the same day (" Account of the explosion in Brandling Main Colliery," by the Rev. J. Hodgson).

1812 (October 6).—Shiney Row.—Explosion which severely scorched one man and six boys, and set the pit on fire (Richardson's *Table Book*, H. D., iii. 120).

1812 (October 10).—Harrington Mill pit, Pensher.—Explosion which killed twenty-four persons, four men and twenty boys (Sykes's *Loc. Rec.*; Holmes's *Coal Mines*, p. 49).

1813 (April 7).—Howdon, or Percy Main.—Explosion in the Riga district of the Howdon pit which burnt twenty-three persons, and broke down the greater number of the doors and minor or "sheth" stoppings in that division; but the principal or "bearing" stoppings, being all secured by pillaring, withstood the shock, and consequently secured the main channels of the ventilation, so that the smaller ramifications only were deranged. "Not a life was lost," says Mr. Buddle, "by the choak damp; but if the pillaring had been wanting, not an individual could have been rescued from its suffocating powers" (*First Report of a Society for Preventing Accidents in Coal Mines*, 1814, p. 14).

1813 (July 17).—Collingwood Main.—Explosion by which eight workmen were killed and two severely injured. The ventilation was obstructed by a creep, and candles were in use (Holmes's *Coal Mines*, pp. 50, 51). The overman, deputies, and others, had gone down to secure the timber, iron, and other materials, which were likely to be lost owing to the creep, and the gas fired at their lights. The mine had previously been in a safe state (*1835 Report*, 1,303-5).

1813 (September 28).—Fatfield, Hall pit.—Explosion which killed thirty-two men and boys. A stone falling from the roof carried along with it a quantity of firedamp, which exploded at the miners' candles (Holmes's *Coal Mines*, p. 54).

1813 (December 24).—Felling.—Explosion which killed twenty-three men and boys (nine men and thirteen boys, according to Richardson), and injured twenty-one more. Firedamp supposed to have ignited at the crane lamp. " In no instance whatever," remarks Mr. Holmes, "has a stronger proof occurred of the inadequate security afforded by ventilation than in this mine. It was reported to be more perfectly ventilated than any other" (*Coal Mines,* pp. 93, 94).

This accident happened about half-past one in the morning, when the men were going to work. "Ten minutes later the greater number of the workmen would have been down. By report, Mr. Haswell (one of the overmen), was much shattered. Some say his head was blown off, or nearly so, and that he was thrown out of the shaft mouth" (Raine's *Life of Hodgson,* i. 131).

1814 (April 5).—Howdon or Percy Main, Howdon pit.—Explosion which killed four persons (Sykes's *List*).

1814 (May 12).—Hebburn.—Explosion which killed eleven persons, viz., the underviewer and all his assistants, who were employed changing the air-current. No one else was in the pit at the time. A sufficient interval had not been allowed for the fire-damp to be cleared away (*1835 Report,* 2,361-63).

1814 (September 9).—Leafield, Chester-le-Street.—Explosion caused by breaking into an old working full of firedamp. No person was killed, though all the workmen employed were much injured (Holmes's *Coal Mines,* p. 96).

Same day a second explosion occurred by which four persons were killed (*ib.*).

1815 (June 2).—Newbottle, Success pit.—Explosion characterized by great violence. Out of seventy-two persons employed, fifty-seven were killed, and the remaining fifteen severely hurt, some of them only surviving till they reached the surface. Supposed to have been caused by breaking into an old working (*ib.*, pp. 100, 101). Flame did not ascend the shaft, but a large column of dust indicated to the workmen above ground the catastrophe that had happened (Sykes's *Loc. Rec.*).

1815 (June 5).—Tyne Main.—Explosion which severely scorched one man, without doing much further damage (Holmes's *Coal Mines,* p. 102).

1815 (July 27).—Sheriff Hill, Isabella pit.—Explosion by which eleven persons perished, three of whom were killed by the blast, and eight suffocated by afterdamp (*ib.*, p. 103; Sykes's *Loc. Rec.*).

1815 (December 18).—Towneley.—Explosion which killed one person (Sykes's *List*).

1816 (April 28).—Walbottle, Wellington pit.—Explosion which "raged with terrific fury through the excavations to a distance of two hundred yards in one continued flame." The workmen made their escape by the Blucher pit, except thirteen (three men and eleven boys, according to Richardson), who were dreadfully bruised or scorched (Holmes's *Coal Mines*, p. 213 ; Richardson's *Table Book*, H.D., iii. 163).

In addition to the foregoing explosions which have been recorded, there was doubtless a long array of small non-fatal explosions, probably from five to ten times more numerous (Holmes, p. 84), scorching and maiming one, two, or three persons at a time, which were never heard of beyond the immediate neighbourhood.

While it can well be imagined that in the other coal districts explosions were as yet neither so frequent nor so destructive as in the deep and fiery mines of the north of England, we have evidence that such disasters did occasionally take place.

Regarding their occurrence in the district over which his survey extended, Farey, in the first volume of his *Agriculture and Minerals of Derbyshire*, etc., published in 1811, makes the following general statement (p. 337): "I heard of explosions having happened in Amoscross Mine, Beggarlee, Boythorp, Codnor nether-park, and Donisthorpe Collieries, Little Pasture Mine, Midhope-stones, Pentrich, and Somercotes-furnace collieries, at Wingersworth Colliery in 1675."

In Cumberland an explosion occurred at Whitehaven in 1806, with the loss of eleven lives (Ryan's *Appeal*, p. 20). At the same colliery we hear of an extraordinary discharge of firedamp coming from the floor, or pavement, in 1816 ; fortunately, however, without resulting in any accident (Davy *On the Safety Lamp*, p. 129).

In Lancashire an explosion occurred in 1806 at St. Helens, with the loss of sixteen lives (Ryan's *Appeal*, p. 20).

In North Staffordshire, about the same time, seven men were killed and several others burnt by an explosion at Fenton Park (Dr. Clanny's paper to the Royal Society in 1813); while notice occurs (*1835 Report*, 3,054-56) of an explosion in the neighbourhood of Dudley, South Staffordshire, by which eight or ten lives were lost.

In Shropshire, in 1816, an explosion occurred in what appears to have been almost a superficial excavation for coal, whereby several men were killed and others severely burnt (Davy *On the Safety Lamp*, p. 4).

Both in North and South Wales in like manner explosions were occasionally taking place :

At Mostyn, about 1806, two explosions occurred, one with the loss of thirty-six and the other of about thirty lives (Ryan's *Appeal*, p. 20 ; *1835 Report*, 2,881).

At Plymouth Collieries, Merthyr Tydfil, Thomas Davis and son were burnt by damp, in September 1806 (*Buried Alive*, by C. Wilkins, p. 4).

At a small colliery worked near Pentrebach, in the Merthyr Valley, 1805-1815, explosions are stated (Mr. Joseph's paper in *Trans. So. Wales Inst.*, vol. vii.) to have occurred almost every Monday morning during the whole time.

At Plas Issa, in 1816, several men were dreadfully burnt and bruised by an explosion (Davy *On the Safety Lamp*, p 131).

In Scotland an explosion occurred at Hurlet, near Paisley, about 1805, causing the loss of eighteen lives. Sixteen funerals left the village for Paisley, and two for Neilston, on the same day (*Child. Employ. Com.*, Append. 1).

Explosions of firedamp have not been peculiar to collieries, similar accidents having already happened, though doubtless on a small scale, in lead mines (*Mining Journal*, iv. 171), and mines of limestone shale (Farey, i. 333). Explosions had also occurred on board ships newly laden with coal. Such an accident happened on August 5, 1816 (Sykes's *Loc. Rec.*), on board a ship at Sunderland, whereby the decks were torn up; and in the following year (July 4, 1817) a similar accident occurred on board the "Fly," of Ely, at Mr. Brandling's staith on the Tyne (*ib.*; see also *Edinburgh Encyclopædia*, 1820, art. Mine).

Explosions in collieries were known by various names, according to the area over which their destructive influence extended. A small local explosion occurring in a single bord, but not affecting other workings in the vicinity, was termed "a flush." If two, three, or four bords were implicated, it was known as "a fire." When it spread over the greater part of a district of workings, it was then called "a heavy fire." While if its violence necessitated its finding relief at the mouth of the pit, it was then designated "a blast" (*1835 Report*, 1,994).

Among the various points connected with the phenomena accompanying explosions, it had been observed that such as happened in confined spaces, as in newly-opened workings, were generally the most violent (*First Report of Sunderland Soc.*, p. 20; see also *Report of South Shields Com.*, art. Ventilation; Dunn's *Win. and Work.*, 2nd ed., pp. 142, 143). That the first explosion was sometimes followed by a second, and even a third one (*First Rep. of Sun. Soc.*, p. 15; Holmes's *Coal Mines*, p. 53). That the large proportion of the victims—as much as three-fourths of the whole—perished by suffocation from the afterdamp, and not from the direct effects of the explosion (*First Rep. of Sun. Soc.*, p. 12).

The liability of coal mines to be inundated by outbursts, or sudden discharges of large volumes of firedamp, was also already well known (*Address in Reply to Dr. Trotter*, 1806, p. 27 ; *First Rep. of Sun. Soc.*, p. 21 ; Dr. Clanny's paper, 1813).

While in almost every case explosions could be traced to the lights (candles or steel mills) used by the miners, in one instance we hear of an explosion being occasioned by lightning. It happened at Lawson Main Colliery, adjoining Walker, and worked by the same owners. The ventilation having become deranged, the whole of the workings underground (420 feet deep) were filled with firedamp, and the pit itself had become a huge gas pipe. Mr. Buddle happened to be near during a thunderstorm, when a flash of lightning ignited the gas, and a very heavy explosion immediately ensued. Mr. Buddle and a great number of other people went to see the havoc which had been made, and he was within 18 feet of the pit when— about an hour and a-half afterwards—another explosion, a most furious one, took place (*1835 Report*, 2,199-2,206).

With a view to confine the gas discharged from exhausted and abandoned workings, these were sometimes dammed completely off. This arrangement was, however, fraught with danger ; leakage through such dams having occasioned the explosion at Harraton in 1808. At other times mere doors were employed to shut off large tracts filled with firedamp. Mr. Holmes was shown such a district, one hundred acres in extent, in Harrington Mill pit, in 1815 (*Coal Mines*, p. 182 n.).

A superior arrangement consisted in using a cast-iron pipe, conveyed from such barred-off districts to the top of the upcast pit— the method pursued, as described above, with the blower encountered in the sinking of Morton West pit at Lambton Colliery. This system was adopted in dealing with the gas in the abandoned workings of the Hutton seam at Harrington Mill pit, the shafts and staples being completely stopped up, and a pipe led to the surface for the escape of the gas (*ib.*, pp. 31, 179, 181). Regarding such gas pipes, Mr. Holmes remarks (p. 123 n.) that though they usually gave out a strong discharge of gas, in certain northerly winds the current became reversed, and the air poured down the pipe.

While accidents due to explosion were extremely numerous, these were not the only great source of danger to which the miners were exposed.

By the bursting in of water from an old working, or waste, at Heaton Colliery, on May 3, 1815, no fewer than seventy-five persons perished. The existence of the waste, which had been abandoned in 1745 (*1835 Report*, 2,368), was perfectly well known, and it had been successfully evaded by means of borings for a lengthened

period.   But the exploring drifts having arrived at a fault, a trouble
of no great size, but which caused the coal to be soft and weak, the
barrier gave way, the flood driving the miners to the higher parts of
the workings, from which there was no possibility of escape, the
colliery having only a single shaft [1] (Dunn's *Win. and Work.*, 2nd ed.,
pp. 193, 194).

On December 11, 1815, the wooden partition, or brattice, at Sheriff
Hill Colliery, took fire from the coal lamp used for ventilating purposes (Sykes's *Loc. Rec.*), whereby five men lost their lives.   The
colliery was worked by a single shaft, which was divided by brattices
into three compartments.   A current of water was kept flowing
down the brattices; but this having been stopped in some way, they
became dry and shortly took fire.   The workmen, finding the want
of air, rushed to the pit.   Five of them (wastemen) did not succeed
in reaching it, and were lost, the remainder being saved with much
exertion.   The brattices continuing to burn, set fire to the coal,
which continued burning for a considerable time.   Mr. Buddle, who
was one of the proprietors, on being made acquainted with the
accident, hastened to the spot, and with great courage and humanity
descended, though the brattice was on fire, in order to render every
assistance in his power (Holmes's *Coal Mines*, pp. 103, 104).

Already the dangers attending the working of a colliery by means
of a single bratticed shaft were beginning to be severely commented
upon (*ib.*, pp. 98, 165).

---

[1] In June, 1809, the pits at East Ardsley, near Wakefield, were suddenly
inundated, when ten individuals perished (*Fossil Fuel*, p. 250 note). ,

CHAPTER XXXIX.

THE NINETEENTH CENTURY.   1801-1816.

Dr. Trotter's proposal to neutralize the noxious gases in coal mines.   Ryan's system of draining off the firedamp.   Mr. Buddle introduces panel-work and compound ventilation.

THE two ordinary methods of combating the inflammable gas, which constituted an element of so much peril in the working of coal mines, have already been referred to, and were now in use in different parts of the kingdom.   The first of these, consisting in the introduction of a ventilating current sufficiently large to reduce the gas below the point of ignition, and sweep it out of the mine as fast as it was produced, has been termed the *diluting system*.   The second method, practised where the ventilation alone was inadequate to remove the gas, consisted in kindling and exploding it at intervals sufficiently short to prevent large accumulations from being formed, and was known as the *firing system*. The frequent repetition of colliery disasters in the early part of the century, led to the proposal of several new schemes for dealing with the noxious gases, and with the firedamp in particular.

Near the close of the year 1805, a new method was suggested by Dr. Trotter, a physician resident in Newcastle-upon-Tyne.   The attention of this gentleman was drawn to the subject, he tells us, in connection with the explosion at Hebburn (October 21, 1805). When on a visit to a sick friend, he happened to pass the churchyard at Jarrow, at the time that thirty-two pitmen, victims of this explosion, were being interred there.   The solemnity of the scene, and the fact that the unfortunate men had left twenty-five widows and eighty-one orphans to bewail their loss, so impressed him as to cause him to prepare and issue (November, 1805) a pamphlet addressed to the coal owners and agents, entitled "A Proposal for Destroying the Fire and Choak Damp of Coal Mines."

Dr. Trotter had been connected with the navy, where fumigation was practised for the destruction of febrile contagion, and in his pamphlet he suggested a scheme for depriving firedamp of its explosive properties by a similar process, to be performed by means of oxygenated muriatic gas—a *neutralizing system* it may be termed. But though the proposal does credit to his humanity, and proved of service in leading to a discussion of the subject, the scheme was open to a number of fatal objections. These were urged with much force by two writers who undertook to reply to Dr. Trotter's proposal, viz., Dr. Dewar, physician to the Manchester Infirmary, and an anonymous writer, who styles himself "A Friend to Rational Schemes of Improvement," both of whom display a knowledge of chemistry and of the interior economy of coal mines superior to that possessed by Dr. Trotter. The chief objections urged against the proposed scheme were, that the gases resulting from the fumigation would be extremely deleterious, and that the cost of the process, assuming the possibility of carrying it out in practice, would be so enormous as to put its employment altogether out of the question.

Dr. Trotter's able critics offered some suggestions of their own for the consideration of the owners and agents of coal mines. Dr. Dewar proposed a substitute for the furnace, in the case of the ventilation of old workings where explosion might be apprehended from it. This consisted in the employment of a tall cylinder of tinned iron, placed over the upcast pit and heated by means of an exterior steam jacket. He admits that this method would be slower than that in common use, but claims that it would be much more safe under the exceptional circumstances referred to. Though the results obtainable by such an arrangement would doubtless have been comparatively trivial, the idea of endeavouring to eliminate the danger inseparable from the use of the furnace was of itself of considerable value.

A suggestion of more immediate practical importance emanated from Dr. Trotter's second critic, "A Friend to Rational Schemes of Improvement." This writer proposed an improved arrangement of the underground ventilation, so as to dispense with the numerous doors required to guide the ventilating current. The inconvenience and danger arising from accumulations of gas taking place in consequence of doors being left open, might, he thought, be obviated "by dividing the mine into a greater number of *independent systems of ventilation*, so disposed that each wagon-road shall form part of an air-course, and shall not intersect any air-course. This measure must, of course, be attended with some expense in making partitions, etc.; but this would be of no great amount, and would be cheaply purchased when it is considered that it would ensure the lives of numbers of persons who may now be brought into danger by the trifling circumstance of inadvertently leaving open a door."

Within a few years after the date when the above pregnant suggestion was published (1806), the plan of adopting "a greater number of independent systems of ventilation" was actually carried out in practice, and was found to be productive of immense benefit in many ways; effecting, indeed, a revolution in the ventilation of coal mines. The introduction of this improvement, however, will be referred to hereafter.

Contemporaneously with Dr. Trotter's proposal to employ chemical agents to destroy the noxious gases, and the suggestions offered by his reviewers, another new scheme for dealing with the inflammable gas was devised by a Mr. James Ryan, who hailed from Donegal. How Ryan was employed in his earlier years we are unable to state; but in 1800 he was engaged as mineral surveyor under the Grand Canal Company in Ireland (*1835 Report*, 2,830). In 1804 (*ib.*, 2,822) we find him employed to examine some coal mines near Bagillt, in North Wales; and in the following year he invented and patented (12th February, 1805, No. 2,822) an improved method of boring, whereby cores could be obtained, and the nature of the strata pierced be ascertained with more certainty than formerly. He also proposed to employ his apparatus for boring out shafts several feet in diameter, which might be used for draining and ventilating mines.

Having in the course of his professional duties acquired a knowledge of the properties of the gases met with in coal mines, Ryan projected a new scheme for clearing them from firedamp. This gas, on account of its light specific gravity, tending always to flow upwards to the higher parts of the workings, he conceived that advantage might be taken of this circumstance for draining it off, in a manner similar to that employed in draining water off land (*ib.*, 2,917). This he proposed to effect by providing small passages, or gas drifts, so arranged as to collect the gas and drain it off at the highest level. His system may be termed the *draining system*.

For some time Ryan was unable to obtain an opportunity of putting his scheme into practice. In 1806 he visited the scenes of the various explosions at Mostyn, St. Helens, and Whitehaven, but his proposals were rejected. In the same year he also visited Newcastle-on-Tyne, and had many conversations with Mr. Buddle on the subject of mine ventilation, in consequence of which he

delivered a course of lectures at Newcastle (*1835 Report*, 2,834-38);
but he failed to induce any coal owner to adopt his system, and
was forced to return home without having obtained a trial of his
scheme in any pit.

In the following year Ryan proceeded to London and waited upon
Sir John Sinclair, President of the Board of Agriculture; and in
April, 1807, he presented the Board with a complete set of his
boring apparatus (Rees's *Cyclopœdia*, art. Coal). Sir John highly
approved of his plans, and introduced him to the Hon. Washington
Shirley, through whose influence he at last succeeded in obtaining
an opportunity of applying his system in a mine in Staffordshire in
1808, viz., at the Netherton mine, belonging to Lord Dudley (*1835
Report*, 2,841 *et seq.*).

Ryan's system was peculiarly suitable for the mines in the thick
coal of the South Staffordshire coalfield. Here, as already mentioned, on account of the liability of the mines to spontaneous
combustion, the working of the coal was carried on in large chambers
or squares, surrounded by barriers of solid coal; and for the same
reason a minimum of ventilation was introduced, this being considered to be less liable to cause ignition to take place. The
ventilation of the chambers was effected by means of small passages, termed air-heads, driven in the coal at the side of the
chamber, which were connected with the downcast pit, and employed
to blow air among the firedamp in order to dilute it—a process
known as "killing the gas"; but inasmuch as the quantity of air
was insufficient to clear away the gas, the firing-line had to be
resorted to in order to dissipate the accumulations in the higher
parts of the chambers.

Having been entrusted with the Netherton mine, which was one
of the most fiery in the district, and was regularly fired, as we have
seen, three times a day, Ryan proceeded to put his ideas to a
practical test; and by a few alterations which he made, succeeded
in clearing the mine from firedamp, and putting the workings into
a safe state, in the short space of about twenty days (*ib.*, 2,854).
This he effected by a re-arrangement of the ventilating current,
connecting a portion of the air-heads in the higher part of the
coal with the upcast instead of the downcast pit, likewise extending
air-pipes from them to the upper workings of the thick coal, and
thus employing them to drain off the gas instead of blowing in air
among it as formerly. In this way the light specific gravity of the
gas, which had previously been a source of difficulty, was made to
aid in its escape.

It cannot be doubted that Ryan's system was a great improvement on the primitive method previously practised in the South Stafford-shire coalfield, and proved of great benefit to the mines. It threw a new light on the subject of mine ventilation, and led to the extensive adoption of top-heads, or passages in the upper part of the thick coal for draining off the gas ; an alteration which rendered the use of the firing line unnecessary, inasmuch as accumulations of gas were prevented from taking place (see *1835 Report*, 3,018, 3,023).

But while the draining system was highly advantageous in South Staffordshire, where the fullest benefit was obtained from it on account of the small areas worked, the small quantity of gas pro-duced, and the lofty character of the chambers in the thick coal, it was less applicable in the case of thin coal seams lying in a level or undulating position, where the workings were carried over extensive areas, and firedamp was met with in great quantities, and where no inducement existed to limit the ventilating current. Hence it is not surprising to find that while Ryan's plans were highly esteemed by many intelligent persons in the midland district, they were regarded with complete apathy, and even contemned in the north of England where the diluting system of ventilation was universally adhered to.

It may be mentioned that a few years later (1815) Ryan again attempted to introduce his system into the north, with the result that in order to satisfy the public mind a deputation consisting of Mr. Buddle, Mr. Hill, viewer of Felling Colliery, and the Rev. J. Hodgson, was sent to Staffordshire to examine and report on it (Dunn's *Coal Trade*, p. 33 ; Raine's *Life of Hodgson*, i. 170 ; *1835 Report*, 2,419), but their report was unfavourable to Ryan. His labours in the cause of the better ventilation of coal mines, and the light which he threw on the subject of ascensional ventilation, were rewarded by the Society of Arts in 1816, by a present of one hundred guineas and their gold medal (Holmes's *Coal Mines*, pp. 87-89) ; and his suggestions were appreciated more highly by later investigators in this country, and by those engaged in working the steep coal seams in Belgium (*Report of S. Shields Com.*, Gas Drifts), than by some of his contemporaries in the mining world.

In connection with Ryan's system allusion may be made to a plan of ventilating coal mines conceived by Lieut. Menzies, of Durham, and published in Dr. Thomson's *Annals of Philosophy* for April, 1816 (Holmes's *Coal Mines*, p. 85 ; *Fossil Fuel*, p. 228). This consisted in placing the upcast pit at the high side, and the downcast pit at the low side of the area to be worked, and connecting them previous to

commencing to work out the coal. It was also part of the scheme
that the transverse excavations should be driven in an oblique or
diagonal direction, in order that all the workings might have a

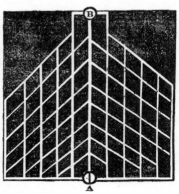

FIG. 37.—MENZIES'S METHOD.

general trend upwards, to facilitate the ventilation and the escape of
the firedamp.   But apart from the delay unavoidable in sinking pits
some distance apart, and connecting them·underground, the proposed arrangement of the workings was unsuitable for practical
application, so that his scheme was never attempted to be carried
out.

Meanwhile, Mr. Buddle had been exerting himself to improve the
methods of working and ventilating the fiery mines of the north of
England, the condition of which was of so dangerous and unsatisfactory a character at this epoch, and nowhere more so than in
the deep and extensive collieries on the Tyne, the management of
which he was called upon to undertake on the death of his father
in 1806.

Between 1807 and 1810 (*1835 Report*, 1,988) this gentleman
employed various substitutes for inducing a ventilating current in
lieu of the ventilating furnace, in cases where its use was attended
with risk of explosion.   Of these the *steam ventilator* was an
apparatus for discharging steam through a cast-iron pipe into the
upcast pit a few fathoms below the surface, the heat of which
rarefied the air and effected the ventilation (*First Report of Sunderland
Soc.*, 1814, p. 7).   This arrangement was applied at Hebburn
Colliery (Dunn's *Coal Trade*, p. 10).   Another expedient was the *hot
cylinder*, which consisted of a cast-iron cylinder, fixed in a brick
furnace, and completely enveloped in flame ; and the mouth of

the upcast pit being covered up, the air-current was passed through this cylinder into a chimney built for the purpose. An old cylinder of a steam engine was quite suitable for this apparatus. This was applied at Wallsend Colliery in reopening a portion of the workings which had been deranged by a creep (Dunn's *Win. and Work.*, 2nd ed., p. 134). An air-pump was also tried, having a piston 5 feet square, and a stroke of 8 feet, and capable of drawing 5,000 or 6,000 cubic feet of air per minute. This was applied at Hebburn Colliery (*ib.*, p. 133), when the discharge of gas during a creep rendered the furnace unsafe, and likewise at Heaton Colliery (*1835 Report*, 919, 1,253). But while these appliances were useful as temporary expedients in cases of difficulty, the results obtained were not sufficiently satisfactory to lead to their adoption in preference to the furnace under ordinary circumstances (Dunn's *Coal Trade*, p. 57).

About 1809-1810, however, Mr. Buddle succeeded in devising, and beginning to put in practice in the collieries under his care, improved methods of working and ventilating, whereby creeps were effectually kept in check, and the difficulties connected with the use of the furnace were in large measure obviated. This he effected by dividing the workings and ventilation into independent systems.

It will be remembered that about the year 1795, when the Main coal at Walker Colliery was exhausted, with the exception of the pillars, a plan was devised by Mr. Barnes whereby he succeeded in effecting a partial working of the pillars without inducing a creep over the whole of the colliery. This he accomplished by dividing the pillars into small areas of ten or twenty acres, around which he built artificial barriers by stowing up the excavations for a breadth sufficient to prevent any creep which might take place within the enclosed tract from extending to the pillars outside. Having proved successful at Walker, the same system was adopted at the adjoining colliery of Bigge's Main soon afterwards, and subsequently at Wallsend (*Trans. Nat. Hist. Soc. Northumberland*, ii. 323). A similar arrangement was also pursued when the working of pillars commenced at Percy Main, in 1810, but a different method of working was adopted,

FIG. 38.—PILLAR WORKING
AT PERCY MAIN.

consisting in the removal of every intermediate pillar and a portion of the adjoining ones, whereby the produce of the seam was increased to 80 or 90 per cent. Still the ultimate effect was that creeps took place, accompanied by danger and loss of coal (*1829 Report*, p. 54).

The above schemes, however, were only expedients adapted to pre-existing conditions, and it occurred to Mr. Buddle that a great improvement might be effected by anticipating the necessity for these artificial barriers in the course of the first working, and apportioning the area to be worked into a number of divisions, or panels, separated from each other by ribs, or barriers, of solid coal; being, in fact, similar to the plan practised in Staffordshire, though on a more extended scale. This course he at once adopted in laying out the Wallsend G pit, which was a separate winning unconnected with the rest of the colliery; and here it was that *panel-work*, as it was termed, was first introduced in 1810 (*Trans. Nat. Hist. Soc. Northumberland*, ii. 333).

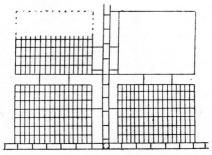

Fig. 39.—Panel Work.

By the adoption of panel-work an effectual check was put to the spread of creeps: the primary object of the arrangement. The working of the pillars in a panel could also be proceeded with as soon as they were all formed, or even made to follow close behind the whole working. It was likewise claimed by Mr. Buddle that the arrangement tended to reduce the risk from explosion by preventing it from spreading into adjoining districts (*1835 Report*, 2,034).

Coincidently with the subdivision of the workings into panels, Mr. Buddle effected a great improvement in the system of ventilating collieries, by dividing the ventilating current. This improvement also was first introduced in the Wallsend G pit in 1810 (*Trans. Nat. Hist. Soc. Northum.*, ii. 333). Mr. Buddle had thought of the arrangement some time previously, but was deterred from putting it into practice because it was not in accordance with the views of many of the old and experienced pitmen, who entertained "a horror of dividing a current of air, inasmuch as they thought that each division, or split, would weaken the principal current" (*1835 Report*, 2,002). As first applied by Mr. Buddle this improvement consisted in the employment of two air-currents instead of one, and was

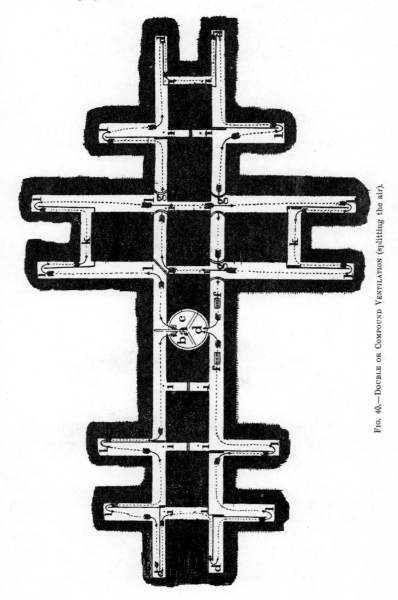

Fig. 40.—Double or Compound Ventilation (splitting the air).

introduced where two downcast pits, or two compartments of the same pit, could be made to discharge their air into one upcast pit (*First Report of Sunderland Soc.*, p. 8). Such was the case at the Wallsend G pit, which was divided into three compartments, two of which were downcast, and the third an upcast pit.

The new system was termed by Mr. Buddle double, or *compound ventilation*. In its simplest form two air-currents were employed, which ventilated separate divisions of the workings, and were discharged by separate passages into the upcast shaft. In both of these passages furnaces were provided, only one of which was kept burning; the passage in which it stood being hence termed the *furnace drift*. The other passage, containing the unlighted furnace, was known as the *dumb drift*. The air-current which ventilated the section of the workings yielding the least quantity of inflammable gas, was passed over the burning furnace. The other current, however loaded it might be with gas, was discharged with safety through the dumb drift, without at all coming in contact with fire on its way. In the event of the state of the workings undergoing a reversal, the furnace in the dumb drift could be lighted, and the other extinguished, in which case the former furnace drift became the dumb drift.

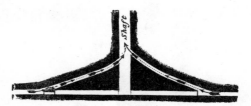

FIG. 41.—FURNACE DRIFT AND DUMB DRIFT.

To maintain an equilibrium between the two currents, sham doors, or *regulators*, were provided, to check the velocity of the shorter run. And, inasmuch as it was sometimes necessary to pass the one current over the other, at the points of intersection passages termed over-casts, or *crossings*—which appear to have been previously used to a small extent under the coursing system—were provided, usually constructed by throwing an arch over the lower airway, and cutting a channel out of the roof for the upper one.

By the introduction of compound ventilation,—now known as the *split-air system*,—not only was much of the danger previously attending the employment of ventilating furnaces obviated, but other import-ant advantages were likewise obtained. Numerous doors were dispensed with, and thus one of the most vulnerable points in Spedding's system of ventilation was overcome.   No air-current had to traverse more than half of the distance formerly necessary; and as more passages were provided, the amount of friction was greatly reduced.   In addition to this, fresh air being supplied in two or more streams instead of one, the atmosphere of the mine was rendered much more wholesome, and the impurities contained in the last of the air immensely lessened.   The expedient of throwing open the main doors, and extinguishing the furnace, frequently necessary under the old system, had rarely to be resorted to under the new one (*Trans. Nat. His. Soc. Northum.*, ii. 334).

No sooner had the system of compound ventilation been successfully applied in the Wallsend G pit, than its use was extended to other parts of the colliery, as well as to the other collieries under Mr. Buddle's care, wherever two or more downcast pits could be made to communicate with one upcast.   Before the close of the year 1813 it had been introduced by him at Percy Main, Hebburn, and Heaton (*First Report of Sunderland Soc.*, p. 9).   It was adopted by Mr. Hill, at Felling Colliery, in the latter part of 1815 (Mr. W. Barkus on "Ventilation," *Trans. N.E. Institute*, 1853).   A few years later it extended to the Wear district.   With shafts of sufficient area, the number of sub-divisions of the ventilating current was found to be capable of indefinite multiplication, and the system underwent great development at the hands of Mr. Buddle and his contemporaries, and continues to be the most approved method of ventilating coal mines at the present day.

The air-currents employed by Mr. Buddle were extremely limited, according to modern ideas.   "The standard air-course, or current of atmospheric air, which I employ in the ventilation of the collieries under my care, abounding in inflammable gas, moves through an aperture from 30 to 40 feet in area, with a velocity of 3 feet per second, which equals from 5,400 to 7,200 cubic feet, or from 525 to 700 hogsheads per minute" (*First Report of Sunderland Society*, 1814, p. 22).   The above quantity would appear to represent the total volume of air employed in the ventilation of a colliery, as Mr. Buddle subsequently states (*1835 Report*, 1,988), "My standard air-courses vary from 2,000 to 3,000 cubic feet per minute; I think the most powerful I have had occasion to employ is about 3,800 cubic feet per minute."

As early as 1814, Mr. John Bedlington, a viewer in the Newcastle-on-Tyne district, issued an address advocating the employment of "more air."

CHAPTER XL.

THE NINETEENTH CENTURY. 1801-1816.

Invention of the safety lamp.

MR. BUDDLE had devised remedies for some of the most pressing evils connected with the working of the northern collieries, and he was sanguine, we are told, that his improvements would do away with colliery explosions altogether (*1835 Rep.*, 2,837); but, alas, other sources of danger remained, which his improvements, valuable as they were, wholly failed to touch.

If the inflammable gas met with in coal mines were invariably discharged into the workings at a uniform rate, and if the ventilating arrangements were at all times in a state of thorough efficiency, it might be possible, by the introduction and proper distribution of sufficient volumes of atmospheric air, to dilute and sweep off the gas as fast as it was produced, and so to maintain the mines in a safe condition. But the ventilation itself is liable to derangement, through the neglect of a door, the failure of a stopping, or a heavy fall obstructing the airway. The quantity of gas given off from the goaves, or wastes, also, varies with the varying pressure of the atmosphere, so that the ventilating current which is adequate at one time may be inadequate at another; while mines are liable to be suddenly inundated with large volumes of gas, either by penetrating unexpectedly into old workings, or by *outbursts* or sudden discharges of gas, which occasionally take place in deep mines, and overpower, for the time being, the strongest ventilation. If, from any of these causes, the atmosphere of a mine has been rendered explosive, it is obvious that the presence of a single light is sufficient to produce disaster and death. Ventilation alone is inadequate to cope with these contingencies. Explosions must inevitably continue so long as firedamp is liable to come in contact with the miners' lights.

The merit of suggesting a new remedy for the dangers connected with the lighting of coal mines, belongs to Dr. Clanny, a medical gentleman residing in Sunderland. His attention was drawn to the subject by the frequency with which explosions took place in the neighbourhood, in consequence of the lights igniting the firedamp; and it occurred to him that some arrangement might be devised for *insulating the miners' lights* so as to prevent them from communicating explosion to the surrounding atmosphere, in whatever condition it might be.

It appears to have been about the end of the year 1811, or in the early part of 1812, that Dr. Clanny first essayed to construct an insulated lamp (Holmes's *Coal Mines*, p. 175). It was "a small lamp of strong glass, the bottom of which was shut, with the exception of a small opening to admit the tube from the bellows, for throwing in the necessary quantity of air to support the combustion of the candle within the lamp." He found, he states, that it safely insulated the candle, but was told that it would never answer the purpose intended, as it was certain to get broken in the mine, and give rise to explosion.

He also tried a lamp insulated by means of valves, but found they would not suit, as the expansive force of explosions within the lamp threw the valves open, and allowed a communication to take place between the candle and the surrounding atmosphere.

At length, however, he succeeded in constructing a strong form of lamp, which was perfectly insulated by the ingenious arrangement of passing the air from the bellows into the lamp through a stratum of water below, while a similar stratum of water above allowed the products of combustion to escape safely at the top. An account of this lamp was communicated by him to the Royal Society, in a paper "On a Steady Light in Coal Mines," read 20th May, 1813.

This lamp of Dr. Clanny's was useful rather as directing attention to the matter, and showing what might be done in the way of providing a greater degree of security in the lighting of coal mines. It was highly approved of by many scientific gentlemen. After having been tested with firedamp in a room, the atmosphere of which had been rendered explosive by gas obtained from the pipe at Harrington Mill pit, it was carried into a dangerous part of the mine by Dr. Clanny, Mr. Holmes, and others, at the risk of their lives (Holmes's *Coal Mines*, pp. 178-182). But the idea was novel, and the lamp being somewhat inconvenient, it did not come into practical use, at least to any extent.

While Dr. Clanny is entitled to the high merit of being the first to conceive and carry to a successful issue the idea of constructing an insulated lamp—for the air-tight lanthorn devised by Humboldt, in 1796, is scarcely deserving of the name, inasmuch as it could only continue to burn so long as the air within sufficed to support combustion—he did not long remain alone in this department of invention, the attention of many minds being drawn to the subject soon afterwards in the following manner :

Brandling Main, or Felling Colliery, where the great explosion occurred on May 25, 1812, was situated in the manor of Felling, which had been a possession of the Brandlings, of Gosforth, since about the year 1590. At the time of the explosion the colliery was the property of Messrs. John and William Brandling, Henderson, and Grace, each of whom held a fourth share.

Felling formed part of the parish of Jarrow and Heworth, of which the Rev. John Hodgson (who afterwards became celebrated as the historian of Northumberland) was the incumbent. As Mr. Hodgson resided at Heworth, this dreadful calamity occurred at his very door, and on him devolved the task of administering the consolations of religion to the bereaved, and of performing the last solemn rites beside the graves of the dead.

Mr. Hodgson was not unacquainted with the details of coal mining operations. He had lived for a considerable number of years in the Newcastle coal district, and had made frequent descents into the mines. At this time the editors of newspapers avoided publishing accounts of colliery explosions, being afraid of giving offence by doing so (Holmes's *Coal Mines*, p. 130). Impressed, however, by the conviction that something further might be done to prevent the recurrence of these calamities, Mr. Hodgson, "contrary to the feelings of the coal owners," determined to make the circumstances connected with the Brandling Main explosion as widely known as possible, with the hope of rousing the attention of scientific men to investigate the causes of these accidents, and find some mode of preventing them. To this end, for many weeks he continued to write notices respecting the accident, to the *Newcastle Courant*; and also wrote and published a particular account of it, accompanied with a plan of the mine and the mode of ventilating it. This publication, the preface of which is dated 4th January, 1813, was widely circulated; and part of it, unknown to Mr. Hodgson, was inserted in Dr. Thomson's *Annals of Philosophy* for May of the same year.

Among those whose sympathies were excited by the recital of the dangers to which the workers in coal mines were exposed, was a Mr. J. J. Wilkinson, a barrister residing in the Temple. During the

Long Vacation in 1813 (*1835 Report*, 285), Mr. Wilkinson went to the north of England, and consulted with many of his friends on the matter, which resulted in his determination to call the attention of the public to colliery explosions with a view to the investigation of the whole subject, to see if any remedy could be found. With this object, on the 1st of September, 1813, he published, and sent into Durham and Northumberland, proposals for the establishment of a society for preventing accidents in coal mines. These proposals having come under the notice of the Bishop of Durham, among others, his lordship wrote to the Rev. Dr. Gray, then Rector of Bishopwearmouth (afterwards Bishop of Bristol), giving him *carte blanche* to aid in the formation of such a society. A meeting of those interested was accordingly arranged for, and was held at Sunderland on the 1st of October, 1813, when the society was duly instituted, and a committee appointed to carry out the objects contemplated as follows :

Patron— His Grace the Duke of Northumberland.

Vice-Patrons—

The Marquis of Bute.
The Earl Percy.
The Earl of Carlisle.
The Viscount Barnard, M.P.
Dr. J. Cornwallis, Bishop of Litch-field and Coventry, and Dean of Durham.
Sir Thomas Henry Liddell, Bart.
Sir J. E. Swinburne, Bart.
Sir Robert J. Eden, Bart.

Sir M. W. Ridley, Bart., M.P.
The Members of the Chapter of Durham.
T. R. Beaumont, Esq., M.P.
J. G. Lambton, Esq., M.P.
Cuthbert Ellison, Esq., M.P.
George Allan, Esq., M.P.
M. J. Davison, Esq.
Adam Askew, Esq.

President—Sir Ralph Milbanke, Bart.

Secretary and Treasurer—Mr. William Burn.

Permanent Committee—

The above Members.
The Rev. Robert Gray, D.D.
The Rev. George Stephenson, M.A.
The Rev. Thomas Baker, M.A.
The Rev. John Hodgson.
The Rev. William Turner.
Stephen Pemberton, M.B.
William Reid Clanny, M.D.
John Armstrong, M.D.
Henry Fearon, M.D.
J. R. Fenwick, Esq.
James John Wilkinson, Esq.
George Robinson, Esq.
Richard Pemberton, Esq.
John Douthwaite Nesham, Esq.

Thomas Hopper, Esq.
Rowland Webster, Esq.
Thomas Wilkinson, Esq.
Addison Fenwick, Esq.
Robert Surtees, Esq.
Mr. William Chapman.
Mr. Stobart.
Mr. John Buddle.
Mr. Thomas Fenwick.
Mr. Matthew Dunn.
Mr. Edward Steel.
Mr. Thomas Croudace.
Mr. Hoyle.
Mr. George Hill.

Honorary Members—
Thomas Thomson, M.D., F.R.S., L. and E.
William Allan, F.R.S.

The society is stated to have issued its first report in the following month [1] (*1835 Report*, 285). This contained a very valuable letter, dated October 18, 1813, voluntarily communicated by Mr. Buddle to Sir Ralph Milbanke, the president, in which was given a detailed account of the various systems employed to effect the ventilation of collieries, "the only method," says the writer, "we are at present acquainted with for the prevention of accidents by fire."

In concluding his letter Mr. Buddle expresses his conviction that any further application of mechanical agency would be ineffectual to prevent explosions in mines exposed to excessive discharges of firedamp, and therefore, he says, "conclude that the hopes of this society ever seeing its most desirable object accomplished must rest upon the event of some method being discovered of producing such a chemical change upon carburetted hydrogen gas as to render it innoxious as fast as it is discharged, or as it approaches the neighbourhood of lights. In this view of the subject it is to scientific men only that we must look up for assistance in providing a cheap and effectual remedy." Mr. Buddle, when he wrote the letter, had evidently in his mind some process for neutralizing the firedamp, such as had been proposed by Dr. Trotter.

It was deemed advisable to invite the aid of Sir Humphry Davy, the distinguished chemist, and Mr. Wilkinson accordingly called at the Royal Institution, but found that he was absent in Paris. Mr. Wilkinson then posted a letter to Sir Humphry, but having neglected to pay the foreign postage, it was returned to Mr. Burn, the secretary of the society.

At this time so little expectation was entertained that any means could be devised likely to prevent explosions in collieries, that the object of the society was regarded as chimerical and visionary. Amidst much difficulty and discouragement, however, and a perpetual harass by the offer of impracticable schemes, they persevered in their meetings, though their humane efforts were for a considerable period attended with little success (Paris's *Life of Davy*, ii. 74, 75).

Ever since the occurrence of the first explosion at Brandling Main Colliery, accounts of similar accidents which took place were regularly forwarded by Dr. Clanny (Holmes's *Coal Mines*, p. 130) to Dr. Thomson's *Annals of Philosophy*, and thus the attention of the

[1] The printed copy in the possession of the writer is, however, dated 1814.

scientific world was kept alive to the matter. The idea of the practicability 'of employing insulated lights, which had never ceased to be advocated by Dr. Clanny—who had exhibited his own lamp to the Sunderland Society at an early period of its history (Thomson's *Annals*, viii. 354)—was gradually gaining ground.

A fresh impulse appears to have been given to the subject by Mr. Murray, a lecturer on chemistry, who, in his *Elements of Chemical Science*, published in June, 1815, proposed the use of an air-tight lamp, which was to be supplied with air through a tube extending downwards to the floor of the mine. A correspondence regarding insulated lights for miners was also commenced by Mr. J. H. H. Holmes in the *Morning Chronicle*, the first letter being dated July 12, 1815. Mr. Holmes was desirous to know, from motives of humanity, whether Dr. Clanny's insulated lamp had been in use in any of the collieries where explosions had recently occurred. This led to a series of letters between Dr. Clanny and Mr. Holmes, which were published successively for a number of weeks ; and were subsequently republished by the latter gentleman in his *Treatise on the Coal Mines of Northumberland and Durham.*

Lamps on the principle suggested by Mr. Murray, and fed with air through flexible tubes, were actually constructed shortly afterwards, by Mr. R. W. Brandling, and Dr. John Murray, of Edinburgh. The former gentleman attached to the top of his lantern a pair of double bellows, by which he drew out the contaminated air, and sucked in fresh air through the flexible tube to supply its place (Paris's *Life of Davy*, ii. 75). His lamp appears to have only formed part of a larger scheme for insulating the miner altogether, by a sort of diving-dress arrangement intended to render him proof alike against chokedamp and firedamp. The lamp itself, according to Mr. Holmes, possessed no security against an explosion within communicating with the surrounding air (*Coal Mines*, p. 185). As Dr. Murray's lamp was based on the supposition of the existence of determinate strata in the air of a mine, which is not the case, it was inapplicable for the purpose intended.

We have seen that the first endeavour of the Sunderland Society to obtain the assistance of Sir Humphry Davy had proved abortive, owing to his absence on the Continent. In the close of the summer of 1815 it was again resolved to apply to him, and a letter was accordingly despatched to London by Dr. Gray, the chairman of the committee, who was generally acquainted with Sir Humphry. Dr. Gray's letter followed Sir Humphry into Scotland, whither he had gone on a visit to Lord Somerville, at Melrose. In his reply, dated

3rd August, 1815, Sir Humphry expresses the great satisfaction it
will give him if his chemical knowledge can be of any use in an
inquiry so interesting to humanity, and begs Dr. Gray to assure the
committee of his readiness to co-operate with them in any experiments or investigations on the subject. He offers at the same time
to visit any place where he might be able to acquire information on
the subject of the coal gas (Paris's *Life of Davy*, ii. 78).

It having been arranged that Sir Humphry should visit the
northern coal district on his way south, he arrived in Newcastle on
the 23rd or 24th of August, where, at Dr. Gray's request (Raine's
Life of Hodgson, i. 173), he was waited upon at the "Turk's Head,"
by Mr. Hodgson, who laid before him all the printed information he
knew of respecting the ventilating and lighting of coal mines, Sir
Humphry entering at once with ardour into the subject. They then
proceeded together to Mr. Buddle's house at Wallsend; Dr. Gray
having arranged that Sir Humphry should see Mr. Buddle.

Mr. Hodgson had, among other things, communicated to Sir
Humphry a theory which he had been led to form regarding the
source of the inflammable gas in coal mines, by some experiments
which he had made (see Raine's *Life*, i. 127), viz., that it existed in
the coal itself. Little was known then on this subject, though
various hypotheses had been suggested. Some thought that it arose
from the decomposition of the water in the mines; others from the
decomposition of the coal, or of the iron pyrites contained in it. At
Mr. Buddle's house, after much general conversation on the subject
of the safe lighting of mines, Sir Humphry took up in his own hand
a bucket of fresh coal and said: "With this I will try Mr. Hodgson's
experiment on coal gas." Carrying it into Mr. Buddle's dining-room,
he begged for a bucket of water, and having put some coal into it,
and stirred it round several times so that no air might remain, he
struck a heavy poker with all his strength on the coal, shattering it
into several pieces, whereupon numerous bubbles rose through the
water. On this Sir Humphry remarked that Mr. Hodgson's experiments were certainly correct and interesting (*ib.*, p. 174). The only
other point he wished to ascertain, he said, was the minimum of
light with which the colliers could see to work. This was exhibited
to him by procuring a steel-mill, and "playing" it in a dark place.
This visit of Sir Humphry Davy and Mr. Hodgson to Mr. Buddle
took place on the morning of the 24th of August, 1815 (Paris's *Life
of Davy*, ii. 80).

From the first Sir Humphry entertained a sanguine hope of being
able to help the miners in their difficulties. Mr. Buddle, on the

contrary, was inclined to be despondent. " I explained to him," he says, " as well as I was able, the nature of our fiery mines, and that the great desideratum was a light that could be safely used in an explosive mixture. I had not the slightest idea myself of ever seeing such a thing accomplished. . . . Just as we were parting he looked at me and said, 'I think I can do something for you.' Thinking it was too much ever to be achieved, I gave him a look of incredulity; at the moment it was beyond my comprehension. However, smiling, he said, 'Do not despair; I think I can do something for you in a very short time'" (*1835 Report*, 2,226).

From Mr. Buddle's house Sir Humphry and Mr. Hodgson proceeded to Coaly Hill, to examine a geological phenomenon mentioned by the latter, which Sir Humphry had expressed a strong desire to see. This consisted of an intrusive dyke of whin or basalt, on the sides of which the coal had been charred for some distance by the heat of the whin when first injected in a molten state (Raine's *Life of Hodgson*, i. 174, 175).

Having inspected several parts of the dyke with great interest, Sir Humphry then accompanied Mr. Hodgson to Hebburn Hall, where they had been invited by Mr. Ellison—who was a very kind friend of Mr. Hodgson's—to dine and spend the night.

On the following morning Sir Humphry visited Hebburn Colliery (Dunn's *Win. and Work.*, 2nd ed., p. 162), and proceeded to Dr. Gray's, at Bishopwearmouth (Raine's *Life of Hodgson*, i. 175). In the course of the day, accompanied by Dr. Gray's eldest son, he called at Dr. Clanny's house, being desirous to see Dr. Clanny and his insulated lamp. Dr. Clanny was not at home; neither was he at home when Sir Humphry called a second time on the same day (*1835 Report*, 336).

Hearing of Sir Humphry's visits on his return home, Dr. Clanny, being much engaged at the time, took the lamp in his carriage, and calling at Dr. Gray's, left it for the inspection of Sir Humphry, who remained at the rectory overnight. And on the following morning Sir Humphry had an interview with Dr. Clanny, who had been invited to breakfast at Dr. Gray's, but did not arrive till after the meal was over, when he found Sir Humphry engaged in making some experiments with his lamp (*ib.*).

After leaving Bishopwearmouth Sir Humphry paid visits to Auckland Castle, Egglestone, Rokeby, and Harwood House, remaining at the latter place till the 30th of September (*A Collection of Letters Relating to Safety Lamps*, 1817, pp. 28, 49).[1]

[1] The full title of the pamphlet is "A Description of the Safety Lamp

On the 29th of September he wrote to Mr. Hodgson desiring him to send a quantity of firedamp from a blower (*ib.*). Six wine bottles were accordingly filled from a violent blower coming from a dyke at Hebburn Colliery, and were transmitted to Sir Humphry on the 5th of October [1] (Dunn's *Win. and Work.*, 2nd ed., p. 163).

In a letter to Mr. Hodgson, dated 15th October, Sir Humphry acknowledged the receipt of the firedamp, and announced that his investigations were progressing well. "My experiments," he says, "are going on successfully, and I hope in a few days to send you an account of them; I am going to be fortunate far beyond my expectations" (*Collection of Letters*, p. 29).

The progress of Sir Humphry Davy in the new path of discovery he had entered upon, was as rapid as it was brilliant, and from time to time he communicated the results of his researches to his friends in the north and to the scientific circles in London.

At the very outset of his investigations Sir Humphry was struck by the low inflammability of firedamp, and speedily discovered the important fact that explosive mixtures could not be fired in metallic tubes of certain lengths and diameters.[2] By diminishing the diameter and shortening the length of the tubes he found that apertures alone, if sufficiently small, were capable of arresting explosion (Paper to Royal Society, 9th Nov., 1815). About the middle of October he had already constructed a lamp which was rendered safe by means of apertures above and below (*Collection of Letters*, p. 30).

This *entirely new method of insulating lights* he announced to Mr. Hodgson, in a letter dated the 19th of October. "I have already discovered," he says, "that explosive mixtures of mine damp will not pass through small apertures or tubes; and that if a lamp, or

invented by George Stephenson and now in Use in Killingworth Colliery. To which is Added a Collection of All the Letters which have appeared in the Newcastle papers, with other Documents relating to Safety Lamps," 2nd ed., London, 1817.

[1] Sir Humphry also obtained some firedamp which had been sent by Dr. Clanny to John George Children, Esq. (see his paper of November 9, 1815; and *1835 Report*, 339).

[2] This had been discovered in the previous year by Mr. Tennant, one of the members of a committee of the Royal Society, appointed at the request of the Secretary of State for the Home Department to investigate the degree of danger which might result from the general introduction of gas into the metropolis, and more especially from the erection of large gasometers in crowded neighbourhoods (Peacock's *Life of Dr. Young*, p. 355). Davy had been absent on the Continent at the time, and was not made acquainted with the circumstance till after he had discovered it for himself (*On the Safety Lamp for Coal Mines*, 1818, p. 31 n.).

lanthorn, be made air-tight on the sides, and furnished with apertures to admit the air, it will not communicate flame to the outward
atmosphere" (*ib.*, p. 29).

On the 25th of October Sir Humphry announced these and other
discoveries to the Chemical Club of London (*ib.*).

On the 30th of October he wrote simultaneously to Dr. Gray and
Mr. Hodgson, enclosing to both a paper entitled, "A notice of
methods for preventing explosions from firedamp," in which he states
that "when a lamp or candle is made to burn in a close vessel
having *apertures only above and below*, an explosive mixture of gas
admitted merely enlarges the light, and gradually extinguishes it
without explosion. Again, the gas mixed in any proportion with
common air, I have discovered will not explode in a small tube, the
diameter of which is less than $\frac{1}{8}$ of an inch, or even a larger tube if
there is a mechanical force urging the gas through the tube" (*ib.*;
Paris's *Life of Davy*, ii. 81-83).

The above communications were not intended to be made public
at this stage. "I consider this at present as a *private* communication," says Sir Humphry in his letter to Dr. Gray; "I wish you
to examine the lamps I have had constructed, before you give any
account of my labours to the committee. I have never received so
much pleasure from the result of any of my chemical labours; for I
trust the cause of humanity will gain something by it."

Again, in a subsequent letter to the same gentleman, he says,
with reference to the letter sent to Mr. Hodgson on October 30:
"My communication to ———— was, like that I made to you,
intended to be *private*" (Paris's *Life of Davy*, ii. 86).

Some manuscript copies of the letter sent to Mr. Hodgson were
circulated among the viewers of the neighbourhood, about the 2nd
or 3rd of November. [Probably Mr. Matthias Dunn, of Hebburn
Colliery, who procured the firedamp for Mr. Hodgson, may have
been one of them. He gives an extract from it in his *View of the
Coal Trade*, p. 31, but by some error has dated the letter 15th
instead of 30th October.] Mr. Hodgson informs us that he records
this fact merely to show that Sir Humphry's discoveries were known
at this time to several gentlemen professionally employed in the coal
mines of the north; not with the desire to have it inferred that any
improper use had been made of the information (*Collection of Letters*,
p. 32).

In an oration delivered on the 4th of November, at the foundation
of the college of the Royal Institution, Mr. Butler alluded, in terms
of exultation, to the process discovered "within these few weeks"

by Sir H. Davy, whereby the firedamp of coal mines had been absolutely subdued (*ib.*, p. 31).

On the 9th of November, Sir Humphry read his first paper to the Royal Society relative to the progress of his discoveries. It is entitled, "On the firedamp of coal mines, and on methods of lighting the mines so as to prevent its explosion." As this paper is published in the *Philosophical Transactions*, and also in Sir Humphry's memoir on the safety lamp (1818), it is unnecessary to enter into any account of the innumerable delicate experiments made before he succeeded in producing lamps which were at once safe and gave a good light. It may be remarked, however, that the results achieved were arrived at by processes which could only have been pursued by an individual conversant with all the resources of chemical science, and with every scientific appliance at his command ; leaving out of view altogether the rare creative genius of Sir Humphry Davy, and the valuable aid which he acknowledges to have received from his talented assistant, Michael Faraday.

The dates at which the various announcements of the progress of Sir Humphry Davy's discoveries were made have been entered into with considerable detail, on account of the claim to priority of invention which was put forward, about a year afterwards, by Mr. R. W. Brandling, on behalf of George Stephenson, who, as we have seen, was at this time employed as engineer, or enginewright, at Killingworth Colliery, near Newcastle-on-Tyne.

It is perfectly clear that for some time, at all events, Sir Humphry and Mr. Stephenson were devoting their energies simultaneously to the invention of an insulated lamp on entirely different principles. The first occasion on which a *rencontre* took place between their respective lamps, was at a public meeting of the coal trade held at Newcastle-on-Tyne on the 10th of November, 1815.

It will be remembered that on the 30th of October, Sir Humphry Davy addressed letters, containing an account of his discoveries, to Dr. Gray and Mr. Hodgson, and that these communications were intended to be kept private. Mr. Hodgson, however, in his zeal for the cause, not only distributed copies of his letter among the viewers of the neighbourhood, but having seen a notice of Sir Humphry's discoveries in the public newspapers, considered it no longer necessary to maintain any reserve; and on his own responsibility attended the above-mentioned meeting, and read to the coalowners the communication which he had received.

The reading of the paper appeared to excite considerable interest. Mr. Hodgson was not aware at the time that Sir Humphry Davy had any rival in the field. But after he had read the paper, some gentlemen from the neighbourhood of Killingworth—and notably Mr. R. Lambert—made mention of Mr. Stephenson's lamp, which Mr. Hodgson then heard of for the first time (*Collection of Letters*, p. 32 ; Paris's *Life of Davy*, ii. 108). We shall therefore proceed to endeavour to elucidate the origin and progress of Mr. Stephenson's endeavours to invent an insulated lamp.

About the month of August, 1815 (*Report upon the Claims of Mr. George Stephenson*, etc., 1817, p. 14), Mr. Stephenson was in the habit of making experiments on blowers of firedamp in the Killingworth pit. He was expostulated with regarding the danger of igniting the gas, but excused himself by stating "generally" that he thought he could make it useful to preserve men's lives (p. 21). Having found that by holding a number of lighted candles on the windward side of the blower he could extinguish its flame by the "burnt air" proceeding from them, he was led to form a theory on which he thought a safety lamp might be constructed. This was that "if a lamp could be made to contain the burnt air above the flame, and to permit the firedamp to come in below in small quantity, to be burnt as it came in, the burnt air would prevent the passing of explosion upwards, and the velocity of the current from below would also prevent its passing downwards" (p. 14).

This theory he communicated to Mr. Wood "about or before the month of August" (p. 16). No steps, however, were taken to carry out the idea till the beginning of the month of October; when a plan was made by Mr. Wood from Mr. Stephenson's directions ; and the lamp was ordered from Mr. Hogg, a tinman in Newcastle, "most probably as early as the 2nd, but *certainly* before the 7th of October" (p. 2).

When Mr. Stephenson first spoke to Mr. Hogg regarding the lamp, he requested the tube might be made $\frac{1}{4}$-inch in diameter ; but Mr. Hogg having suggested that it probably would not burn, it was made $\frac{1}{2}$-inch in diameter, and a slide attached to it in order to lessen it, if necessary (p. 21). A glass for the lamp was also ordered at the Northumberland Glass House. It was conical in shape, and open at the top (p. 14).

The lamp was received from the manufacturer on October 21, and was tried at the blower in Killingworth Colliery on the evening of the same day. It was found that when the slide was so far shut that the lamp burnt "but feebly" in good air, when exposed to the current of the blower, "within a few inches of its mouth," the flame of the lamp increased in size, and then went out (p. 15). When in this condition the lamp was easily put out by motion (p. 17), and required to be carried " very steadily" (*1835 Rep.*, 1,537).

Mr. Stephenson's biographer has constructed a "pretty story" about the trial of this lamp, in which he states, with considerable emphasis, that the very first experiment with it was made by Mr. Stephenson in the mine at the risk of his own life. Mr. Wood, however, who was present, explains that "the danger was not quite so great as represented. At most," he says, "an explosion might have burnt the hands of the operator, but would not extend a few feet from the blower" ("Address on the two late eminent engineers, the Messrs. Stephenson," by N. Wood, Newcastle, 1860).

Whatever was proved by the trials to which the lamp was put, it was found that the tube and slide arrangement was a failure. If it was safe at all, it was only when the flame of the lamp was reduced to such a degree as to be practically valueless, as it could not bear being carried about. It was consequently determined to make alterations ; and as Mr. Stephenson conceived that the cause of the lamp going out with such facility was owing to the "burnt air" hanging about the flame, he determined to apply three smaller tubes instead of the one large one, and to place them round the flame and point them towards it in order to dislodge the air (*Report on the Claims*, etc., pp. 15, 16). The lamp was accordingly forthwith entrusted to a Mr. Matthews, a tinman in Newcastle, who made the alterations ; but they were of such a trivial character that the transaction was not entered in his books, and no particulars were preserved by him either of the date or of the size of the tubes (*ib.*, p. 22). They are stated, however (p. 4), to have been made "according to those dimensions which it was supposed the previous experiments with the slide had determined to be the dimensions of safety"—the safety, we presume, ascribed to "the velocity of the current from below."

The altered lamp—usually referred to as Mr. Stephenson's second lamp—was delivered to Mr. Stephenson on the 4th of November, and tried in Killingworth Colliery on the same day (p. 3). The accounts of the trial are somewhat laconic. Mr. Stephenson says it was "found safe" (p. 16). Mr. Wood states that it was "found to burn better than the other, but still not well; still, however, the explosion did not pass downwards" (pp. 17, 18). The overman states that the lamp was tried in a very foul place, and the effect was the same as before ; the flame increased and then went out. Also that Mr. Stephenson thought, and he agreed with him, that this altered lamp burnt better than the former one (p. 19).

Whether the tests which were applied to the altered lamp can be regarded as satisfactory evidence of its safety is certainly questionable. It is scarcely probable that either Mr. Stephenson, or his companions, knew at the time that undiluted firedamp extinguishes lights, or were acquainted with the proportions of gas and air which form the most explosive mixture. Again, was the lamp proof against passing explosion upwards? However this may be, it is evident that the lamp burned badly. Even Mr. Stephenson was disappointed with it. "It did not entirely answer my expectations," he says (*A Description of the Safety Lamp*, etc., 1817, 2nd ed., p. 8); nor is this surprising, inasmuch as, according to his *theory*, his lamp was to *burn* among firedamp, whereas it did exactly the reverse.

Mr. Stephenson's theory was no doubt erroneous, whatever may be said either as to the safety or utility of the lamp which he had produced. Two subsequent sets of experiments were made with it, however, which are worthy of note. We are told that "on the 17th of November it was tried at Killingworth office, with inflammable air, before Richard Lambert, Esq., and on the 24th of November before R. W. Brandling, Esq., C. J. Brandling, Esq., and Mr. Murray" (*Collection of Letters*, p. 5); and we also learn that at the latter date Mr. Stephenson had a new lamp in the hands of the manufacturer (*A Description of the Safety Lamp*, etc., 2nd ed., p. 10).

What transpired at Killingworth office on the 17th of November, we do not know. It is possible that Mr. Lambert, who championed Mr. Stephenson's cause at the meeting of the coal trade on the 10th of the month, may have made no reference to that episode, nor to the communication from Sir H. Davy which he had heard read, in which mention was made of the safety of lamps "having apertures only above and below." This, however, we do know, that immediately afterwards Mr. Stephenson set about constructing a new lamp, which differed in several essential particulars from his first lamp, and was apparently based on a different theory altogether. In the new lamp the air was admitted through a double series of apertures, the one placed above the other, and escaped through a covering full of apertures at the top of the chimney. The plan of this lamp was not drawn by Mr. Wood, but by a Mr. Henry Smith, clerk to Mr. Robert Watson, plumber, in Newcastle (*Report on the Claims*, etc., p. 24). It was ordered about the 19th or 20th of November, and was made and delivered to Mr. Stephenson in a few days (*ib.*).

This lamp—usually called Mr. Stephenson's third lamp, though, strictly speaking, it was his second new lamp—was tried in Killingworth pit on the 30th of November, "and found to be perfectly safe and burn extremely well"; and on the 5th of December it was exhibited and experimented upon with firedamp before a general meeting of the Literary and Philosophical Society of Newcastle-on-Tyne (*Collection of Letters*, p. 5).

We are told that at the above meeting Mr. Wood attempted to explain the *rationale* of the lamp, but was unable to do so, whereupon Mr. Stephenson stepped forward and described it "down to its minutest details." The account given by a gentleman who was present at the meeting—viz., Mr. J. H. H. Holmes, who was extremely interested in the subject of insulated lamps for miners, and who figures and describes the various lamps of the period, including the one exhibited by Mr. Stephenson at the above meeting, in his *Treatise on the Coal Mines of Durham and Northumberland*, published in 1816—is somewhat different:

"Mr. Stephenson," he says (p. 187), "undoubtedly claims great merit, if the invention produced was from his own genius. . . . The principle of this lamp (p. 188) is its being supplied with air through small perforations at the bottom, which, when in pure atmospheric air, enables the light to burn something similar to the radiance of a rush light. . . . In regard to this lantern having been tried in a mine six weeks previous to its appearance at the meeting, I must express some doubts, as it certainly did not wear the appearance of so old a practitioner, and as Mr. Stephenson appeared totally ignorant of the manner in which the air and gases operated upon the light. Nothing was heard or said of it previous to the private meeting before spoken of [held on the 28th of November], which was exclusively for the purpose of taking into consideration the methods of lighting collieries."

Mr. Holmes did not consider the tests which were applied to this lamp, at the meeting, as affording satisfactory evidence of its safety (p. 189).

There is a lamp now in the possession of the Literary and Philosophical Society of Newcastle-on-Tyne, which is stated to be the identical lamp exhibited at the above meeting. If it be so it is not in the same condition as it then was; *e.g.*, the lamp exhibited had a conical glass and no trimmer; the lamp now in the possession of the society has a cylindrical glass and the Davy trimmer.

From what has been already stated, it must be obvious that the claim to priority of invention put forward by Mr. R. W. Brandling, on behalf of Mr. Stephenson, was altogether preposterous. And it cannot but be admitted that some of the devices resorted to in the pamphlets published in support of Mr. Stephenson's alleged claim could only be justified on the principle that "all's fair in love and war."

The discovery which Sir Humphry Davy had made, that explosion would not pass through small apertures and tubes, was only a stepping stone to still higher achievements; and before the close of the year 1815 he gave to the world the *wire gauze* safety lamp. This was the last, the most splendid, the crowning triumph of his labours—the "metallic tissue permeable to light and air and impermeable to flame."

The first Davy lamps—as the wire gauze lamps were named after their illustrious inventor—arrived in the north of England on the 8th of January, 1816; and on the following day were experimented upon by the Rev. J. Hodgson, Mr. Dunn, and others, at the blower in Hebburn Colliery from which the firedamp had been obtained, with the most satisfactory results (Raine's *Life of Hodgson*, i. 178).[1] On the 17th of the month they were put to still more severe tests in the same mine by Mr. Hodgson, Mr. Buddle, and Mr. Dunn; and on this occasion were carried into a dangerous working-place, to the intense alarm of a solitary pitman, who was working by the glimmering light of a steel mill, and who threatened to send his pick into the man who was rash enough to advance with what he took to be an ordinary candle (*ib.*, pp. 182-83).[2]

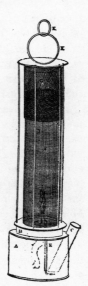

FIG. 42.—DAVY LAMP.

By no one was the invention more eagerly welcomed than by Mr. Buddle; no one was a better judge of its inestimable value. "I first tried it," he says, "in an explosive mixture on the surface, and then took it into a mine, and to my astonishment and delight, it is impossible for me to express my feelings at the time when I first suspended the lamp in the mine, and saw it red hot; if it had been a monster destroyed, I could not have felt more exultation

[1] There is a slight discrepancy between this account and Mr. Dunn's (*Win. and Work.*, 2nd ed., p. 166), who speaks of having tried the lamp on the 1st of January.

[2] The two Davy lamps used on the above occasions were presented by Mr. Hodgson to Miss Emma Trevelyan in 1836, by whose brother they were subsequently placed in the Museum of Practical Geology, London (Raine's *Life of Hodgson*, i. 183).

than I did.   I said to those around me, 'We have at last subdued this monster'" (*1835 Report*, 2,226).

In the autumn of this year (1816), Sir Humphry Davy accompanied Mr. Buddle into some of the fiery mines of the north, to see his lamp in actual use.   "Sir Humphry was delighted," says Mr. Buddle, "and I was overwhelmed with feelings of gratitude to that great genius which had produced it" (*ib.*; Paris's *Life of Davy*, ii. 132).

Mr. Buddle remonstrated with Sir Humphry for not securing the invention by a patent, from which he might have derived an income of five or ten thousand a year.   "The reply of this great and noble-minded man," he says, "was 'No, my good friend, I never thought of such a thing, my sole object was to serve the cause of humanity, and if I have succeeded, I am amply rewarded in the gratifying reflection of having done so.'"

On the occasion of this visit, Sir Humphry drew attention to a point requiring to be observed in the use of his lamp, viz., that it should not be exposed to a strong current of explosive mixture without being protected, and gave instructions that under such circumstances a shield partly encircling the gauze should be employed.   This source of danger he demonstrated experimentally, at the pipe which conveyed the gas from the blower in the shaft at the Morton West pit, Lambton Colliery, up to the surface, in the presence of a large party, as thus described by Mr. Buddle :

"We took a length of hose from an extinguishing engine, with the jet-pipe upon it, and attached that to the blower pipe at the top of the pit; it was held horizontally, and the jet was thrown very forcibly out of the nozzle of the pipe; the blower was sufficiently strong to propel the stream of gas across the engine-house.   I well recollect the pipe was held at the entrance of the engine-house, and the jet passed the explosion to the far end of the room, for it was very powerful; the distance that the blower fired it was from nine to twelve feet, I should think.   I held the lamp in the direction of the jet, and not having seen it before, I was not very apprehensive of its firing.   It did not fire at first, but as I approached the end of the nozzle pipe the gauze became red-hot and passed the explosion. The flame was as long, or longer, than the breadth of the engine-room; I remember that it burnt the nap off my great coat and spoiled it.   This experiment was repeated over and over again. Lord Durham himself was present, and a great many other persons, professional men and others, were present on this occasion.   The force of Sir Humphry's remarks at the time was : 'Now, gentlemen, you see the nature of the danger to which you are exposed in using

he lamp, and I caution you to guard against it in the manner I
have shown you. This is to show the only case in which the lamp
will explode, and I caution and warn you not to use it in any such
case when you can avoid it, without using the shield'" (*1835 Report*,
2,227).

An account of the above experiments, made in September, 1816,
was also given by Sir Humphry Davy in his memoir, *On the Safety
Lamp*, published in 1818 (p. 137).

As early as March, 1816, a deputation of the northern coalowners
requested the honour of an interview with Sir Humphry Davy, and
presented him with a letter containing an expression of the united
thanks of the coalowners for his great discovery (Paris's *Life of
Davy*, ii. 109, 110). A few months later it was felt that some mark
of acknowledgment and respect should be presented to Sir Humphry
by the coal trade; and a meeting was held on August 31, when
resolutions were passed accordingly.

At an adjourned meeting of the coalowners, held October 11,
1816, Mr. William Brandling demurred to the presentation to Sir
Humphry Davy, bringing forward the claims of Mr. Stephenson,
and requesting that an investigation should first be made to ascertain who was the real inventor. This proposal was submitted to
the meeting and negatived (*ib.*, 115). The same meeting, however,
voted one hundred guineas to Mr. Stephenson, as an acknowledgment
of his labours in the same direction.

The presentation to Sir Humphry was made at a dinner held at
the "Queen's Head," Newcastle, on the 11th of October, 1817, Mr.
J. G. Lambton (afterwards Earl of Durham) presiding. It consisted
of a service of plate worth £2,500 (*1835 Report*, 2,418).

Mr. Stephenson's supporters held a meeting on November 1, 1817,
with C. J. Brandling, Esq., in the chair, when a committee was
appointed to collect subscriptions on his behalf, of which Richard
Lambert, Esq., was treasurer, and R. W. Brandling, Esq., secretary.
The amount collected, added to the sum previously voted by the
coalowners, reached the handsome total of about £800. This,
together with a silver tankard, was presented to Mr. Stephenson
by C. J. Brandling, Esq., at a public dinner held in the Assembly
Rooms, Newcastle, on the 12th of January, 1818 (*Philosophical
Mag.*, li. 70).

The claims of Dr. Clanny, who is entitled to the highest credit on
account of his originating the idea of the insulated lamp, were long
overlooked, beyond his receiving the gold and silver medals of the
Society of Arts. It was not till as late as 1846 that steps were

taken to procure for him some public acknowledgment of his labours in the cause of humanity in connection with colliery explosions. An appeal having been made on his behalf, a purse of gold (amounting to 100 sovereigns) was collected, which, together with a silver salver, was presented to him at the Athenæum, Sunderland, on 3rd February, 1848 (Dunn's *Win. and Work.*, 2nd ed., p. 162; *Min. Jour.*, xviii. 70).

The invention of the Davy lamp was regarded by Dr. Gray as a sufficient reason for dissolving the Sunderland Society for the Prevention of Accidents in Mines (*1835 Report*, 330).

The share which the Rev. J. Hodgson had in the steps which led to the invention of the Davy lamp, was no small one. It was he who, braving the displeasure of the affluent Brandlings, had vividly portrayed and laid before the public eye, in his little pamphlet on the explosion at their colliery, the awful spectacle presented by a coal mine devastated by "whirlwinds of tempestuous fire," and aroused the attention of the humane to the perils to which the workers in fiery collieries were exposed. The assistance he had given in forwarding the invention afforded him some solace even in his last illness.[1]

Sir Humphry Davy in after life always dwelt with peculiar satisfaction and delight upon the invention of his safety lamp. "I value it," he said, "more than anything I ever did. It was the result of a great deal of investigation and labour ; but if my directions be only attended to, it will save the lives of thousands of poor labourers. I never was more affected than by a written address which I received from the working colliers, when I was in the North, thanking me, on behalf of themselves and their families, for the preservation of their lives." He was also delighted to show to his friends the service of plate which had been presented to him (Paris's *Life*, ii. 139).

Not only has the safety lamp been instrumental in saving thousands of lives, but it introduced a new era in coal mining. It enabled untold millions of tons of coal to be rescued from the bowels of the earth, which without its aid would have been irrevocably lost. It rendered possible the entire removal of the pillars of coal, great part of which had been previously left underground in fiery

---

[1] To Mr. Hodgson belongs the honour of suggesting some permanent organization for affording relief to sufferers from accidents in coal mines, and also to aged and infirm colliers—a proposal which was endorsed by Mr. Buddle immediately afterwards, and took the form of the Permanent Fund at a later period.

mines. It led to the re-opening of many collieries which had been abandoned, after having been worked out as far as was practicable by means of candles and steel mills.

The safety lamp began to be made use of at Whitehaven in February, 1816. It was introduced at a colliery at Plas Issa, in Wales, in June of the same year, *immediately after, and in consequence of,* an explosion of firedamp having occurred there. Here the manager of the mine had some difficulty in getting it tried, partly on account of the opposition of the colliers' wives, who, by their noise and lamentations, indicated the contempt and scepticism with which they regarded the invention (Davy, *On the Safety Lamp,* 1818, pp. 129-131). But for a long period the chief field for the employment of the lamp was in the most dangerous parts of the fiery mines of the north of England.

The safety lamp did not put an end to colliery explosions; it never got the opportunity of doing so, or the catalogue of these calamities would, to say the least of it, have been vastly curtailed. But where employed it rendered inestimable aid. Indeed, it may be said that deep coal mining would have been beset with insuperable difficulties, had science not armed the miners with the wonderful insulated lamp, which warns them of the presence of their invisible enemy, and protects them from its power.

Well might Mr. Surtees exclaim (*Hist. of Durham,* ii. 89), "What fairer triumph, what brighter extension of the empire of science, has marked the annals of philosophy, than this victory over the swart demon of the mine!"

CHAPTER XLI.

THE NINETEENTH CENTURY. 1801-1816.

Feared scarcity of colliers in the north in 1804. Alteration of date of binding, and strike of 1810. Destruction of small coal by burning. Mr. Benjamin Thompson invents the drop, and improves the screening arrangements. Proposed legislative control over collieries, for the preservation of mining records, and introduction of improvements. Estimates of the production of coal.

IN connection with the annual binding of the pitmen in the north, a custom had arisen of giving two or three guineas to each collier, or hewer, as binding or bounty money; but in the year 1804, in consequence of an extraordinary demand for coal having arisen, and the collieries of Sir H. Vane Tempest, at Pensher and Rainton, having become greatly extended under the management of Mr. Arthur Mowbray, a general scramble for hewers and putters took place when the binding time arrived. So great was the fear of not procuring a necessary supply of men, that twelve or fourteen guineas per man were given on the Tyne, and eighteen guineas on the Wear, and likewise exorbitant bounties to putters, drivers, and others. Drink was lavished in the utmost profusion, and every sort of extravagance committed; and a positive increase of wages established to the extent of 30 or 40 per cent. (Dunn's *Coal Trade*, p. 28).

The high wages brought many labourers and their families into the mines. But the period of excitement soon passed over, and matters returned to their normal level. An attempt was even made by the coalowners to reduce the gratuities almost to a nominal sum. In 1809 the amount of binding money to be given to hewers was fixed at 5s. on the Tyne and 10s. 6d. on the Wear, to such as were householders, and at 8s. on the Tyne and 13s. 6d. on the Wear to single men (*Trans. N.E. Inst.*, xv. 217). But this arrangement appears to have been frustrated by the opposition of the pitmen.

At this time the coalowners became desirous to remove the ceremony of binding from the long-accustomed month of October, to January, as calculated to suit the trade better, and determined to bind the pitmen for three months only, in order to make the alteration. Instead of carrying out this, however, they seem to have sought to bring about the same result by extending the period of binding for a longer term than usual. But when the old binding time came round in October, 1810, a general strike took place to have it re-altered to October. To this the coalowners would not consent, and the law was had recourse to, with the result that great numbers of the pitmen were imprisoned, and Durham gaol was so full that 300 of them were immured in the Bishop's stables (*ib.*, 219; Dunn's *Coal Trade*, p. 30). By the intervention of the Rev. Mr. Neshfield the differences were at length adjusted, and from this time April 5 was adopted as the binding day. Under Mr. Neshfield's proposals the amount of binding money was to be continued the same as the year preceding, viz., five guineas per man (Sykes's *Loc. Rec.*, ii. 403).

In this era, and indeed for a long time subsequently, a great destruction of small coal was going on, the amount of duty chargeable upon it, combined with the small price obtainable for it, operating together to reduce its sale to a minimum. What could be left in the pit was allowed to remain there ; what must necessarily be brought to the surface was thrown on a heap at the pit bank, which, whether ignited spontaneously (Dunn's *Win. and Work.*, 2nd ed., p. 227) or on purpose, was usually a burning or fiery heap. "Masses of valuable coal," says Mr. Chapman (pamphlet, 1815, p. 26), "frequently exceeding 3,000 or 4,000 London chaldrons each, enlighten the surrounding country during the night, as may be almost generally witnessed by all travellers on the great north road from Durham to Morpeth." It was estimated that from one-fourth to one-fifth of all the coal brought out of the pits was extracted by the process of screening, some of which was consumed in making cinders, or coke, and some for making mineral tar, but the remainder was simply destroyed by burning. In some instances even one-third of the whole output of a colliery was so destroyed (Thompson's *Inventions*, etc., 1847, p. 2).

Among the various useful improvements in the mechanical department of colliery engineering introduced by Mr. Benjamin Thompson after he became managing partner of Urpeth or Bewicke Main Colliery in 1811, was the invention of the apparatus known as the "drop," for lowering the wagon down to the vessel's hold in order to save the breakage incurred by the coal in falling from a height. A similar arrangement had been devised and patented by Mr. W. Chapman in 1800, and applied at Benwell staith, but it did not prove satisfactory and was abandoned. Mr. Thompson's drop was, however, original with him, and was a great improvement on Chapman's arrangement. It was first set to work at Bewicke Main staith in 1812 (Thompson's *Inventions*, etc., 1847, p. 3), and subsequently came into extended use.

The same gentleman effected great improvements in the arrangements for the screening of coals. At this time the screens were very short, and the bars from $\frac{1}{2}$ inch to $\frac{5}{8}$ inch and even $\frac{3}{4}$ inch apart, with the result that the coal was both badly cleared of small, and much valuable coal passed between the bars. Mr. Thompson lengthened the screens to more than twice their former length, and reduced the space between the bars to $\frac{3}{8}$ inch, thus at the same time more effectually extracting the very small part, and likewise preventing any of the better part from being lost (*ib.*, p. 23). This improvement was introduced at Urpeth Colliery in 1812.

Mr. Thompson also introduced the use of a second screen, having bars $\frac{3}{16}$ inch apart, for the purpose of re-screening the small coal and extracting the dust. This was first applied at Ouston Colliery in 1815 (*ib.*, p. 24). His arrangements were found to answer well, particularly as a reduction of duty was made in the following year on coal passed through a screen the bars of which did not exceed $\frac{3}{8}$ inch apart, when such was exported oversea (*ib.*, p. 64).

Cast iron was now used for making screen bars in some cases (*ib.*, p. 65). Cast-iron props for underground work were patented in 1802 (Farey's *Agriculture*, etc., i. 348).

An attempt was made to introduce circular sheet-iron tubs in lieu of the wicker corves universally employed in raising coal in the north, at Washington Colliery, in 1812. As they had to pass each other in the shaft, they were found unsuitable and abandoned (Dunn's *Coal Trade*, p. 61).

Illustrative of the progress being made in the underground department of colliery engineering, and the change which was taking place from vehicles dragged over the floor of the mine, to carriages running on rails, it may be mentioned that, subsequent to his appointment as colliery engineer at Killingworth, in 1812, Mr. George Stephenson introduced tram roads there, in lieu of the sledges previously employed (*Trans. N.E. Inst.*, viii 41) in the conveyance of the coal from the working-places to the main roads.

He was also one of the earliest to employ the steam engine in hauling coal from the dip of the shaft.

The subject of the preservation of mining records, which had been brought forward by Mr. Thomas, of Denton, in 1797, and again in 1808 (Holmes's *Coal Mines*, p. 214), was revived by Mr. Wm. Chapman immediately after the great inundation at Heaton, in 1815. But while the scheme suggested by Mr. Thomas only contemplated a voluntary registration of records in the Newcastle-on-Tyne district, Mr. Chapman's proposal went much further, recommending that such a movement should be initiated in all the coal mining districts, and setting forth that the preservation of plans of abandoned and exhausted workings was a matter worthy of the attention of the Legislature, and should be made compulsory by Act of Parliament.

The idea of legislative control being invoked to enforce the preservation of mining records in this country, appears to have been suggested to Mr. Chapman by a translation of a French pamphlet relative to the coal mines at Liége, published by the Rev. J. Hodgson in the *Newcastle Courant* in 1814. His paper—entitled "Observations on the Necessity of Adopting Legislative Measures to Diminish the Probability of the Recurrence of Fatal Accidents in Collieries, and to Prolong the Duration of the Coal Mines of the United Kingdom,"—like that of Mr. Thomas, was read before the Literary and Philosophical Society of Newcastle-on-Tyne ; and, with a liberality and public spirit deserving of all praise, this society published the two papers together, at its own expense, in 1815.

The proposals of Mr. Thomas and Mr. Chapman were chiefly designed for the benefit of posterity, but, immediately after the paper of the latter gentleman was produced, Mr. Holmes, in the correspondence in the *Morning Chronicle* already adverted to, warmly advocated the desirability of legislative supervision over the working of collieries with a view to secure the introduction of improvements such as the safety lamp ; and reiterated the same ideas in his treatise on the coal mines, published in the following year (see Holmes's *Coal Mines*, pp. 138, 142, 144, 156, 172). The movement failed to elicit any response at the time, but the fact that the efforts of private individuals to compass the safe and efficient working of collieries required to be supplemented by aids of a more comprehensive character continued to gain ground from this time forward.

Mr. Chapman, in his paper above mentioned, estimated the

annual consumption of coal in Great Britain, exclusive of waste, to be as follows, in 1815 :

	Tons.
In the iron and other manufactories in the coal counties, about.	4,000,000
Coals paying coast duty ; about 3,600,000 ch. Winchester, or	5,040,000
Coals consumed for culinary and other purposes, in the counties not paying duty, about	4,000,000
Total,	13,040,000

In the following year we have another and somewhat more detailed estimate. The nothern coalowners were now beginning to find themselves driven out of many of their ancient markets, by coals coming from the other coalfields which were duty free, and the quantity of which was gradually becoming larger and larger simultaneously with the improved facilities afforded by the extension of canals and railways. In order to obtain some information on this point, a deputation was sent from the River Wear in 1816 to collect statistics (*1829 Report*, p. 95). The quantity of coals conveyed by canals and railways in different parts of the kingdom at this date, as estimated by them, is given below in chaldrons, together with the same reduced into tons, as given by Samuel Salt in his *Statistics and Calculations* (1845, p. 63) :

	Chaldrons.	Tons.
Yorkshire,	967,406	2,563,626
Derbyshire,	355,554	942,218
Nottinghamshire,	186,666	494,665
Leicestershire,	66,666	176,665
Warwickshire,	162,962	431,849
Staffordshire,	300,000	795,000
Quantity that passes towards the eastern sea,	2,039,254	5,404,023
And there is good reason for believing that an equal quantity passes towards the west and south,	2,039,254	5,404,023
Quantity supposed to be sold annually without paying duty, and carried by canals and railways,	4,078,508	10,808,046
If to the figures given above we add the vend from the northern ports for the same year, viz. (Dunn's *Coal Trade*, p. 72),	1,125,551	2,982,710
We obtain—exclusive of waste, local sale, and the production of Scotland and Ireland— total for year 1816,		13,790,756

CHAPTER XLII.

THE NINETEENTH CENTURY. 1817-1835.

Collieries of the Tyne and Wear. Sinkings through the Magnesian Limestone. Opening up of the South Durham district.

THE sight of the safety lamp in the hands of some hundreds of miners in the Newcastle-on-Tyne neighbourhood, who spoke of them with a mixture of gratitude and affection under the name of *Davys*, we are told by a writer who visited the north shortly after the lamp came into use, made his heart glow at the thought of the greatness of the benefits conferred on humanity by the invention of the wire gauze safe lamp (Mr. Knight, *Phil. Maga.*, January, 1817).

The introduction of the Davy lamp gave a new lease of life to the deep collieries of the Tyne basin. Walker Colliery, after having been completely worked out as far as was practicable by means of candles and steel mills, and having been abandoned in 1811, was re-opened in 1817 with Davy lamps, and has continued working ever since. Great part of the formerly relinquished workings of Walls-end, Willington, Percy Main, Hebburn, and Jarrow, were likewise recovered and again brought into work by its aid, as also parts of Elswick and Benwell, on the west side of Newcastle, and several collieries on the Wear (Prof. Phillips's *Report*, p. 9; Paris's *Life of Davy*, ii. 136).

Few new sinkings were made in the immediate vicinity of the Tyne at this period, but a number of the collieries were deepened to lower seams.

At Wallsend the A pit was sunk to the Bensham seam—which lay about 870 feet below the surface—in 1820, and a small portion of the seam worked by means of a brattice; four other shafts being sunk to it subsequently (*Trans. Nat. Hist. Soc. Northumberland*, ii. 350-51). The working of the Main coal or High Main seam at this colliery, was discontinued in 1831 (*Proc. Inst. Mechan. Eng.*, 1847-49, p. 31).

The St. Hilda pit, at South Shields Colliery, was sunk to the Bensham seam in 1825, at a depth of about 858 feet from the surface, the shaft being divided into an upcast and downcast by means of a brattice (Hair's *Sketches*, p. 34).

About the same time Jarrow Colliery was sunk to the Bensham seam, at a depth of 1,050 feet (*ib.*, p. 31), by means of a staple from the Main coal; and a similar staple was sunk to the Bensham seam at Willington Colliery in 1831, where it lay at a depth of 870 feet from the surface (*ib.*, p. 16).

On the western edge of the Tyne basin High Heworth Colliery was sunk to the Low Main coal in 1821, at a depth of 817 feet (*London and Edinburgh Phil. Maga.*, iii. 98).

An event of some importance in the history of the collieries of this tract was the erection of a large pumping engine at Friar's Goose, by Messrs. Losh, Wilson, & Bell, of Walker Ironworks, in 1823, for the purpose of drawing off the water in the High Main seam at Tyne Main Colliery, situated about a mile and a-half east of Gateshead. The cylinder of the engine was 6 feet in diameter, with a stroke of 9 feet, the stroke of the pumps being 7 feet 2 inches. It worked three sets of pumps, each 16½ inches in diameter, and raised 1,170 gallons of water per minute from a depth of 330 feet. Its power was estimated at 180 horses; and it continued for a long period to be the most powerful engine on the Tyne (Hair's *Sketches*, pp. 20, 36; *Industrial Resources of the Tyne*, etc., 2nd ed., p. 294; *Iron and Coal Trades Review*, lvi. 297).

The erection of the above engine led to the re-opening of St. Lawrence Colliery, or Picton Main, on the opposite side of the Tyne, in 1831; where, after an unsuccessful attempt to obtain coal in the High Main seam, a new sinking was effected to the Low Main seam in 1833 (Latimer's *Loc. Rec.*, p. 14). Mr. Matthias Dunn entered upon the management of the colliery in 1832, and the sinking was executed in the short space of eight months, the depth being 564 feet.

Among other sinkings made in the more outlying portion of the Tyne district, a new colliery was established near the hamlet of Wide-open, about five and a-half miles north of Newcastle, where the High Main coal lay at a depth of 480 feet. Here sinking was commenced in April, 1825, and coals drawn in May, 1827. The railway from this colliery to the shipping place near Percy Main was close upon ten miles (nine and three-quarter miles 193 yards) in length; and there were five fixed engines, and several locomotives employed to work it (Hair's *Sketches*, pp. 24, 25). Of what construction the locomotives were we are not informed. The wagons employed were peculiar, carrying only half a chaldron of coal.

At the same period a sinking of an exceptional character was made by Messrs. Brandling at Gosforth, three miles north of Newcastle. The coal to be won lay on the north side of the great fault or dislocation, which intersects the coalfield from east to west, and is known as the Ninety Fathom Dyke, from the circumstance of its depressing the strata on the north side to that extent at one of the points where it was pierced, though the extent of the depression at Gosforth was nearly twice as much. In order to avoid the watery strata on the north side of the fault, the pits were sunk on its south side, and the coal won and worked by means of horizontal tunnels through the dyke.[1]

Sinking was commenced at Gosforth in 1825, and finished in October, 1827; the depth of the east pit being 1,130 feet, and of the west pit 1,086 feet. The High Main coal was cut 584 yards from the pits, and the extent of the depression on the north side of the dyke found to be 960 feet (*London and Edinburgh Phil. Maga.*, iii. 30-34). The coal was won on January 31, 1829, and on February 6th the event was celebrated after a unique fashion, a grand subterranean ball being given to the workmen and others, at which between 200 and 300 persons were present, nearly one-half of whom were females (Sykes's *Loc. Rec.*).

On the south side of the Tyne, Springwell Colliery, belonging to Lord Ravensworth and partners, and situated about three miles south-east of Gateshead, commenced shipping coal in January, 1826 (*ib.*).

Taken as a whole the collieries of the Tyne were now in a declining state, and were gradually losing the premier position in the coal trade which they had so long held. But little whole coal now remained to work in the famous High Main seam. So far as it was concerned, most of the collieries were reduced to the old pillars which had been left for their supplies of coal, which were now being recovered, at greatly increased cost, by a second, and sometimes even a third working (*1829 Report*, p. 82; *1830 Report*, pp. 259-301).

Simultaneously with the decline of the collieries of the Tyne,

[1] On account of the peculiar situation of the sinking, the shafts passed through the whole series of workable coal seams from the High Main to the Brockwell. For much interesting information relating to Gosforth Colliery, see Mr. Embleton's paper in *Transactions N.E. Inst.*, vol. xxxviii.

those on the Wear began to take the foremost position in the market, and to command the highest prices for their coal. Here also an important discovery was made in this era, which led to a commencement being made to open up a large tract of country hitherto regarded as wholly barren of good coal (*1830 Report*, p. 231), but which now became a field for the establishment of deep and extensive collieries.

In the eastern, and more particularly in the south-eastern portion of the county of Durham, the coal measures are overlapped and concealed by a more recent and unconformable formation belonging to the Permian system, and known as the Magnesian Limestone. The depth at which the coal lay, added to the unpromising character of the surface, had hitherto presented an effectual barrier to the development of this part of the coalfield; to say nothing of the belief prevalent among the mining engineers in the north that the coal deteriorated when it passed under the limestone rock.

This opinion appears to have originated from the following circumstances. As the High Main seam trended away southwards from the Tyne, a small band of stone made its appearance in the middle of it, which gradually increased in thickness until the two sections were so completely separated as to render the seam unworkable. This band of stone was known as the Heworth band, doubtless from its having been first encountered in the workings of the colliery there, but was found to range from west to east through the collieries of Hebburn, Jarrow, and South Shields, destroying the High Main seam in the southern portion of these collieries.

Various unsuccessful borings had also been made to obtain coal near the limestone. Thus Edington, writing in 1813, speaks of Messrs. Hurrey & Ismay's bore, made to the east of South Shields Colliery to a depth of 600 ft. without finding coal, and states that it was supposed they had not gone deep enough; "but," he remarks, "as the limestone put in, we seldom find coal and limestone together" (*Coal Trade*, p. 140).

A more favourable boring is mentioned by Holmes, in 1816 (*Coal Mines*, p. 11), as having been made by a Mr. Goodchild near his quarries west of Sunderland. "After trying to a great depth, the argillaceous shale which generally accompanies coal was found, and next came the regular coal strata; but the investigation ended here, as the expense of sinking shafts, etc., would have been too great, while seams nearer the surface are workable."

Borings are also mentioned (*London and Edinburgh Phil. Maga.*, iii. 99) as having been made near Scots House in the vicinity of the

Boldon Hills, but they were not sufficiently encouraging, and the opinion prevailed that no mine would be worked to profit near or under the Magnesian Limestone.

This idea appears to have likewise received support from the fact of an inferior seam of coal having been worked under the limestone near Ferryhill, in the southern part of the coalfield, in the latter part of the eighteenth century. Hence the opinion continued to prevail that this large tract was barren of good coal, giving rise to the dictum, "No coal under the Magnesian Limestone"—an opinion which was held by many of the proprietors of estates situated on the limestone at the time of William Smith's visit to Durham in 1821-22, though he at once perceived the fallacy of it, and estimated that coal could be got at workable depth at Haswell, under the estate of Colonel Braddyll, which he was employed to survey (Professor Phillips's *Memoirs of W. Smith*, p. 102).

Just at this period the first sinking within the edge of the limestone was successfully effected, and the illusion regarding the barren nature of the strata underneath it was gradually dispelled, leading to this extensive area—hitherto looked upon as of no value—becoming the scene of some of the largest, deepest, and most costly collieries that had yet been opened out.

The work of piercing through the limestone to the coal measures beneath was in some cases attended with extraordinary difficulty and expense. This was partly occasioned by the open character of the rock itself, which, being intersected by numerous large fissures, discharged vast quantities of water into the shafts ; but a still more formidable difficulty presented itself when the bottom of the limestone was reached. Here, at the break between the two unconformable formations, a bed of loose sand existed, of varying thickness and consistency, but nearly always yielding great feeders of water, to penetrate which was at times a task of immensely greater difficulty than cutting the hardest rock.

An attempt to sink at Hetton, near Houghton-le-Spring, was made by Mr. Lyons as early as 1810,[1] but was abandoned on account of the sand being found to prove an insuperable obstacle (Fordyce's *Coal and Iron*, p. 93). Ten years later, however, another attempt was made by the Hetton Coal Company which proved successful. On meeting with the sand the sinkers endeavoured to draw it off by engine power, but were obliged to desist as the ground for a con-

---

[1] Mr. Lyons is stated (*Min. Jour.*, xi. 85) to have bored to the coal under the limestone, in 1810, but the fact does not appear to have been made public.

siderable distance round sunk in. Recourse was then had to a cast-iron cylinder, consisting of segments bolted together, and sunk by pressure, by which means the first pit was carried through the sand, though at great expense (Dunn's *Win. and Work.*, 2nd ed., p. 44). Of the two pits sunk, the Blossom pit was begun December 19, 1820, and reached the Main coal September 3, 1822, at a depth of 649 feet. The Minor pit (45 yards west of the Blossom pit) was begun December 23, 1820, and carried down to the Hutton seam at a depth of 882 feet. The limestone was 156 feet thick, and the soft sandstone, at the break between it and the coal measures, was only 4 feet 4 inches in thickness. The feeders of water amounted to nearly 2,000 gallons per minute (*London and Edinburgh Phil. Maga.*, iii. 200-4).

To connect this colliery with the shipping port of Sunderland necessitated the construction of a private railway about seven or eight miles in length, the superintendence of which was entrusted to Mr. George Stephenson, who still held the position of engineer to Lord Ravensworth and partners, and resided at Killingworth—an appointment for which he was probably indebted to the influence of his brother Robert Stephenson, who was engineer at Hetton Colliery at this time (*Min. Jour.*, xi. 85). The railway was constructed in accordance with Mr. Stephenson's ideas, and laid with a form of cast-iron rail designed and patented by himself and Mr. Losh, of Walker Ironworks, in 1816 (Wood's *Railroads*, p. 30). As the character of the country to be traversed precluded the formation of a level railway, it was necessary to employ various forms of hauling power. The line was opened for traffic on November 18, 1822 ; the machinery employed to work it consisting of "five of Mr. George Stephenson's patent travelling engines, two 60 h.-p. reciprocating engines, and five self-acting incline planes" (Sykes's *Loc. Rec.*).

The locomotives, however, did not prove a success. From a MS. report on Hetton Colliery, made in 1827, we learn that three of them had then been abandoned, and supplanted by fixed engines ; and it was recommended by the reporters as well worthy of consideration whether the two remaining locomotives should not likewise be taken off the line, and their place also be filled by reciprocating engines. These two locomotives hauled trains consisting of sixteen wagons, and worked a portion of the railway one and a-quarter miles in length.

Within a few years after the establishment of Hetton Colliery, a sinking which exhibited remarkable boldness of conception was projected by Messrs. Pemberton in what was in large measure unknown ground, near the coast, at Monkwearmouth. This famous undertaking was commenced in May, 1826, and notwithstanding great difficulty the works were pushed forward with spirit and determination. But progress was slow, and it was not till after five years' labour that the first unequivocal stratum of the coal formation was reached in August, 1831. This consisted of a seam of coal 1½ inches in thickness, found at the depth of 344 feet from the surface. The thickness of the covering of limestone was 325 feet, and the stratum of sand was 5 feet thick. The feeders of water amounted to 3,000 gallons per minute; but this was soon dammed back by a casing of cast-iron tubbing, which was carried from the little seam of coal above mentioned to within 78 feet of the surface.

For a considerable distance into the coal measures the outlook seemed very unpromising, as a greater thickness of barren strata was pierced than had ever been encountered previously. A new feeder of water was also met with at a depth of 1,000 feet, requiring fresh pumps, and a fresh outlay of money. In the eyes of most men the prospects of the enterprising adventurers seemed dark indeed; by many of the viewers the project was denounced as hopeless. But Messrs. Pemberton boldly persevered, sinking deeper and deeper, until in February, 1834, their pluck was rewarded by the shaft coming upon a seam of coal of considerable thickness and value at the depth of 1,578 feet. This seam was found to be identical with the Bensham seam of the Tyne, or Maudlin seam of the Wear. The winning of this colliery is stated to have cost between £80,000 and £100,000 (*Fossil Fuel*, p. 187; Latimer's *Loc. Rec.*; Fordyce's *Coal and Iron*, p. 73).

In the meantime a number of other sinkings had been carried down through the limestone. The Hetton Coal Company opened out additional pits at Elemore and Eppleton; the Hutton seam being won at the latter colliery in June, 1833, at a depth of 930 feet (*Trans. N.E. Inst.*, xv. 234). The Elemore pits are situated a mile south-west, and the Eppleton pits about a mile north-east of the Hetton pits.

Another sinking was made in the northern part of the township of Haswell, by Colonel Braddyll and partners—the South Hetton Coal Company—which, after piercing 342 feet of limestone, and 30 feet of sand, reached the Hutton seam at a depth of 1,080 feet (Fordyce's *Coal and Iron*, p. 93). The colliery was opened, amidst great festivities, on August 5, 1833 (Latimer). The pits were

15 feet in diameter, and divided by brattices into three equal parts (*Child. Employ. Com.*, Appendix i., p. 149).

The first attempt made by the Haswell Coal Company to effect a sinking in the same township was abandoned after an expenditure of £60,000, on account of the stratum of quicksand encountered at the bottom of the limestone, proving 120 feet thick, and yielding 4,000 gallons of water per minute (Dunn's *Win. and Work.*, 2nd ed., p. 6). The second attempt was more fortunate. By means of boring, a spot was found free from quicksand, and here a shaft was sunk which reached the Hutton seam, after five years' labour, at a depth of 930 feet, on March 11, 1835 (Fordyce's *Coal and Iron*, p. 94 ; Latimer).

At Thornley Colliery, about two miles south of Haswell, coal was won on January 29, 1834 (Latimer).

In the first quarter of the present century, and even later, some of the collieries in the South Durham district continued in a highly primitive condition ; being wholly dependent for their trade on the landsale of the surrounding district. At Brandon Colliery, near Brancepeth, a whim gin was employed in raising the coal ; and instead of being a horse gin as usual, a bull was yoked to the machine (Fordyce's *Coal and Iron*, p. 97). At another colliery, near Witton-le-Wear, the coals were drawn by an ass, and banked out and sold by an old woman ; while the western dales of Yorkshire were supplied with coals from Butterknowle Colliery, carried on the backs of droves of mules (*Trans. N.E. Inst.*, xv. 236, 179).

But this district was now to be awakened from its slumbering mediæval simplicity. The twenty miles intervening between the coalfield and the sea, which had hitherto presented an effectual barrier to the development of the collieries, was about to be bridged over by an iron road, and the snort of the iron horse to be heard in the neighbourhood.

In 1821 an Act of Parliament was obtained for the formation of the Stockton and Darlington Railway (Richardson's *Table Book*, H.D., iii. 231)—a project which appears to have been chiefly promoted by Mr. Edward Pease. This was the first public railway of any importance, and Mr. George Stephenson, having obtained the appointment of engineer, left Killingworth to superintend its construction. The laying of the rails was commenced in May 1822, and the line was opened for traffic from Stockton to Witton Park Colliery, a length of twenty-five miles, in September 1825 (*ib.*, p. 317).

In the formation of this railway malleable-iron rails were partially employed—the first time they had been so to any extent. The process of rolling these rails, in lengths of 12 to 15 feet, was invented and patented by Mr. Birkenshaw, of Bedlington Ironworks, Northumberland, in 1820 (Wood's *Railroads*, 2nd ed., p. 39); and it was determined to lay one-half of the railway with cast-iron and the other half with malleable-iron rails.

The country through which the railway passed admitted of the construction of a more level line than that at Hetton Colliery, it being necessary to employ only one fixed engine. The remainder of the line being suitable either for locomotive engines or horses, it was decided to employ both in the work of haulage. Five locomotives were in all procured—viz., four from Mr. Stephenson and one from Mr. Robert Wilson, of Newcastle; but one of Mr. Stephenson's engines having burst, four were in use, while the major part of the traffic was carried on by means of horses. After two years' trial the working of the locomotive engines appears not to have been regarded with any degree of satisfaction, and it is stated to have been under consideration in 1827, whether horses should not be alone employed to the exclusion of locomotives (Colburn's *Locomotive Engineering*, p. 21; Burn's *History of the Steam Engine*, 2nd ed., p. 114).

It was at this time that Hackworth, the manager of the working department of the railway, set about improving the engine obtained from Mr. Robert Wilson, which, in addition to its not having worked satisfactorily, had been damaged in a collision. This engine had originally four steam cylinders—two to each pair of wheels— and a single fire tube. Hackworth placed the boiler (which was of greater length than usual) on six wheels; introduced a return fire tube into it; removed one pair of cylinders; and by throwing the exhaust steam into the chimney through one pipe instead of two (Stretton's *Locomotive Engine*, 5th ed., p. 25) obtained a more powerful steam blast than had hitherto been used. The engine thus altered was known as the "Royal George," and proved the most substantial success in steam locomotives which had yet been attained.

The immense superiority of the coupled engine was quickly appreciated, and from the date of its introduction by Wilson, in 1826, locomotives of the Blenkinsop and George Stephenson type went out of date. The clumsy overhead gearing formerly employed was abandoned; and in all the newer engines the cylinders were placed on opposite sides of the boiler, and the power transmitted more directly and efficiently to the driving wheels.

Soon afterwards followed another innovation of great consequence in locomotive construction, viz., the multitubular boiler, which was adopted by Mr. Robert Stephenson in the "Rocket" engine, built in 1829, at the suggestion of Mr. Booth, secretary of the Liverpool and Manchester Railway (Wood's *Railroads*, ed. 1831, p. 387; Booth's *Account of the Liverpool and Manchester Railway*, 2nd ed., 1831, p. 75), who, according to his own statement, took the idea from the double tube of Hackworth's engine. This was the third great improvement of the locomotive. By the happy combination in the "Rocket" of the coupled engine, multitubular boiler, and

FIG. 43.—HACKWORTH'S LOCOMOTIVE, THE "ROYAL GEORGE."

powerful steam blast, Mr. R. Stephenson made the locomotive at last a brilliant success [1] (see *The Northern Year Book* for 1829, pp. 270-273; *The Mechanics' Magazine*, October and November, 1829, vol. xii.; *A Practical Treatise on Railroads*, by Nicholas Wood, 2nd ed., 1831, p. 363 *et seq.*; see also *Address on the Two Late Eminent Engineers, the Messrs. Stephenson*, by Nicholas Wood, in the *Transactions of the North of England Institute of Mining Engineers*, vol. viii., 1859-60).

---

[1] The cylinders of locomotive engines began soon afterwards to be placed horizontally, to obviate difficulties with the springs. The coupled engine of the locomotive type subsequently became the favourite form of engine for winding coals out of pits.

Previous to the opening of the Stockton and Darlington Railway, coal had been an article of *import* into the Tees (Hair's *Sketches*, p. 5); but from this time the South Durham collieries were enabled to share in the maritime trade, and we begin to hear of the Crowtrees Wallsends, Old Etherley Wallsends, etc., of this district—an anomaly which led to a Stockton coal merchant being asked by the committee on the Coal Trade in 1830 as to whether there was "any place called Wallsend" in that neighbourhood. The explanation given was that "coals are not known by any other name in London; they hardly consider they are coals unless they have that name" (*1830 Report*, p. 125).

FIG. 44.—ROBERT STEPHENSON'S LOCOMOTIVE, THE "ROCKET."

The coalowners of the Tyne and Wear did not regard the introduction of the coal of this district into the market with any degree of relish, and were inclined to look upon the new exporters from the Tees as outsiders and interlopers in the coal trade (*Fossil Fuel*, p. 329).

From this time the facilities for exporting coal from the Durham collieries underwent rapid improvement, by the construction of lines of railway and the formation of docks and harbours along the coast. An Act of Parliament for the Clarence Railway was obtained in 1829 (Richardson's *Table Book*, H.D., iv. 22). Seaham Harbour, the foundation-stone of which had been laid in 1828, commenced shipping coal in 1831 (*ib.*, p. 90).

In the same year Middlesbrough Dock was opened, when a block of coal weighing $3\frac{1}{2}$ tons was shipped, being the largest piece of coal ever sent from the northern coalfield. It was sent from Blackboy Colliery by Mr. T. Y. Hall, to the Coal Exchange in London, where it long continued to be an object of curiosity and interest (Account of Mr. Hall in Fordyce's *Hist. of Durham*).

In 1834 the Stanhope and Tyne Railway was opened (*Trans. N.E. Inst.*, xv. 234). And in 1835 Hartlepool Dock and Harbour was opened, the first coal shipped being from Thornley Colliery (*ib.*, 235). Hartlepool had in ancient times been the emporium of the fleets of the prince palatine bishops of Durham (Hair's *Sketches*, p. 5), but with the rise of the coal trade on the Tyne had fallen into a state of decay ; to be again revived by the extension of the coal trade into the south-eastern part of the coalfield in the present century.

From the period of the successful establishment of the Liverpool and Manchester Railway, constructed by Mr. Stephenson and laid entirely with malleable-iron rails, intense public interest began to be taken in railway conveyance (*Fossil Fuel*, p. 353). The formation of lines proceeded apace in all parts of the kingdom, and George Stephenson and his son Robert were borne aloft on the rising tide to fame and fortune.

CHAPTER XLIII.

THE NINETEENTH CENTURY. 1817-1835.

The northern coalowners agitate for relief from the coal duties. Anomalies of the coal trade. Parliamentary inquiries. Repeal of the coal duties. Substitution of weight for measure in the sale of coal. Estimates of the annual consumption of coal. Estimates of the duration of the Northumberland and Durham coalfield.

THE coalowners of the Tyne and Wear were beginning to find themselves differently circumstanced from what they had been in times bygone. They no longer held the coal trade entirely in their own hands. They no longer could fix the prices of coal and regulate the vend among themselves at their own will. Competitors were springing up far and near. Year by year they were being driven more and more out of markets which they formerly possessed, by the inland coals, which were duty free ; as well as by the seaborne coals from Wales, now becoming a considerable trade.

In their altered circumstances the northern coalowners began to find the duties on seaborne coal, which had been imposed for the most part when Newcastle possessed almost a monopoly of the trade, coming to be an insupportable burden, and to agitate for relief.

For the Tyne coalowners in particular matters had changed very much for the worse. With their best seam nearly exhausted,[1] their coal was becoming of less value. At the same time, with a large portion of the produce of the collieries obtained from crept pillars, the cost of production had been greatly enhanced. And in addition to this they had a grievance peculiar to themselves in the Richmond

---

[1] The Main coal was, as noted, abandoned at Wallsend in 1831. The royalty comprised 1,250 acres (*Trans. Nat. Hist. Soc. of Northumberland*, ii. 311, 322). In its palmy days the colliery is stated (Dunn's *Win. and Work.*, 2nd ed., p. 323) to have returned £50,000 or £60,000 per annum.

shilling tax, which had been levied uninterruptedly since the composition made between Queen Elizabeth and the hostmen in 1599 ;
and which was now in the hands of the Government, having been
purchased from the Richmond family in 1799.

We have seen that a reduction had been made in 1816, on the
duty chargeable on small coal passed through a $\frac{3}{8}$ inch screen when
exported oversea : the duty on it being then made the same as that
payable on culm—a term applied in Wales to small coal, which was
largely exported for lime burning (*Trans. Nat. Hist. Soc. Northumberland*, i. 92, 96) ; and of which the word "gum," applied to small
coal in the west of Scotland, is probably a corruption.   In 1823 the
amount of duty chargeable on small coals and culm, when so
exported, was 4s. 6d. per Newcastle chaldron ; and upon coal above
that size 17s. per Newcastle chaldron (Bunning's *Account of the
Duties on Coal*, 1883, p. 8 ; *1829 Report*, p. 67).

In the case of coal carried to London a concession of 3s. 4d.
per London chaldron was made in 1824 (*1829 Report*, p. 7), leaving
the duty payable on coal sent to London and the coast at 6s. 6d.
per London chaldron on the Tyne, and 6s. on the Wear (*ib.*, p. 51).
And in the following year a Small Coal Act was passed whereby
the duty on coal which passed through a $\frac{3}{8}$ inch screen when
carried to London and coastwise, was reduced to 1s. per imperial
or London chaldron (*ib.*, pp. 37, 61).

The coalowners of the Tyne and Wear, however, continued to
agitate either to have the duties on seaborne coal entirely abrogated,
or to have the same duties imposed upon the inland coals, so as
to place them on a par with their competitors.   They considered it
hard that coal coming to the same town, if brought from an
inland colliery, should be duty free, while if brought by sea
from the north of England, should be chargeable with 6s. per
chaldron of duty.

At this period the coal trade was becoming full of anomalies
of one kind and another, some of recent, some of ancient growth ;
which not only fostered a system of frauds and abuses, but almost
rendered it an impossibility for the most honest-minded to conduct
their business in a just and truthful manner.

Even the recent Small Coal Act had given rise to a curious
anomaly.   It was now customary to employ three sizes of screens in
preparing coal for the market.   The first screen, the bars of which
were usually $\frac{1}{2}$ inch or $\frac{3}{4}$ inch apart, was used to prepare coal for
the coasting and London trade ; after this was a screen with bars
$\frac{3}{8}$ inch apart ; and after this again another screen, of still smaller

dimensions, was used for taking out the smallest dust, or "duff," as it was called. The result of this was that while the coal which passed through the $\frac{3}{8}$ inch screen—known as beans and peas—could be sold both at home and abroad at a reduced duty, the better coal, made between it and the first screen—known as nuts and walnuts—being chargeable with the full duty, was destroyed to a very large extent, sometimes as much as 90 or 100 chaldrons per day being wasted at a single colliery. They were also constantly used in the mending of roads (*1829 Report*, pp. 70, 72, 117).

Other anomalies arose from coal being loaded in the north by weight, and sold in London and on the coast by measure. While in the north every effort was made to send away the coal in as large a condition as possible, in order to please customers,[1] from the moment it was put on board ship it became the interest of everyone through whose hands it passed to break it up, on account of small coals yielding an increased measure ; and the crew, or small boys, were sometimes deliberately employed to smash it as it entered the ship's hold (*ib.*, pp. 60, 79).

The quantity of coal which a ship delivered, as measured at its destination, being frequently considerably greater than the quantity which it received by weight at the port of shipment, and an excess of 5 per cent. only being allowed by Government, the coal fitters were under the necessity of making out the ship's certificate for some chaldrons more than were actually loaded into it, in order to avoid the seizure of the excess of measure, which sometimes amounted to as much as 19 per cent. (*ib.*, p. 35).

In the metage of the coal also there was great opportunity for the perpetration of frauds, though to some extent the opposing influences tended to counteract each other ; the meter being bribed by the ship's captain to increase the quantity as much as he possibly could ; and being likewise bribed by the buyer to measure it out as little as he possibly could (*ib.*, p. 80 ; *1830 Report*, p. 207).

The frauds and abuses, anomalies and grievances, of the coal trade, were made the subject of inquiry by a committee of the House of Lords in 1829, and by a committee of the House of Commons in 1830.[2]

---

[1] To avoid breakage of coal, the practice of employing eight large square tubs, instead of loading coals into the keels in bulk, was introduced on the Wear in 1818, the tubs holding a chaldron each (*Trans. N.E. Inst.*, xv. 226 ; Thompson's *Inventions*, etc., p. 14).

[2] An earlier inquiry regarding the coal trade had been made by a Parliamentary Committee in the year 1800.

The following table, compiled by Mr. Hugh Taylor, by whom it was submitted to the first of the above committees (*1829 Report*, p. 126), exhibits the

COAL MEASURES USED IN DURHAM AND NORTHUMBERLAND.

Cubic inches.	Old Ale gallons.	O. Corn gallons.	Imperial gallons.	Pecks.	Cwts.	Bolls.	Foth.	Chal-drns.	Keels	Tens.
282	1									
268⅘	·9532	1								
277·274	·9832	1·0315	1							
1209·6	4·289	4½	4·362	1	·309					
9676·8	34·315	36	34·899	8	2·23⅓	1				
77414·4	274·31	288	279·198	64	17·14⅔	8	1			
232,243½	823·5	864	837·59	192	53	24	3	1		
	6588·4	6912	6700¾	1536	424	192	24	8	1	
	14412·2	15120	14657·9	3360	927½	420	52½	17½	2³⁄₁₆	1

"By the above," says Mr. Taylor, "it appears that a Newcastle chaldron of twenty-four coal bolls ought to contain 232·243½ cubic inches, whereas in reality the standard weight of 53 cwt. requires only 217·989 cubic inches, which is the Custom House measurement, being a difference of 14·245½ cubic inches = 6·14 per cent., or 22·526 instead of twenty-four bolls."

The London chaldron was based upon the Winchester or imperial bushel, between which and the Newcastle chaldron no standard existed (*1829 Report*, p. 150). The bushel was a circular vessel, 19½ inches in diameter, the sides of which were 7⅞ inches in height; and in filling it a cone was raised 6 inches high, measuring 11½ inches from the apex to the rim (*1830 Report*, plate iii.). Three bushels made a sack; and twelve sacks, or thirty-six bushels, made a London chaldron.

Roundly speaking, the Newcastle chaldron—sometimes called the double chaldron—was nearly equal to two London chaldrons. A witness examined before the committee in 1830 (*Report*, p. 126), declared the proportions to be as eight to seventeen. This would make the London chaldron 25 cwt. The proportion adopted by the Custom House officials for revenue purposes (*1829 Report*, p. 148; *1830 Report*, p. 140) was as eleven to twenty-one, making the London chaldron 28 cwt. The committee of 1830, after having a series of experiments made, decided that, so far as north country coal was concerned, 25½ cwt. might be taken as the average weight of a London chaldron (*Report*, p. 14).

But great changes were about to be made in the coal trade, whereby many of its features, which had been handed down from former ages, were to be swept away. The trade was now on the eve of being reorganized and modernized.

As the result of the inquiries which had been made, and perhaps in some measure in consequence of a petition presented by the Marquess of Londonderry to the House of Lords in 1830 (*Trans. N.E. Inst.*, xv. 232), Parliament repealed the duties on coal consumed within the kingdom, which ceased to be levied from 1st March, 1831; including the Richmond shilling, one of the oldest taxes in the coal trade, which had existed in one form or another for at least five or six centuries (*1836 Report*, pp. xxv., xxvi.).

Weight was also substituted for measure in the sale of coal in January, 1832, and the office of coal meter was abolished (*ib.*, p. 23); whereas, in 1369, four coal meters appear to have sufficed for the London coal trade, the staff had grown into a small regiment consisting of fifteen principal meters, and 158 deputy or working meters (*1830 Report*, p. 4).

The connection which had so long existed between the coal trade and the chaldron was now brought to an end, and it ceased altogether to be a legal measure of coal, though the Newcastle chaldron wagon continues to be largely used on the private colliery railways in the north of England at the present day.

The keel, as representing a certain weight of coal (21 tons), continued to be used by the northern coal merchants for some time longer; but in 1863 the leading firms in Newcastle resolved to abolish it, as a source of trouble and inconvenience (*Trans. N.E. Inst.*, xv. 258). This ancient craft, so long identified with the coal trade of the north, is now gradually becoming obsolete.

At the same time that the home duties on coal were repealed, those on coal exported oversea were reduced; and a further reduction was made in 1834 (*1836 Report*, p. 24). In 1845 they were abolished as regards British ships; and in 1850 they were repealed altogether (Bunning's *Account of the Duties on Coal*, p. 10).

The following estimate of the annual consumption of coal in

England and Wales was furnished by Mr. Buddle to the Lords'
Committee in 1829 (*Report*, p. 113).

London Chaldrons.

From inland collieries—

Manufactories,	3,500,000
Household consumption,	5,500,000
Total consumed from inland collieries,	9,000,000
Sent coastwise and chargeable with duty,	3,000,000
Total,	12,000,000

(or 15,300,000 tons).

Mr. Hugh Taylor arrived at a similar conclusion by a different
method. This gentleman estimated that the annual vend, together
with the home consumption of Durham and Northumberland,
amounted to 3,960,000 tons, and that this quantity sufficed for
the requirements of 5,000,000 persons. At the same rate, and
supposing the whole population of Great Britian to be 15,000,000
persons :

Tons.

The quantity of coals consumed by the populace would be (*1829 Report*, p. 125),	11,880,000
Consumed by ironworks, etc.,	3,000,000
	14,880,000
Exported to Ireland, say	700,000
Total tons, exclusive of foreign exportation,	15,580,000

The committee, however, appear to have been of the opinion that
the above estimates were much too low, and that the total consumption of coal, exclusive of manufactures of iron, lime, and glass, might
be about 30,000,000 tons (*1829 Report*, p. 114).

With regard to the probable duration of the supply of coal from
the great northern coalfield, as to which various estimates had
already been presented by Bailey, Dr. Thomson, Bakewell, etc. :
Mr. Taylor supposed it equal to supply the then annual vend of
3,500,000 tons for a period of 1727 years (*ib.*, p. 124 ; see also
Mr. M. Walton Brown's paper, *Trans. N.E. Inst.*, vol. xxxvii.,
p. 9).

Professor Sedgwick, on the other hand (*1830 Report*, p. 237), was
of opinion that the best beds of coal were not likely to last more
than 350 or 400 years.

Dr. Buckland likewise considered Mr. Taylor's estimate much
exaggerated, and thought it should be cut down to 400 years
(*ib.*, pp. 242, 244). Both he and Professor Sedgwick, however,

entertained unfavourable views regarding the large and as yet little explored tract under the Magnesian limestone.

None of the other English coalfields were supposed to possess a supply of coal much in excess of their own requirements, and already attention was being directed to the great coalfield of South Wales, as the source from which the fuel supply of the future must be obtained.   Here Mr. Bakewell estimated sufficient coal existed to supply England with fuel for a period of 2,000 years, after all the English coalfields were worked out (*ib.*, p. 244).

CHAPTER XLIV.

THE NINETEENTH CENTURY.   1817-1835.

Combination among the pitmen in the north.   Strikes of 1831 and 1832.

THE decline in the prosperity of the older northern collieries in this era, to which allusion has been already made, appears to have proved oppressive to the colliers no less than to the coalowners.

In 1825 was published at South Shields (*Child. Employ. Com.*, Appendix i., p. 516) a pamphlet entitled *A Voice from the Coal Mines, or a Plain Statement of the Various Grievances of the Pitmen of the Tyne and Wear*. In this, complaint is made of low prices, fines, bonds, and bad ventilation. It is stated that "Sir H. Davy's invention of the safety lamp has been an advantage to the coalowners, but a great injury to the comfort and earnings of the pitmen, for while the former remain indifferent about the safety of the mine, and neglect to form the proper supply of atmospheric air to the inner parts of the pit, on account of the great power of the lamp to resist combustion or explosion, the poor miner has to suffer the most awful agony in an exceedingly high temperature, inimical to his health, comfort, and even life" (*Trans. N.E. Inst.*, xv. 227, 228). This appears to have been one of the first notes of a strong feeling of discontent with their condition, which was rising among the pitmen in the north.

While combinations for regulating the vend of coals, so as to secure a remunerating price, had existed among the coalowners in the north for over two centuries, only now do we begin to hear of the colliers combining to regulate the production of coal, with a view to obtaining better terms for their labour. That the tendency to combine had manifested itself among the workmen at an earlier period, is evidenced by the fact of this being prohibited, as we have seen, in colliery bonds belonging to the year 1763.

In 1826 the "Association of Colliers on the rivers Tyne and Wear" consisted of upwards of four thousand persons (*Fossil Fuel*, p. 299

note).[1] The objects intended to be promoted by the union, as set forth in their articles of association, were : "To make provision for themselves and families in cases of death, sickness, or other accidents or infirmities, and to unite in a firm manner, in order to obtain a more suitable recompense for, and to regulate the hours of, labour."

In the latter connection one of the rules provided "that no member should earn more than four shillings and sixpence per day, while employed underground in the mines," nor be allowed to work as "a hewer in shift-work above eight hours in every twenty-four hours"; nor, when hired by the day, should he labour underground above twelve hours in the twenty-four.[2]

In this year another publication was issued at Newcastle, entitled "An Appeal to Coal Owners and Viewers" (ib., p. 300 note), setting forth various grievances of the pitmen relating chiefly to matters connected with the annual bond. Objections were urged against the amount of idle time, the amount and method of collecting forfeits for short measure, or mixing the coal, etc. A strike is stated to have taken place for a period of seven weeks (Trans. N.E. Inst., xv. 228), with what result we are not informed.

It was customary for the coalowners, under the yearly bond system, to guarantee the pitmen a wage of 2s. 6d. per day, or 15s. per week, whether the pit worked or not (1829 Report, p. 23), together with a house and fuel for the nominal sum of 3d. a week. When working the colliers were invariably paid by the piece, and could earn 5s. per day (ib., p. 53).

In 1828 the upstanding wage was reduced to 14s. per week, and in 1830 it was withdrawn altogether by a section at least of the coalowners, with the result that in many collieries wages fell very low, as low as 8s. or 10s. per week (1830 Report, p. 274), owing to want of work.

Under the circumstances it is not surprising that the pitmen should have commenced an agitation to better their condition. On February 26, 1831, 8,000 or 10,000 pitmen met on Black Fell, near Chester-le-Street, when they entered into resolutions to demand higher wages (Richardson's Table Book). Another meeting for the same purpose was held on Black Fell on March 12 ; and on the 21st of March they assembled on Newcastle Town Moor, to the number

---

[1] This combination was formed immediately after the repeal of the Combination Laws, by Act of Parliament, 5 George IV., c. 95.

[2] The policy of restriction was not new in British mining, having been practised by the lead miners in ancient times, as we learn from Pliny.

of nearly 20,000. When the bonds expired on April 5, a general strike took place.

Among the incidents of the strike it is recorded that on April 18, 1,200 or 1,500 pitmen visited the collieries in the neighbourhood of Blyth and Bedlington, which they laid off work, besides doing considerable damage (Sykes's *Loc. Rec.*).

The pitmen held meetings at Jarrow on April 21, and at Black Fell on May 5; and on May 16 riots occurred at South Shields and Hebburn, in connection with which Mr. Nicholas Fairless, a highly respectable magistrate of the former place, appears to have been called upon to maintain the principles of law and order.

In his second letter addressed to the pitmen, dated May 23, a writer who styles himself Philanthropos recommended that the points remaining in dispute should be referred to arbitration. Whether the suggestion was adopted we are not informed, but the strike terminated soon afterwards, after a stoppage of seven weeks; the coalowners having conceded an advance of at least 30 per cent. in wages, together with several alterations in the general clauses of the annual bond, in favour of the pitmen (*An Impartial Enquiry*, etc., by Scrutator, 1832, p. 3). The working hours of the pits were also reduced from 14, or even at times 16, to 12 hours per day (*Child. Employ. Com.*, Appendix i., pp. 630-647).

It was estimated (second letter, by Philanthropos), that during the strike the men lost in wages £100,000, and that when to this was added the loss of the coalowners, keelmen, sailors, and others, £200,000 would not cover the total amount.

Towards the end of the strike coals were actually imported into Newcastle, as evidenced by the following handbill:

"Just arrived from Berwick, and is now selling from the 'Facility,' Captain Cromby, a Cargo of good household coals, fit for any purpose. Apply to the master on board, at the Low End of the Quay, or James Lunn, Broker, Quayside, Newcastle, 18th May, 1831."

After the redress of grievances and the liberal advance in wages granted by the coalowners, it might have been expected that the old and amicable relations which had previously existed between them and the pitmen would have again revived. But so far from this being the case, the leaders of the union appear to have made use of the advantages which had been gained for the purpose of strengthening the association by binding the members together in such a way as to deprive them altogether of the power of independent action, and of making restriction more stringent. By the seventh article of the rules and regulations it was provided (Scrutator's *Impartial Enquiry*, p. 6): "That if any member of this society have a desire to leave his colliery to go to any other, he be required to get a certificate from the colliery he belongs to and lay it before the committee of the colliery he intends to go to, before he goes to make a bargain or agreement with the master he intends to agree with, or be excluded from the society." It was thus sought to debar coalowners from employing any workpeople save such as were duly *chartered* by the union. Nor did the aggressive action of the unionists stop here. At Hetton, the most extensive colliery in the north, they demanded the dismissal of the principal viewer, or otherwise they would not hire on any terms, and even refused to allow the viewer to read to them the terms proposed by the owners.

With regard to restriction, the eighth article of the regulations provided: "That no members of this society earn more than four shillings per day, clear of fines and offtakes, while employed as a hewer." During part of the year 1831 (*ib.*, p. 9) the limitation of 4s. was reduced to 3s. per day, with the result that the supply of coal fell far short of the demand.

The agitation continued to be kept up by holding meetings from time to time; and recourse was even had to acts of violence and intimidation against those who kept aloof from the union.

On August 13, 1831, a meeting of 10,000 or 12,000 pitmen was held at Boldon Fell (Sykes's *Loc. Rec.*).

On December 4, 1,000 pitmen riotously assembled at Waldridge Colliery, stopped the pumping engine while thirty or forty men were in the pit, and threw tubs and corves down, with the intention of killing those at work. A reward of five hundred guineas was offered for the apprehension of the parties concerned in this outrage. Six men were tried at the ensuing Durham Assizes, and sentenced to imprisonment for various terms (*ib.*). The rioters here and at other places are stated to have been protected by the union (Scrutator's *Impartial Enquiry*, p. 9).

On March 3, 1832, between 7,000 and 8,000 pitmen met at Boldon Fell for the purpose of arranging not to agree with the masters for the next twelve months, unless some of the clauses were struck out of the bonds, also to urge the support of the union (Sykes's *Loc. Rec.*). A strike was commenced on the same day (*Hair's Sketches*, p. 32).

Meanwhile the coalowners had not been idle. A committee had been appointed to make investigation regarding the frequent disputes between the coalowners and the pitmen, in order to discover whether the latter had any just cause of complaint, and if so, to point out the proper remedy.

In their report, read at a general meeting of the coalowners, March 10, 1832, the committee stated that since their engagement in May last two-thirds of the hewers had obtained, without extraordinary exertion, 4s. a day in six hours, and the remaining one-third the same sum in seven hours ; able-bodied young men, or two boys acting as putters, 4s. in eleven hours; shifters, 3s. for eight hours ; drivers 1s. 3d., and trappers from 10d. to 1s. per day not exceeding twelve hours.

The committee pointed out that eight hours had always been considered as the customary day's work for a hewer, and that since the last engagement the working hours had been considerably reduced ; and the workmen acknowledged that this had taken place in consequence of a regulation among themselves that no hewer should earn more than 4s. a day. The loss of production resulting from this restriction was estimated at 171,606 Newcastle chaldrons, or 454,755 tons.

It was further stated that owing to the loss and inconvenience sustained by this action on the part of the men, some of the coalowners had been compelled to introduce strange workmen into the mines to assist in raising a sufficient supply of coal. This was resisted by the pitmen, and many acts of violence and outrage had been committed, which stopped their collieries for a time ; but the proprietors had persevered, and procured a supply of labourers, who experienced no difficulty in executing the work, and were perfectly satisfied with the wages they received.

The committee came to the conclusion that the disputes had not originated in real grievances, but had been caused and kept alive by the workmen allowing themselves to be persuaded that they could secure constant work and high wages by a secret combination to control the free circulation of labour. They adverted to the character of the combination as indicated by the various riots and outrages which had taken place, and by the threats and intimidation used to induce individuals to join the general confederacy. They pointed out that the state of matters could not be remedied by the mere payment of liberal wages, or by the coalowners timidly abandoning their rights. And they recommended that the terms of all agreements made with the workmen should be as clear and explicit as possible ; that the decided and proper course adopted by those coalowners who had successfully resisted the unlawful demands of their pitmen should be pursued in all cases where they violated their voluntary engagements ; and, above all, that the trade generally should afford complete indemnity to every individual for any loss he might sustain in seeking protection and redress from the laws of his country.

The coalowners being determined to resist to the utmost the demands of the pitmen, the pitmen being sanguine of forcing further concessions from the coalowners, the strike of 1832 was fierce and prolonged, and produced a great commotion in the district and surrounding country.   After it had continued for some time, and there seemed no prospect of an agreement being arrived at, the coalowners advertised for workmen in remote mining districts, holding out the fairest prospects of good wages and personal protection.   The pitmen, on the other hand, employed every means to counteract this, and spread about broad-sheet lists of the accidents by "fire and flood" which had occurred in the northern collieries.

"Notwithstanding this," says a writer who visited the north at the time (*Fossil Fuel*, pp. 302-3), "great numbers of persons, particularly from Wales, left their houses, removed their families, and went to work in the north.   The northern coaches were crowded with the adventurers, and the stage-waggons were piled with their bedding and boxes ; many from the shorter distances of Staffordshire or Yorkshire, walked or hired light vehicles—and certainly to see the numerous haggard pedestrians, or the cart loads of squalid women and children, in and about the town of Newcastle, going and returning, was a grievous sight.   Many of the strangers found matters so little flattering, that they hastily bent their steps back again; others staid and entered upon their work; not a few, especially of the Welsh strangers, fell victims to the cholera, which raged sorely at several of the collieries ; in almost all cases the condition of the new comers was irksome in the extreme.   It was no uncommon thing to see the native pitmen idly reposing on the grass, or unaccountably traversing the neighbourhood, while a policeman with a drawn sword in his hand, or a firelock on his shoulder, was walking to and fro, on the adjacent pithill, to protect the party at work within.   The police were out every night on duty about the several collieries, to prevent damage to the works or outrage to the men."   Viewers were obliged to travel with arms.

Many acts of violence and several murders were committed.   On April 21, during a riot at Hetton Colliery, a man who had left the union was murdered, being shot with two marbles by the unionists (Sykes's *Loc. Rec.* ; Scrutator's *Impartial Enquiry*, p. 9).   On May 1, on the occasion of turning the pitmen out of their houses at Friar's Goose Colliery, it was found necessary to call out the military to quell the rioters. On June 11, Mr. Nicholas Fairless, a magistrate of South Shields, already referred to, was attacked and ill-treated by two pitmen, named Jobling and Armstrong, in consequence of which he died. The latter succeeded in escaping, but Jobling was tried and executed at Durham, and his body hung in chains at Jarrow Slake, close to the spot where the murder had been committed.

The author of *Fossil Fuel* tells us (p. 304) that on returning one evening from the delightful marine village of Tynemouth to Newcastle, during the disturbances, seeing a crowd about a public-house he inquired what was the matter, and received the reply that "The police have shot a pitman," which turned out to have been really the case in a fray that had just ended.

At last, however, the determined and united action of the coal-owners in resisting and refusing to recognize the union prevailed, and in the latter part of September the union was dissolved, and the men recommenced work, after a loss in wages estimated at £80,000 (Fordyce; *Trans. N.E. Inst.*, xv. 234).

It seems not improbable that this association, designated "The Coal Miners' Friendly Society," began its career with benevolent and perfectly legitimate objects in view, but that in the hands of unscrupulous leaders it degenerated into a machinery of tyranny and intimidation, fostering lawlessness and violence, and rendering the relations between the coalowners and the pitmen altogether intolerable.

The number of persons engaged in connection with the coal trade of the rivers Tyne and Wear was estimated by Mr. Buddle, in his evidence before the Lords' Committee in 1829 (*Report*, p. 87), as follows :

On the Tyne—Under ground, Men, . . 4,937		
Boys, . . 3,554		
	8,491	
Above ground, Men, . . 2,745		
Boys, . . 718		
	3,463	
		11,954
On the Wear, ...		9,000
Total at collieries, ...		20,954
Seamen and boys in 1,400 vessels, ...		15,000
Keelmen, etc., ...		2,000
		37,954
In London—Whippers, lightermen, etc., . . 5,000		
Factors, agents, etc., . . . 2,500		
		7,500
Total (exclusive of persons employed at outports). .		45,454

CHAPTER XLV.

THE NINETEENTH CENTURY. 1817-1835.

Sizes of shafts, and depth attained in different districts. Coal supply of Manchester, Liverpool, Sheffield, Leeds, Birmingham. Mining by day-levels still extensively pursued in South Wales. Production of iron.

WHILE the shafts at the northern collieries were almost invariably circular in form, they were made of a variety of sizes. Where no partition or brattice was intended to be introduced, they were commonly of a diameter of 6 or 8 feet (*Fossil Fuel*, p. 180). If intended to be divided into two sections, they were made 8 or 10 feet in diameter; while the deeper shafts, which were at this time frequently divided into three or four compartments, were usually sunk of a diameter ranging from 11 to 14 or 15 feet.

The maximum depth attained in the north was at Monkwearmouth Colliery, which was situated near the trough or deepest part of the coalfield. Here (*ib.*, p. 188) the shaft had been carried down to a distance of 1,590 feet below the surface, and was still being further deepened. The time occupied in running a load in this pit was $2\frac{1}{8}$ minutes (*1835 Report*, 1,837).

In several instances, viz., at Jarrow, Gosforth, and South Hetton, depths of about 1,100 feet had been reached. At Jarrow, the oldest of these, and situated in the deepest part of the Tyne basin, the coal was raised in two, or it might be said three stages (*Fossil Fuel*, p. 200). One engine lifted it in the principal shaft from the Main coal to the surface, a distance of about 780 feet; another engine, placed underground, raised it in a staple from the Bensham seam, which lay 270 feet deeper; while a third engine worked an inclined plane, and brought up the coal from a district which by a succession of faults had been depressed 72 feet deeper still: the three stages making a total depth of 1,122 feet.

The cost of opening out collieries in the north was now in some

instances becoming very formidable, ranging from £10,000 to
£150,000 (*1829 Report*, pp. 45, 50); a single pit sometimes costing
£30,000 and even £40,000 (*ib.*, p. 50; *1835 Report*, 2,150). Under
these circumstances there was a strong inducement to sink as few
pits as possible, and to work as large an area as was practicable
from each establishment.

The three winnings belonging to the Hetton Coal Company, at
Hetton, Eppleton, and Elemore, for example, were placed at distances of about a mile apart (London and Edinburgh *Phil. Maga.*,
iii. 203, 204), a pair of pits being sunk at each point. This colliery
(including the three establishments), already referred to as the most
important mining concern in the coalfield, was said to be capable of
working 200,000 Newcastle chaldrons or 530,000 tons annually.
It proved most prosperous and profitable; indeed, the profits are
characterized as extravagant. A sum of £80,000 is said to have
been cleared the first year (*Min. Jour.*, xi. 85). One of the partners
who disposed of his share in the concern realized at the rate of
£324,000 for the whole (*1836 Report*, pp. 174, 177); and within a
few years subsequently shares were frequently bought and sold at
the rate of upwards of £500,000 (Dunn's *Coal Trade*, p. 237).

Little change had been made in the size of pillars employed in
the Newcastle district, if we may accept the statement of the author
of the *History of Fossil Fuel* (p. 217), who speaks of them as 20 yards
by 9, or, in some instances, square cubes of about the latter measurement on each side. Mackenzie, however, writing in 1825 (*View of
Northumberland*, 2nd ed., p. 90), speaks of the mode of working coal
having been much improved within the last few years. "From
seven-eighths to nine-tenths of the coal," he says, "is at present
raised, whilst formerly but one-half, and frequently less, was all that
could be obtained." This doubtless refers to the general commencement to remove the pillars, now rendered practicable by the aid
afforded by the Davy lamp.

At Howgill Colliery, Whitehaven, the workings had been carried
more than 1,000 yards under the sea, at a depth of about 600 feet
below its bottom (*ib.*, p. 143).

In the Lancashire coalfield in 1835, the town of Manchester drew
supplies of coal from various sources, comprising collieries extending
almost from the town itself to near Bolton, a distance of about eight
miles; from Worsley, seven or eight miles off; from pits lying
between Manchester and Oldham; from others between Manchester
and Ashton; some from the Rochdale side of the town; and many
of the best coals from Wigan (*ib.*, p. 424).

At the same period Liverpool was chiefly supplied with coal from Wigan, distant twenty-two miles; also from St. Helens, twelve miles off; and from Prescot, eight miles distant; the carriage being by canal and railway (*ib.*, p. 429). Large quantities of coal from the Wigan district were likewise exported from Liverpool to America, the best qualities being known as "Orrell coal," after the colliery of that name, just as on the east coast the term "Wallsend" became generally adopted by the trade.

The collieries of the Bolton district—comprising Kersley, Farnworth, Worsley, Bolton, and Little Lever—were of little depth, not exceeding 300 feet (*1835 Report*, 4,103, 4,120). The Duke of Bridgewater's collieries at Worsley were still worked by an adit navigable for barges used in conveying the coal, and which at this period had attained an extent of about thirty miles (*Fossil Fuel*, p. 189).

In the Ashton and Oldham districts the pits were much deeper (*1835 Report*, 4,120). Mention occurs of two shafts at Ashton, one of which was 10 feet 6 inches or 11 feet in diameter, and 750 feet deep; and the other 11 feet 6 inches in diameter, and 954 feet deep, and was being sunk lower (*ib.*, 3,753). Here the shafts were sunk nearly a mile apart, usually in pairs, or sometimes three together (*ib.*, 3,651).

In Yorkshire, Staffordshire, and other places, where the sinkings were of moderate depth, and effected with comparatively little difficulty and expense, the shafts were made of small diameter (commonly 7 or 8 feet), and were more numerous, and worked more limited areas. It was the usual plan to sink separate shafts for pumping, ventilating, and drawing coal; the latter being in some instances oval in form (*Fossil Fuel*, p. 180). Instead of two engines winding out of one shaft, as was sometimes the case in the large divided pits in the north of England, the same engine was frequently employed to raise the coal out of two or more separate shafts.

The mean depth of the pits at Sheffield in 1819 (Hunter's *Sheffield*, p. 8) was 360 feet, the mouth of the principal excavation being then within the town. The oldest pits from which Sheffield drew its supplies of coal in 1835 (*Fossil Fuel*, pp. 423, 424), are spoken of as situated at the Manor, the Intake, and Birley, in a south-easterly direction, and at distances of two, three, and four miles, the coal being chiefly conveyed by large numbers of one-horse carts. Considerable quantities of coal were also brought by canal on the north side of the town from Rotherham and Attercliffe and Tinsley

Common, as well as from the Low Manor pits, which were worked by a company who were understood to be realizing immense profits out of the various collieries in the neighbourhood leased from the Duke of Norfolk, and who themselves supplied 159,000 tons per annum to the town.

The process of manufacturing coke, in ordinary bee-hive ovens, as pursued at this period at the Duke of Norfolk's collieries, is minutely described by Parkes in his *Chemical Catechism* (ed. 1822, p. 453). There were a great number of these ovens in the Sheffield neighbourhood in 1835 (*Fossil Fuel*, p. 411). Coke was also produced by piling large coals in long rows without ovens.

In the Leeds neighbourhood, in 1835, coal was being worked at depths varying from 80 to 420 feet, the latter depth having been attained at Middleton collieries, belonging to the Rev. R. H. Brandling (*1835 Report*, 4,024), and comprising the Day Hole and the Venture and West pits. The town also drew supplies from Thorp Hall collieries, about two and a half miles off, where seven or eight pits were being worked by W. Fenton, Esq.; Rothwell Haigh Colliery, where three pits were worked by J. & J. Charlesworth, Esqs., who also had a pit at Lofthouse; and from other collieries situated at Beeston Park, Beeston, Manston, Garforth, and Colton, some of which were of very little depth (*Fossil Fuel*, pp. 425-428).

In addition to vertical pits, many of the Yorkshire collieries still possessed sloping roads, or "futterils," to the underground workings (*ib.*). A noted instance was at Earl Fitzwilliam's collieries at Elsecar and Rawmarsh, near Rotherham, where we are told that the ladies from Wentworth House sometimes went down to witness the operations, and to see the impressions of organic remains which abounded in some parts of the strata.

The Earl's colliery at Rawmarsh was wilfully set on fire in 1833, but the conflagration was extinguished by discharging the contents of a reservoir into the mine (*ib.*, 233, 254).

In the South Staffordshire coalfield the pits were remarkably numerous and close together. There were few pits deeper than 450 or 600 feet (*1835 Report*, 3,048). They were seldom more than 300 yards apart, or worked more than 10 acres (*ib.*, 3,027, 3,023-24). The common practice was to sink a pair of pits—called "a plant," or plantation—so near together as to be worked by the same gin, or whimsey (*Fossil Fuel*, pp. 192, 200). In addition to flat and round hemp ropes, chains were likewise employed in raising the coal.

The town of Birmingham drew its supplies of coal from Tipton,

Oldbury, Bilston, West Bromwich, Wednesbury, and Dudley; the greatest quantity coming from West Bromwich, and the best quality from Wednesbury. It was chiefly brought by canal, though some was carted into the town by the small proprietors (*ib.*, p. 425).

In North Staffordshire part of the mines were still very shallow, but in some instances a considerable depth had been attained. As early as 1818 (*Mining Journal*, xi. 59) a depth of 1,030 feet had been reached at Fenton Park Colliery. In 1835 one mine is spoken of as upwards of 1,200 feet (*1835 Report*, 2,514). This was doubtless a mine at Apedale, mentioned in Smith's *Miner's Guide*, published in 1836, as having attained a depth of 725 yards 2 feet, or 2,177 feet—a most exceptional depth at this period, and probably the greatest yet reached anywhere in England.

In this district also the custom of working a single rope in a shaft, so prevalent at the time, was pursued, the size of the shaft mentioned being 7 feet diameter (*1835 Report*, 2,667-68).

In Warwickshire the mines appear to have still been of comparatively little depth (*Fossil Fuel*, p. 145); but in the Ashby Wolds districts of Leicestershire, coal was being extensively worked by the Marquess of Hastings, and others, at depths of about 1,000 feet (*ib.*, pp. 115 note, 145).

Further south, the Gloucestershire and Somersetshire districts were remarkable for the extreme smallness of the pits employed, which were still, and for some time subsequently, mere well holes, measuring only 4 or 5 feet across (*First Report*, 1853, p. 107). Notwithstanding this, in the neighbourhood of Bath, a depth of 1,200 feet is stated (*1835 Report*, 2,901) to have been already attained.

While the early systèm of obtaining coal by means of horizontal galleries had become well-nigh obsolete in most of the coalfields, on account of the exhaustion of the coal above the level of free drainage, it continued to be still largely available, and extensively pursued in the Forest of Dean and South Wales (*ib.*, 2,476, 2,471).

In South Wales the coal measures attained to elevations ranging from 1,000 to 1,800 feet (*Trans. Nat. Hist. Soc. Northumberland*, i. 89), and the coalfield being intersected by numerous deep valleys, extraordinary facilities were presented for obtaining immense supplies of coal and ironstone by means of levels driven into the hill sides. The natural advantages were further improved upon by the construction of canals, and in some cases also railways, along the valleys; so that the mines not only admitted of being opened out and worked inexpensively, but were likewise provided with convenient outlets for their produce. The adits into the mines are stated (*Fossil Fuel*,

p. 189) to have been commonly used as canals for bringing out the coal.

Under the circumstances above mentioned it is not surprising that even in the early part of the present century the pits in this coalfield were still of little depth. The maximum depth reached in 1806 (*Phil. Trans.* for the year 1806, p. 344) did not exceed about 480 feet. In 1827 the Dunraven pit, at Adair Colliery, was sunk by Mr. F. Forster to a depth of 660 feet (*Trans. Nat. Hist. Soc. Northumberland*, i. 106, 107), being probably one of the deepest sinkings in the coalfield at this date.

Regarding the consumption and export of coal in South Wales in this era, the following particulars are given (*ib.*, p. 114) for the year 1828 :

		Tons.
Consumed by the ironworks, ...		1,500,000
,, other manufactures and domestic use, .		350,000
Home consumption, ...		1,850,000

Coal and culm exported :

	Tons of coal.	Tons of culm.	Coal and culm.
Cardiff, . .	32,109	—	32,109
Newport, .	422,878	—	422,878
Swansea, . .	144,198	195,213	339,411
Llanelly, . .	84,386	7,758	92,144
Milford, . .	8,303	10,051	18,354
	691,874	213,022	904,896

Consumption and export, ...		2,754,896

Little or no coal was shipped at Newport at the commencement of the present century (*Fossil Fuel*, pp. 394, 395). The great development of this shipping port compared with Cardiff was owing to an exemption which it enjoyed from a duty of 4s. per ton within a large area of the Bristol Channel, from which Cardiff was excluded, though its harbour lay only about half a mile beyond the boundary line.

The custom of mixing Welsh and Newcastle coal had already been partially adopted in London. In South Wales the peasantry mixed the small, or culm, of the stone coal with clay, and formed it into balls, which constituted the principal article of fuel used in the cottages of Glamorganshire, Carmarthenshire, and Pembrokeshire. The balls burned for a great length of time, and the fire was never allowed to go out, in some cases for many years (*Trans. Nat. Hist. Soc. Northumberland*, i. 91-93).

In the manufacture of iron with coal South Wales now held the lead. Shropshire, which led the van in the eighteenth century, owing to its limited resources had fallen far behind its richer rivals, Staffordshire and South Wales, whom it had taught the secret of the manufacture. The make of pig iron in 1827, immediately preceding the invention of the hot blast by Neilson, was as follows (*ib.*, p. 115):

	Furnaces.	Tons.
Staffordshire,	95	216,000
Shropshire,	31	78,000
South Wales,	90	272,000
North Wales,	12	24,000
Yorkshire,	24	43,000
Derbyshire,	14	20,500
Scotland,	18	36,500
	284	690,000

This period witnessed the final extinction of the once famous charcoal iron manufacture of the Weald of Sussex, which dates from the time of the Roman occupation, if not earlier. The last furnace was that of Ashburnham, which was dismantled in 1828 (see the *Antiquary*, July, 1896).

The coal supply up till 1835 may be said to have been entirely obtained from mines not exceeding a depth of 1,000 feet, though a commencement had now been made in various districts—Northumberland and Durham, Lancashire, North Staffordshire, and Somersetshire—to penetrate below this level.

As recently as 1830 it was considered to be doubtful whether it would be possible to work coal profitably at a greater depth than 1,200 feet.

CHAPTER XLVI.

THE NINETEENTH CENTURY. 1817-1835.

Watt's improved steam engines being generally adopted at the deeper colleries. Invention of the tub, cage, and guide-rod system of raising coal. Employment of gunpowder in coal-getting.

IN the mechanical department of colliery engineering, no less than in matters affecting the coal trade, considerable progress was made at this period in the direction of modern arrangements.

Though the Newcomen steam engine was still extensively used, both for pumping water and drawing coal, in the shallower collieries of the midland counties and Scotland, in the case of the deeper mines in the North of England, and elsewhere, Watt's improved engines were now being generally adopted (*Edinburgh Encyclopædia*, xiv. 335, 358; Mackenzie's *Northumberland*, 2nd ed., i. 88). In the former instance the engines employed were usually on the second motion (*Fossil Fuel*, pp. 202, 203; Dunn's *Win. and Work.*, 2nd ed., p. 123); but at the deeper mines direct-acting engines were used.

A form of winding engine which came much into favour in the North of England, consisted in placing the cylinder in a vertical position, with the drum, or rope roll, immediately overhead. This necessitated the building of a tall engine house, a feature observable at many of the older northern collieries at the present day, where this style of winding engine is still largely employed. Messrs. Thomas Murray & Co., of Chester-le-Street, are said to have been noted builders of this description of engine.

With the greatly increased efficiency of Watt's engines, resulting in large measure from the employment of steam of a higher pressure, the Newcomen engine became more and more supplanted by them from this time forward, and gradually fell out of use. But even in the North of England one of the old engines of the most primitive form, with the cylinder on the top of the haystack boiler, and the steam passing between them through a slide-valve, is spoken of in 1852 (Mr. Wood's inaugural address to Mining Institute) as having "only very recently" been abandoned. A few of them, as the writer has been credibly informed, were still at work in the midland counties within the last twenty years. Nor is the machine yet altogether extinct. One of them continues in use at Caprington Colliery, near Kilmarnock, in Ayrshire, pumping water at the Earlston pit. It has a cylinder 28 inches in diameter, and works with steam of a pressure of 1 lb. per square inch above the atmosphere (*Colliery Guardian*, May 7, 1897, p. 855). An old giant engine of this kind is likewise still employed in pumping water at the William pit, Whitehaven Colliery. It was erected in 1805 or 1810, after the expiration of Watt's patent, and is provided with a separate condenser. It works with steam of a pressure of 5 lb. above the atmosphere, using only the exhaust steam from another engine. Its cylinder is 80 inches in diameter; this patriarchal atmospheric engine being one of the largest, as it is one of the last of its race (*Trans. Cumberland and Westmoreland Antiq. and Arch. Soc.*, iii. 293; *Trans. Fed. Inst.*, vii., p. 262).

Since the time when the steam engine came to be applied to the raising of coal in the pits, in other respects the machinery employed in this work had undergone little alteration in the North of England collieries. The coal continued to be drawn to the surface in the ancient corve, or basket made of hazel rods. As the depths of the pits increased, the size of the corves had been enlarged, until they commonly carried 5 or 6 hundredweights of coal. In many collieries, too, it had become customary to draw two or three corves at a time, attached to the rope, one above the other, at short distances apart. But they were still swung loosely up and down the shafts, and suffered great damage from striking against each other, or against the sides of the pit, in ascending and descending. At times these collisions resulted in the empty corve being carried back again to the surface, perched on the top of the ascending full one (*Mining Journal*, September and October, 1858). The only improvement in the drawing arrangements consisted in dividing the shaft by a timber brattice throughout its whole length, thus providing separate passages for the ascending and descending corves. This effectually put a stop to direct collisions, but did not alleviate the damage sustained against the sides.

The use of corves was attended with many other inconveniences. Being high, they were difficult to fill at the hewer's working place.

At the junction between the branch lines and the main horse roads, they required to be lifted from the small trams used by the putters, and placed on the horse rolley by means of a crane. They were unwieldy to handle, both at the top and bottom of the shaft, and required endless repairs. And as a moderate speed of winding could only be attained, the output of coal was limited. It is true there is mention (Thompson's *Inventions*, etc., p. 28) of between 400 and 500 tons of coal being drawn up a shaft at Ouston Colliery, upwards of 360 feet deep, by a pair of ropes in twelve hours, in 1816. But this must have been quite an exceptional performance. In 1835 Mr. George Stephenson stated (*1835 Report*, 1,842) that he thought the largest quantity he had known brought out of a pit in a day of twelve hours was 300 tons.

Under the corve system, particularly in shafts where no brattice existed (*ib.*, 1,162), the arrangements for lowering and raising the men and boys were of the most primitive description. Their security depended almost entirely on the tenacity with which they clung to the rope. The general practice in ascending and descending was for two men to sit each with a leg in a noose or loop of the chain, and frequently five or six boys would cling to the rope, one above another, trusting their lives to their capability of holding fast while they traversed the whole length of the shaft, a distance, it might be, of 1,000 feet or more. So inured were the boys to this hazardous mode of travelling, which was known as "topping," that it was regarded by them as fine fun. Mr. Buddle (*ib.*, 2,385) relates an instance of a boy who fell asleep while descending a pit 600 feet deep, with his arms clasped round the rope, and in this condition was brought back to the top again, when he was taken off by the banksman, and even then was only awakened by a slap.

The ingenious arrangements introduced by Mr. Curr in the latter part of the eighteenth century for raising coal in carriages suspended under a cross-bar running in guides, were found to answer well in shallow collieries, and were generally adopted about Leeds, Barnsley, and Sheffield (*Fossil Fuel*, p. 208). We also hear of guides being introduced at Duckmanton Colliery, Chesterfield, in 1825, and being employed at Radstock Colliery, Somersetshire, shortly after this date (*Trans. N.E. Inst.*, xv. 227); though whether in conjunction with carriages or wicker corves, we are not informed.

The guide-rod system, however, was not sufficiently matured to lead to its general adoption in deep collieries. One of its defects lay in the circumstance that the movable platform arrangement, usually employed for landing the load at the surface, was somewhat clumsy and tedious (Ure's *Dictionary*, 1839, p. 983). An improvement was introduced at Mr. Sparrow's colliery at Lane End, in Staffordshire, where, on the load arriving at the top of the shaft, and the winding engine being reversed, a self-acting mechanism came into play, whereby the corve was pushed to one side and placed on the saddle-boards, or landing-stage, automatically (*1835 Report*, 1,831). But so long as the carriage, or corve, was suspended under a cross-bar, it was scarcely practicable to raise more than one at a time, and hence the system only admitted of limited outputs of coal.

An improved arrangement had come into use at some of the collieries in the south, where the carriage, instead of being suspended, was drawn sitting on a platform (*ib.*, 1840). This appears to have been introduced in connection with the balance-tub system of winding, which, as already mentioned, found most favour in Wales, owing to the facilities existing for getting rid of the water let down into the mine by means of adits ; the carriage sitting on the top of the water cistern. The arrangement was simple and efficient, admitting of 300 or 400 tons being drawn in a day from a depth of 300 or 360 feet. Its use, however, appears to have been limited to raising one carriage at a time, under the peculiar circumstances above mentioned.

We have seen that an attempt to dispense with wicker corves, and to substitute sheet iron tubs for them, was made at Washington Colliery, Durham, in 1816, but proved unsuccessful. Another attempt to improve upon the old-established system was made by Mr. Thomas Easton, at Hebburn Colliery, about 1827 (Mr. Hall's paper to N.E. Inst., Dec., 1853), of the nature of which we have no very clear account ; but owing to the difficulties encountered in putting the scheme into practice, partly due to the objections of the putters, he was compelled to fall back upon the former arrangement.

Shortly afterwards the subject of improvements in the winding and haulage arrangements in vogue at the northern collieries was taken up by Mr. T. Y. Hall, and a series of trials made with a view to the disuse of wicker corves, which resulted in the abolition of this system, and the introduction of a new and immensely superior one.

Mr. Hall was a native of the village of Greenside, near Ryton-on-Tyne. In his early youth he is stated to have undergone an unusual amount of drudgery as a common pit-boy. Subsequently he served an apprenticeship under his father and Mr. Buddle, at Towneley, Whitefield, and Crawcrook collieries, situated in his native parish. From thence he removed in 1826 to take the management of North Hetton Colliery, and after holding this position for a period of four years, and spending a like period as manager of Blackboy, or Tees Wallsend Colliery, he was appointed to the management of South Hetton Colliery (*Memoir of T. Y. Hall*, compiled from Fordyce's *Hist. of Durham*).

It was at South Hetton Colliery, belonging to Colonel Braddyll and partners, the sinking of which to a depth of 1,080 feet was completed, as we have seen, in 1833, that Mr. Hall first attempted to employ substitutes for the wicker corves. His earliest experi-ment, made in the summer of this year, consisted in the employment of iron tubs of two sizes, viz., large circular tubs holding 80 pecks or 24 cwt. of coal, and without wheels, to be used in the shaft and on the rolley-ways, or horse-roads; and small oblong tubs holding 8 cwt. each, and fixed on wheels, to be used by the putters in the workings; the contents of three small tubs being intended to be emptied into one large one, at the points to which the latter were brought on the horse rolleys. In order to steady the large tubs while being raised in the shaft, and prevent them from suffering or causing damage by oscillation, the compartments in which they travelled were cleaded or lined round with timber, thus presenting a smooth passage only slightly larger than the size of the tub itself.

Mr. Hall's new scheme was, however, open to a number of serious objections; and after it had undergone about six months' trial, and its superiority to the ordinary corves was rather doubtful, the owners of the colliery employed Messrs. Nicholas Wood and George Johnson to report upon it. These gentlemen accordingly visited the colliery early in 1834, and inspected Mr. Hall's arrangements, but with the result of being led to report unfavourably of the tub system. The drawbacks to it, which they pointed out, were the difficulty of properly screening the contents of the large tubs, the impossibility of discriminating between the colliers who sent clean and those who sent dirty coals, the breakage of coal occasioned by the emptying of the small tubs into the large ones, and the expense incurred in making the extra height required on the rolley-ways for the large tubs, and also in making the quays for transferring the contents of the small tubs into the large ones.

Being dissatisfied with the condemnation of his scheme, Mr. Hall, on April 5, 1834, requested two other mining engineers to examine into the matter, who in their report, dated April 10, recommended that a further trial should be given to it. The owners of the colliery accordingly did not interfere. But soon afterwards Mr. Hall succeeded in devising another and much superior system, whereby the objections urged by Messrs. Wood and Johnson were entirely obviated. This was to dispense altogether with the large tubs, and to take the small tubs themselves to the shaft standing athwart the rolleys, and to raise them to the surface, two at a time, in a two-decked iron cage, or chair.

No time was lost by Mr. Hall in making arrangements for the trial of his new scheme. Another pit was prepared for the reception of cages. Passages for them to travel in were cleaded with timber so as to limit the amount of oscillation, in a manner similar to that employed in guiding the large iron tubs, and the cage system was brought into operation in December, 1834 (*Trans. N.E. Inst. of Colliery Engineers*, ii. 26). But shortly afterwards Mr. Hall left South Hetton to undertake the management of collieries in the vicinity of Ryton, which he had leased conjointly with Messrs. Buddle and Potter.

In its imperfect state as applied at South Hetton, the cage and tub system proved unsatisfactory, and it was discontinued and circular tubs again had recourse to soon after Mr. Hall's departure, these being less liable to accident in the shaft than the rectangular cages. But Mr. Hall, being convinced of the great capabilities of this new method of raising coal, at once proceeded to apply it in an improved form, at the Glebe pit, Woodside, near Ryton. Here *guide-rods* were applied (three to each cage), and the cages were provided with *shoes* closely embracing them, enabling the raising and lowering of the cages to be performed with great rapidity and perfect smoothness and safety. Keeps, or *keps*, also were applied to rest the cages upon and steady them during the process of changing the tubs. With the addition of these improvements the immense superiority of the new system was quickly felt, from the circumstance that the pit was able to raise twice as much coal as was possible under the corve system.

A model of a pit shaft fitted up on the cage-and-guide system, is stated (*Mining Journal*, September and October, 1858; Mr. Hall's paper to N.E. Inst., December, 1853) to have been made in 1835, by Mr. Thomas Sopwith; which was exhibited in the Polytechnic Exhibition at Newcastle, and was presented in 1853 to the Museum of Practical Geology, London.

The great value of Mr. Hall's innovations was soon recognized.

WAL
FIREDAMP ESCAPE

ERY.

OR VILLAGE PIT.

Large numbers of persons visited the Glebe pit to see the new system of raising coal in operation ; and the success which attended it led to its being speedily adopted at one colliery after another. The rolleys which were used at first in conveying the tubs on the horse roads were subsequently dispensed with (Dunn's *Win. and Work.*, 2nd ed., pp. 91, 123 ; *Trans. N.E. Inst.*, xv. 239), and the simpler arrangement adopted of conveying the tubs on their own wheels directly from the hewer's working place to the pit bottom.

The introduction of the new system was productive of many highly important advantages. Leaving out of view the economy which resulted from it as compared with corves, it enabled the men and boys to be lowered and raised with immensely greater comfort and safety ; while the rapidity with which the winding of coal could be carried on, enabled double the quantity of coal to be drawn. From this time the use of corves rapidly declined, and the employment of cages and tubs—as the small wheel-carriages continue to be termed in the north of England—soon became general.

Mr. Hall also adopted edge rails and flanged wheels (*Trans. N.E. Inst.*, vii., p. 6), in lieu of the tram plates and sharp wheels which were still in general use. Thus, he perfected the improvements which Mr. Curr had begun, and established the system of drawing and conveying coal in carriages, as universally practised at the present day.

Wicker corves survived at a few places for a considerable time. They were still used at Shilbottle Colliery, near Alnwick, in 1864 (*Epitome of Evidence, 1864 Report*, p. 289), and at the William pit, Whitehaven, even later. At the latter pit—which the writer had the privilege of visiting in the autumn of 1871, making the descent in a corve—they were used under exceptionally favourable circumstances. The seam of coal being 10 feet thick admitted of the use of large corves carrying 11 cwt. of coal, while by means of an ingenious self-acting mechanism, consisting of a shutter running in guides with a lever attached, the corves were lifted off, and placed on, the rolleys at the top and bottom of the shaft, by the winding engine, with ease and despatch. Within a year or two afterwards, however, they were superseded by the tub-and-cage system.

A curious result of the disuse of the hazel twig corves in raising coal, was that it permanently lowered the price of hazel nuts in the London market. " ' Where there are no bushes there can be no nuts,' says the Spanish proverb, and the effect of the change from corves to tubs was to leave the hazel bushes to bear nuts" (*Newcastle Daily Chronicle*, September 30, 1881, p. 3).

Another innovation of modern times, which appears to have been initiated, or at all events rapidly developed in this era, was the employment of gunpowder in coal-getting. We have seen that this agent had long been in use at collieries for blasting stone; having begun to be used in shaft sinking in the early part of the eighteenth century. Also that it had come into use for cutting through faults in the underground workings by the middle of the century; and that it was being used for shooting down the stone necessary for making height in the horse roads early in the present century (*Account of Felling Explosion*).

At what precise period gunpowder began to be employed for the purpose of blasting down coal does not seem to be recorded, but it would appear to have been little if at all so used even during the early years of the present century. Daniell in the account of his visit to the Whitehaven mines in 1813 (*Voyage Round Great Britain*, ii. 157), mentions hearing blasting at a fault, but tells us nothing of any further use of gunpowder. Holmes in his treatise on the *Coalmines of Durham and Northumberland* in 1816 (p. 224) speaks only of the wedging process in coal-getting.

It would appear, however, from later evidence, that a commencement was made to apply gunpowder to this work in the north of England just about this period. We find the underviewer at Hetton Colliery, examined by Mr. Leifchild in 1841 (*Child. Employ. Com.*, Appendix i., p. 649), stating that "about twenty-eight years since gunpowder was introduced for blasting, which renders the hewers' work very much easier." This would make the date of the introduction of this innovation to be 1813.

The earliest contemporary allusion to the use of gunpowder in coal-getting which the writer has met with, occurs in Mr. Bald's article in the *Edinburgh Encyclopœdia* (art. Mine) which belongs to the year 1820. Here, in describing the division of labour usually adopted under the Shropshire method or longwall system of working coal, after referring to the operations of the "holers," who undermine the coal, he proceeds to speak of the "getters" who succeed them, and who set wedges along the roof to bring down the coal; "or," he adds, "if the roof is very bound the coal is blown down with gunpowder."

About, or soon after this time, gunpowder must have been very commonly used in blasting down coal in the north of England. Being a great saving in labour, and enabling coal to be worked at a reduced cost, its use was an advantage in these respects, both to the coalowners and the workmen.

The old method of wedging, and the new method of blasting, are thus contrasted by the author of *The Pitman's Pay*, in 1828[1] (*The Newcastle Magazine*, vol. vii., p. 9):

> "Here agyen had awd langsyners
> Mony a weary, warken' byen,
> Now unknawn to coaly Tyners,
> A' bein' mell-and-wedge wark then.

> "Aw've bray'd for hours at woody coal,
> Wi' airms myest droppen frae the shouther;
> But now they just pop in a hole
> And flap her down at yence wi' pouther."

Writing in 1835, the author of the *History of Fossil Fuel* (p. 245) speaks of the system of blasting down the coal as then generally prevailing in the deep mines of the north, whereas in Yorkshire and other places wedging it down was still mostly practised (see also *1835 Report*, 3,839). But at this date the use of gunpowder was increasing very much in the south as well (*ib.*, 1868).

Bickford's safety fuse was patented in 1831 (*Trans. N.E. Inst.*, xvii. 61). A wedging apparatus for bringing down coal was invented and patented by Mr. W. Wood, of Newcastle, in 1830. One cargo of coals was wrought by it at Gosforth Colliery, but owing to the extra expense it was soon laid aside (*Fossil Fuel*, p. 246). Mr. E. F. Boyd stated, in 1869 (*Trans. N.E. Inst.*, xix. 13), that he had once seen it.

---

[1] *The Pitman's Pay* was originally published in three parts in *The Newcastle Magazine* for the years 1826, 1828, 1830.

CHAPTER XLVII.

THE NINETEENTH CENTURY. 1817-1835.

Increased prevalence and higher pressure of firedamp in the Tyneside collieries. Blowers and outbursts. Firedamp in other districts.

THOUGH the burning wells of Lancashire still existed in this era over a line of country ten miles in length (*1835 Report*, 2,897), it was becoming generally accepted that, as a rule, the quantity of fire-damp encountered in coal mines increased coincidently with their increasing depth (*ib.*, 361, 1,798, 2,552, 3,047). This fact was pointed out by Mr. Buddle to the Lords' Committee in 1829 (*Report*, p. 46), and to the Commons' Committee in 1835 (*Report*, 2,318), though he seems subsequently to have been disposed to dispute the point, on account of less gas having been met with than was to have been expected in the deep collieries on the Wear (Sykes's *Account of Wallsend Explosion*, p. 10). But he had to admit that such had been the case in his own experience at Wallsend, and that the Bensham seam, which lay about 200 feet below the Main coal, and about 850 or 900 feet from the surface, was the more fiery of the two.

When the Bensham seam was first sunk to in the A pit at Walls-end in 1820, "this unfortunate seam" was, to use Mr. Buddle's expression, "prodigiously fiery" (*1835 Report*, 2,024, 2,094). The coal itself afforded gas enough to light the pit. All that was necessary was to drill a hole in the seam, and stick a tin pipe into the aperture, clay it up tight, and apply a light to it, when a gas light was obtained. On placing a candle against the coal, it ignited the gas issuing from a thousand fissures; and when shots were fired for blasting down the coal, they generally set fire to the gas, which had to be beaten or "doused" out by the men with dusters or wet sacks. In the Main coal, in the same colliery, as the gas was at times ignited in places inaccessible to the dusting or dousing process, two cannons were kept in readiness to extinguish the flame by concussion ; and on one occasion in the Bensham seam, as the "guns" were not at hand, the underviewer had recourse to a blown-out shot, which successfully answered the purpose : a proceeding for which Mr. Buddle gave him the highest credit (*ib.*, 2,095-98). The underground railways at Wallsend are described as so dusty that they were obliged to lead water in tubs to water them, or the people would have been almost suffocated with dust (*ib.*, 2,184).

A severe explosion having taken place in the Bensham seam at the A pit, before much more had been accomplished than forming the shaft pillars, the working of the seam was suspended for a time to admit of other shafts being sunk to the coal.

When the working of pillars was subsequently prosecuted in this seam, the discharge of gas was greatly augmented by the strata breaking up to the Yard seam, situated about 70 feet above (*ib.*, 2,023). The gas-pipe drifts, or return air-courses, from the pillar or broken districts, were generally in an explosive state (*Trans. Nat. Hist. Soc. of Northumberland*, ii. 351).

A remarkable illustration of the large discharge of gas from the Bensham seam workings was exhibited in the great gas light, burning at the C or village pit, which formed a noted feature of Wallsend Colliery for a long period. Here the gas issuing from a detached and barred-off district of workings, five acres [1] in extent, was conveyed to the surface by a 4-inch cast iron pipe. The quantity of gas discharged from this tract amounted to about 2 cubic feet per second, [2] or 120 cubic feet per minute, and the noise which it made in escaping resembled the roaring of a blast furnace ; the discharge being most vehement when the wind blew from the south-east. It produced a pennant of flame 8 or 9 feet in length, which formed a conspicuous object to a considerable distance. This great stream of gas continued to flow uninterruptedly, with a slightly diminishing volume, for a period of at least nineteen years (*ib.*, 2,030, also p. 179; *Fossil Fuel*, p. 230 note ; *South Shields Report*, art. Safety Lamp ;

[1] Mr. Buddle, both in his evidence before the 1835 Committee and at Wallsend inquest, says five acres. The author of *Fossil Fuel* says about four acres. The South Shields Committee say not more than five acres. There appear to have been two pipes at first, and two are shown in Hair's sketch of this pit ; one of them, however, discharging very little gas. See also Mr. Buddle's narrative of the explosion at Wallsend, in the *Transactions of the Natural History Society of Northumberland* (vol. ii., p. 371), and the plan of the workings in the Bensham seam, where the tracts are marked P and R.

[2] So said by Mr. Buddle in his evidence before the 1835 Committee (*Report* 2,030). At Wallsend inquest he puts it at "11 hogsheads per minute," equal to 113 cubic feet (*ib.*, p. 179).

T. J. Taylor, *Trans. N.E. Inst.*, 1853; Professor Phillips's *Report*, p. 10).

Not only was firedamp more abundant in the deeper seams, but it existed under a higher degree of pressure, or tension; and blowers and outbursts begin to be more frequently heard of.

Shortly after the Bensham seam was sunk to at Jarrow Colliery (Hair's *Sketches*, p. 31), by means of the staple or underground pit already mentioned, a blower of gas was encountered, which occasioned a severe explosion in 1826, and which continued to discharge gas for at least ten years afterwards (*Trans. Nat. Hist. Soc. of Northumberland*, ii. 388).

In the same seam a sudden and violent outburst of gas occasioned another explosion, attended with a large loss of life, in 1830. So great had been the pressure of the pent-up gas, that it forced forward a massive block of coal six tons in weight (Professor Phillips's *Report*, Append. iv.), and tore open a passage for itself along the top and down one side of it, giving to the excavation all the appearance of having penetrated into old workings (*Trans. Nat. Hist. Soc. of Northumberland*, i. 197). In this instance no trace of gas remained after the explosion.

Similar outbursts of gas occurred at Jarrow within a few months afterwards, forcing off masses of coal, but of less magnitude. In all the cases the eruption of gas took place at small faults in the seam (*ib.*, p. 205). It had been already noted that gas was sometimes met with at faults even in collieries where it was not otherwise found (*Edin. Encyclopæd.*, xiv. 362).

At Willington Colliery, when the Bensham seam was sunk to in 1831, also by means of a staple from the Main coal, a blower of gas was encountered which led to the abandonment of the workings, and their being filled with water. The pressure of the gas issuing from the blower, however, produced a water-blast which occasioned an explosion in the seam above. So great was the discharge of gas from the staple that it was closed up by a strong cap of iron, from which a 3-inch iron pipe was led to the surface, where the gas was burnt, producing a flame about a yard in height (*1835 Report*, 1262, 1279).

At Benwell Colliery, west of Newcastle, a burst of gas occurred from the thill, or pavement, of the Beaumont seam in 1830; but happily an explosion was prevented by the vigilance of the overman and his deputy (*Trans. Nat. Hist. Soc. of Northumberland*, i. 188).

In the Wear district a burst of gas from the roof produced an explosion in the I pit, Washington Colliery, in 1828 (*ib.*, p. 187).

Instances illustrative of the high pressure of gas are also recorded in this era (the locality not being specified), where in driving an excavation 4 feet in width under a fiery seam, with 7 feet of argillaceous strata between, the gas forced down the intervening measures in seeking vent for itself (*Edinburgh Encyclopædia*, xiv. 362).

The danger arising from sudden discharges of pent-up firedamp was pointed out by Mr. Buddle to the Lords' Committee in 1829 (*Report*, p. 47) as one of the great risks attendant upon colliery enterprises. "In the course of pursuing the workings of collieries into the whole coal," he says, "they frequently cut across those fissures, which are in the roof above, and full of inflammable air in the compressed state I have described; they frequently, even before we come near them by a considerable distance, break away the coal or the stone, when it becomes too weak to resist the elastic force of the compressed gas; and I have known within my own practice, in a very short time, in a few minutes, from a state of perfect safety a pit become completely charged to the point of explosion, from an immense quantity of gas rushing out of those fissures, which we technically call blowers; precisely the same thing as if we had made a communication with an old working; this discharges the gas into the working, and overpowers the ventilation. . . . If there is more than one volume of inflammable air to fourteeen of atmospherical air, it then is an explosive mixture, and of course it explodes at the first naked light it falls in with."

Elsewhere the same gentleman, in speaking of the various causes of explosion (*Trans. Nat. Hist. Soc. of Northumberland*, i. 187), remarks that "this may be considered the most dangerous case, as it frequently happens that a large quantity of gas bursts out from those cavities, which occur in the roof and pavement, as well as in coal. . . . The great danger in this case arises from the suddenness and great force of the eruption, without giving sufficient warning for the escape of the colliers, or for allowing the persons in charge of them time to adopt the necessary measures of precaution. Many accidents have happened from this cause, but there have also been innumerable instances of escape from it. The technical name adopted by our colliers for this sort of occurrence is 'a bag of foulness.'"

Reference has been made to the circumstance of firedamp proving less formidable than was to have been expected in the new and deep collieries opened out at this period in the Wear district. But it is perhaps doubtful whether this apparent anomaly was not to some extent due to the more capacious shaft room and improved ventilation adopted at these collieries.

Next to the great northern coalfield, the exporting districts of limited area about Whitehaven, in Cumberland, and on the estuary of the Dee, in North Wales, appear to have been most largely infested with firedamp up till this period, in both of which explosions occurred periodically.

In the Lancashire coalfield many of the mines were now becoming explosive, in the neighbourhood of Newton, Wigan, and Ashton (*1835 Report*, 1,759-1,765, 2,443, 3,472).

The mines in the West Riding of Yorkshire are described as explosive, but in a very slight degree (*ib.*, 2,429). Firedamp was, however, giving some annoyance in the Leeds district, also at Wakefield, and in the neighbourhood of Bradford (*ib.*, 4,028, 3,717, 3,763). In Derbyshire and Leicestershire the quantity of firedamp was comparatively small (*ib.*, 1,226, 1,768).

That the South Staffordshire mines yielded a little gas we have already seen. One or two of the coal seams in North Staffordshire were also becoming somewhat fiery (*ib.*, 2,522-27, 2,606-7). We hear of a blower being encountered at a fault in a pit only 63 feet deep (*ib.*, 2,761-65). In Shropshire also gas was occasioning accidents.

In Warwickshire, the Forest of Dean, and Somersetshire, the mines appear to have been either altogether free from or very little infested with explosive gas.

In the South Wales coalfield, the great proportion of the coal being still obtained from shallow workings, the production of firedamp was as yet neither extensive nor dangerous, and few explosions had occurred (*Trans. Nat. Hist. Soc. of Northumberland*, i. 112; *1835 Report*, 4, 2,473-74).

A project for dealing with firedamp was patented by a Mr. Wood in 1826, whose idea was to set a clock to fire the mine by means of phosphorus when the men were out (*Trans. N.E. Inst.*, xvii. 34).

CHAPTER XLVIII.

THE NINETEENTH CENTURY. 1817-1835.

*Colliery explosions. Northumberland and Durham. Cumberland. North
Wales. Lancashire. Yorkshire. Staffordshire. South Wales.*

IN this era the great scene of colliery explosions still lay in the
Northumberland and Durham coalfield, as appears from the following records :

1817. June 30. Harraton, Row pit.—Violent explosion, by which
thirty-eight men and boys were killed. Corves, trams, and several
utensils used at the bottom of the shaft (492 feet deep), were blown
into the air, together with the bodies of two of the unfortunate
workmen, one with the head off, and the other cut in two in the
middle (Sykes's *Loc. Rec.*).

Mr. Buddle, who was an eye-witness of this explosion, and who
cited it to the Lords' Committee in 1829 (*Report*, p. 49) as a marked
instance of one man's wilfulness causing the destruction of a large
number of his fellow-workmen, gives the following account of it
(*1835 Report*, 2,955-87) :

"There was a very decent man, his comrade, working in the
same place with him ; the overman went in with them in the
morning and showed them the danger ; for although there was
no gas in the place they were working in, at about 12 yards
from them, in what we call the *return* from the place, which is
the way the current of air was going, he actually took them in
and showed them that it was explosive. He cautioned them by
no means to expose a naked light, inasmuch as they were subject
to the operation of what we call backing of the foulness, against
the current of air upon their lights. He gave them this caution
and went about his business. When this headstrong fellow told
his comrade that he could not see with that thing, meaning the
Davy, and would insist on screwing off the gauze cylinder and

taking his candle, the other remonstrated with him, told him he
was aware of the danger, and he really durst not stop if he per-
sisted in unscrewing the Davy; however, after what I have stated,
after two or three attempts at the lamp, he obstinately took off the
top of it.   I am not quite certain whether he lighted a candle, but
he worked with a naked light.   The other man was so sensible of
the danger that he immediately went away, and in going out-bye
he saw the overman and requested him to go immediately in to
Moody, as he was quite sure he would do a mischief.   He then
came to the surface; he then rode, as we call it; he came up the
pit, and in a very few minutes the explosion happened.   I happened
to be in a situation where I saw this explosion; it was rather an
eruption than an explosion.   It was a most curious phenomenon; it
continued for above five minutes to vomit out a column of black
smoke, which ascended an immense height into the air, like a water-
spout.   It was a very fine day, there was only a gentle breeze of
wind from the west, and I saw it feeding till the mass of black
smoke and coal-dust formed an immense cloud immediately over
the pit, with a narrow stalk to it, the diameter of the shaft.   A
kind of explosion took place at length, which cut off the stalk from
the top of the pit, and then this immense cloud was carried away by
the gentle breeze, and deposited its contents over the country for
perhaps two or three miles.   I made the best of my way to the pit,
and when I arrived there, everything was blown away from its
mouth; the metal pulleys that the ropes go over were carried to
a distance, the shaft framing was totally blown away, the ropes
were blown out, and there were two mangled carcasses lying within
a little distance of the mouth of the shaft.   There was a body cut
in two, the trunk and arms without the head were lying in one
place, and the legs and thighs lying at four or five yards from it.
At about twelve yards from the pit there was a body lying without
a head.

   " ' What was the depth of the shaft ? '—Eighty fathoms (480 feet).
   " ' How far do you conceive those workmen were from the bottom
of the shaft at the time the explosion took place ? '—We ascertained
that accurately afterwards, for one of them was the body of a boy
whose father was the onsetter at the bottom of the pit; and it shows
how a little shelter in some cases on those occasions will protect a
man.   The onsetter always has a little recess, in which he keeps
what we call the chalking board, on which he chalks down the
quantity of work done by each collier; and this little boy (it was
his first day of being at work) was at a door very near the shaft,

and he frequently came to his father in the course of the day; he had just come to him; at the instant the explosion happened the man held the boy's hand with one of his, while with the other he was chalking on his board, his body being within the recess niche in the coal; the boy was carried up the pit in the way I have described, and the man was not the least injured.   The other man, whose name was Allen, I believe, was standing at the bottom of the pit, leaning with his elbows on a corf, talking to the onsetter; he disappeared in an instant, and was blown out at the top of the pit. It was clear from the appearance after we got down the pit to seek for the bodies, that the fire had taken place where Moody was working, as the very first stroke of the fire had been there, for his body was almost burnt to a cinder, and the poor unfortunate over-man was found within about 40 yards of him; he had never reached him."

This is the last explosion known to the writer in which bodies are stated to have been blown to the surface from the bottom of the pit, at a colliery in England.

Two days later (July 2) eight men who went down the Nova Scotia pit, at the same colliery, were killed by the afterdamp which had entered the workings, supposed from the Row pit, subsequent to the explosion (Sykes's *Account of Wallsend Explosion*, p. 33 n.).

1817. July 21. Sheriff Hill.—Explosion which killed one person (*ib.*).

1817. September 25. Jarrow.—Explosion by which six lives were lost (Sykes's *Loc. Rec.*).

1817. November 3. Ouston.—Explosion by which one was killed and three burnt (*ib.*).

1817. December 18. Rainton, Plain pit.—Explosion by which twenty-seven were killed (eleven men and sixteen boys). It happened before all the workmen had descended. Had it occurred a little later there would have been 160 men and boys in the pit (*ib.*).

1818. August 5. Wallsend.—Explosion by which four were killed.

Two men and two boys were employed in drifting in a creep in the G pit, and were using the Davy lamp.   One of the men extinguished his lamp while trimming it, and sent a boy to the stationary light in the fresh air to relight it.   When the boy was returning with the lamp, and had arrived within a distance of 20 yards, the man, being impatient, called to him to make haste, whereupon he began to run, but fell, and all were instantly enveloped in fire.

On proceeding to the spot Mr. Buddle found that when the boy had fallen, the Davy lamp had struck against the corner of a tram plate, whereby an aperture was made large enough to admit the blade of a penknife, and he had no doubt that this damage to the lamp was the cause of the explosion (*Trans. Nat. Hist. Soc. of Northumberland*, ii. 332; Sykes's *Acc. of Wallsend Explosion*, p. 33 n.).

1819. July 19. Sheriff Hill.—Explosion which killed thirty-five, viz., two men and thirty-three boys. It happened after the hewers had left work (Sykes's *Loc. Rec.*).

1819. October 9. Lumley (or Lambton), George pit.—Explosion with loss of thirteen lives (Sykes's *List*). Another account gives the number as eleven men and boys, and ascribes the accident to a bord having been worked into with a naked light (Sykes's *Loc. Rec.*; *1835 Report*, 460).

1820. April 28. Jarrow.—Explosion, with loss of two lives (Sykes's *List*).

1821. July 9. Rainton, North pit.—Explosion, with loss of one life (*ib.*).

Coxlodge.—Explosion, with loss of one life (*ib.*). Scott, who gives some account of this explosion in his *Scenes and Incidents*, etc. (pp. 56, 57), dates it 1823; and states that while a number of others were maimed and burnt, the young man who was killed was not burnt

1821. October 23. Wallsend, A pit.—Explosion, with loss of fifty-two lives. Out of fifty-six persons who were in the pit only four survived.

This accident is stated to have "shook the ground like an earthquake, and made the furniture dance in the neighbouring houses" (*Loc. Rec.*). It occurred in the Bensham seam, to which the A pit had been sunk in the previous year, and the workings in which only extended to a short distance (not more than 100 yards in any direction) from the shaft. The pit was divided into two sections, upcast and downcast, by means of a timber brattice.

The workings, Mr. Buddle states, were liable to be charged with gas to the firing point, "but accidents had always been avoided by the vigilance of two young men—the overmen of the pit. It was, however, deemed prudent in consequence of the dangerous nature of the pit, to place it under the care of the most experienced overman in the colliery. In a short time afterwards this fatal accident happened, but as the overman, together with his deputies, and nearly all the people who were in the pit at the time perished, the immediate cause of the accident could not be distinctly ascertained. We had, however, very strong presumptive proof that it had been occasioned by the too great confidence of the overman in his own judgment, and that he had not given the usual alarm 'Put out the lows' (*i.e.*, extinguish the lights) in due time" (*Trans. Nat. Hist. Soc. of Northumberland*, i. 185-86).

In a later notice relating to this accident (published subsequent to Mr. Buddle's death), it is ascribed to the furnaceman secretly leaving the furnace in order to be present at some feast which was being held (*Min. Jour.*, xiii. 372).

A fatal feature of this accident was the blowing out of the brattice, whereby those who were not killed by the explosion were suffocated (*1835 Report*, 1,988, 2,090-94; *Trans. Nat. Hist. Soc. of Northumberland*, ii. 352).

1821. Felling.—Explosion with loss of six lives (Sykes's *List*).

1823. February 21. Ouston.—Explosion by which four men were killed, and two severely burnt (Sykes's *Loc. Rec.*).

1823. November 3. Rainton, Plain pit.—Explosion with loss of fifty-nine lives (Sykes's List; in *Loc. Rec.* the number is given as fifty-three men and boys). The safety lamp was in use in the pit; but regarding one department there is some uncertainty whether lamps or candles were used (*1835 Report*, 645).

1822. Killingworth.—Explosion by which several men were burnt; the majority of whom recovered, but some were thought (by Mr. Stephenson) to have died (*ib.*, 1,400).

This was not improbably the occasion on which Mr. N. Wood was burnt, along with three or four more; the accident being caused by the temporary neglect of a door, in a part of the mine where there was a blower of gas (*ib.*, 1,117, 1,129).

Mr. Wood informed a Parliamentary Committee that he wished to throw himself down, but was unable to do so, the air being so dense that his body floated in it (*Third Report*, 1853, p. 19).

1824. October 25. Lumley, George pit.—Explosion with loss of fourteen lives (Sykes's *List*).

1824. November 19. Newbottle, Dolly pit.—Explosion causing loss of eleven lives, viz., eight deputy overmen and wastemen who were below at the time, and also three of five others who afterwards descended in search of the dead bodies. The shaft was divided by a brattice, which was blown out and fell to the bottom (Sykes's *Loc. Rec.*).

1825. July 3. Fatfield, Judith pit.—Explosion with loss of eleven lives (Sykes's *List*). Another account calls it the Juliet pit, Harraton

Outside (Sykes's *Loc. Rec.*). Fatfield formed part of the original Harraton estates.

1825. October 5. Hebburn.—Explosion with loss of four lives. The firedamp was ignited by the sparks of a steel mill, which was being used while the Davy lamps were cooling.[1] The men were suffocated by the afterdamp (Sykes's *Loc. Rec.*). It is stated (*South Shields Report*, p. 11 n.) that on November 27, 1830, two men met their death from the same cause in the same place.

1826. January 17. Jarrow.—Explosion by which thirty-four men and boys were killed, and some others much burnt (*ib.*; Sykes's *Loc. Rec.*).

This accident occurred in the Bensham seam, which had recently been sunk to (Hair's *Sketches*, p. 31). According to one account (*South Shields Report*, art. Boys in Mines), it was caused by a young boy having left a trap-door open; but this is seemingly incorrect, as there is evidence of a very circumstantial character that it was due to a sudden discharge of inflammable gas. Ten years afterwards, we hear of a sample of gas being obtained for analysis, from the Bensham coal seam, Jarrow Colliery, collected from a blower, which caused the accident in 1826 (*Trans. Nat. Hist. Soc. of Northumberland*, ii. 388).

1826. May 30. Towneley Main, or Stella.—Explosion with loss of thirty-eight lives (Sykes's *Loc. Rec.*).

1826. September 5. Heworth—Explosion by which five were killed, and ten others scorched and burned (*ib.*).

1826. October 27. Benwell, High pit.—Explosion by which two young men were killed, and several others injured. There were upwards of one hundred men and boys in the mine at the time (Hair's *Sketches*, p. 27). The accident was ascribed to a candle having been taken into a part of the mine where it had been cautioned not to go (Sykes's *Loc. Rec.*).

1827. July 20. Lumley, Charles pit.—Explosion by which nine men were burnt, one of whom died. Ascribed to a candle being taken into the wrong part of the pit (*ib.*).

The pit was partly worked with safety lamps and partly with candles. The blast came from the part where the candles were used (*1835 Report*, 466-470).

1827. September 5. Fawdon.—Explosion by which three young men were much burnt, two of whom died (Sykes's *Loc. Rec.*).

---

[1] When Mr. T. E. Forster was serving his time at Hebburn, the top part of the Davy lamp was always red hot, but never fired the gas (*Trans. N.E. Inst.*, xv. 145).

1828. March 15. Jarrow.—Explosion with loss of eight lives (*ib.*).

1828. September 1. New pit, Houghton-le-Spring.—Explosion with loss of seven lives. Door left open, causing an accumulation of gas on Monday morning (*ib.*).

1828. November 20. Washington, I pit.—Explosion with loss of fourteen lives. There were fifteen persons in the pit, of whom only one escaped, who was much burnt. "The report was awfully loud, and the blast so powerful that the machinery on the mouth of the pit was blown down and scattered to some distance, with corves and other weighty bodies from the bottom of the shaft. The colliery had been examined in the morning, and was considered to be in a perfect state of ventilation " (*ib.*).

The accident was occasioned by a burst of gas, or "bag of foulness," breaking down from the roof of the air-course bord, behind the workmen, which at the same time stopped the ventilation by the fall of the roof it occasioned (*Trans. Nat. Hist. Soc. of Northumberland*, i. 187).

Mr. T. J. Taylor cites this accident as a noted instance of an explosion being caused by an eruption of gas (*Trans. N.E. Inst.*, 1853).

1829. May 13. Killingworth, West Moor pit.—Explosion which burnt several, one of whom died (Sykes's *Loc. Rec.*).

1829. June 26. Newbottle, Dorothea pit.—Explosion by which one man was killed, followed by a second explosion. During a period of twenty-four hours explosions occurred every one or two hours. The mine being on fire, two pits were closed up (*ib.*).

1829. December 3. Willington.—Explosion, accompanied by a rush of water from some old workings, causing the loss of four lives (*ib.*).

1830. August 3. Jarrow.—Explosion by which forty-two men and boys were killed (*ib.*). Ten more were also much injured. There were 120 men in the mine when the explosion took place (at 5.40 a.m.), of whom seventy were in the Besham seam, where the blast took place (Hair's *Sketches*, p. 31).

This accident was caused by the sudden outburst of gas, which forced out the mass of coal, as already mentioned. An account of it, illustrated by plans and diagrams, was read by Mr. Buddle to the Natural History Society of Northumberland, on the 18th of October following, and published in their *Transactions* (vol. i., p. 184 *et seq.*).

Though so fatal in its consequences, the range of the fire was not of very great extent. Mr. Buddle characterizes it as a smart fire—

not a heavy one. The hewer who was working at the point where the burst of gas took place was not burnt, and no marks of fire appeared for about eight yards back from the face; where, at the end of a "stenting," or crossholing, the gas had become sufficiently mixed with air to render it explosive.

Mr. Buddle presented the society, among other things, with a specimen of the "charred coaldust," which, he says, "is deposited in every part of the workings within the range of the fire. This dust flies in all directions in luminous sparks, similar to those discharged from the chimney of an engine, which are frequently propelled by the force of the explosion to a considerable distance beyond where the flame of the ignited gas reaches. They scorch and wound those who may happen to be within their reach, and frequently set fire to any combustible substance they may fall upon—sometimes the coal itself." [1]

The district of workings where the explosion occurred was lighted with candles. Mr. Buddle's remarks on this point will be adverted to hereafter.

1831. July 9. Wreckenton, King pit.—Explosion with loss of three lives (two men, one boy); supposed to have been caused by a door being left open (Sykes's *Loc. Rec.*).

1831. September 20. Willington, High pit.—Explosion, by which eight were killed (four men and four boys), and seven severely scorched. This accident was caused by the water-blast in the Bensham seam staple already referred to; the gas igniting at the candles of the workpeople in the Main coal (*1835 Report*, 1,262). The whole complement of men were in the mine at the time, but the greater part were enabled to effect their escape by means of another shaft (Hair's *Sketches*, p. 16).

1832. October. Wallsend, C pit.—Explosion with loss of one life. Gas supposed to have ignited at the ventilating furnace (Sykes's *Account of Wallsend Explosion*, pp. 22, 34).

1832. November 13. Heaton.—Explosion with loss of one life (*ib.*, p. 34).

1833. May 9. Springwell, B pit.—Explosion by which forty-seven persons (ten men, thirty-seven boys) were killed, and a number

---

[1] In an article on fires in collieries, contributed to Jameson's *Journal* in 1828 (p. 101), Mr. Robert Bald, the eminent Scotch mining engineer, remarks that they were sometimes caused "by the blast of an explosion, which is a magazine of blue and white flame of intense heat, which sets fire to the small coaldust of the roads in the mines." And he further states (p. 106) that when the fire was in the coaldust of the roads small extinguishing engines were used, and sometimes concussion.

of others much injured. "The pit," says Latimer (*Loc. Rec.*, p. 10), "had generally been worked with open candles, but on the morning of the accident, a 'blower' (a crevice through which a stream of gas issued) having been opened by a workman, the overman ordered the men to use safety lamps, and the cause of the explosion was shrouded in complete mystery."

This accident has been cited as affording evidence of the insecurity of the Davy lamp. If we may accept the testimony of Mr. Buddle on the point this is altogether erroneous. "I know," he says (*1835 Report*, 2,224), "that it is affirmed the late explosion at the Springwell Colliery took place from the Davy lamp; now I am utterly at a loss to conceive how that notion has prevailed. I was called in to a consultation, with other professional men, the day after the explosion there; and to the best of my recollection, all the evidence that we had about the cause of the accident was not that it had happened from the lamps, but from the want of the lamp; the intelligence I received was that one particular part of the pit was discovered to be in a dangerous state, the overman sent the boy for the Davys; the last man that got out met that boy going in with the Davys, but whether he had ever arrived at his point of destination is unknown."

Notwithstanding this refutation at the hands of so high and well-informed an authority as Mr. Buddle, in a list of accidents published some years subsequently (*Report of South Shields Committee*), appended to the notice of this explosion, we find the remark, "Davy lamps employed."

This explosion occurred in the Hutton seam, at a depth of 720 feet from the surface (Latimer's *Loc. Rec.*, p. 10).

1833. May 24. Great Lumley.—Explosion with loss of two lives (Sykes's *List*).

1833. November 8. Black Fell.—Explosion with loss of three lives (*ib.*; Latimer, p. 18).

1833. November 29. Low Moorsley pit.—Explosion by which Mr. Appleby, viewer, Mr. Dawson, overman, and four men, were dreadfully burnt (Sykes's *Account of Wallsend Explosion*, p. 34 n.).

1834. November 24. St. Lawrence.—Explosion by which three men were killed. Two of the men were masons, and had been building a wall with a naked candle, by which it was supposed the gas became ignited (Latimer's *Loc. Rec.*, p. 32).

1835. June 18. Wallsend.—Explosion causing the loss of 102 lives : twenty-seven men and seventy-five boys.

This accident happened in the Bensham seam, about 2 o'clock

in the afternoon.   Of about ninety hewers who had gone to work in
the morning, all had left the pit with the exception of six.   Hence
the bulk of those in the pit at the time of the accident consisted of
young persons, such as putters, drivers, trappers, etc., employed
in getting out the coal.   The six hewers left were working in the
whole coal with candles; naked lights being used in two divisions
of the workings.

The indications at the surface of an explosion having occurred
were very slight.   One of the banksmen at the G pit had just
unhooked the lowest full corve from the rope and placed an empty
corve in the pit, when a gust of wind blew it out and carried his hat
over the headgear.   The same individual in the course of a few
minutes saw smoke issuing from the C pit.   This is described as of
a lightish colour, and as being only a single puff which ceased almost
immediately.

Two furnacemen, employed at the A and B pits, succeeded in
escaping by the C pit, and four persons were found alive at the
bottom of the G pit, one of whom, however, died a few days afterwards ; while 101 bodies were found in the mine.

Of the unfortunate victims some were burnt and some not,
though lying near each other.   Many of them had left the place
where they were working, and travelled a considerable distance—as
much as 500 yards (*1835 Report*, 2,993)—before succumbing to the
deadly afterdamp.

Subsequent examination elicited the fact that the explosion had
not originated in any of the working districts.   The indications of
greatest violence appeared to be in the vicinity of the shaft (the G
pit), near which there were no workings.

It was then traced to a point where two men were employed in
blasting down the roof in a rolley-way leading to the B pit to make
height for a horse road.   These men were allowed to use naked
lights where the blasting was going on, but were restricted to safety
lamps at the place where the stones were deposited a short distance off.

In the neighbourhood of where these men were working there was
a pair of doors leading into a highly dangerous part of the mine ;
and from the position in which the cistern, or bottom portion of the
lamp of one of the men was found, it was concluded that he had
incautiously approached the doors with the naked light, causing an
explosion of the gas accumulated in two tracts of abandoned and
unventilated workings.

The most fatal feature of the explosion was the blowing out of the
brattice in the G pit.   In consequence of his experience in connection

with the explosion in the same seam at the A pit in 1821, Mr. Buddle adopted the expedient of sinking the G pit from the Main coal downwards, in the form of two pits 6 feet diameter, separated by a partition of natural rock. But the arrangement unfortunately failed to answer his expectations. One hundred and eighty feet of the timber brattice above the Main coal was carried away, which fell down the shaft and closed the mouths of the two shafts to the Bensham seam. But for this untoward event, Mr. Buddle was of opinion that one-half, or more, of the lives might have been saved (*1835 Report*, 1,988, 2,122-26, 2,040-52, 2,068, 2,307; also pp. 177-188, where evidence at inquest is given; Sykes's pamphlet; Mr. Buddle's narrative, *Trans. Nat. Hist. Soc. of Northumberland*, vol. ii.).

This accident has been cited as an instance of an explosion having occurred where Davy lamps were employed (*Report of South Shields Committee*, art. Safety Lamp; also Append. E).

1835. November 19. Burdon Main.—Explosion with loss of eleven lives (three men, eight boys). Ascribed to a door having been left open (Latimer's *Loc. Rec.*, p. 46).

Of those who perished by explosions in the northern coalfield, the great majority were suffocated by the afterdamp, or killed by concussion (*1835 Report*, 684-692), while only about one-fourth of the victims were burnt to death.

Up till this time five ships are stated (*ib.*, 2,931) to have been blown up on the Tyne and Wear.

In 1834-35 an attempt was made to collect statistics relative to the number of lives lost in the mines of England and Wales during the previous twenty-five years. The returns obtained are admitted to have been very defective. From some counties no information was forthcoming; in other cases the nature of the accidents was not mentioned. Northumberland and Durham are omitted. Imperfect, however, as it purports to be, the following summary is not devoid of interest (*1835 Report*, Preface):

	Lives lost.		
Cumberland,	140	Firedamp and chokedamp.	
Chester,	7	Do.	do.
Flint,	39	Do.	do.
Lancashire (no returns from several districts),	135	Do.	do.
York, West Riding,	23	Chokedamp.	
Do. do.,	93	Firedamp.	
Do. do.,	230	Accidents not specified.	
Do. North Riding,	29	Firedamp and chokedamp.	
Derby,	19	Do.	do.

Lives lost.

Nottingham,	.	.	.	18	.	Firedamp and chokedamp.
Stafford (one district),		.		104	.	Do. do.
Warwick,	.	.	.	3	.	Do. do.
Salop, .	.	.	.	89	.	Do. do.
Gloucester, .	.	.	.	3	.	Do. do.
Somerset, .	.	.	.	1	.	Do. do.
Monmouth, .	.	.	.	3	.	Do. do.
Brecon,	.	.	.	15	.	Not specified.
Do.,	.	.	.	3	.	Explosions.

$$\overline{954}$$

The following notices are met with relative to particular explosions which occurred in the above districts during the years 1817-35 :

In the Cumberland coalfield, between 1817 and 1824, an explosion occurred at Saltonlow Bottom (*1835 Report*, 3,427-3,434), by which three men were killed. During the same period the William pit, Whitehaven, exploded (*ib.*, 2,297, 2,308-2,310, 3,401-6) with the loss of thirty-three lives, including a number of women. While in September, 1833, there were fourteen men killed and several severely hurt (*Fossil Fuel*, p. 283) at Mr. Curwen's colliery at Workington.

In North Wales an explosion, regarding which we have no particulars, is alluded to (*Phil. Maga.*, xlix. 104-5) as having occurred in Mr. Roscoe's colliery at Bagillt, in 1816 or 1817. And in the same district a like catastrophe is stated (Boyd's *Coal Mines Inspection*, Append.) to have happened at Flint, on May 20, 1828, with the loss of eleven lives.

In Lancashire there is mention (*ib.*) of an explosion at Pemberton, Wigan, on April 24, 1830, with the loss of nine lives. In the neighbourhood of Newton an explosion occurred in 1833-34 (*1835 Report*, 1762), with the loss of twelve lives. A considerable number of lives are also stated (*ib.*, 4,110) to have been lost by an accident at Wigan in 1835; and in the same year reference is made (*ib.*, 1,764) to an accident in the neighbourhood of Ashton.[1]

In Yorkshire, though a considerable number of lives were evidently being lost by firedamp, scarcely a notice occurs of particular accidents. We hear of a small explosion at Middleton Colliery, about 1823-25 (*ib.*, 4,064), by which two men were killed.

In the South Staffordshire coalfield an explosion occurred at Oldbury, near Dudley, on September 1, 1833 (*ib.*, 1,819; *Fossil Fuel*, p. 283), whereby thirteen persons were greatly injured, three

---

[1] Some account of accidents which had occurred in the Ashton neighbourhood is given in a small work entitled *An Address to Coal Miners*, printed in 1832, and edited by John Howcroft (*1835 Report*, 4,129).

of whom died. Another explosion took place at Pump-house Colliery, near Dudley Port, West Bromwich, on November 2, 1835 (*Mining Journal*, vol. i., pp. 90, 99), by which sixteen men were killed and five more or less burnt.

In North Staffordshire we hear of an explosion at Apedale (*1835 Report*, 2,594-96), causing the loss of ten or more lives; of another at Shelton (*ib.*, 2,743) whereby a number of persons were burnt, of whom four or five died; and of another at Greendock pit (*ib.*, 2,558), by which one man was killed and a second severely burnt.

In the Ashby-de-la-Zouch portion of the Leicestershire coalfield, there is mention (*Child. Employ. Com.*, Append. i., p. 99) of an explosion occurring at Swadlincote Colliery about 1833, by which two men were burned.

In the South Wales coalfield we have no mention of any large explosion of firedamp having yet occurred, and the loss of life from this cause appears to have been as yet very small. There is a notice of some accidents having happened at the Hendreforgan mine (*1835 Report*, 1,223); the manager on one occasion being very much burnt along with some others. Another explosion also occurred at a colliery near Llanelly, about 1827, by which thirteen persons were much burned (*Child. Employ. Com.*, Append. ii., p. 695).

Among accidents of other kinds various inundations took place in this era.

Towneley Colliery (Stella) was inundated by a high flood on the Tyne, December 1, 1828. One man was drowned, whose remains were recovered in opening out Stargate pit to the Brockwell seam in 1880.

Beamish Colliery was inundated March 7, 1832, when two persons were drowned (Sykes's *List*).

Kingswood Colliery, Northumberland, was inundated May 2, 1833, when five persons were drowned (Latimer's *Loc. Rec.*, p. 10).

The Lady and Isabella pits at Workington, Cumberland, were inundated from old workings in the same year (1833). There were thirty men underground at the time, who were rescued, with the exception of four (*Fossil Fuel*, p. 250).

At St. Helens, Lancashire, in 1835, seventeen persons were drowned by the water from a river above bursting into a mine (*1835 Report*, 3,709, 4,123).

Few instances are recorded of persons having been suffocated in the mines of the great northern coalfield, except in connection with the afterdamp resulting from explosions. A singular case occurred at Nesham's colliery, at Newbottle, on October 19, 1821, when six

men were suffocated by some noxious gas in which the candles continued to burn (Sykes's *Loc. Rec.*; *1835 Report*, 1,853).[1]

Accidents from ropes breaking appear to have been somewhat
frequent at this period. By the breaking of a rope at Burradon
Colliery, Northumberland, in 1822, four persons (two men and two
boys) were killed (Richardson's *Table Book*). On December 21,
1832, three persons were killed by the breaking of a rope at
Harrington, Durham (Latimer's *Loc. Rec.*, p. 6). At Hartley Colliery four lives were lost by the breaking of a rope on November
24, 1834 (Sykes's *List*). And at Burdon Main Colliery six lives
were lost from the same cause in 1835 (*1835 Report*, 2,997).

Notices of accidents of various other kinds, connected with the
shaft and surface machinery, are met with in the local records of
Northumberland and Durham, but of the long list of miscellaneous
accidents underground little or nothing is heard.

An early instance of cast iron tubbing bursting occurred at
Houghton pit, belonging to Lord Durham, on October 15, 1832
(Sykes's *Account of Wallsend Explosion*, p. 34 note). An immense
stream of water gushed out, which filled the workings of the pit.
No human life was lost, but all the horses in the pit at the time
were drowned.

[1] See a notice of similar cases at Hartley and Tyne Main collieries (*1835
Report*, 880-81).

CHAPTER XLIX.

THE NINETEENTH CENTURY. 1817-1835.

Attack on the Davy lamp. Appointment of a Select Committee of the House of Commons in 1835. The Davy lamp and gunpowder. Tampering with the lamp. Improved discipline with regard to its use.

WE have seen that Sir H. Davy had himself been the first to point out the danger of exposing the wire-gauze lamp to a strong explosive current, and that he had cautioned the miners in his memoir *On the Safety Lamp* against such a proceeding. This had been duly attended to, and the lamp carefully handled, in the Newcastle district; but in other parts of the kingdom neither the lamp nor the inventor's instructions received much attention at that time.

In making experiments with wire gauze and explosive mixtures, in 1822 (*1835 Report*, 9), Goldsworthy Gurney, Esq., discovered that an explosive mixture "such as is found in coal mines" would pass flame through meshes of wire gauze if moving at the rate of 300 feet per minute. This he published in his *Lectures on the Elements of Chemical Science* in 1823; and he further drew attention to this source of danger in connection with the use of the wire-gauze lamp in mines, in the *Times* newspaper in 1824 (*ib.*, 50, 69).

A few years afterwards a more persistent and determined attack was commenced upon the Davy lamp, and an attempt made to prove that it afforded little or no protection to miners, and had probably been itself the cause of explosions taking place.

The prime movers in this agitation were Messrs. Upton and Roberts, a firm of lamp manufacturers in London. Upton, who was most pronounced in his allegations against the Davy lamp, was neither a chemist nor a miner, and had never been in a mine in his life (*ib.*, 1879). Roberts belonged originally to St. Helens, in Lancashire, and had worked as a miner in many different parts of the kingdom. While still a miner, he had invented a safety hood for use among noxious gases, and had visited London at the suggestion and with the assistance of Mr. Curwen, of Workington, to exhibit the contrivance to the Society of Arts (*ib.*, 3,351-3,361). Eventually he settled down in London as Mr. Upton's partner.

Messrs. Upton and Roberts had invented a safety lamp based upon the principle of security discovered by Sir H. Davy, which they claimed to be an improvement on the Davy lamp, and which they wished to see substituted for it. This lamp was protected by a patent, and its inventors left no stone unturned to damage the reputation of the Davy, and establish the superiority of their own lamp.

They drew the attention of various scientific gentlemen in the metropolis to the insecurity of the Davy lamp in an explosive current of coal gas and air, and the capability of resisting this possessed by their own lamp, *e.g.*, Mr. Pereira, Mr. Partington, Mr. Hemming, Dr. Turner, and Dr. Birbeck (*ib.*, 1,916-1,932). They also visited South Staffordshire in March 1834, and invited the mineowners to meet in order to witness experiments in proof of the insecurity of the Davy lamp; when about forty gentlemen assembled at the Gasworks at West Bromwich, and were much surprised to see the Davy lamp made to explode the gas (*ib.*, 1,937). Mr. Roberts also performed the experiment in a coal mine at Dudley, though not in the working part of the mine, but with a bladder of gas brought into a safe part (*ib.*, 1,936, 3,499-3,509).

As the result of Messrs. Upton and Roberts's demonstrations in Staffordshire a petition was presented to the House of Commons in March 1834, by Mr. Littleton, M.P. for South Staffordshire, on behalf of the "Coal Masters and Miners of the Staffordshire collieries, and of the collieries in the neighbourhood of Dudley," praying "that some legislative measure may be provided, appointing a scientific board to examine all lamps intended to be offered for sale to the public as safety lamps to be used in collieries, and to direct the stamping of all such as they shall approve, and to prohibit the sale of any as safety lamps, which shall not be so approved; and also to examine a safeguard to enable workmen, when necessary, to enter places infected with mephitic gases" (*Fossil Fuel*, p. 283).

The petitioners then proceed to enumerate various explosions whereby more than one hundred men had been killed or injured within the preceding eight months (viz., at Springwell, Oldbury, Workington, etc.), without referring to any connection between these explosions and the Davy lamp; but, seemingly taking it for granted that they were caused, or partly caused by it, they proceed

to say that "many fatal accidents have been attributed to the carelessness of the workmen in the use of their lamps, but we humbly
submit to the sense of this enlightened assembly that the charge
should not be received unless supported by strong evidence.   For it
is contrary to the natural principle of self-preservation that men
should, when the dreadful consequences are well known, be thus
indifferent to their own safety."

This was a very strenuous attempt to stamp out the Davy lamp,
to make way for Messrs. Upton and Roberts's patent instrument.
The petition came, be it observed, from a district where, in answer to
the question, "Had they been accustomed to use the lamp?" the
reply elicited was, "Seldom or ever to work by" (*1835 Report*,
1,955).

In consequence of this petition (Dunn's *Win. and Work.*, 2nd ed.,
p. 243), in the following year (1835), on the motion of Mr. Pease,
member for South Durham, a Select Committee of the House of
Commons was appointed on the 2nd of June "to enquire into the
nature, cause, and extent, of those lamentable catastrophes which
have occurred in the mines of Great Britain, with the view of
ascertaining and suggesting the means of preventing the recurrence
of similar fatal accidents."   The committee entered upon its task on
the 17th of June; just the day before the great explosion took place
at Wallsend Colliery.

The committee were particularly struck by the circumstance that
the invention of Sir Humphry Davy's safety lamp had not resulted
in any diminution of the number of lives lost through colliery explosions; but that on the contrary, more lives had been lost during the
eighteen years following its introduction, than in the eighteen years
preceding its invention (*Report*, Preface).

There were two different ways of accounting for this apparent
anomaly.   Mr. Buddle ascribed it to the circumstance of more
dangerous mines being now worked, which could not have been
in existence but for the aid afforded by the Davy lamp (*1829 Report*,
p. 47; *1835 Report*, 2,392-93); while Messrs. Upton and Roberts, and
others, maintained that Sir Humphry Davy had been mistaken as to
the safety of his lamp, and that the lamp itself occasioned explosions
(*1835 Report*, 22, 1,884, 1,940, 1,948).

There was another important element in the case.   Almost at the
same moment that science had armed the miners with the safety
lamp, the "demon of the mine" had been powerfully reinforced by
the introduction of the practice of employing gunpowder in the
getting of the coal.

Had the Davy lamp been universally employed in the mines in lieu of open lights, then indeed the continuance of explosions might, with some degree of reason, have been held to indicate a fatal error in relying upon it. But so far from this being the case, for a period of twenty years after its invention, in most of the coalfields the lamp was only used occasionally, and to a very small extent; while even in the north of England—where alone, and at Whitehaven and Workington, the Davy lamp was regarded and employed as a working implement (*ib.*, 2,223)—its use was almost solely confined to the pillar or "broken" working; the first, or "whole mine" working, continuing to be carried on with candles.

The only collieries where safety lamps appear to have been exclusively used at this period, were those of Walker (Prof. Phillips's *Report*, p. 9), and perhaps Heaton (*1835 Report*, 2,896) on the Tyne —at both of which probably pillars alone were being worked—and at some pits on the Wear similarly situated (*ib.*, 483, 492). But the idea of using the safety lamp exclusively, under ordinary circumstances, had scarcely begun to be entertained, nor indeed was such an arrangement regarded as desirable (*ib.*, 1,307-9). The system of mixed lights may be said to have been the universal rule in fiery mines in the north in this era, and for some time subsequently; and, indeed, is not uncommon at the present day where the quantity of gas evolved is not considerable.

The explanation of the restriction of the safety lamp to pillar working is a simple one. At this period the use of the lamp was generally, and very naturally, supposed to be altogether incompatible with the employment of gunpowder in the getting of the coal. In the pillar working gunpowder was unnecessary, and here the safety lamp was at once adopted as a welcome substitute for the steel mill. But in the case of working in the whole mine, gunpowder was regarded as indispensable (*ib.*, 989), and the safety lamp was consequently dispensed with, while naked lights and gunpowder bore sway. Mr. Wood, it is true, used safety lamps in conjunction with blasting at one of the Killingworth pits for a time, but resorted again to naked lights, on the plea that any use of the lamp, except where absolutely necessary, tended to give rise to carelessness on the part of the miners (*ib.*, 1,099, 2,588).

That it was gunpowder which stood in the way of the more extended use of the Davy lamp, and contributed more than anything else to perpetuate the employment of naked lights in the working of the whole coal in the fiery mines of the north, is admitted with perfect frankness. Take, for example, Mr. Buddle's remarks on the subject, in his account of the explosion at Jarrow Colliery in 1830 (*Trans. Nat. Hist. Soc. of Northumberland*, 1,202-3).

"It will be observed," he says, "that the *immediate* cause of the explosion was the ignition of the gas at the flame of some of the candles used by the workmen, as candles were very generally used in this part of the colliery.

"Here the question, why were candles used at all, and why was not the safety lamp exclusively adopted? suggests itself. The reason why the safety lamp was not generally used, nor can be generally used in future, is, that the use of gunpowder in the working of the coal is quite indispensable, and as the inflammable air ignites at the explosion of gunpowder, our main dependence must, in all such cases, rest chiefly upon the efficiency of the ventilation. Without the use of this powerful auxiliary, it is not practicable to work the coals out of this part of the mine in a marketable state, nor at a price that would pay for the working. Many collieries are similarly circumstanced, and a certain degree of risk must, therefore, be unavoidably incurred, or they must cease to be worked" (see also *1835 Report*, 2,402; Paris's *Life of Davy*, ii. 135).

Similar testimony is afforded by Mr. N. Wood, another eminent viewer (*1835 Report*, 1096).

"I will explain," he says, "the reason why I use candles in that mine in preference to lamps; the reason is, the coal is of such a nature that it cannot be wedged down. The mode of working coal is either by blasting or by wedging; the coal of that part of Killingworth Colliery is of that hard nature, and the tenacity with which it sticks to the roof is such that I believe it cannot be worked to profit without blasting; and my reason, therefore, for working it with candles is, that it would not, with the use of the lamp, be worked to profit."

That naked lights should have continued to be used in fiery mines after the invention of the safety lamp, for reasons of economy, is perfectly intelligible, but when the two able authorities above quoted proceed to maintain that this practice was conducive to safety, they enter upon more doubtful ground.

Mr. Wood, as we have seen, after employing safety lamps in a pit where blasting was carried on, "abandoned this mode of proceeding from the conviction that the mine was much safer by having candles entirely in it, than by using lamps occasionally, and setting men to blast the gunpowder" (*1835 Report*, 1,099). Mr. Buddle, questioned as to whether it was safe to use candles at any time (*ib.*, 2,071-72), replied, "Yes, I consider it a very great protection, the using of candles. It keeps every man upon the alert; we never can by the use of the Davy lamp judge of the quantity of air passing so well as we can do with the candle."

The liability of fiery mines to be suddenly inundated by eruptions of firedamp has been already adverted to as a feature of mining, to guard against which the invention of an insulated light was greatly desiderated. The existence of this danger was freely admitted by Mr. Wood (*1835 Report*, 846-47) and Mr. Buddle, and yet these gentlemen advocated the continued use of naked lights in working the whole mine, where it was that such eruptions took place. Mr. Wood—in whose experience only one small explosion had occurred from such a contingency—examined by the 1835 Committee upon the point, said (*ib.*, 994) he did not "think that any very extensive explosion would take place in such a case, if the ventilation is perfect," admitting at the same time, that "such explosions sometimes operate and destroy the men by the stoppings being blown down and the atmospheric air destroyed." Mr. Buddle, on the other hand, in whose wider experience extensive explosions had occurred from this very cause (*e.g.*, Washington and Jarrow), classed them among accidents arising "from causes which we cannot control" (*ib.*, 2,016), and characterized explosion in general as "a casualty that is incidental to the nature of coalmining" (*ib.*, 2,408).

The 1835 Committee were doubtful whether it was justifiable to carry on a colliery in which it was necessary to sacrifice fifty or one hundred men every ten or fifteen years (*ib.*, 3,760).

Mr. Buddle emphasized the danger of pillar working, and the comparative ease and safety with which the whole mine working was conducted. "Our difficulties," he says (*ib.*, 2,020), "only commence with the working of the pillars; comparatively it is only child's play till we come to the working of the pillars." And yet, strange to say, the working of the pillars had been rendered so safe by the exclusive employment of the safety lamp in this department, that the scene of the explosions at Wallsend, Jarrow, Willington, etc., was in the whole mine working, and places under the naked lights and gunpowder *régime*.

In other districts very little progress had yet been made in the employment of the Davy lamp. Mr. Buddle states (*ib.*, 2,223) that in any part where he had been (exclusive of Northumberland and Durham, and Cumberland) it was considered as a matter of curiosity, or precaution, to inspect certain places in the mine to discover where gas may be found, rather than considering it as a working implement belonging to the mine.

This view of the use of the lamp had been publicly advocated in the Midland counties. Mr. Farey, sen., a mineral surveyor in Derbyshire, had insisted that reliance should be placed on ventilation for safety, and that the lamp should only be used for examining the workings on Monday mornings: a recommendation which appears to have been acted upon to a large extent in the district to which he belonged; but which provoked the following rejoinder from Mr. J. Murray—already referred to as the proposer of a tube safety lamp in 1815—who was a great admirer of Davy's invention, and a warm advocate for its general use in mines, at this period :

"The recommendation of an *occasional* use of the safety lamp," he says, in a communication to the *Philosophical Magazine*, dated February 3, 1817 (vol. xlix., p. 104), "is one which will not be followed, nor can I conceive anything more absurd or ridiculous than to employ the instrument on a Monday, and *then hang it up* the week through. The fatal effects of such a procedure have been recently awfully exemplified in the last colliery which I descended. I *entreated* Mr. Roscoe to the continued use of Sir H. Davy's safe lamp—to be uniform and universal. The neglect of the precaution has accelerated that event which I hope will be a fence against any impressions from the doctrines of Mr. Farey, sen. Sir H. Davy's lamp was used in the Bagillt Colliery, and some were ordered from Mr. Newman, of Lisle Street, by Mr. Roscoe, to whom I submitted Mr. N.'s address; but such has been only occasional, or used in parts of the mine as were too alarming to be disregarded. I would not for a moment be understood to impeach either the prudence or precaution of Mr. Edward Roscoe, whose attention and care are highly honourable to him."

Nevertheless the occasional use of the safety lamp, and its restriction to alarming parts of the mine, continued to be the general rule in the Midland districts, even in 1835. Considerable difficulty was experienced in some localities in inducing the miners to work with the lamp, on account of the diminished light which it afforded, which was only equal to one-fourth part of that of a candle. It was consequently necessary to give them additional remuneration, when circumstances rendered it imperative that the lamp should be employed.

The very limited use of the lamp in Lancashire—regarding which abundance of direct evidence otherwise exists—is illustrated by the following clause in the rules of Pendleton Colliery, near Manchester, in 1832; at this time under the management of Robert Stephenson, civil engineer, brother of George Stephenson, and which appears to have been one of the earliest collieries in which the salutary arrangement of establishing a code of rules was adopted :

"The overmen and deputies must thoroughly understand what is generally termed trying the candle, in parts of the mine where it is expected inflammable gas may accumulate, to ascertain whether it is near the firing point or not; if in any degree dangerous, none must be allowed to go there without using the safety lamp, and not the naked candle. The parts most likely to be charged with inflammable gas will be on the rise side of the workings, it being much lighter than the common atmosphere. It will require their greatest attention on Monday morning, or when the pit has not been worked for a few days" (*1835 Report*, 3,792).

Instances might be multiplied to show the very limited extent to which the colliery proprietors of the Midland coalfields had availed themselves of the protection of the safety lamp. It was not until explosions began to become alarmingly formidable and frequent, coincidently with the further deepening of the mines, that the absolute necessity of substituting the lamp for naked lights in fiery mines began to be realized.

Various cases were cited before the 1835 Committee in which flame was supposed to have passed through the wire gauze of the Davy lamp. The explosion at Saltonlow Bottom, according to Mr. Roberts, was occasioned by two men placing their Davy lamp in the air-course, and proceeding to beat out the firedamp from their working-place with their coats. They were both burnt to death, and a young man at a distance of 140 yards was killed by concussion. Whether he had a safety lamp or a naked light is not stated (*ib.*, 3,427-3,436).

The explosion at the William pit, Whitehaven, was supposed by the same witness to have been caused by the Davy lamp, though it was ascribed to someone having removed the top of their lamp (*ib.*, 3,402-8).

Mr. Roberts likewise mentioned a case told him by a steward of Squire Willis's Colliery, near Prescot, in Lancashire, whose story was that a Davy lamp had been introduced in that colliery, and that he looked at it and said, "It will be very strange if this be safe; if this thin wire gauze is such a protection as to keep itself below the heating point of ignition." He then took the lamp and placed it up where the inflammable air was, and after a few minutes had elapsed there was an explosion (*ib.*, 3,512). —This seems altogether incredible, assuming the lamp to have been a proper Davy lamp.

Of cases mentioned by other witnesses, the explosion at Green-dock pit, North Staffordshire, was ascribed to this cause (*ib.*, 2,558). There was a pair of pits 942 feet deep. The colliery had been standing for a while, and the agent took down two men, and left them with a safety lamp to work with. When he came up, water was thrown down to increase the ventilation, and an explosion occurred immediately, one of the men being killed and the other much burnt.

Another witness, belonging to the same district, stated (*ib.*, 2,735-38) that he had himself seen the lamp fire the gas in a "thirling." The current was so strong that it would blow a candle out. The ignited gas flew away with the air and went out. It seemed to fly close from the gauze.

Mr. T. W. Embleton also mentioned the explosion at Middleton Colliery, which he had heard was occasioned by the two men entering with Davy lamps into a very strong current of air, highly impregnated with carburetted hydrogen (*ib.*, 4,064).

Whether any of the above cases were *bonâ-fide* instances of flame passing through the wire gauze of the Davy lamp, arising from neglect or ignorance of the warning given by Sir H. Davy, or whether the lamps themselves were defective, it is impossible to determine. It is somewhat singular that they should all have occurred in districts where the number of lamps in use must have been insignificant.

In the north of England, on the contrary, where many hundreds of Davy lamps had been in constant use during the nineteen years which had elapsed since its introduction, no case was known of the lamp having caused explosion. The viewers in the north had perfect confidence in it when properly used, and were ready to entrust their lives to its protection. None of them knew it ever to have failed. "I never did," says Mr. Buddle (*ib.*, 2,233), who had had more extended experience of the Davy lamp than any other individual; "I can only say that from the time of the invention of this lamp and getting them introduced as quickly and extensively as possible, I am quite certain that I have not for many years had less than 1,000 lamps a day using, and frequently 1,500, and I can state that I never have known an explosion happen from the Davy lamp, not even one solitary instance. I have seen them in operation, and been with them myself in all possible varieties of explosive mixtures to which they can be exposed in our mines. From my experience I have perfect confidence in them; and when I state during the number of years (nearly twenty) which I have had those lamps in daily use, that I do not know of one single accident having happened from them, at least so far as my own experience goes, I think I am warranted in pronouncing the Davy lamp to approximate as nearly to perfection as any instrument of human invention can do."

Even in the north it was found necessary to keep a watchful eye upon the wire gauze employed in the manufacture of Davy lamps. For this purpose Mr. Buddle carried in his pocket a small lens, the same as used by the Paisley manufacturers for examining their muslins. In the frame of the lens there was an aperture $\frac{1}{4}$ inch square, and by placing the little instrument on the gauze he was enabled to ascertain the number of apertures in a quarter of an inch, as a multiple for the whole inch. This he called his gauze gauge (*ib.*, 2,217). The standard size of gauze employed by Mr. Buddle contained about 784 apertures per square inch.

We have seen that the South Staffordshire petitioners against the sale of unsafe lamps, begged the House of Commons not to credit the statement that men would tamper with the lamp. But what were the real facts of the case where the lamp was extensively used? Mr. Buddle informed the Lords' Committee in 1829 (*Report*, p. 50) that scarcely a month occurred without the punishment of some of the workpeople for the mismanagement of the Davy lamp. "They have been fined, and the magistrates have sent them to the house of correction for a month, yet they will screw off the top of the Davy and expose the naked flame." [1]

At first the pitmen were disposed to sympathize with the culprits in such cases, but a more sensible feeling was beginning to prevail. An instance occurred at Benwell Colliery (*1835 Report*, 2,255) where a man was sentenced by the magistrates to three months' imprisonment for taking the top off his lamp in a dangerous place. On Mr. Buddle being requested by the friends of this man to intercede with the magistrates for a mitigation of the sentence, he referred the matter to the pitmen themselves to decide; with the result that they held a meeting and came to the conclusion that the man should undergo the full term of imprisonment—a decision which Mr. Buddle considered to be highly creditable to them. In another case at Gosforth Colliery, near the close of the year 1835 (*Min. Jour.*, i. 139), a

[1] A curious case of foolhardiness in the use of naked lights was that of a collier who undertook to write his name on the roof with a candle. He lay down on his back and began the attempt, when the gas fired on him (*1835 Report*, 3,663).

punishment of three months' imprisonment with hard labour was imposed on a pitman for unscrewing the top off his Davy lamp.

Instances of lamps being tampered with was matter of common knowledge among the northern witnesses examined by the 1835 Committee. Indeed, long after this period it was found necessary to take more and more stringent measures to prevent wilful pitmen from endangering their own and other people's lives by unscrewing the top off the lamps for the momentary advantage of obtaining a better light.

Improved discipline with regard to the use of the Davy lamp was gradually being introduced in the northern collieries. It is clear that at the first introduction of the lamp it was customary to work with it in an explosive atmosphere. We also hear (ib., 3,253) of colliers working for hours together with the lamp red hot in Earl Fitzwilliam's collieries, and in the neighbourhood of Bradford. But the danger attendant upon this proceeding, in the event of any accident happening to the lamp, had led to its abandonment, and it was now generally regarded by the viewers in the north as imprudent to use the lamp in this way, and had become the rule to withdraw the men when the gas fired in their lamps, and only to employ the lamp as a matter of precaution (ib., 1,083), as a second line of defence.

It was also now becoming customary to lock the safety lamps, though the practice was not yet general. We find Mr. Buddle stating in 1830 (Report, p. 273), that lamps in the hands of boys, and of workmen employed in dangerous places, were locked. But in 1835 (Report, 530-1) it had become usual, at the best collieries, to invariably lock all safety lamps. Pipes also were prohibited where danger was apprehended (ib., 515).

Quite a number of different safety lamps were already in the field. The 1835 Committee witnessed experiments on nine varieties in the laboratory of London University. In all cases, with the exception of Upton and Roberts's lamp, the flame was made to pass through the gauze, by explosive currents. This lamp was consequently recommended by the committee, but it never came into use in the north, nor indeed anywhere to any extent.[1] The northern viewers were well satisfied with the Davy lamp, and the danger of the lamp encountering explosive currents in the mines was somewhat remote. Such currents did not exist in the ordinary working-places (ib., 910), nor were the men required to go where there was an explosive atmosphere (ib., 739). The return airways were almost the only part

[1] In addition to being heavy, it was so easily put out as to be perpetually leaving the miner in darkness.

of the mine where any danger might be feared from this cause, but these were only travelled by the wastemen, who were invariably old and experienced pitmen, and who carefully sheltered their lamps in rapid currents, if for nothing else than to prevent their being blown out (*ib.*, 2,227-29, 3,481).

Among the lamps were those of Dr. Clanny and Mr. G. Stephenson, in both of which all Sir Humphry Davy's inventions had been adopted—including the wire-gauze envelope itself.

CHAPTER L.

THE NINETEENTH CENTURY. 1817-1835.

*Commencement to employ greatly increased volumes of air to ventilate
collieries in the Wear district. Backward state of ventilation in the
Midland coalfields. Difficulties with goaves, or wastes, in fiery mines.
Proposals of Goldsworthy Gurney and John Martin. Conclusions of
the 1835 Committee. Beginning of mining literature.*

In this era a commencement was made to employ volumes of air to
ventilate mines vastly greater than had previously been attempted,
or even thought of.

Though the system of compound ventilation, or splitting the air,
had been devised by Mr. Buddle, and put in practice by him at
Wallsend Colliery, as early as 1810, the object which he aimed at
had not been to obtain an increased quantity of air, but to overcome
difficulties connected with the ventilating furnace; and, accustomed
as he had been to the small volumes of air which could alone be
introduced under the coursing system, he continued to entertain
what to us appear very circumscribed views on the subject of
ventilation.

It is true that he informed the Lords' Committee in 1829 (*Report,*
p. 47), that a colliery of which he was viewer required 18,000 cubic
feet of air per minute to keep it in a safe working state—perhaps
Percy Main Colliery, where he elsewhere states that eight separate
air-currents were employed for the ventilation of the workings (*Trans.
Nat. Hist. Soc. of Northumberland*, ii. 334). But this he evidently
quotes as an exceptionally large quantity of air; and at Wallsend
Colliery, at the time of the great explosion in 1835, when it was
ventilated by three downcast and two upcast pits, the three air-
currents employed measured from 1,500 to 1,800, or 2,000 cubic feet
each per minute, and the aggregate quantity 5,000 cubic feet per

minute[1] (*1835 Report*, 2,081, 2,973). A velocity of 3 feet per second, or 2 miles per hour, which had been Mr. Buddle's standard in 1813, was still considered a very good current in the Tyne district (*ib.*, 909, 2,314).

Under these circumstances it is not surprising that the mines were in a very precarious condition, and that transitions from a state of safety to a state of danger were rapid and frequent. In some mines mere variations of the atmospheric pressure were sufficient to change the complexion of the workings; a low barometer being tantamount to the mine being in an explosive state, while with a dense condition of the air, gas was scarcely perceptible—a lowering of the atmospheric pressure being stated (*Trans. Nat. Hist. Soc. of Northumberland*, i. 185) to have sometimes rendered the whole circulating current of a pit's workings explosive in the course of fifteen or twenty minutes.

It was in the collieries of the Wear district, which, as we have seen, were taking the lead in the coal trade at this period, that the new era in mine ventilation began. Here the system of splitting the air was introduced about 1820-25 (*1835 Report*, 474, 497, 537, 700); and at the same time a commencement was made to cause greatly increased volumes of air to sweep through the mines. This was effected by employing larger airways; also larger, and in some cases several furnaces; and great assistance was at times obtained from the fires of boilers placed underground in connection with steam machinery for hauling the coal, which was coming into common use as a substitute for horses.

Immediately after Mr. Buddle had assured the 1835 Committee that the volume of air passing through Wallsend Colliery was not less than 5,000 cubic feet per minute, he was questioned regarding evidence furnished to the committee by a previous witness, Ralph Elliot (father of Sir George Elliot), relative to the ventilating currents employed at a colliery belonging to Lord Londonderry, situated at Pensher, on the Wear. This colliery, like Wallsend, was ventilated by three downcast and two upcast pits; and regarding the performance of one of the upcasts 6½ feet in diameter, which had been specially sunk for ventilating purposes, Elliot had made the following statement:

The rate of the air in the D pit was 12 feet 6 inches per second, the area 40 feet, and the quantity of air 30,240 feet. In the same pit the total in three divisions in the Hutton seam, uniting and

[1] The hewers are stated to have very frequently complained of there being too much ventilation (*1835 Report*, 2,039).

passing over a steam engine furnace into the upcast shaft at the rate of 7·5 feet, the area 42 feet, the quantity was 18,900; the total being 49,100 feet, ascending a pit 6½ feet in diameter, at the rate of 24 feet per second (*1835 Report*, 2,978-80).

Strange to say, though Mr. Buddle was chief viewer to Lord Londonderry, he was unaware of this great acceleration and augmentation of the ventilating currents effected at Pensher, and could only confess that he had never measured the quantities, and indeed was at a loss to know how to accomplish it in the case of ascending currents. The circumstances came upon him altogether as a surprise. Dr. Clanny relates (*1849 Report*, p. 499) that "When he (Elliot) came out I was proceeding on the street with Mr. Buddle and Mr. Pease, and Mr. Buddle said, 'What do you mean by this, Mr. Elliot? You have spoken of a ventilation at the rate of ten miles an hour; do you ever effect such a current? I never heard of more than three or four miles.' 'Yes, I do frequently,' said Mr. Elliot, 'and hence the safety of so rapid a current; and another consequence is' the preservation of the timber and the materials of the mine, by reason of the pureness of the air.'"

The ventilation achieved at Pensher was, however, exceeded by that of the great colliery at Hetton. Here the volume of air employed in 1835 (exclusive of Elemore), amounted to 96,300 cubic feet per minute (Prof. Phillips's *Report*, p. 30), and it subsequently underwent enormous augmentation.

Though artificial ventilation by means of fire had been practised in some of the midland districts long before it had extended to the great northern coalfield, it had continued to be applied in most cases after a primitive fashion. Underground furnaces had only of recent years (about 1815) begun to be introduced in Lancashire (*1835 Report*, 3,384-87, 3,607). They were doubtless also now being used in Yorkshire (*Fossil Fuel*, p. 215), and on a small scale in North Staffordshire (*1835 Report*, 2,535). But at most of the collieries in the Midland districts, where artificial ventilation was resorted to at all, the means employed consisted of firepans, or coal lamps, hung in the pit, or in lateral shaft, or placed at the bottom. Such, Professor Phillips states (*Report*, p. 35), were the only methods practised in Derbyshire up till the year 1836. While further south, in Warwickshire and the Forest of Dean, artificial ventilation had scarcely begun to be made use of at all.

In some collieries substantial stoppings of brick and lime were provided, but in others, even in Lancashire, they consisted of mere heaps of rubbish, admitting of great leakage of air (*1835 Report*,

3,380-83); and no brattices were employed to carry the air close to the face of the workings. The practice of letting out the furnace on Saturday night and lighting it again on Monday morning—a fruitful cause of accident—was now, however, being abandoned in Lancashire (*ib.*, 3,739).

In the South Wales coalfield ventilation by fire never obtained any strong footing; the mines of this district, being to a large extent horizontal, presented an unfavourable field for the employment of this agency.

Though the name "fireman" continues to be applied even at the present day, in some parts of the kingdom, to the individual who examines the workings of a colliery previous to the entrance of the workmen in the morning, the duties of this official had become much less risky and exciting than formerly. It was no longer necessary for him to search for and explode the firedamp with his pole and lighted candle. The presence of the enemy could now be discovered with ease and safety by means of the Davy lamp, and the colliers now disposed of it by sweeping it out with their coats when necessary (*1835 Report*, 3,428; Dunn's *Win. and Work.*, 2nd ed., p. 101).

The process of beating with a cloth, in order to dissipate noxious gases, though only heard of in connection with coal mining at this period, was in reality the oldest of all methods of artificial ventilation. It was employed in the metalliferous mines of Germany in the time of Agricola (who gives a figure of two men shaking a piece of cloth between them), and is likewise referred to even in the pages of Pliny (*H.N.*, xxxi. 28).

Now that the working of pillars was a recognized and regular branch of coal mining, the formation of large goaves, or wastes, had become general. In fiery mines these goaves were found to be a source of much difficulty and danger, particularly in the case of flat seams, where there was no natural drainage of the gas. The question of what should be done with the goaves was a problem regarding which a variety of opinions existed.

We have seen that under the system of working pursued in South Staffordshire (where the quantity of firedamp was small), the compartments, or sides of work, were shut off completely after all the coal that could be got had been obtained, with a view to the prevention of ignition by spontaneous combustion.

A similar plan was practised in the case of goaves yielding gas in the Potteries district of North Staffordshire, and this course of procedure was not without its advocates in other districts (*1835 Report*,

3,726). But already an accident had taken place at Apedale from this arrangement, and even in the same coalfield some of the mine managers would not permit it to be done (*ib.*, 2,590-94).

Mr. Buddle tried different arrangements. In the case of exhausted panels in the C pit, he adopted, as has been seen, the method of shutting them completely off and conducting the gas in pipes to the surface. In the G pit, on the other hand, the entrances to the exhausted compartments were left in free communication with the return airway, into which the exuding gas was allowed to escape, to be carried away by the ventilating current. Thus huge magazines of gas were formed in the mine, the only safeguard against accident from which consisted in the rigid exclusion of naked lights from their vicinity. The unsatisfactory character of this method, however, was shown by the fact that it was supposed to have occasioned the great explosion in 1835. But Mr. Buddle knew of no better system, and was even of opinion that increased ventilation would be of little avail. "It does not signify," he says (*1835 Report*, 2,982) "what form of ventilation you have, if it cannot be applied to dislodge the gas ; and so long as the current of air can only be applied merely to the skirts or margin of the goafs, to carry off the feeders of gas exuding from them, by the gas drifts through the dumb furnaces, no improvement whatever is effected ; unless, therefore, some mode can be devised of completely expelling the gas from those lodgments, nothing can be done for us that has not already been done. All the schemes which have been devised for removing or drawing off the gas by pipes, or anything of that kind, really amount to nothing ; for until some effectual plan can be devised for dislodging and expelling the gas entirely and effectually from those lodgments occasioned by working the pillars, the chief cause of all our accidents will, I fear, remain unabated."

The formation of detached and imperfectly closed goaves in the interior of a mine, has at all times been a source of difficulty in fiery mines, and may perhaps be regarded as one of the defects inherent in the bord-and-pillar system of working coal, and especially so under some of its peculiar developments.

Among the more novel suggestions brought under the notice of the 1835 Committee for the safer working of collieries, was Mr. Gurney's proposal to exclude fire or flame altogether from the mines, which he proposed to effect by lighting them by means of reflected light, and ventilating them by jets of high-pressure steam. His plan of reflected light does not seem ever to have been seriously entertained by anyone except himself ; but regarding ventilation by high-pressure steam, which had been applied previous to this time at a colliery in South Wales, more will be heard hereafter.

Among various proposals made by Mr. John Martin, one was to substitute a fan in lieu of the ventilating furnace. This was not new either, though to him probably belongs the merit of suggesting an arrangement whereby coal was enabled to be drawn at the upcast pit. The proposal received little attention at the time, but soon afterwards mechanical ventilation began to be more highly thought of.

Mr. Martin also proposed a plan of working coal designed to ensure ascensional ventilation and the drainage of the gas upwards. It may be regarded in a manner as the counterpart of Lieut. Menzies's scheme, and consisted in surrounding the area to be worked by drifts in the first instance, and then proceeding to work the coal from the extremities inwards.

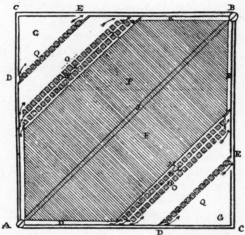

FIG. 45.—J. MARTIN'S PLAN OF WORKING AND VENTILATING.

Nearly all the witnesses examined by the 1835 Committee—and notably Mr. Buddle—were unfavourable to an inspection of mines on the part of the Government, and of legislative interference in mining operations, though Mr. George Stephenson considered that the sinking of two shafts should be made compulsory (*Report*, 1,659). No objections, however, were entertained to scientific gentlemen visiting the mines, the immense advantages accruing to the coal trade from Sir H. Davy's labours not having been forgotten.

The question of the establishment of codes of rules for the guidance and discipline of the workpeople was also regarded with favour and soon after began to be commonly carried out.

It seems very paradoxical that the scientific witnesses examined by the Committee should have been ranged against the Davy lamp, and that the most eminent mining witnesses, though placing complete reliance on the lamp, should have given their emphatic support to the continued use of naked lights in working the whole mine in fiery collieries, notwithstanding the repeated disasters resulting therefrom.

With the conflicting and perplexing evidence furnished to them, it is not surprising that the 1835 Committee did not arrive at any very decided conclusions as to the course which should be adopted by the Legislature.

They thought it desirable that notice of accidents, involving a large loss of life, should be sent as soon as possible to the Secretary of State for the Home Department, and that some fit and proper person should be directed to attend the inquest to assist the coroner and jury in their deliberations.

They considered that in the case of some mines more shafts were required for ventilating purposes than were ordinarily provided; and that the system of employing brattices in ventilating shafts was deservedly reprobated. Also, that the foul and free air-courses were frequently too near each other, and the stoppings between them of too temporary a nature.

They were of opinion that in some mines lighted by the ordinary means, the use of the safety lamp ought to be compelled by the owners. The necessity for maps and plans showing the state of the workings, and also indicating the position of adjacent abandoned mines which might be filled with gas or water, they regarded as sufficiently obvious.

They had also considered how far legislative enactments might aid the miner, but conceived that the great dissimilarity of mines in different parts of the kingdom rendered it impossible for the time to lay down any precise directions or form any rules of universal application; but were sanguine that great benefit might be anticipated from men of known ability being encouraged to visit the mines, whether as chemists, mechanics, or philanthropists.

They also thought that great advantages might be expected from the establishment of associations similar to the Polytechnic School recently formed in Cornwall. And that a vigilant oversight on the part of owners, viewers, and managers, might prevent many accidents.

On account of the objections which had been made to any inspection of the mines on behalf of the Government, the committee

abstained from expressing any opinion upon the necessity or expediency of such a course.

Thus their ably-conducted and elaborate inquiry led to no decisive recommendations being made; but it cannot be doubted that the dissemination of the information collected, throughout the mining districts, proved of considerable service to the cause of mining.

The year 1835 may almost be regarded as the period of the commencement of mining literature, for although some few books, and numerous papers and pamphlets, had been issued previous to this time, such had been only fitful and intermittent. This year, however, witnessed not only the publication of the valuable Parliamentary Report above referred to, but likewise the anonymous *History of Fossil Fuel*, a work of varied interest ascribed by Professor Jevons to John Holland. In this year also one of the mining periodicals was established, which has continued to be published uninterruptedly down to the present day.

INDEX.

A

Adits, aqueducts, or watergates, earliest mention of, in the north of England, 46, 53; different names in different districts, 56.

Agricola, Georgius, pseudonym of writer on mining and metallurgy in Germany, 83, 109, 110, 152, 154, 176, 297, 521.

Air-pump, invention of the, 236-7; applied to the steam engine, 288; applied to ventilate mines, 415.

America, silver from, 23; tar from, 343; Fulton establishes steam navigation in, 386.

Anglo-Saxons, or early English, coal not used by the, 7; keels brought to Britain by the, 38.

Anthrax, or charcoal, 1, 6, 12.

Association of colliers on the Tyne and Wear, 464.

Atmosphere, discovery of the pressure of the, 183, 236.

Atmospheric, or vacuum engines, attempts to invent, 237; effected by Newcomen, 238.

B

Baku, holy fires of, 109.

Balance-tub system of winding coal, 276, 481.

Barnes, Thomas, 309, 312, 316, 318, 319.

Bearing system, 57, 58, 66, 120.

Beaumont, Master, 151, 157, 201.

Belgium, 17, 18 note, 194, 225, 413.

Bell, or bee-hive pits, 32-4.

Bell's, Henry, steamboat "Comet," 386.

Birmingham, 239, 289, 300, 312, 331, 364, 474.

Blackett, Mr., of Wylam, 374, 375, 376, 379, 380.

Blenkinsop, John, establishes steam locomotion, 377-383.

Blowers of fire damp, 291, 293, 347, 400, 407, 489, 497, 500.

Boll, or barrow measure, 57.

Bord, or board, meaning of term, 176.

Bord-and-pillar system of working: Northumberland and Durham, 70, 74, 91, 168, 176, 180-182, 254, 255, 267, 273, 279, 283, 293, 313, 315-318, 341, 362, 395, 472. Cumberland, 180, 279, 346, 352, 353, 362. Scotland, 180, 341. South Wales, 181. Derbyshire, 187. South Staffordshire, 192, 332. Yorkshire, 254 note.

Boring process, 152, 153, 174, 184, 189, 283, 411, 412, 448.

Bratticed shafts, 389, 408.

Brown, William, builds many Newcomen engines, 260; invents screens, 284; erects a water gin, 297-8; constructs an iron man, 305.

Buckets, chain of, 157.

Buddle, John, sen., born 1743, 308; becomes manager at Wallsend, 309.

Buddle, John, jun., born 1773, 308; becomes assistant to his father, 309; succeeds his father at Wallsend, 414; invents panel work, 416; invents splitting the air, 416.

Burning, or boiling wells, 188-9, 336-7, 364, 487.

By-products of coal, 204, 306, 333, 339, 343, 365.

C

Cage-and-tub system, invention of the, 482-484.

Canals, 229, 329, 330, 331, 335, 339, 343, 359, 360, 366. See also Navigation.

London, incipient use of coal by limeburners and smiths in, 21, 29; prohibition of its use by brewers, etc.,
on account of smoke, 30; regularly
imported and used by smiths
and limeburners in the fourteenth
century, 50; commencement of its
use for domestic purposes in
fifteenth century, 63; complaints
against high prices in sixteenth
century, 96; dislike of it and restriction of its use in reign of Queen
Elizabeth, 122, 123; comes into
general use in reign of King James
I., 127; one half of coal fleet required for supply of, 138; attempts
to fix prices, 141, 143; extreme
scarcity during civil and Dutch
wars, 142, 145; importation of coke,
285, 313; Trevithick's circular
railway at, 375.

Long wall, or long way, method of
working coal: Shropshire, 203-4;
Somersetshire, 341; Cumberland,
356-7; Northumberland, 357; Scotland, 357-8.

Lyell, Sir Charles, 4.

M

Macclesfield, 61.

Mackworth, Sir Humphry, 223.

Manchester, 5, 303, 329, 385, 456,
472.

Martin, John, 523.

Mary Queen of Scots, 115.

Menzies, Lieutenant, 413.

Menzies, Michael, 276, 278.

Mine, original meaning of term, 25.

Miner, The Compleat, 173.

Mines, Royal, 19, 227.

Mining records, preservation of, 319,
443.

Monmouthshire. See South Wales
and Monmouthshire coalfield.

Murdock, William, 364, 371.

N

Navigation, inland, 189, 228, 229,
326, 329, 330. See also Canal.
steam, 386-7.

Neath, 119, 125, 223, 224, 359.

Newcastle-on-Tyne, *passim*; increase
of revenue from coal trade, 24;
royal grants of coal to, 41, 42;
obtains conservatorship of the
Tyne, 86; acquires the Grand
Lease, 97.

Newcastle-on-Tyne coalfield. See
Northumberland and Durham.

Newcomen, Thomas, inventor of the
steam engine, 238; builds the first
engine at Wolverhampton, 239; his
death, 244.

Newport, 360, 476.

North, Roger, 156, 160, 161, 162,
163, 167, 189.

North Staffordshire. See Staffordshire, North.

North Wales. See Wales, North.

Northumberland, Earl of, 49, 50, 64,
111; Duke of, 423.

Northumberland and Durham, North
of England, Newcastle-on-Tyne, or
Great Northern coalfield, annals
relating to the: previous to 1066, 4,
5, 8; Norman period, 13-15; thirteenth century, 20-25, 33; fourteenth century, 37-58; fifteenth
century, 64-76; sixteenth century,
82-108; seventeenth century, 129-
182; eighteenth century, 231-235,
247-285, 290-299, 307-319; nineteenth century, 388-405, 409-472,
478-491, 492-502. See also Explosions, Railways.

Nottingham, 26, 114.

Nottinghamshire coalfield. See Yorkshire, Derbyshire, and Nottinghamshire.

Noxious gases, or damps, 108-110,
121, 160, 174-5, 179, 183, 186-7,
188-9, 193-4, 197, 214, 234, 279,
282, 326, 327, 329, 330, 352, 393,
409-413, 488, 504. See also Blowers,
Outbursts, Explosions, Firing system, Safety lamps, Ventilation.

O

Open-cast working, 32, 192, 339.

Ornaments of coal, 4, 188, 329.
of iron, 2.

Orrell Colliery, 382, 473.

Outbursts of firedamp, 397, 405, 406,
420, 489, 498.

Outram, Benjamin, 178, 327.

Owen, George, author of a *History of
Pembrokeshire*, 120.

Oxley, Joseph, 277.

P

Paisley, 406, 515.

Panel-work, 416.

Papin, Denis, 237, 238, 288, 371.

raising water, 158-9 ; stoop and room method of working coal, 177, 180, 181, 341, 358 ; use of peat in whisky manufacture, 186 note ; family of Hacket in Fife, 225 ; smelting silver ore with coal, 228 note ; building of steam engines, 244, 261, 262, 263 ; cast-iron pipes used in mine pumps, 266 ; Watt repairs model of Newcomen engine at Glasgow, and invents separate condenser, 286-288 ; water wheel for winding at Alloa, 297 ; production of iron in 1788, 304 ; iron railways, 304, 367 ; hard nature of Scotch coal, 317 ; first iron boat, 338 ; Pennant's tour, 353 ; employment of steam engine in raising coal, 354 note ; long way of working, 357-8 ; expansion of iron manufacture, 363 ; William Murdock a native of, 364 ; first locomotive engine, 385 ; steam navigation, 386; production of iron in 1827, 477.

Screens, 284, 442, 458.

Sea coal, applied to coal gathered on the Northumberland coast, 20 ; controversy as to meaning of, 108, 109, 127 ; applied to coal under the sea, 127.

"Sea-coale, Char-coale, and Small-coale" pamphlet, 142.

Sea Coal Lane, London, 29.

Serfdom in England, 49, 75 ; in Scotland, 76.

Shafts, round, 174 and *passim* ; oval, 283, 347 ; rectangular or square, 176, 320, 340 ; bratticed, 389.

Sheffield, 59, 302, 321, 325, 326, 369, 473, 480.

Shropshire coalfield, annals relating to the : previous to 1066, 5 ; thirteenth century, 27 ; fourteenth century, 61 ; sixteenth century, 117 ; seventeenth century, 202-205; eighteenth century, 336-340 ; nineteenth century, 372. See also Explosions, Railways.

Smeaton, 242, 261, 295, 298, 314, 321, 331, 335.

Smelting with coal. See Copper, Iron, Lead, Tin.

Smiths, the earliest patrons of coal, 1, 2, 12, 21, 30, 32, 80.

Somersetshire coalfield, annals relating to the : previous to 1066, 6 ; sixteenth century, 118 ; seventeenth century, 176, 212, 214 ; eighteenth century, 341-343 ; nineteenth century, 475, 491. See also Explosions.

South Wales. See Wales, South.

Spedding, Carlisle, 344-351.

Spedding, James, 344, 351.

Splitting the air, 418.

Square work, 193, 332.

Staffordshire, North, coalfield, annals relating to the : thirteenth century, 28 ; seventeenth century, 193 ; eighteenth century, 334 ; nineteenth century, 475, 491, 503. See also Explosions.

Staffordshire, South, coalfield, annals relating to the : thirteenth century, 28, 33, 34 ; fourteenth century, 60 ; sixteenth century, 115, 116 ; seventeenth century, 191-193 ; eighteenth century, 330-334 ; nineteenth century, 363, 412, 413, 473, 474, 491, 503. See also Explosions, Railways.

Steam engine, invention of the Newcomen, 238 ; extensively used for pumping water at collieries and mines, 261-263 ; the separate condenser invented by Watt, 286-288 ; the double-acting engine invented by Watt, 301 ; the high pressure engine brought into use by Trevithick, 369.

Steam locomotion, 371-386.

Steam navigation, 386, 387.

Steel mill, invention of the, 279, 348.

Stephenson, George, builds his first locomotive, 383 ; his claim to the invention of the safety lamp, 430-435 ; constructs the Hetton Colliery railway, 450 ; the Stockton and Darlington railway, 452 ; the Liverpool and Manchester railway, 456 ; approved of a measure of legislative control over mines, 523.

Stephenson, Robert, sen., engineer at Hetton Colliery, 450 ; manager of Pendleton Colliery, 512.

Stephenson, Robert, jun., his locomotive engine "Rocket," 386, 454.

Strikes, 1765, 270, 273 ; 1810, 441 ; 1826, 465 ; 1831 and 1832, 466-470.

Sunderland Society, for preventing accidents in coal mines, 423.

Swansea, 29, 32, 128, 223, 358, 359, 476.

Sweden, 243, 256, 285 note.

T

Tar, manufacture of, 204, 305, 333, 339, 343, 365, 441.

Taxation of coal, 47, 68, 98, 120, 140, 146 ; chimneys, 141 ; windows, 149 ; repeal of coal duties, 461.

Ten measure, the, 45, 87, 100, 136, 146, 147, 267, 274.

Thompson, Benjamin, 441.

Thrusts, 168. See also Crushes.

Tin, pre-emption of, 141 ; smelting with coal, 195 note, 215, 228.

Tithes of coal, 52, 60, 69, 82.

Tram, 177, 305, 352.

Trevithick introduces high pressure steam engine, 368 ; his attempts to establish steam locomotion, 371.

Triewald, Sir Martin, 243, 285, 345.

Trotter, Dr., proposes to neutralize noxious gases in mines, 409.

Tubbing, wood, 174, 258, 311, 392 ; stone (?), 223 ; iron, 311, 312, 392.

Tynemouth, mining operations of the monks of, 23, 38, 42, 65, 86, 106.

U

Upton & Roberts, Messrs., 506.

Uriconium or Wroxeter, coal used by the Romans at, 5.

V

Vacuum, discovery of the true nature of the, 236.

Vacuum engines, attempts to invent, 237 ; its successful accomplishment in the Newcomen steam engine, 238.

Ventilation :

By falling water, 231.

By fire, 175, 186, 187, 194, 253-4, 282, 326-7, 361, 393, 520.

By hot cylinder, 410, 414.

By machinery, 277, 415, 523.

By steam, 414, 522.

Natural, 160, 179, 285, 351.

See also Face-airing, Coursing the air, Splitting the air, Furnace, Fire-lamp.

W

Wains, marking of, 101 ; size fixed, 146.

Wales, North, annals relating to the coalfield of : Norman period, 17 ; thirteenth century, 29, 33 ; fourteenth century, 62 ; fifteenth century, 78 ; sixteenth century, 121 ;

seventeenth century, 219-223 ; eighteenth century, 358 ; nineteenth century, 439, 491, 543. See also Explosions.

Wales, South, and Monmouthshire, annals relating to the coalfield of : previous to 1066, 3 ; thirteenth century, 29, 34 ; fourteenth century, 62 ; sixteenth century, 119-121 ; seventeenth century, 223, 224 ; eighteenth century, 358-361 ; nineteenth century, 363, 373, 475, 491, 503. See also Explosions, Railways.

Wallsend Colliery, winning of, 290.

Warwickshire coalfield, annals relating to the : the Norman period, 15 ; sixteenth century, 117 ; seventeenth century, 198-200 ; eighteenth century, 334, 335 ; nineteenth century, 475, 491.

Water-gates. See Adits.

Watt, James, invents the separat condenser, 286 ; invents the double-acting engine, 301.

Wayleaves, 21, 26, 27, 40, 53, 66, etc.

Wells, burning or boiling, 188, 336, 364, 487.

Wilson, Robert, 374, 375, 386.

Winding coal by water balance, 276, 278 ; by water wheels, 278, 297-299, 325, 335, 343, 368 ; by steam engines, 277, 278, 297, 313, 314, 325, 327, 329, 334, 339, 342, 343, 355, etc.

Windmills. See Sailing engines.

Women, employment of, in mines, north of England, 91, 232, 233, 234, 305 ; Cumberland, 354, 503 ; Scotland, 57.

Y

Yearly bond, 76, 269, 270, 440, 465.

Yorkshire, Derbyshire, and Nottinghamshire coalfield, annals relating to the : previous to 1066, 5 ; thirteenth century, 26, 33, 34 ; fourteenth century, 59, 60 ; fifteenth century, 76 ; sixteenth century, 111-114 ; seventeenth century, 184-188 ; eighteenth century, 320-327 ; nineteenth century, 377, 379, 473, 491, 503. See also Explosions, Railways.

Z

Zwickau, coalfield of, in Saxony, 11.